PHYSICAL ORGANIC CHEMISTRY

Physical Organic

Chemistry

Kenneth B. Wiberg

Professor of Chemistry, Yale University

John Wiley & Sons, Inc.

New York · London · Sydney

Library of Congress Catalog Card Number: 63-20644
Printed in the United States of America

Preface

The field of physical organic chemistry may easily be considered to have originated with the publication of Hammett's classic text bearing that title. Much good work of this type had been done previously. However, the development of this field as one of major interest to organic chemists occurred in the mid 1940's after the publication of Hammett's book. More recently, several related works have appeared. The trend in these books has been to concentrate on the organic chemical aspects and to minimize the physical chemistry involved.

The present work represents an experiment in producing a useful text which would concentrate on the more physical chemical aspects. Since it was designed as a text rather than as a reference book, it has been necessary to select the topics considered with some care, and many interesting subjects and extensions of the subjects covered have been omitted in order to pare the mass of information which is available into an amount which could be covered in a reasonable length of time. My choice of subjects will undoubtedly not be universally agreeable. However, if the experiment proves to be a reasonable success, the experience gained by those who use this book will be a guide to future improvement.

The work is designed for a one-year graduate course, possibly in conjunction with a text which will present the more organic chemical aspects. The latter have been minimized herein because of the availability of texts emphasizing this aspect and because of a desire to minimize duplication of material.

The subject has been divided into three parts: Bonding and Spectra, Equilibria, and Kinetics. A considerable amount of integration has been possible so that material presented in one part is used as much as possible in a later part. The first sections of each part contain material which often will be covered in other courses. This material is included mainly as a review. Throughout the work, specific examples have been considered so that the student may see how the material presented may be applied to the study of organic compounds. Problems and reading lists have also been provided for many sections in order to help the student in gaining a good understanding of the material.

The final section, the Appendix, contains a variety of material which is designed to be useful. It contains a review of matrix algebra, tables of constants and other numerical data, and discussions of the practical treatment of nuclear magnetic resonance data and of kinetic data for reactions having complex rate laws. The final section of the Appendix includes a discussion of computer programming, since this subject is becoming of increasing importance to organic chemists, and since computers are now becoming fairly generally available. This is followed by some examples of computer programs which may be of interest to organic chemists.

Finally, I must acknowledge the contributions of former teachers and colleagues who started and nurtured my interest in physical organic chemistry. I should like especially to recognize the contribution of those at the University of Washington from whom I learned much and from whom I "borrowed" many ideas on how to present this material. Much of the work was written in Karlsruhe, Germany, during tenure of J. S. Guggenheim and A. P. Sloan fellowships. I wish to thank these organizations for their assistance and Professor R. Criegee, also, for making facilities available at the Technische Hochschule in Karlsruhe.

KENNETH B. WIBERG

New Haven, Conn.
November 1963

Contents

PART ONE

Bonding and Spectra

1-1 Introduction

Any consideration of the theoretical aspects of organic chemistry must begin with a discussion of the nature of covalent bonding. Ideas of bonding have always played a central role in the development of organic chemistry, and the greatest achievement of organic chemistry—the development of the structural theory—is a direct outgrowth of the early, qualitative attempts to find an explanation for the attractive forces between atoms.

A modern consideration of the nature of covalent bonding and other attractive forces cannot be made without using quantum chemistry as the frame of reference. In order to do this as expeditiously as possible, the following discussion will first consider the principal approximation methods which are available and then some applications of these methods to problems of interest to organic chemists.

It will also be seen that a quantitative treatment of bonding will lead directly to the energy levels of each state of bonding of a given molecule. Since the observed spectra of molecules are related to the transition from one of these energy states to another, the following treatment will also permit a consideration of the spectral properties of compounds.

1-2 The Wave Nature of the Electron

In many ways electrons exhibit wavelike properties. For example, electrons will be diffracted in much the same way as ordinary light, the main difference being in the wavelength and thus in the spacing in the grating required in order to observe an effect. With ordinary light, a grating ruled with 1 to 10 thousand lines per centimeter is satisfactory, but with an electron beam, because of its shorter wavelength, no ordinary grating is adequate, and a crystal with its small distance between nuclei is used in order to observe diffraction.[1]

Accepting the wave nature of an electron, we can first qualitatively consider the effects of restraint on a species of this type. Suppose the particle having wavelike character were contained inside a one-dimensional box (Fig. 1-1) (i.e., it is permitted to move only along the x axis for a distance a). In order for the electron to be in a stationary state (of which more will be said later), we must also assume that the wave starts and finishes at the ends of the box. Thus the first wave we may draw is one which begins and finishes at the ends of the box and has no nodes. The next wave would have one node, the third would have two nodes, and so on.

Since for a wave of a given amplitude the energy increases with increasing frequency, it is apparent that the wave having no nodes has the lowest energy, what with one node is of higher energy, and that the energy of the state increases as the number of nodes increases. As will be seen later, for a given system this is, in general, the relationship between the possible wave functions and the energies.

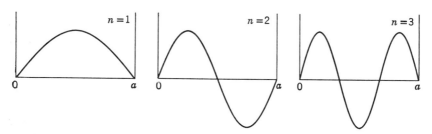

Fig. 1-1. Possible waves for a particle in a box.

[1] For a review of the application of electron diffraction in studying molecular structure, see L. O. Brockway, *Revs. Modern Physics*, **8,** 231 (1936).

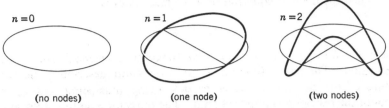

$n = 0$ $n = 1$ $n = 2$

(no nodes)   (one node)   (two nodes)

Fig. 1-2. Possible waves for a particle on a circle.

Another simple case is the particle on a circle. The particle is restrained to move along the circumference of the circle, and the waves corresponding to it are perpendicular to the plane of the circle. In order to obtain a stationary state the wave must return on itself, and therefore the possible wavelengths will be determined by the size of the circle. The first wave will have an infinite wavelength and no nodes, the second will have a nodal line bisecting the circle, and the next will have two nodal lines perpendicular to each other (Fig. 1-2). Again, the energy of a state will be a function of the number of nodes, that with no nodes having the lowest energy.

Reference

Development of Wave Mechanics:
> J. C. Slater, *Quantum Theory of Atomic Structure*, McGraw-Hill Book Co., New York, 1960, vol. I, pp. 1–50.

1-3 The Postulatory Basis of Wave Mechanics

The preceding treatment will, of course, not give the energies of the possible states for these systems and cannot easily be extended to the more complex cases. Therefore we shall now examine the treatment of some of these cases by the use of wave mechanics. Certain postulates are fundamental to wave mechanics and have been developed by a consideration of the nature of the equations describing classical systems which are best considered as involving particles on the one hand and those considered as involving waves on the other. In a sense the postulates are not capable of direct proof, their validity being demonstrated by one's ability to calculate precisely the results of measurement by their use. The postulates may be stated in a number of possible ways. One way, which will be convenient for our purposes, is the following.

1. The fundamental equation of wave mechanics is

$$\alpha\psi = \lambda\psi$$

where α is an operator, ψ is the wave function or eigenpsi, and λ is the eigenvalue. The wave function is an expression describing the wave nature of the electron or other particle being considered, taking into account the restrictions imposed on it. The operator α simply does something to the wave function on which it operates. For example, the operation might be differentiation with respect to the coordinate, x. The nature of the operator to be used in a given problem will be discussed in more detail below. The eigenvalue λ is the value of the quantity corresponding to the nature of the operator used. Thus, for example. if one used the total energy operator, the value of λ would be the energy of the system.

2. For every dynamical quantity in classical physics, such as the distance, momentum, kinetic energy, and potential energy, there is a corresponding wave mechanical operator. In order to obtain the latter one writes the classical equation and replaces x by x and p (momentum) by $(-ih/2\pi)(\partial/\partial x)$. Thus the kinetic energy T is given by

$$T = \tfrac{1}{2}mv^2 = \frac{p^2}{2m} \qquad (\text{since } p = mv)$$

and the kinetic energy operator T_{op} is

$$T_{\text{op}} = \frac{p_{\text{op}}{}^2}{2m} = \frac{\left[\dfrac{-ih}{2\pi}\left(\dfrac{\partial}{\partial x}\right)\right]^2}{2m} = \frac{-h^2}{8\pi^2 m}\left(\frac{\partial^2}{\partial x^2}\right)$$

For a three-dimensional system, the latter is taken over all three co-ordinates.

3. For every state there is a corresponding wave function. The square of a wave function gives a probability. If a wave function is a description of the wavelike nature of a particle, then the square of the wave function should be analogous to an intensity (the square of the amplitude of a light wave gives the intensity of the light). The only meaningful concept of this type is the probability of finding the particle.

4. The only possible results of the measurement of a dynamical variable are the eigenvalues obtained from the wave equation. Thus there is an exact one-to-one correspondence between the values which are measured and those obtained from the wave equation.

In order to have the wave functions correspond to physical reality, they must have certain properties. First, the integral of ψ^2 taken over all space must be finite:

$$\int_{-\infty}^{\infty} \psi^2 \, d\tau = \text{a finite value}$$

This follows from the statement that ψ^2 gives a probability. The integral then gives the total probability, which for a real case must be finite. Further, the wave function must be continuous and single valued. If this were not the case, then at some point in space there would be more than one value of the wave function and more than one value of the probability. This is impossible for any real case. These are the restrictions which make the wave function "well behaved."

1-4 *Some Simple Examples*

We can understand these postulates best by considering some simple examples. The simplest case we may treat is that of a free particle, which has only kinetic energy. Let us first obtain the possible results of a measurement of the momentum of the particle. We can write

$$p_{op}\psi = \bar{p}\psi$$

where p_{op} is the momentum operator and $\bar{p}$ represents the eigenvalues of the momentum. According to postulate 2, we replace p_{op} by $(-ih/2\pi)(\partial/\partial x)$ and obtain

$$-\frac{ih}{2\pi}\left(\frac{\partial\psi}{\partial x}\right) = \bar{p}\psi$$

The form of ψ must now be determined. It can be seen that in order to obtain a satisfactory wave function for this problem, the first derivative of ψ with respect to x must be equal a number times ψ. The type of function which will have this property is e^{ax} for

$$\frac{d}{dx}e^{ax} = ae^{ax}$$

It can be shown that for this case a is equal to $2\pi i/l$,[2] where l is the wavelength of the wave associated with the particle. Making this substitution,

[2] K. S. Pitzer, *Quantum Chemistry*, Prentice-Hall, New York, 1953, p. 15.

one obtains

$$-\frac{ih}{2\pi}\frac{\partial}{\partial x}e^{2\pi ix/l} = \bar{p}e^{2\pi ix/l}$$

$$-\frac{ih}{2\pi}\frac{2\pi i}{l} = \bar{p}$$

$$\frac{h}{l} = \bar{p}$$

This dependence of momentum on Plank's constant divided by the wavelength has been verified for a number of particles. In particular, electron diffraction experiments are a good test, for the momentum of the electron is a function only of the voltage used to accelerate it, and its wavelength may be determined from the spacings in the electron diffraction patterns of compounds whose crystal structure have been determined by X-ray studies. The above may be considered a partial justification for the nature of the wave function and operator which was used.

It should be noted that this result does not indicate any restrictions on the values of momentum which are allowed. This is the general result for all cases in which the particle is not bound (restricted to a certain portion of space).

We may now determine the results of a measurement of the energy of a free particle. The particle has only kinetic energy, and this is given by

$$T = \tfrac{1}{2}mv^2 = \frac{p^2}{2m}$$

The wave equation is then

$$T_{op}\psi = E\psi$$

or

$$\frac{p_{op}^2}{2m}\psi = E\psi$$

where E is the value of the energy. Making the previously described substitution for p_{op}, we obtain

$$-\frac{h^2}{8m\pi^2}\frac{\partial^2\psi}{\partial x^2} = E\psi$$

The ψ used in determining the momentum will still apply here, and thus

$$-\frac{h^2}{8m\pi^2}\frac{\partial^2}{\partial x^2}e^{2\pi ix/l} = Ee^{2\pi ix/l}$$

Performing the indicated operation, we obtain

$$\frac{h^2}{2ml^2} = E$$

Here again the value of E is not quantized (restricted to certain definite values), but, rather, any values are possible, depending only on the wavelength of the particle.

We may now turn to two problems in which the particle is bound and in which we would expect to obtain a set of discrete energy levels. These are the particle in a box and the particle on a circle, the cases which were considered in a qualitative way in Section 1-2. For the particle in a box the wave function can be well behaved in the sense that it is single valued only if the wavelength l is related to the length of the box a by

$$l = \frac{2a}{n} \qquad n = 1, 2, 3, \ldots$$

(cf. Fig. 1-1).[3] Introducing this value of l into the wave function used previously, we obtain

$$\psi = e^{i\pi x n / a}$$

The permissible energy levels are then obtained from

$$T_{\text{op}}\psi = E\psi$$

$$-\frac{h^2}{8m\pi^2}\frac{\partial^2}{\partial x^2}e^{i\pi x n/a} = Ee^{i\pi x n/a}$$

$$\frac{h^2 n^2}{8ma^2} = E$$

Here we see that only certain values of energy are possible and that these are a function of the size of the box and of the quantum number n. The energy distribution is then

$$n = 3 \;\underline{\hspace{5cm}}\; E = 9h^2/8ma^2$$

$$n = 2 \;\underline{\hspace{5cm}}\; E = 4h^2/8ma^2$$

$$n = 1 \;\underline{\hspace{5cm}}\; E = h^2/8ma^2$$

It may be noted that the energy required in going from one level to the next decreases as the size of the box increases. A simple molecular analogy to this case is a linear conjugated system. Here the box consists of the p orbitals which make up the π molecular orbital. Thus the length of the box is the length of the conjugated system. Consider the case of the polymethinium systems having m equal to 1, 2, 3, and 4.

$$(CH_3)_2N\!\!-\!\!(CH\!\!=\!\!CH)_m\!\!-\!\!CH\!\!=\!\!\overset{+}{N}(CH_3)_2$$

[3] This may perhaps be more easily seen by writing the wave function of the energy operator in the equivalent form $\psi = \sin(2\pi x/l)$, where l is again the wavelength of the particle.

The spacing between the energy levels will vary with m because of the change in length of the conjugated system. The bond lengths are not known but may be taken as approximately 1.40 Å. Since alkyl groups are known to stabilize positive charges (cf. Section 1-15), the methyl groups probably contribute something to the length of the conjugated system, and this contribution was taken as approximately $\frac{1}{3}$ the C—C bond distance. Thus the values used were 6.53, 9.33, 12.13, and 14.93 Å for m equal to 1–4, respectively. The energy diagram for these conjugated systems calculated from the particle in a box approximation is given in Fig. 1-3. The x's represent the electrons in the conjugated system and are placed two to an energy level in accordance with the Pauli exclusion principle.

The lowest energy ultraviolet transition for these compounds would

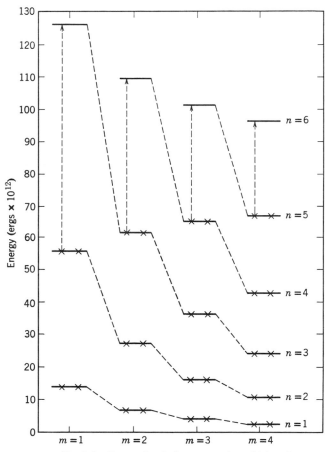

Fig. 1-3. Energy levels for some polymethinium ions.

correspond to the excitation of an electron from the highest filled level to the lowest unfilled level. This is shown by the vertical dotted lines in Fig. 1-3. The difference in energy may be converted to the frequency of the light which would be absorbed in causing this transition by the relationship $\Delta E = h\nu$, and the wavelength λ would be given by $\lambda = c/\nu$, where c is the velocity of light (3.00×10^{10} cm/sec). The calculated wavelengths and the corresponding observed values[4] are shown in Table 1-1. Considering the very simple approximation used, the agreement between the calculated and observed values is remarkably good.

Table 1-1 Spectra of Some Polymethinium Ions

m	*Calculated*	*Observed*
1	2830	3100 Å
2	4120	4120
3	5420	5100
4	6720	6600

A particle on a circle may be treated in the same way. In order for the wave function to be single valued and continuous, the wavelengths must be

$$l = \frac{2\pi r}{n} \qquad n = 0, 1, 2, \ldots$$

where r is the radius of the circle (cf. Fig. 1-2). Substitution into the wave function previously used gives

$$\psi = e^{i x n / r}$$

The wave equation is then

$$T_{op}\psi = E\psi$$

$$-\frac{h^2}{8m\pi^2}\frac{\partial^2}{\partial x^2}e^{i x n / r} = E e^{i x n / r}$$

$$\frac{h^2 n^2}{8\pi^2 m r^2} = E$$

With the exception of the first energy level where $n = 0$ and $p = 0$, each of the energy levels may arise from either $+p$ or $-p$ as the momentum (corresponding to the particle moving around the circle in a clockwise or a counterclockwise direction). Thus for every value of n above the first there

[4] H. J. Dauben, Jr. and G. Feniak, unpublished results.

are two states with the same energy. They are referred to as degenerate states. The energy level distribution for a particle on a circle is then

$n = 3$ $=\!=\!=\!=\!=\!=\!=\!=\!=$ $E = 9h^2/8\pi^2 mr^2$

$n = 2$ $=\!=\!=\!=\!=\!=\!=\!=\!=$ $E = 4h^2/8\pi^2 mr^2$

$n = 1$ $=\!=\!=\!=\!=\!=\!=\!=\!=$ $E = h^2/8\pi^2 mr^2$

$n = 0$ $\rule{3cm}{0.4pt}$ $E = 0$

Having this result, we may again look for a physical system which resembles this case and then try to apply the result as an approximation. A particularly good analogy is benzene, in which we may consider the electrons in a given energy level as being relatively free to travel in a circle of a radius equal to that of the ring. Again, placing two of the unsaturation electrons in each energy level, the distribution of these electrons in benzene would be

$=\!=\!=\!=\!=\!=\!=\!=\!=$ $n = 2$

$\rule{2cm}{0.4pt}$ xx   xx $\rule{1cm}{0.4pt}$ $n = 1$

$\rule{3cm}{0.4pt}$ xx $n = 0$

where the x's represent the electrons. A transition from the highest filled level ($n = 1$) to the lowest unfilled level ($n = 2$) would require the energy

$$\Delta E = \frac{(4 - 1)h^2}{8\pi^2 mr^2}$$

Using the additional relationships, $\Delta E = h\nu$ and $\lambda = c/\nu$, the wavelength corresponding to this transition would be given by

$$\lambda = \frac{8\pi^2 mr^2 c}{3h}$$

If we make the appropriate substitutions ($h = 6.63 \times 10^{-27}$ erg-sec, $m = 9.04 \times 10^{-28}$ g, and $c = 3.00 \times 10^{10}$ cm/sec), this becomes

$$\lambda = 10.76 \times 10^{10} r^2$$

In benzene the energy levels are split because of interelectronic effects. However, the center of gravity of the bands which result is at about 2000 Å. Using this value and solving for r, a value of 1.38 Å is obtained which may be compared with the value 1.397 Å determined from the rotational Raman spectrum.[5] The agreement between the two values is remarkably good—in fact, too good considering the approximations. These simple calculations indicate how complex systems may often be treated by rather crude approximations and still give remarkably good results.

1-5 The Harmonic Oscillator

Another example which may give us an insight into problems of chemical interest is the harmonic oscillator. This is a reasonable approximation to the behavior of diatomic molecules and also may be used as an approximation to the behavior of electrons in atoms. Again we will follow the procedure previously described, first writing the classical total energy operator (the Hamiltonian operator) and then making the necessary substitutions to obtain the quantum mechanical operator.

Consider the classical case of a weight attached to a spring. If it is moved a distance x from its equilibrium position, it will have a potential energy V equal to $\frac{1}{2}kx^2$, where k is the force constant which is related to the strength of the spring. The total energy H will at any time be the sum of the potential and the kinetic energy, the latter being $p^2/2m$.

$$H = T + V = \tfrac{1}{2}kx^2 + \frac{p^2}{2m}$$

In terms of the classical frequency of oscillation (v) of a weight attached to a spring, the force constant k is given by

$$k = 4\pi^2 m v^2$$

Making this substitution, and the previously mentioned substitution for p, we obtain

$$-\frac{h^2}{8\pi^2 m}\frac{\partial^2 \psi}{\partial x^2} + 2\pi^2 m v^2 x^2 \psi = E\psi$$

where E represents the possible results of a measurement of the energy. In order to get this into a convenient form for solution, we multiply both

[5] B. P. Stoicheff, *Can. J. Phys.*, **32**, 339 (1954).

sides by $8\pi^2 m/h^2$ and make the substitutions

$$\lambda = \frac{8\pi^2 mE}{h^2}$$

$$\alpha^2 = \frac{4\pi^2 mk}{h^2} = \frac{16\pi^4 \nu^2 m^2}{h^2}$$

where λ represents a reduced energy and α a reduced force constant. Then

$$\frac{\partial^2 \psi}{\partial x^2} + (\lambda - \alpha^2 x^2)\psi = 0$$

This may be solved by using an equation of the form $f_{(x)}e^{-\alpha^2 x^2/2}$ for ψ. In order for ψ to fulfill the extra requirements that it be single valued, continuous, and that the integral of ψ^2 taken over all space be finite, it can be shown that the following relationship between λ and α must hold.[6]

$$\frac{2n - \lambda/\alpha + 1}{(n + 1)(n + 2)} = 0$$

where n is any integer. Multiplying both sides by the denominator, we obtain

$$\lambda/\alpha = 2n + 1$$
$$\lambda = 2\alpha(n + \tfrac{1}{2})$$

Introducing the values of λ and α, we obtain

$$E = h\nu(n + \tfrac{1}{2}) \qquad n = 0, 1, 2, 3, \ldots$$

A plot of the wave functions which correspond to these energy levels is shown in Fig. 1-4. It should be noted that the lowest energy level (which has no nodes) has the energy $\tfrac{1}{2}h\nu$, and thus this treatment leads directly to the zero-point energy for the lowest level. This is an example of the operation of the Heisenberg uncertainty principle, which states that the product of the uncertainties in position and momentum must be on the order of Planck's constant h. Thus if the lowest energy level were at the minimum in potential energy, the momentum would be zero, and the uncertainty in position would be infinity. This being impossible, the lowest level is one in which the uncertainty in momentum is finite, permitting a finite value of the uncertainty in position. In particular, for this case the maximum value of the momentum would be given by

$$\frac{p^2}{2m} = E_0 = \tfrac{1}{2}h\nu$$

[6] The proof of this statement will not be given here, for it adds little to an understanding of the problem. For the details, see K. S. Pitzer, *Quantum Chemistry*, Prentice-Hall, New York, 1953, pp. 35–39 or L. Pauling and E. B. Wilson, Jr., *Introduction to Quantum Mechanics*, McGraw-Hill Book Co., New York, 1935, pp. 72–76.

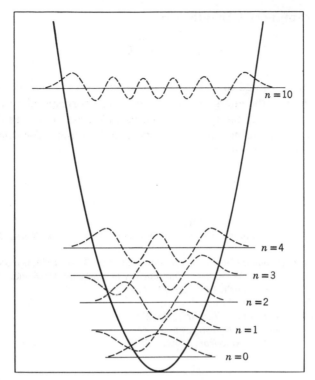

Fig. 1-4. *Wave functions for a harmonic oscillator. The parabola represents the maximum excursions of a classical oscillator having the same force constant.*

Making the substitution for ν in terms of the force constant, we get

$$p^2 = 2mE_0 = \frac{mh}{2\pi}\sqrt{\frac{k}{m}}$$

$$p = \pm\sqrt{\frac{mh}{2\pi}\sqrt{\frac{k}{m}}}$$

Since the momentum has both positive and negative values, the uncertainty in the momentum is the difference between these values or $\Delta p = 2p$. Similarly, the maximum value of x would be given by

$$\tfrac{1}{2}kx^2 = E_0 = \tfrac{1}{2}h\nu$$

$$x^2 = \frac{2E_0}{k} = \frac{h}{2\pi k}\sqrt{\frac{k}{m}}$$

and thus

$$\Delta x = 2\sqrt{\frac{h}{2\pi k}\sqrt{\frac{k}{m}}}$$

The product of Δx and Δp is therefore

$$\Delta x\,\Delta p = \frac{2}{\pi}\,h$$

It may further be noted that the only one of the cases we have considered which has zero as the energy of the lowest level, corresponding to $p = 0$ and therefore no uncertainty in p, is the particle on a circle. In this case the uncertainty in the position of the particle is infinite, for one has no knowledge as to its position.

References

Treatment of the Harmonic Oscillator:
    W. Kauzmann, *Quantum Chemistry*, Academic Press, New York, 1957, pp. 201–208.
    K. S. Pitzer, *Quantum Chemistry*, Prentice-Hall, New York, 1953, pp. 35–39.
    L. Pauling and E. B. Wilson, Jr., *Introduction to Quantum Mechanics*, McGraw-Hill Book Co., New York, 1935, pp. 72–76.
The Heisenberg Uncertainty Principle:
    W. Kauzmann, *Quantum Chemistry*, pp. 235–246.
    K. S. Pitzer, *Quantum Chemistry*, pp. 35–39.
    G. Gamow, *Scientific American*, January 1958.

1-6 The Hydrogen Atom

One case which will supply information necessary for developing the theory of bonding is that of the hydrogen atom. Here we wish to determine the possible energy levels for an electron which is in the field of a proton. Since the total energy is desired, it is necessary to consider both the kinetic and potential energy, and thus the wave equation will be written as

$$(T_{\text{op}} + V_{\text{op}})\psi = E\psi$$

where T_{op} and V_{op} are the kinetic and potential energy operators, respectively, and E represents the possible energy values for the system. The potential energy is simply that due to the Coulombic attraction of a proton for an electron and is given by

$$V = -\frac{e^2}{r}$$

The expression for the kinetic energy operator is considerably simplified by using the nucleus as the center of the coordinate system. Doing so is practical in this case, since we are not interested in translation of the whole system but only in the relative motion of the two particles, and since the center of mass effectively coincides with the position of the nucleus. Furthermore, the use of polar coordinates is more convenient than Cartesian coordinates, so that instead of writing the kinetic energy operator in the form

$$-\frac{h^2}{8\pi^2 m}\left(\frac{\partial^2}{\partial x^2} + \frac{\partial^2}{\partial y^2} + \frac{\partial^2}{\partial z^2}\right)$$

we will use the equivalent in polar coordinates, which is

$$-\frac{h^2}{8\pi^2 m}\left(\frac{1}{r^2}\frac{\partial}{\partial r}\left(r^2\frac{\partial}{\partial r}\right) + \frac{1}{r^2 \sin\theta}\frac{\partial}{\partial\theta}\left(\sin\theta\frac{\partial}{\partial\theta}\right) + \frac{1}{r^2 \sin^2\theta}\frac{\partial^2}{\partial\phi^2}\right)$$

in which m refers to the mass of the electron. The relationship between the polar coordinates and Cartesian coordinates is shown in Fig. 1-5.

The wave equation therefore takes the form

$$-\frac{h^2}{8\pi^2 m}\left[\frac{1}{r^2}\frac{\partial}{\partial r}\left(r^2\frac{\partial\psi}{\partial r}\right) + \frac{1}{r^2 \sin\theta}\frac{\partial}{\partial\theta}\left(\sin\theta\frac{\partial\psi}{\partial\theta}\right) + \frac{1}{r^2 \sin^2\theta}\frac{\partial^2\psi}{\partial\phi^2}\right]$$

$$-\frac{e^2}{r}\psi = E\psi$$

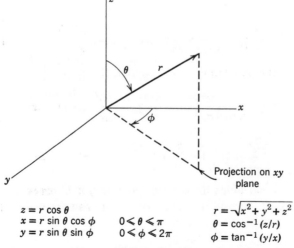

$$z = r\cos\theta$$
$$x = r\sin\theta\cos\phi \qquad 0 \leqslant \theta \leqslant \pi$$
$$y = r\sin\theta\sin\phi \qquad 0 \leqslant \phi \leqslant 2\pi$$

$$r = \sqrt{x^2 + y^2 + z^2}$$
$$\theta = \cos^{-1}(z/r)$$
$$\phi = \tan^{-1}(y/x)$$

Fig. 1-5. Relationship between Cartesian and polar coordinates.

In order to separate the variables, let us try the assumption that ψ may be written as

$$\psi = R\Theta\Phi$$

where Θ is a function only of θ, Φ is a function only of ϕ, and R is a function only of r. Thus

$$-\frac{h^2}{8\pi^2 mr^2}\left[\Theta\Phi\frac{\partial}{\partial r}\left(r^2\frac{\partial R}{\partial r}\right) + \frac{R\Phi}{\sin\theta}\frac{\partial}{\partial\theta}\left(\sin\theta\frac{\partial\Theta}{\partial\theta}\right) + \frac{R\Theta}{\sin^2\theta}\frac{\partial^2\Phi}{\partial\phi^2}\right]$$
$$-\frac{e^2}{r}(R\Theta\Phi) - E(R\Theta\Phi) = 0$$

Then, multiplying by $\dfrac{r^2\sin^2\theta}{R\Theta\Phi}$, we obtain

$$-\frac{h^2\sin^2\theta}{8\pi^2 m}\left[\frac{1}{R}\frac{\partial}{\partial r}\left(r^2\frac{\partial R}{\partial r}\right) + \frac{1}{\Theta\sin\theta}\frac{\partial}{\partial\theta}\left(\sin\theta\frac{\partial\Theta}{\partial\theta}\right)\right]$$
$$-\frac{h^2}{8\pi^2 m}\left[\frac{1}{\Phi}\frac{\partial^2\Phi}{\partial\phi^2}\right] - e^2r\sin^2\theta - Er^2\sin^2\theta = 0$$

Now, one part of the expression contains only one variable, ϕ. We may then make the substitution

$$-m^2 = \frac{1}{\Phi}\frac{\partial^2\Phi}{\partial\phi^2}$$

where $-m^2$ must be a constant, since the rest of the expression does not contain ϕ, and since the entire expression is equal to zero. Making this substitution and dividing by $\sin^2\theta$, we obtain

$$-\frac{h^2}{8\pi^2 m}\left[\frac{1}{R}\frac{\partial}{\partial r}\left(r^2\frac{\partial R}{\partial r}\right) + \frac{1}{\Theta\sin\theta}\frac{\partial}{\partial\theta}\left(\sin\theta\frac{\partial\Theta}{\partial\theta}\right) - \frac{m^2}{\sin^2\theta}\right] - e^2r - Er^2 = 0$$

Applying the same reasoning, it is apparent that

$$-\beta = \frac{1}{\Theta\sin\theta}\frac{\partial}{\partial\theta}\left(\sin\theta\frac{\partial\Theta}{\partial\theta}\right) - \frac{m^2}{\sin^2\theta} = \text{constant}$$

and

$$-\frac{h^2}{8m\pi^2}\left[\frac{1}{R}\frac{\partial}{\partial r}\left(r^2\frac{\partial R}{\partial r}\right)\right] - e^2r - Er^2 - \beta = 0$$

Now that the variables have been separated, it is necessary to obtain expressions for R, Θ, and Φ. The last is obtained from the m equation above:

$$\frac{\partial^2\Phi}{\partial\phi^2} = -m^2\Phi$$

An acceptable solution of this is

$$\Phi = \frac{1}{\sqrt{2\pi}} e^{im\phi} \qquad m = 0, \pm 1, \pm 2, \ldots$$

which may be verified by substitution. The factor $1/\sqrt{2\pi}$ is introduced as a normalization factor so that the integral of Φ^2 taken over all space will be unity.

The other two differential equations may also be solved giving R and Θ. In order to solve the β equation for Θ, it is necessary to introduce a new quantum number, l, which may have the values $|m|$, $|m| + 1$, $|m| + 2$, etc. The details of the solution will not be given here, but the value of the product $\Phi\Theta$ for various values of m and 1 are given in Table 1-2.

Table 1-2   Angular Part of the Wave Function for the Hydrogen Atom

$l = 0$ $\quad$ $m = 0$ $\qquad$ $\Theta\Phi = \left(\dfrac{1}{4\pi}\right)^{\frac{1}{2}}$

$l = 1$ $\quad$ $m = 0$ $\qquad$ $\Theta\Phi = \left(\dfrac{3}{4\pi}\right)^{\frac{1}{2}} \cos\theta$

$l = 1$ $\quad$ $m = \pm 1$ $\qquad$ $\Theta\Phi = \left(\dfrac{3}{8\pi}\right)^{\frac{1}{2}} \sin\theta\, e^{\pm i\phi}$

$\qquad\qquad\qquad\qquad$ or $\left(\dfrac{3}{4\pi}\right)^{\frac{1}{2}} \sin\theta\cos\phi$

$\qquad\qquad\qquad\qquad$ and $\left(\dfrac{3}{4\pi}\right)^{\frac{1}{2}} \sin\theta\sin\phi$

$l = 2$ $\quad$ $m = 0$ $\qquad$ $\Theta\Phi = \left(\dfrac{5}{16\pi}\right)^{\frac{1}{2}} (3\cos^2\theta - 1)$

$l = 2$ $\quad$ $m = \pm 1$ $\qquad$ $\Theta\Phi = \left(\dfrac{15}{8\pi}\right)^{\frac{1}{2}} \sin\theta\cos\theta\, e^{\pm i\phi}$

$\qquad\qquad\qquad\qquad$ or $\left(\dfrac{15}{4\pi}\right)^{\frac{1}{2}} \sin\theta\cos\theta\cos\phi$

$\qquad\qquad\qquad\qquad$ and $\left(\dfrac{15}{4\pi}\right)^{\frac{1}{2}} \sin\theta\cos\theta\sin\phi$

$l = 2$ $\quad$ $m = \pm 2$ $\qquad$ $\Theta\Phi = \left(\dfrac{15}{32\pi}\right)^{\frac{1}{2}} \sin^2\theta\, e^{\pm 2i\phi}$

$\qquad\qquad\qquad\qquad$ or $\left(\dfrac{15}{16\pi}\right)^{\frac{1}{2}} \sin^2\theta\cos 2\phi$

$\qquad\qquad\qquad\qquad$ and $\left(\dfrac{15}{16\pi}\right)^{\frac{1}{2}} \sin^2\theta\sin 2\phi$

s orbital *(r = constant)*

p orbital *(r = cos θ)*

d orbital *(r = 3cos²θ −1)*

d orbital *(r = cos θ sinθ)*

Fig. 1-6. Angular part of the wave function for the hydrogen atom.

It may be seen that the states which have $m = 0$ and $l = 0$ have no dependence on θ and ϕ. Thus the whole wave function will be spherically. symmetrical and will correspond to what is commonly known as an s state For the states having $l = 1$, there are three possible values of m. With $m = 0$, the angular dependence is on $\cos \theta$, which corresponds to a direction along the z axis (cf. Fig. 1-5). Similarly, dependence on $\sin \theta$

cos ϕ corresponds to direction along the x axis, and sin θ sin ϕ corresponds to direction along the y axis. These are commonly known as p states. With $l = 2$, there are a total of five states corresponding to $m = -2, -1$, 0, $+1$, and $+2$. With $m = 0$, the dependence is again on cos θ, which corresponds to the z direction; $m = \pm 1$ corresponds to the z direction and either x or y, and thus the wave function lies principally in the zy and zx planes; and $m = \pm 2$ corresponds to the x and y directions, and therefore it lies principally in the xy plane. The states correspond to the wave functions which are commonly known as d states. Figure 1-6 shows the angular relationships in diagrammatic form.

We must now consider the radial distribution. In order to solve the equation containing r as the only variable, it is necessary to introduce another quantum number n, which may have any integral value. For a given value of n, the maximum possible value of l is $n - 1$. The values of R for various values of n, l, and m are given in Table 1-3, where the nuclear charge Z has been introduced in order to make these more general (see below). In the case of the hydrogen atom, $Z = 1$. All the parts of the total wave function which have been given have been normalized so that the integral of the total wave function squared will equal unity.

Table 1-3 Radial Part of the Wave Function for Hydrogen-like Atoms

$$n = 1 \quad l = 0 \qquad R_{1s} = 2\left(\frac{Z}{a_0}\right)^{3/2} e^{-\sigma}$$

$$n = 2 \quad l = 0 \qquad R_{2s} = \left(\frac{Z}{2a_0}\right)^{3/2} (2 - \sigma)e^{-\sigma/2}$$

$$n = 2 \quad l = 1 \qquad R_{2p} = 3^{-1/2}\left(\frac{Z}{2a_0}\right)^{3/2} \sigma e^{-\sigma/2}$$

$$n = 3 \quad l = 0 \qquad R_{3s} = \frac{2}{27}\left(\frac{Z}{3a_0}\right)^{3/2} (27 - 18\sigma + 2\sigma^2)e^{-\sigma/3}$$

$$n = 3 \quad l = 1 \qquad R_{3p} = \frac{1}{81\sqrt{3}}\left(\frac{2Z}{a_0}\right)^{3/2} (6 - \sigma)\sigma e^{-\sigma/3}$$

$$n = 3 \quad l = 2 \qquad R_{3d} = \frac{1}{81\sqrt{15}}\left(\frac{2Z}{a_0}\right)^{3/2} \sigma^2 e^{-\sigma/3}$$

$$a_0 = \frac{h^2}{4\pi^2 me^2} = 0.529 \times 10^{-8} \text{ cm} = 0.529 \text{ Å}$$

$$\sigma = Zr/a_0$$

$$E = -\frac{Z^2 e^2}{2a_0 n^2}$$

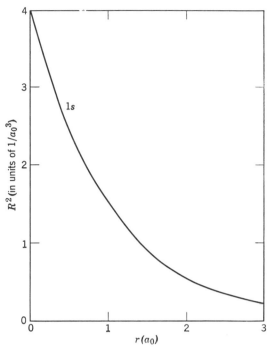

Fig. 1-7. Probability distribution for the radial part of the hydrogen atomic wave functions.

The probability of finding an electron at a given distance from the nucleus is of some interest, and this is given by the square of R for that point. The value of R^2 as a function of the distance from the nucleus is shown in Fig. 1-7. It can be seen that the maximum probability is at the nucleus for an s state and is at some distance from the nucleus for the other states. This probability function, however, gives a rather distorted view of the situation, for the volume element involved increases as r^2, and thus the probability of finding an electron in a shell of thickness dr at a distance r from the nucleus is given by r^2R^2. A plot of this function against distance is shown in Fig. 1-8. It can be seen that the maximum probability of finding an electron on this basis for a $1s$ state is at a distance a_0, corresponding to the distance which was calculated using the old Bohr atomic model. With the $2s$ state there is a nodal sphere in the wave function, leading to a point at about $2a_0$ at which the probability of finding an electron is zero. Similarly, with the $3s$ state there are two nodal spheres, leading to two points on a line drawn from the nucleus at which the probability of finding an electron is zero. Thus in this case, also, states of

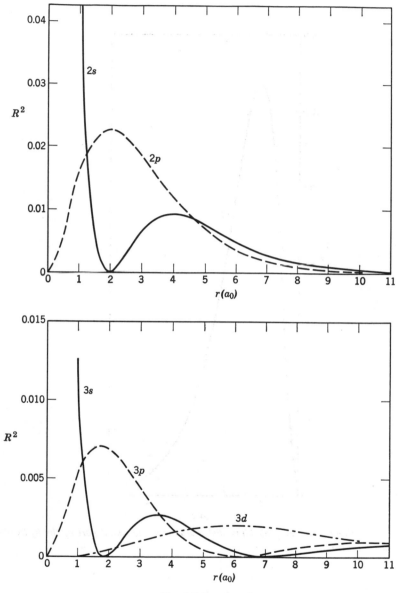

Fig. 1-7 (continued)

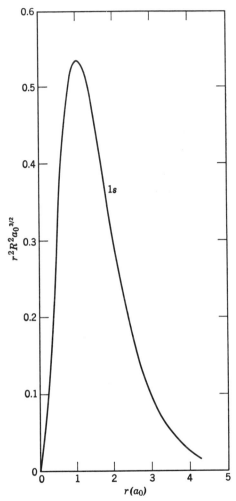

Fig. 1-8. Volume weighted probability distribution for the radial part of the hydrogen atom wave functions.

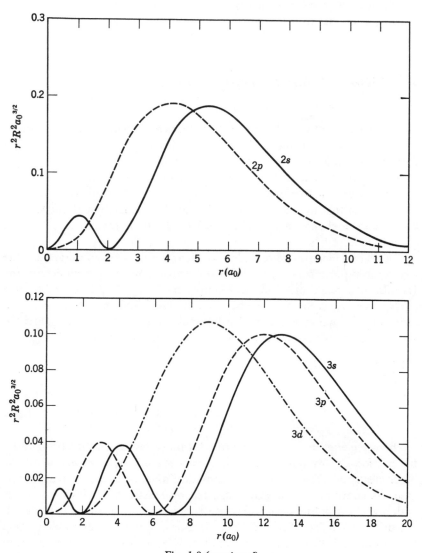

Fig. 1-8 (continued)

increasing energy have increasing number of nodes in the wave function. It may also be noted that the distance at which the maximum probability is found decreases in the order s, p, d.

1-7 Other Atoms: Hybridization

We have now obtained the wave functions and energies for the ground state and the excited states of a hydrogen atom. It is possible to use the data thus obtained in considering other atoms? First, we might consider the case of an ion consisting of one electron and two or more protons in the nucleus. Here the treatment would be the same as that for the hydrogen atom, except that the nuclear charge Z would no longer equal unity. This will result in a change in both the energy levels and in the radial part of the wave functions.

If a second electron were added to such an ion, a new interaction, the electronic repulsion between the two electrons, must be included in the Hamiltonian operator. This will simply involve the addition of a term e^2/r_{12}, where r_{12} is the distance between the two electrons. Another set of terms of this type would be added for each additional electron. Thus the wave equation for the case of three electrons would be

$$\left[\frac{-h^2}{8\pi^2 m}\left(\frac{d^2\psi}{dx^2} + \frac{d^2\psi}{dy^2} + \frac{d^2\psi}{dz^2}\right) + \left(-\frac{e^2}{r_{1a}} - \frac{e^2}{r_{2a}} - \frac{e^2}{r_{3a}}\right)Z\right.$$
$$\left. + \left(+\frac{e^2}{r_{12}} + \frac{e^2}{r_{13}} + \frac{e^2}{r_{23}}\right)\right]\psi = E\psi$$

The wave equation, thus constituted, cannot be solved directly because the motion of any one electron is dependent on the motions of all the other electrons. Thus some approximation must be made in treating this case. A common one is that suggested by Hartree[7] in which one deals with one electron at a time and considers its interaction with the smeared-out distribution for all of the other electrons. Since the terms containing the coordinates of two electrons are thereby eliminated, the wave equation may then be solved, usually by numerical methods.

The procedure begins by assuming a set of wave functions for all of the electrons except one and calculating the electron density distribution which would result. The wave equation, including the interaction of the one electron with the calculated electron density distribution, may now be

[7] D. R. Hartree, *Proc. Cambridge Phil. Soc.*, **24**, 89, 111, 426 (1928).

written and solved for the wave function for that one electron. The procedure may then be repeated for the second electron, the third electron, and so on for all the electrons in the atom.

Once this calculation has been carried out for all the electrons and a set of improved wave functions has been obtained, the calculation is repeated using these new wave functions, and a set of further improved wave functions is obtained. The calculation is continued until the wave functions which result are the same as those which were used in calculating the electron density distribution. Thus the calculation converges on a set of wave functions which are self-consistent. The results of such calculations are in fairly good agreement with the experimental values.

One qualitative observation may be made concerning this treatment. Since a symmetrical potential distribution was used in the calculation, the angular properties of the wave functions which result must be similar to those with which one started (the hydrogen atom wave functions). Thus we can still talk about the resultant orbitals as s, p, d, and f, and the shapes of the orbitals will be similar to those previously discussed for the hydrogen atom. The radial properties of the wave functions will, of course, be changed by the calculation.

The wave functions which result are obtained in the form of a table rather than as analytical functions, and hence they are inconvenient to use. Even the simple hydrogenlike wave functions are of an inconvenient form for use in other calculations, and therfeore the approximate wave functions suggested by Slater,[8] in which the parameters have been chosen so as to give agreement with the experimental data, are very commonly used. The Slater orbitals are as follows:

$$\psi(1s) = N_{1s}e^{-cr} \qquad \psi(2s) = N_{2s}re^{-cr/2} \qquad \psi(3s) = N_{3s}r^2e^{-cr/3}$$

$$\psi(2p_x) = N_{2p}xe^{-cr/2} \qquad\qquad \psi(2p_y) = N_{2p}ye^{-cr/2}$$

$$\psi(2p_z) = N_{2p}ze^{-cr/2} \qquad\qquad \psi(3p_x) = N_{3p}xre^{-cr/3}$$

$$\psi(3d_{xy}) = N_{3d}xye^{-cr/3} \qquad\qquad \psi(3d_{xz}) = N_{3d}xze^{-cr/3}$$

$$\psi(3d_{yz}) = N_{3d}yze^{-cr/3} \qquad\qquad \psi(3d_{x^2-y^2}) = N_{3d}\frac{x^2 - y^2}{2}e^{-cr/3}$$

$$\psi(3d_{z^2}) = N_{3d}\frac{z^2}{2}e^{-cr/3}$$

[8] J. C. Slater, *Phys. Rev.* **36**, 57 (1930); P. M. Morse, L. A. Young, and E. S. Haurwitz, *ibid.*, **48**, 948 (1935); W. E. Duncanson and C. A. Coulson, *Proc. Roy. Soc. Edinburgh*, **62A**, 37 (1944).

The constants N are normalization factors, the values of which are

$$N_{1s} = \left(\frac{c^3}{\pi}\right)^{1/2} \qquad N_{2s} = \left(\frac{c^5}{96\pi}\right)^{1/2} \qquad N_{3s} = \left(\frac{2c^7}{5\cdot3^9\pi}\right)^{1/2}$$

$$N_{2p} = \left(\frac{c^5}{32\pi}\right)^{1/2} \qquad N_{3p} = \left(\frac{2c^7}{5\cdot3^8\pi}\right)^{1/2} \qquad N_{3d} = \left(\frac{2c^7}{3^8\pi}\right)^{1/2}$$

The distances are measured in units of Bohr radii, $a_0(0.529$ Å$)$, and the values of the effective nuclear charge, c, are obtained using the following rules:

1. $c = Z - S$, where Z is the atomic number of the atom and S is the shielding constant.
2. The shielding constant is the sum of the following contributions:
    a. Nothing from any shell ouside the one being considered.
    b. An amount 0.35 from each other electron in the group considered (except in the $1s$ group, where 0.30 is used). Each group consists of atoms with the same principal quantum number and which are in an s or p orbital or in a d of f orbital. The s and p electrons are considered together, and so are the d and f electrons.
    c. If the group being considered is an s,p group, an amount 0.85 from each electron in the next inner shell and 1.00 from each electron further in. If the group is a d,f group, an amount 1.00 for each electron inside it.

For example, with carbon, the effective nuclear charge for the $1s$ electrons is $6 - 0.30$ or 5.70, and for the $2s$, $2p$ electrons it is $6 - 3 \times 0.35 - 2 \times 0.85$ or 3.25.

It can readily be seen that the $1s$, $2p$, and $3d$ Slater orbitals are identical with the corresponding hydrogenlike wave functions. However, the radial distribution for the $2s$ Slater orbital is the same as that for the $2p$ orbital (cf. Fig. 1-8 for the hydrogenlike orbitals), and the former has no spherical node. Similarly, the radial distribution for the $3s$, $3p$, and $3d$ Slater orbitals are the same, and only the angular part is different. At distances encountered in chemical bonding, the hydrogenlike and the Slater orbitals are, however, very similar.

The importance of hybrid atomic orbitals in forming bonds to carbon and to a number of other elements is well recognized. Having obtained the wave functions for a hydrogen atom, and having presented a justification for the use of hydrogenlike atomic orbitals in considering other elements, it would seem appropriate to consider how the hybrid orbitals are formed and to what extent they are unique descriptions of the wave functions for a given system.

Let us first consider the sp^3 type orbitals which are used by carbon in forming saturated compounds such as methane. In the ground state, the carbon atom has two electrons in the $2s$ orbital and one electron in each of two $2p$ orbitals. This configuration, having only two unpaired electrons, would permit only the formation of the highly reactive compound CH_2 but could not account for the formation of a compound with four atoms attached to carbon. In order to obtain the latter one of the electrons in the $2s$ orbital must be promoted to the empty p orbital. This state has an energy 96 kcal/mole higher than that of the ground state.[9] The promotion energy is more than counterbalanced by the formation of an additional two bonds having bond energies on the order of 80 to 110 kcal/mole. However, the formation of bonds using this state would not lead to a methane molecule in which all of the C-H bonds were identical, whereas experimental data have shown the latter to be the case.

Pauling and Slater[10] have shown that the observed nature of the bonding in methane could be accounted for if one assumes that hybrid orbitals involving linear combinations of the s and p orbitals are formed. The new, hybrid orbitals may be written as

$$\psi_1 = a_1 s + b_1 p_x + c_1 p_y + d_1 p_z$$
$$\psi_2 = a_2 s + b_2 p_x + c_2 p_y + d_2 p_z$$
$$\psi_3 = a_3 s + b_3 p_x + c_3 p_y + d_3 p_z$$
$$\psi_4 = a_4 s + b_4 p_x + c_4 p_y + d_4 p_z$$

The constants a_i, b_i, c_i, and d_i must be chosen so that the resultant wave functions are normalized and orthogonal. Thus, since the atomic orbitals s and p are normalized and orthogonal, the requirements are satisfied by the relationships:

$$a_i{}^2 + b_i{}^2 + c_i{}^2 + d_i{}^2 = 1 \quad \text{(normalization)}$$
$$a_i a_j + b_i b_j + c_i c_j + d_i d_j = 0 \quad (i \neq j) \quad \text{(orthogonality)}$$

There are a total of 4 normalization equations and 6 orthogonality relationships, making a total of 10 equations, whereas there are 16 unknowns. Of the remaining 6 unknowns, 3 will result only in changing the orientation in space, and hence only 3 parameters are required to indicate the nature of the hybridization.

The set of parameters which will lead to the sp^3 hybrid is $a_1 = b_1 = c_1 = d_1$, which represent only three independent variables because of the

[9] A. G. Shenstone, *Phys. Rev.*, **72**, 411 (1947).
[10] L. Pauling, *Proc. Nat. Acad. Sci.* **14**, 359 (1928); *J. Am. Chem. Soc.* **53**, 1367 (1931); J. C. Slater, *Phys. Rev.* **37**, 481 (1931).

normalization requirement. It can readily be seen that the normalization and orthogonality requirements are then met by the set of wave functions:

$$\psi_1 = \tfrac{1}{2}(s + p_x + p_y + p_z)$$
$$\psi_2 = \tfrac{1}{2}(s + p_x - p_y - p_z)$$
$$\psi_3 = \tfrac{1}{2}(s - p_x + p_y - p_z)$$
$$\psi_4 = \tfrac{1}{2}(s - p_x - p_y + p_z)$$

It may be noted that the contribution of s and p character to the hybrid orbitals is given by the squares of the appropriate coefficients. Thus, for each of the above orbitals, the s contribution is $\tfrac{1}{4}$ and the p contribution is $\tfrac{3}{4}$.

The geometrical relationship between these hybrid orbitals is easily seen. The s part has no effect on the geometry, for it is spherically symmetrical. With ψ_1 there is a sum of the three p orbitals. Since the positive side of the orbitals is normally taken as lying on the positive side of the corresponding coordinate axis, a point on the axis of the orbital described by ψ_1, will be equidistant from the $+x$, $+y$, and $+z$ axes. Similarly, with ψ_2, a point on the axis of the new orbital will be equidistant from the $+x$, $-y$, and $-z$ axes. This may perhaps be best visualized by considering a cube, the center of which is the origin of the coordinate system (Fig. 1-9). The first hybrid orbital will be directed towards the forward upper right-hand corner of the cube, the second toward the rear upper left-hand corner, and so on.

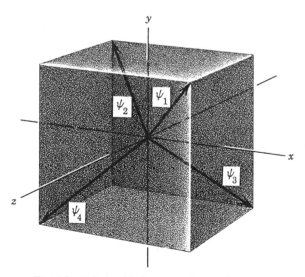

Fig. 1-9. Relationship between sp³ wave functions.

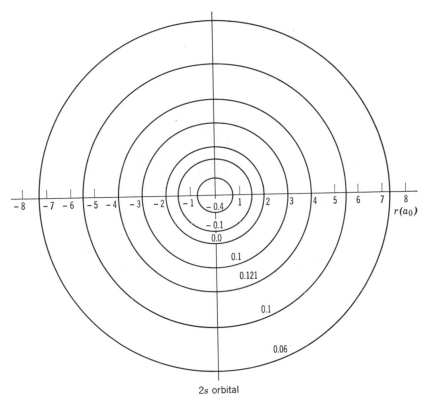

2*s* orbital

Fig. 1-10. Shapes of some atomic orbitals and hybrid orbitals. The numbers on the contours give the value of ψ.

It is of interest to compare the sp^3 hybrid orbitals with the starting atomic orbitals, and such a comparison is shown in Fig. 1-10. It can be seen that the hybrid orbital concentrates the electron density distribution on one side of the nucleus, which results in a large degree of overlap with the wave functions of other atoms which form bonds with these orbitals. The greater overlap in turn leads to a stronger bond.

Another possible choice of parameters would be $a_1 = b_1 = c_1$, $d_1 = 0$. This results in the wave functions:

$$\psi_1 = \frac{1}{\sqrt{3}}(s + p_x + p_y)$$

$$\psi_2 = \frac{1}{\sqrt{3}}(s + 0.366p_x - 1.366p_y)$$

$$\psi_3 = \frac{1}{\sqrt{3}}(s - 1.366p_x + 0.366p_y)$$

$$\psi_4 = p_z$$

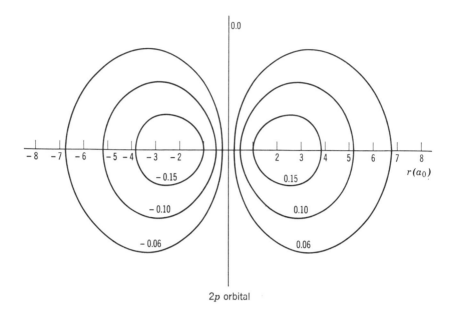

2p orbital

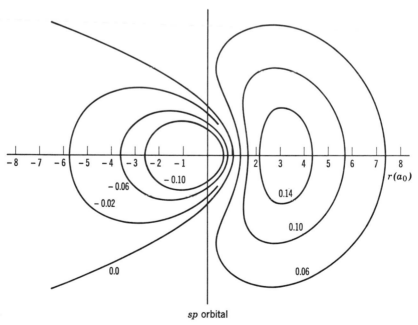

sp orbital

Fig. 1-10 (continued)

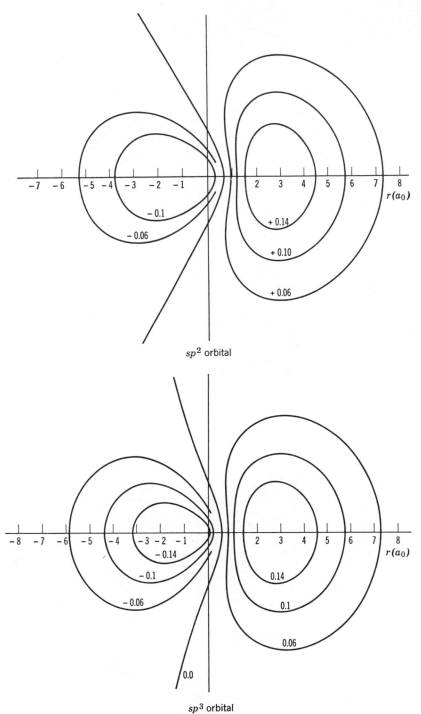

sp^2 orbital

sp^3 orbital

Fig. 1-10 (continued)

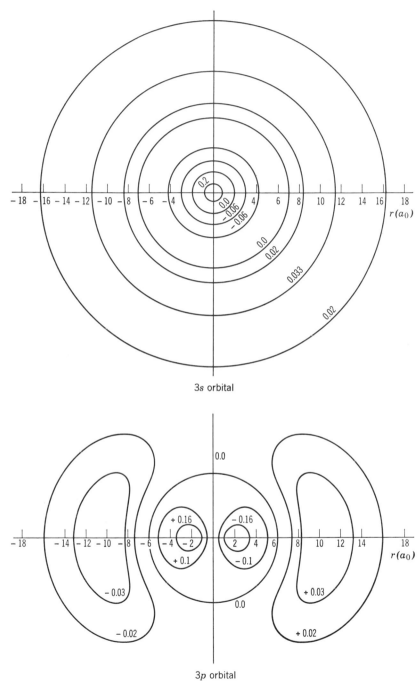

3s orbital

3p orbital

Fig. 1-10 (continued)

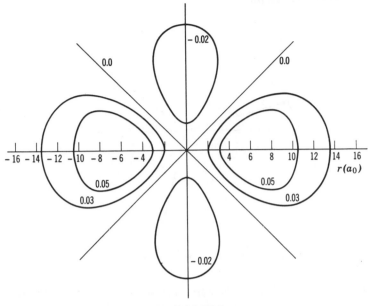

3d orbital ($3d_z$)

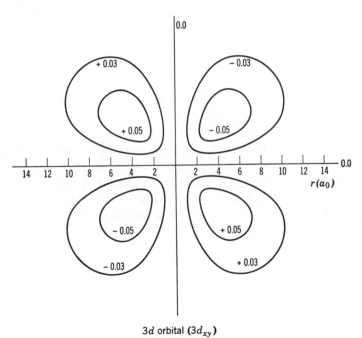

3d orbital ($3d_{xy}$)

Fig. 1-10 (continued)

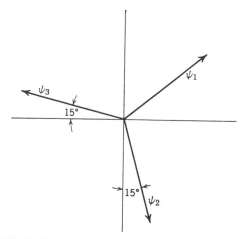

Fig. 1-11. *Relationship between sp² wave functions.*

the first three of which are hybrid sp^2 orbitals, leaving a p_z orbital which is perpendicular to the plane of the other orbitals. The three orbitals must all lie in the xy plane, for the p orbitals which form them lie on the x and y coordinates, respectively. The first will have its axis between that of the $+x$ and $+y$ axes, since the coefficients for the p_x and p_y orbitals are equal (Fig. 1-11). The second will lie close to the $-y$ axis and will make an angle, α, with it of

$$\cos \alpha = \frac{1.366}{\sqrt{0.366^2 + 1.366^2}} = 0.966$$

$$\alpha = 15°$$

and it will lie in the $+x$ direction. Similarly, the third orbital will make an angle of 15° with the $-x$ axis and will lie in the $+y$ direction.

The three sp^2 orbitals are more commonly drawn with the axis of one of the orbitals coinciding with the x axis (Fig. 1-12). This corresponds to a rotation of the coordinate axes and gives the equivalent set of hybrid orbitals:

$$\psi_1 = \frac{1}{\sqrt{3}} (s + \sqrt{2}p_x)$$

$$\psi_2 = \frac{1}{\sqrt{3}} \left(s - \frac{\sqrt{2}}{2} p_x + \frac{\sqrt{6}}{2} p_y \right)$$

$$\psi_3 = \frac{1}{\sqrt{3}} \left(s - \frac{\sqrt{2}}{2} p_x - \frac{\sqrt{6}}{2} p_y \right)$$

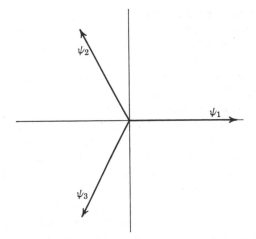

Fig. 1-12. Relationship between sp² wave functions after rotation of coordinates.

By using either of these equivalent sets, it can readily be seen that each orbital is formed from $\frac{1}{3}$ of an s orbital and $\frac{2}{3}$ of a p orbital.

A third set of parameters would be $a_1 = b_1$, $c_1 = d_1 = 0$. This leads to the wave functions:

$$\psi_1 = \frac{1}{\sqrt{2}}(s + p_x)$$

$$\psi_2 = \frac{1}{\sqrt{2}}(s - p_x)$$

$$\psi_3 = p_y$$

$$\psi_4 = p_z$$

Here, since the only directional component is in the x direction, the two hybrid orbitals ψ_1 and ψ_2 must also lie in the x direction. With ψ_1 we have a sum of the s and p_x orbitals. The wave function for the p_x orbitals has a positive sign in the $+x$ direction, and the wave function for the s orbitals is positive everywhere except for the part within the nodal sphere. However, the latter lies relatively close to the nucleus and may be neglected for the present purpose. The s and p_x orbitals therefore reinforce each other in the $+x$ direction, whereas there is partial cancellation in the $-x$ direction. Hence $\psi_1{}^2$ will be large for $+x$ and small for $-x$, corresponding to a higher probability of finding the electron in the $+x$ than in the $-x$ direction. Similarly, for ψ_2, the sign of p_x is changed, and the higher probability of finding an electron will be in the $-x$ direction.

We may now inquire if these are the only hybrid orbitals which may be formed from s and p wave functions. It may easily be seen that these are the only sets of equivalent hybrid orbitals, but since the choice of the values of a_1, b_1, and c_1 was arbitrary, an infinite set of hybrid orbitals may be formed from the set of s and p orbitals. The only requirements are that the new hybrid orbitals are normalized and orthogonal. These orbitals are of considerable importance, for in most unsymmetrical cases the orbitals used are not one of the simple equivalent orbitals described above, but, rather, they are one of the other hybrid orbitals.

An example of this is the water molecule. The bond angle in water is 104.5°, which is significantly different from the angle derived from pure p orbitals (90°) and from sp^3 orbitals (109°28'). Thus, assuming coaxial bonds, some other hybrid must be used. Let us try to obtain a set of orbitals which will lead to this bond angle. To do so it is convenient to consider the p orbitals as vectors directed along the axis of the orbital. We can then take linear combinations of the p orbitals to form new p-type orbitals which will be directed in the appropriate directions. Let us take two such p-type orbitals, p_i and p_j (Fig. 1-13), and see what relationships must hold in order for the angle between them to have a given value.

The hybrid formed from p_i will be ψ_1:

$$\psi_1 = \frac{1}{\sqrt{N_1}}(s + \lambda p_i)$$

where N is the normalization constant ($1^2 + \lambda^2$) and λ is the mixing constant which determines the relative weight of the s and p orbitals. Similarly, the hybrid orbital formed from p_j will be

$$\psi_2 = \frac{1}{\sqrt{N_2}}(s + \delta p_j)$$

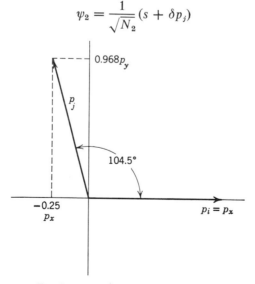

Fig. 1-13. p-atomic orbitals for water.

where δ is a mixing constant. For these orbitals to be orthogonal,

$$\frac{1}{\sqrt{N_1 N_2}} \int (s + \lambda p_i)(s + \delta p_j)\, d\tau = 0$$

and thus

$$\int s^2\, d\tau + \int \lambda s p_i\, d\tau + \int \delta s p_j\, d\tau + \int \lambda \delta p_i p_j\, d\tau = 0$$

The first term is unity because the original wave function was normalized, and the second and third terms are zero because of the orthogonality of the original wave functions. Therefore

$$1 + \lambda \delta \int p_i p_j\, d\tau = 0$$

and because of the vector character of the wave functions $p_i p_j$, the integral of their product can be replaced by the cosine of the angle between them, θ_{ij}. The required orthogonality condition is then

$$\lambda \delta = -\frac{1}{\cos \theta_{ij}}$$

In this case, θ_{ij} is equal to 104.5°, and thus the product $\lambda \delta$ is equal to 4.00. We wish to construct two equivalent orbitals, since the two O—H bonds in water are equivalent, and thus we shall set both λ and δ equal to the square root of this quantity, namely 2.00. For convenience let us have p_i lie along the x axis. Then the first x hybrid orbital will have the wave function

$$\psi_1 = \frac{1}{\sqrt{5}}(s + 2p_x)$$

The second orbital (Fig. 1-13) may be obtained by forming the projections of p_j on the x and y axes, and this leads to the wave function

$$\psi_2 = \frac{1}{\sqrt{5}}(s - 0.500p_x + 1.936p_y)$$

The other two orbitals may be constructed in a similar manner. However, it may be more easily done using the normalization relationships. It can be seen that each of the above orbitals has 0.2 of an s orbital. The remaining orbitals, if they are to be equivalent, must then have 0.3 of an s orbital each. Thus they may be written as

$$\psi_3 = \sqrt{0.3}(s + a_3 p_x + b_3 p_y + c_3 p_z)$$
$$\psi_4 = \sqrt{0.3}(s + a_4 p_x + b_4 p_y + c_4 p_z)$$

One of the remaining orbitals must be in front of the xy plane and the other behind. Thus the signs of c_3 and c_4 must be opposite. Furthermore, the normalization condition requires that $0.3(c_3)^2 + 0.3(c_4)^2 = 1$, for the probability of finding an electron in a p_z orbital is unity. Thus $c_3 = 1.291$ and $c_4 = -1.291$. Similarly, since these latter two orbitals have identical p_x and p_y components, the remaining coefficients may be evaluated so that the total probability of finding an electron in a p_x orbital and in a p_y orbital is unity. The entire set of wave functions then is

$$\psi_1 = \frac{1}{\sqrt{5}} (s + 2p_x)$$

$$\psi_2 = \frac{1}{\sqrt{5}} (s - 0.5p_x + 1.936p_y)$$

$$\psi_3 = \sqrt{0.3}\, (s - 0.5p_x - 0.646p_y + 1.291p_z)$$

$$\psi_4 = \sqrt{0.3}\, (s - 0.5p_x - 0.646p_y - 1.291p_z)$$

It would now be of interest to obtain the angle between the orbitals described by the wave functions ψ_3 and ψ_4. For two vectors having the components x_i, y_i, z_i, and x_j, y_j, and z_j, respectively, the cosine of the angle is given by

$$\cos \alpha = \frac{(x_i x_j) + (y_i y_j) + (z_i z_j)}{\sqrt{(x_i^2 + y_i^2 + z_i^2)}\,\sqrt{(x_j^2 + y_j^2 + z_j^2)}}$$

and using the above values, the angle is found to be 115.5°. This is the basis of the common assumption that if steric or other factors tend to increase one bond angle on a carbon, the angle formed from the other two orbitals on that carbon will tend to decrease.

Why should the bond angles deviate from the tetrahedral arrangement? A simple, yet in many ways very satisfactory, argument proceeds as follows:[11] Two principles govern the distribution of electrons about an atom. The first is the repulsion between the electrons which tends to place the electrons as far from each other as possible, and the second is the Pauli exclusion principle, which states, in effect, that electron pairs are energetically more favorable than assemblies of three or more electrons. Thus, in any atom having eight electrons about it, the electrons would prefer to be located as pairs at the corners of a tetrahedron (and, similarly, if there were six electrons, they would be located as pairs at the corners of a triangle).

In water, two pairs of electrons would be in elongated orbitals forming bonds with the hydrogens, whereas the other two pairs would be in orbitals relatively more concentrated near the nucleus. The repulsion between the

[11] P. G. Dickens and J. W. Linnett, *Quart. Revs.*, **11**, 291 (1957); R. J. Gillespie, *J. Am. Chem. Soc.*, **82**, 5978 (1960); J. W. Linnett, *J. Am. Chem. Soc.*, **83**, 2643 (1961).

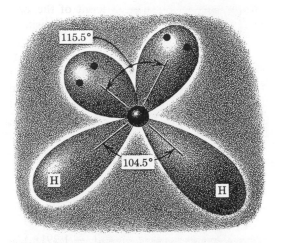

Fig. 1-14. Molecular orbitals for the water molecule.

electrons in the latter two orbitals will therefore be greater than that between the electrons in the bonding orbitals. Thus the angle between the unshared pairs will be greater than that between the bonding orbitals (cf. Fig. 1-14).

We may now inquire if the amount of s and p character in a bond, as calculated from the bond angle, has a quantitative significance. Unfortunately, the answer is probably "No," for the use of hydrogenlike wave functions is in itself only an approximation for a many electron case and since the $3s$, $3p$ and $3d$ orbitals were not included in the scheme. How ever, in a semiquantitative, comparative sense, it provides a way of thinking about bonds which do not fit the simple picture of sp, sp^2, and sp^3 hybrid orbitals.

There are two reasons why hybrid orbitals are more favorable than the hydrogenlike orbitals. First, as mentioned above, the hybrid orbitals are directed so as to minimize interelectronic repulsion. Second, these orbitals concentrate the wave function in the direction of bonding, leading to a greater amount of overlap with the wave function of the other atom and resulting in a stronger bond. It is therefore of interest to compare the strengths of bonds formed by the several types of hybrid orbitals. Figure 1-15[12] shows how the overlap integral between two atoms, such as carbon, varies with the percentage of s character in the bond. Although pure p or s orbitals result in overlap integrals less than 0.5, it can be seen that the hybrid orbitals give values of the overlap integral of over 0.8.

The curve has a maximum at about the sp hybrid, and thus it might be

[12] A. Maccoll, *Trans. Faraday Soc.* **46**, 369 (1950).

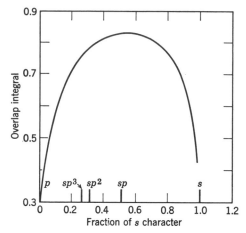

Fig. 1-15. Overlap integral between two similar hybrid atomic orbitals as a function of s character. (A. Maccoll, *Trans. Faraday Soc.*, **46**, 369 (1950).)

expected that this hybrid orbital leads to the strongest bond and then is followed by the sp^2 and sp^3 orbitals.

Justification for this point of view is found in Table 1-4, which compares the bond strengths of bonds to hydrogen by the various types of hybrid orbitals on carbon.[13] It can be seen that the bond energies decrease in the expected order, and, further, the stretching force constants and the bond lengths change in the expected fashion.

Table 1-4   Properties of CH Bonds Involving Different Hybridization

Hybridization	Molecule	C—H Bond Length	Stretching Force Constant	Bond Energy (kcal/mole)
sp	Acetylene	1.057	5.88	121
sp^2	Ethylene	1.079	5.05	106
sp^3	Methane	1.094	4.88	101
p	CH radical	1.120	4.09	80

Throughout this section we have discussed bonding in terms of s and p hydrogenlike orbitals. Although this gives a fairly satisfactory description of the compounds in question, it appears likely that the orbitals forming the bonds have some d and f character. Pauling[14] has considered the bonding

[13] A. D. Walsh, *Trans. Faraday Soc.*, **43**, 60 (1947).
[14] L. Pauling, *Proc. Nat. Acad. Sci.* **44**, 211 (1958); *The Nature of the Chemical Bond*, Cornell University Press, Ithaca, New York, 3rd ed., 1960, pp. 126–128, 143; *Theoretical Organic Chemistry, Kekulé Symposium*, Butterworths Scientific Publications, London, 1959.

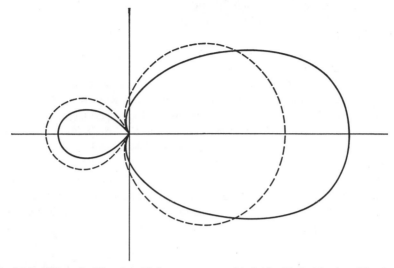

Fig. 1-16. *Effect of adding d and f character to an sp³ hybrid orbital. The dotted line is the wave function for an sp³ orbital and the solid line is the same wave function to which 4% d character and 2% f character has been added.* (L. Pauling, *Nature of the Chemical Bond,* 3rd ed., 1960, p. 128, © 1960 by Cornell University; used by permission of Cornell University Press, Ithaca, N.Y.)

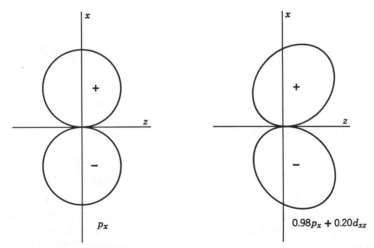

Fig. 1-17. *Effect of adding 4% d character to a p atomic orbital* (L. Pauling, *The Nature of the Chemical Bond,* p. 143).

energy of sp^3 orbitals to which $3d$ and $4f$ character was added. Although the d and f orbitals have a higher energy than the $2s$ or $2p$ orbitals, a new orbital is formed which is more concentrated along the bonding direction than the sp^3 orbital (Fig. 1-16). Up to a certain point, the increase in bonding energy thus produced more than counterbalances the higher energy of the d and f orbitals, and the best orbital was that having about 4% d character and 2% f character. In the same way, the addition of a small amount of d character to a p orbital produces a considerable change in the shape of the orbital (Fig. 1-17), and this may have important consequences in the consideration of π-orbital overlap.[14]

Finally, it should be noted that the use of s and p orbitals as the basis functions for forming hybrid orbitals arises from the mathematical formalism in treating the hydrogen atom. We could just as well consider the sp^3 wave functions as the basis functions and form the other orbitals as linear combinations of these orbitals.

References

Pauli Exclusion Principle:
    L. Pauling, *Nature of the Chemical Bond*, Cornell University Press, Ithaca, N.Y., 3rd ed., 1960, pp. 47–57.
    G. Gamow, *Scientific American*, July 1959, p. 74.
Self-Consistent-Field Model of an Atom:
    C. A. Coulson, *Valence*, Oxford University Press, London, 1952, pp. 32–34.
    W. Kauzmann, *Quantum Chemistry*, Academic Press, New York, 1957, pp. 334–336.
Hybridization:
    C. A. Coulson, *Valence*, Oxford University Press, London, 1952, pp. 187–222.
    L. Pauling, *Nature of the Chemical Bond*, Cornell University Press, Ithaca, N.Y., 3rd ed., 1960, pp. 108–142.

1-8 The Variation Method

The cases in which organic chemists are particularly interested are those involving three or more particles. The wave equation for these cases cannot be solved directly, for the equation is not of a suitable form. However, two powerful approximation methods have been developed which permit the solution of a wide variety of problems. Since these are the key to the application of quantum chemistry, they will be considered in some detail.

The first is the *variation method*, which is based on the theorem that[15]

$$\int \psi_{\mathrm{arb}} H \psi_{\mathrm{arb}} \, d\tau \geqslant \int \psi_0 H \psi_0 \, d\tau = E_0$$

Here ψ_{arb} is an arbitrarily chosen ψ which meets all the requirements (single valued, continuous, etc.) for the operator in question and is normalized, H is the Hamiltonian operator, which is the sum of the kinetic and potential energy operators, ψ_0 is the true wave function for the particular case, E_0 is the true energy, and $d\tau$ indicates that the integration is to be taken over all coordinates of the system (i.e., x, y, and z if Cartesian coordinates are used). If it can be shown that this theorem is correct, then the limitation on the accuracy of the value of the energy obtained will depend on how good a guess we make for ψ_{arb}, and, in any case, the energy obtained will be equal to or higher than the true energy.

The equality on the right side of the equation should first be shown. Since $H\psi_0 = E_0\psi_0$, it may be written as

$$\int \psi_0 E_0 \psi_0 \, d\tau = E_0$$

The E_0 may be taken out from under the integral sign, since it is a constant; and since the integral of $\psi_0{}^2$ is equal to unity, it reduces to $E_0 = E_0$.

In order to prove the theorem we must first develop the expansion theorem, which states that an arbitrary ψ (provided that it meets the usual requirement) may be expanded in terms of the true wave functions for the system in question

$$\psi_{\mathrm{arb}} = c_0\psi_0 + c_1\psi_1 + c_2\psi_2 + c_3\psi_3 + \cdots = \sum_i c_i\psi_i$$

where ψ_0, ψ_1, ψ_2, ... are the wave functions for the energy levels E_0, E_1, E_2, ..., respectively, and correspond to different values of the quantum number, n. We will assume that the ψ's are normalized so that

$$\int \psi_i \psi_i \, d\tau = 1$$

The true wave functions for any case are orthogonal, so that

$$\int \psi_i \psi_j \, d\tau = 0$$

[15] It should be noted that this and all similar expressions should be written using the complex conjugate of ψ. However, since real wave functions will be used throughout this presentation, this notation will not be used.

Now, if both sides of the equation are squared and an integration performed over all coordinates, this becomes

$$\int \psi_{\text{arb}}\psi_{\text{arb}} \, d\tau = \int \sum_{ij} c_i\psi_i c_j\psi_j \, d\tau$$

or

$$\int \psi_{\text{arb}}\psi_{\text{arb}} \, d\tau = \int c_0\psi_0 c_0\psi_0 \, d\tau + \int c_0\psi_0 c_1\psi_1 \, d\tau$$

$$+ \int c_0\psi_0 c_2\psi_2 \, d\tau + \cdots + \int c_1\psi_1 c_1\psi_1 \, d\tau$$

$$+ \int c_1\psi_1 c_2\psi_2 \, d\tau + \cdots$$

From the above properties of the wave functions it can be seen that the terms in which a given ψ is multiplied by itself will give unity times the square of the coefficient and that terms which contain two different ψ's will give zero on integration. Thus

$$1 = \int \psi_{\text{arb}}\psi_{\text{arb}} \, d\tau = c_1{}^2 + c_2{}^2 + c_3{}^2 + \cdots = \sum_i c_i{}^2$$

and the requirement for the equation to hold is that the squares of the coefficients be equal to unity.

It is apparent from the foregoing that the following expression also holds:

$$\int \psi_{\text{arb}} H \psi_{\text{arb}} \, d\tau = \int \sum_i c_i\psi_i H \sum_i c_i\psi_i \, d\tau$$

and we may evaluate it term by term:

$$\int \psi_{\text{arb}} H \psi_{\text{arb}} \, d\tau = \int c_0\psi_0 H c_0\psi_0 \, d\tau + \int c_1\psi_1 H c_1\psi_1 \, d\tau$$

$$+ \cdots = c_0{}^2 E_0 + c_1{}^2 E_1 + c_2{}^2 E_2 + \cdots$$

where again the terms having different ψ's drop out because they are orthogonal:

$$\int c_0\psi_0 H c_1\psi_1 \, d\tau = E_1 \int c_0\psi_0 c_1\psi_1 \, d\tau = 0$$

and

$$\int c_0\psi_0 H c_0\psi_0 \, d\tau = E_0 \int c_0\psi_0 c_0\psi_0 \, d\tau = c_0{}^2 E_0$$

It can be seen that the integral is equal to the weighted average of the energies $E_0, E_1, E_2, \ldots$. These energies are the true energies of the successively higher energy states of the system in which we are interested. Since all the energies after the first term are greater than E_0 (the ground state), the weighted average will be equal to or greater than E_0, which is that which was to be proved. If the ψ_{arb} were chosen so that the coefficients greater than c_0 are small, the energy obtained using ψ_{arb} would be very close to the true value, and, if not, it might be considerably higher.

The utility of this theorem lies in the fact that ψ_{arb} may also be expanded in terms of other wave functions, ϕ, which meet the requirements for wave functions in general and are linearly independent but need not be the wave functions of the operator and need not be orthogonal.

$$\psi_{arb} = c_1\phi_1 + c_2\phi_2 + c_3\phi_3 + \cdots = \sum_i c_i\phi_i$$

Now, if it were possible to take a complete set of these wave functions and to determine the values of the coefficients which would minimize the energy, we should obtain a good approximation to the true energy, for we know that the lowest energy which can be calculated in this way is the true energy, provided that the correct operator is used. Our problem is then to evaluate the coefficients.

The energy may be written as

$$E = \frac{\displaystyle\int \psi_{arb}H\psi_{arb}\,d\tau}{\displaystyle\int \psi_{arb}\psi_{arb}\,d\tau}$$

where the denominator is the normalization factor, which is included in case ψ_{arb} has not been normalized. In the expanded form, using only three ϕ's in this example, it will be

$$E = \frac{\displaystyle\int (c_1\phi_1 + c_2\phi_2 + c_3\phi_3)H(c_1\phi_1 + c_2\phi_2 + c_3\phi_3)\,d\tau}{\displaystyle\int (c_1\phi_1 + c_2\phi_2 + c_3\phi_3)(c_1\phi_1 + c_2\phi_2 + c_3\phi_3)\,d\tau}$$

We wish to determine what values of c_1, c_2, and c_3 will result in giving a minimum value of E. The minima and maxima of any equation are obtained by setting the derivative with respect to that variable equal to zero. Thus we set

$$\left(\frac{\partial E}{\partial c_1}\right)_{c_2,\,c_3} = 0 \qquad \left(\frac{\partial E}{\partial c_2}\right)_{c_1,\,c_3} = 0 \qquad \left(\frac{\partial E}{\partial c_3}\right)_{c_1,\,c_2} = 0$$

In order to differentiate the expression, let us write it with all of the terms multiplied out.

$$[c_1c_1\phi H\phi_1 + c_1c_2\phi_1H\phi_2 + c_2c_2\phi_2H\phi_2 + c_2c_1\phi_2H\phi_1 + \cdots]\,d\tau$$
$$= E[c_1c_1\phi_1\phi_1 + c_1c_2\phi_1\phi_2 + c_2c_2\phi_2\phi_2 + c_2c_1\phi_2\phi_1 + \cdots]\,d\tau$$

Note that the cross terms (such as $c_1c_2\phi_1\phi_2$) do not necessarily drop out, for the wave functions are not necessarily orthogonal. In order to abbreviate this we shall write

$$H_{ij} = \int \phi_i H \phi_j \, d\tau$$

$$\Delta_{ij} = \int \phi_i \phi_j \, d\tau$$

which gives the expression:

$$c_1{}^2 H_{11} + c_1 c_2 H_{12} + c_2{}^2 H_{22} + c_2 c_1 H_{21} + c_1 c_3 H_{13} + c_3 c_1 H_{31} + c_2 c_3 H_{23}$$
$$+ c_3 c_2 H_{32} + c_3{}^2 H_{33} = E(c_1{}^2 \Delta_{11} + c_1 c_2 \Delta_{12} + c_2{}^2 \Delta_{22} + \cdots)$$

It is now differentiated with respect to c_1:

$$(2c_1 H_{11} + c_2 H_{12} + c_2 H_{21} + c_3 H_{13} + c_3 H_{31}) =$$
$$\left(\frac{\partial E}{\partial c_1}\right)_{c_2, \, c_3} (c_1{}^2 \Delta_{11} + c_1 c_2 \Delta_{12} + c_2{}^2 \Delta_{22} + \cdots)$$
$$+ E(2c_1 \Delta_{11} + c_2 \Delta_{12} + c_2 \Delta_{21} + c_3 \Delta_{13} + c_3 \Delta_{31})$$

and $\dfrac{\partial E}{\partial c_1}$ is set equal to zero. In this case H_{12} is the same as H_{21} (just a different order of performing the operations), and thus the equation becomes

$$c_1 H_{11} + c_2 H_{12} + c_3 H_{13} = E(c_1 \Delta_{11} + c_2 \Delta_{12} + c_3 \Delta_{13})$$

The equation is also differentiated with respect to c_2 and c_3, giving

$$c_1 H_{21} + c_2 H_{22} + c_3 H_{23} = E(c_1 \Delta_{21} + c_2 \Delta_{22} + c_3 \Delta_{23})$$
$$c_1 H_{31} + c_2 H_{32} + c_3 H_{33} = E(c_1 \Delta_{31} + c_2 \Delta_{32} + c_3 \Delta_{33})$$

Thus in order to solve for the energy and the coefficients, we must solve the set of three simultaneous equations:

$$c_1(H_{11} - \Delta_{11}E) + c_2(H_{12} - \Delta_{12}E) + c_3(H_{13} - \Delta_{13}E) = 0$$
$$c_1(H_{21} - \Delta_{21}E) + c_2(H_{22} - \Delta_{22}E) + c_3(H_{23} - \Delta_{23}E) = 0$$
$$c_1(H_{31} - \Delta_{31}E) + c_2(H_{32} - \Delta_{32}E) + c_3(H_{33} - \Delta_{33}E) = 0$$

For any set of simultaneous equations of this type, the necessary and sufficient condition for a solution is that the determinant of the coefficients be equal to zero. In this case the determinant is

$$\begin{vmatrix} H_{11} - \Delta_{11}E & H_{12} - \Delta_{12}E & H_{13} - \Delta_{13}E \\ H_{21} - \Delta_{21}E & H_{22} - \Delta_{22}E & H_{23} - \Delta_{23}E \\ H_{31} - \Delta_{31}E & H_{32} - \Delta_{32}E & H_{33} - \Delta_{33}E \end{vmatrix} = 0$$

and it is commonly known as the secular determinant. (It should be evident that there will be as many rows and columns as there are ϕ's.)

Its solution (the method of procedure is described in Appendix 2), taking the lowest root, gives the value of E. The latter may be resubstituted into the original equations to give the values of c_1, c_2, and c_3. This requires the assumption of a value for one of the c's (for example, call $c_1 = 1$), and once the relative values have been obtained, they are normalized by dividing by $\sqrt{c_1{}^2 + c_2{}^2 + c_3{}^2}$.

It may be noted that the secular determinant gives as many values of energy as the number of trial wave functions used in the summation. Not only is the lowest root the approximation to the ground state, but also the higher values are approximations to the successively higher energy levels for the system in question. The wave functions for the excited states of the system may be obtained by finding the coefficients which satisfy the original equations for each of the higher values of the energy.

There is an interesting property of this treatment. It is that the error in the energy is one order of approximation less than that of the ψ_{arb} which was used in calculating it. This may be shown by considering the case in which

$$\psi_{\mathrm{arb}} = \psi_0 + \epsilon\psi_1$$

where ϵ is an infinitesmal of the first order. This is normalized, since ψ_0 and ψ_1 are the true wave functions and are therefore orthogonal, and since ϵ^2 is effectively zero (the square of a small number being very small). The energy is given by

$$E = \int (\psi_0 + \epsilon\psi_1) H (\psi_0 + \epsilon\psi_1)\, d\tau$$

and this is equal to E_0, the true energy, since

$$E = \int \psi_0 H \psi_0\, d\tau + \int \epsilon\psi_1 H \psi_0\, d\tau + \int \psi_0 H \epsilon\psi_1\, d\tau + \int \epsilon^2 \psi_1 H \psi_1\, d\tau$$

and the last three terms will equal zero, remembering that $\epsilon^2 \simeq 0$ and that the ψ's are orthogonal. Thus even with a relatively poor wave function we may still get an answer which is reasonably close to the correct one.

The use of this theorem is best illustrated by an example. Let us consider the case of a particle in a box again since we know the energy of the lowest energy state. For convenience the center of the box will be taken as the origin of the coordinate system.

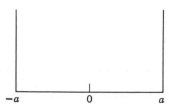

The first guess as to a reasonable wave function will be

$$\psi_{arb} = (a^2 - x^2)$$

The energy will then be given by

$$E = \frac{H_{11}}{\Delta_{11}} = \frac{\displaystyle\int_{-a}^{a} (a^2 - x^2)H(a^2 - x^2)\,dx}{\displaystyle\int_{-a}^{a} (a^2 - x^2)(a^2 - x^2)\,dx}$$

where H is, as before, $\dfrac{-h^2}{8\pi^2 m}(\partial/\partial x)$. The solution of this equation gives $E = 0.03164h^2/ma^2$ as compared to $E_0 = 0.03125h^2/ma^2$ (the true energy). Thus the calculated value is 1.3% higher than the true value. A comparison of the shapes of ψ_0 and ψ_{arb} is shown in Fig. 1-18.

Another guess as to a reasonable wave function might be

$$\psi_{arb} = (a^4 - x^4)$$

Here the energy would be given by

$$E = \frac{H_{11}}{\Delta_{11}} = \frac{\displaystyle\int_{a}^{a} (a^4 - x^4)H(a^4 - x^4)\,dx}{\displaystyle\int_{-a}^{a} (a^4 - x^4)(a^4 - x^4)\,dx}$$

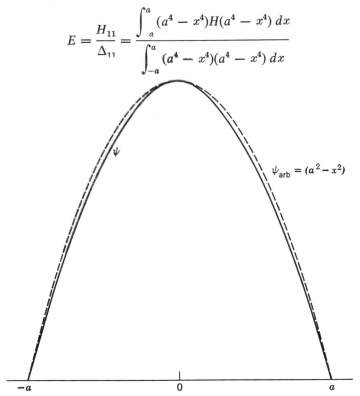

Fig. 1-18. *A comparison of the true and approximate wave functions for a particle in a box.*

and this gives as the solution, $E = 0.0402h^2/ma^2$, which is 29% above the true answer. Since both assumptions gave answers which are reasonable approximations to the true answer, we should be able to get a very much better answer by using a linear combination of the two assumed values. Thus we shall use

$$\psi_{arb} = c_1\phi_1 + c_2\phi_2 = c_1(a^2 - x^2) + c_2(a^4 - x^4)$$

For this case the secular equation would be

$$\begin{vmatrix} H_{11} - \Delta_{11}E & H_{12} - \Delta_{12}E \\ H_{21} - \Delta_{21}E & H_{22} - \Delta_{22}E \end{vmatrix} = 0$$

where

$$H_{11} = \int_{-a}^{a} (a^2 - x^2) \frac{-h^2}{8\pi^2 m} \frac{d^2}{dx^2} (a^2 - x^2) \, dx = \frac{8}{3} a^3 \frac{h^2}{8\pi^2 m}$$

$$H_{12} = \int_{-a}^{a} (a^2 - x^2) \frac{-h^2}{8\pi^2 m} \frac{d^2}{dx^2} (a^4 - x^4) \, dx = \frac{16}{5} a^5 \frac{h^2}{8\pi^2 m}$$

$$H_{22} = \int_{-a}^{a} (a^4 - x^4) \frac{-h^2}{8\pi^2 m} \frac{d^2}{dx^2} (a^4 - x^4) \, dx = \frac{32}{7} a^7 \frac{h^2}{8\pi^2 m}$$

$$\Delta_{11} = \int_{-a}^{a} (a^2 - x^2)(a^2 - x^2) \, dx = \frac{16}{15} a^5$$

$$\Delta_{12} = \Delta_{21} = \int_{-a}^{a} (a^2 - x^2)(a^4 - x^4) \, dx = \frac{128}{105} a^7$$

$$\Delta_{22} = \int_{-a}^{a} (a^4 - x^4)(a^4 - x^4) \, dx = \frac{64}{45} a^9$$

Introducing these values and solving for E, we find that the value is $0.03125h^2/ma^2$ or identical with the true value of E. Having the value of E, it is possible to obtain the coefficients c_1 and c_2, for

$$c_1(H_{11} - \Delta_{11}E) + c_2(H_{12} - \Delta_{12}E) = 0$$

Introducing the values of H_{11}, H_{12}, Δ_{11}, and Δ_{12}, we find that for the case where a is unity, $c_1/c_2 = -5.52$. The normalization factor is $\sqrt{1^2 + 5.52^2}$ or 5.61. Thus $c_1 = 0.984$ and $c_2 = -0.178$. The negative value for c_2 is expected, for both ϕ_1 and ϕ_2 lie above ψ_0.

1-9 The Perturbation Method

In using the variation method, we knew the correct operator for the problem but did not know the correct wave functions. The latter were approximated by using a linear combination of trial functions and then minimizing the eigenvalue derived from the wave equation. Thus, by using the total energy (Hamiltonian) operator, the coefficients of the trial functions were adjusted so as to minimize the energy.

In other cases the problem is similar to one which has been solved and may be considered to be a perturbation of the latter. Then the operator, which in this example will be the Hamiltonian operator, may be written as

$$H = H^{(0)} + \lambda H^{(1)}$$

where $H^{(0)}$ is the simple part of the operator for which the correct wave functions are known, and $H^{(1)}$ represents the perturbation of the more simple system. The quantity λ gives the magnitude of the perturbation. As before, the wave equation is

$$H\psi_i = E_i \psi_i$$

in which the subscript i indicates the state which is being considered. Thus if $i = 0$, we would be considering the ground state.

Let us expand ψ in terms of a series

$$\psi_i = \psi_i^{(0)} + \lambda \psi_i^{(1)} + \lambda^2 \psi_i^{(2)} + \cdots$$

where the enclosed exponents refer to the order of approximation and not to a power. Thus $\psi_i^{(0)}$ is the correct wave function for the ith state of the unperturbed problem, the zeroth approximation being that there is no perturbation. Also, let us expand the energy in terms of a similar series.

$$E_i = E_i^{(0)} + \lambda E_i^{(1)} + \lambda^2 E_i^{(2)} + \cdots$$

Since

$$(H^{(0)} + \lambda H^{(1)})\psi_1 = E_i \psi_i$$

we may substitute the above series expansions in the latter, giving

$$(H^{(0)} + \lambda H^{(1)})(\psi_i^{(0)} + \lambda \psi_i^{(1)} + \lambda^2 \psi_i^{(2)} + \cdots)$$
$$= (E_i^{(0)} + \lambda E_i^{(1)} + \lambda^2 E_i^{(2)} + \cdots)(\psi_i^{(0)} + \lambda \psi_i^{(1)} + \lambda^2 \psi_i^{(2)} + \cdots)$$

This may be rearranged to give

$$[H^{(0)}\psi_i^{(0)}] + \lambda[H^{(1)}\psi_i^{(0)} + H^{(0)}\psi_i^{(1)}] + \lambda^2[H^{(0)}\psi_i^{(2)} + H^{(1)}\psi_i^{(1)}] + \cdots$$
$$= [E_i^{(0)}\psi_i^{(0)}] + \lambda[E_i^{(1)}\psi_i^{(0)} + E_i^{(0)}\psi_i^{(1)}]$$
$$+ \lambda^2[E_i^{(0)}\psi_i^{(2)} + E_i^{(1)}\psi_i^{(1)} + E_i^{(2)}\psi_i^{(0)}] + \cdots$$

To the zeroth approximation, λ and higher terms are zero, giving

$$H^{(0)}\psi_i^{(0)} = E_i^{(0)}\psi_i^{(0)}$$

Similarly, to the first approximation, λ^2 and higher terms are zero. The above equality may be subtracted out and the remaining expression divided by λ, giving

$$H^{(1)}\psi_i^{(0)} + H^{(0)}\psi_i^{(1)} = E_i^{(1)}\psi_i^{(0)} + E_i^{(0)}\psi_i^{(1)}$$

which is the expression for the first order perturbation. The second order perturbation expression may be obtained in the same way, giving

$$H^{(0)}\psi_i^{(2)} + H^{(1)}\psi_i^{(1)} = E_i^{(0)}\psi_i^{(2)} + E_i^{(1)}\psi_i^{(1)} + E_i^{(2)}\psi_i^{(0)}$$

In order to put the first order perturbation expression in usable form, let us multiply both sides of the equation by $\psi_i^{(0)}$ and integrate over all space:

$$\int \psi_i^{(0)} H^{(1)} \psi_i^{(0)} \, d\tau + \int \psi_i^{(0)} H^{(0)} \psi_i^{(1)} \, d\tau$$
$$= \int \psi_i^{(0)} E_i^{(1)} \psi_i^{(0)} \, d\tau + \int \psi_i^{(0)} E_i^{(0)} \psi_i^{(1)} \, d\tau$$

We may now expand $\psi_i^{(1)}$ in terms of the true ψ's for the unperturbed case.

$$\psi_i^{(1)} = c_0\psi_0^{(0)} + c_1\psi_1^{(0)} + c_2\psi_2^{(0)} + c_3\psi_3^{(0)} + \cdots$$

except that the state corresponding to i will be left out. Thus if we were considering the ground state, $i = 0$, and $\psi_0^{(0)}$ would be left out of the expansion. The terms of the above expression may now be evaluated term by term. Since the integral of $(\psi_i^{(0)})^2$ is equal to unity,

$$\int \psi_i^{(0)} E_i^{(1)} \psi_i^{(0)} \, d\tau = E_i^{(1)}$$

and since the expansion of $\psi_i^{(1)}$ does not contain $\psi_i^{(0)}$, the integral of $\psi_i^{(1)}\psi_i^{(0)}$ is equal to zero. Thus

$$\int \psi_i^{(0)} E_i^{(0)} \psi_i^{(1)} = 0$$

and, also,

$$\int \psi_i^{(0)} H^{(0)} \psi_i^{(1)} = 0$$

Thus we have that

$$E_i^{(1)} = \int \psi_i^{(0)} H^{(1)} \psi_i^{(0)} \, d\tau$$

and

$$\lambda E_i^{(1)} = \int \psi_i^{(0)} \lambda H^{(1)} \psi_i^{(0)} \, d\tau$$

The utility of this result lies in the fact that the correct wave functions for the simple case (which are known) may be used with the perturbation operator to give the value of the perturbation energy.

This may be illustrated by an example. Suppose we consider the case of a particle in a box with a step, where the height of the step is $\frac{1}{3}E_0$ and E_0 is the ground state energy for the unperturbed case in which there is no step. The correct value for the energy of the ground state of the perturbed case may be shown to be $1.1597E_0$.

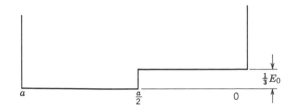

Here the perturbation will simply be the potential energy of the step and thus

$$H = T + \tfrac{1}{3}E_0$$

where T is the kinetic energy operator. The wave equation using the ground state wave function for the unperturbed case is then

$$E = \int_0^a \psi_0\left(-\frac{h^2}{8\pi^2 m}\frac{d^2}{dx^2}\right)\psi_0 \, dx + \frac{1}{3}\int_0^{a/2} \psi_0 E_0 \psi_0 \, dx$$

where the limits of integration on the perturbation part are 0 and $a/2$ because the perturbation extends over only one half the box. The first part gives E_0 and the second gives $\tfrac{1}{6}E_0$, and thus the energy of the ground state of the perturbed system is calculated to be $1.1667E_0$, which is only 0.6% larger than the true energy.

We are now in a position to obtain the wave functions for the perturbed case. It was previously found that

$$H^{(1)}\psi_i^{(0)} + H^{(0)}\psi_i^{(1)} = E_i^{(1)}\psi_i^{(0)} + E_i^{(0)}\psi_i^{(1)}$$

This expression is multiplied by $\psi_j^{(0)}$, where j is any state except i and the integration is performed over all space:

$$\int \psi_j^{(0)} H^{(1)}\psi_i^{(0)} \, d\tau + \int \psi_j^{(0)} H^{(0)}\psi_i^{(1)} \, d\tau = \int \psi_j^{(0)} E_i^{(1)}\psi_i^{(0)} \, d\tau + \int \psi_j^{(0)} E_i^{(0)}\psi_i^{(1)} \, d\tau$$

But since $\int \psi_j^{(0)}\psi_i^{(0)} d\tau$ is equal to zero, the third term is zero. In order to evaluate the last term, let us expand $\psi_i^{(1)}$ in terms of the true ψ's,

$$\psi_i^{(1)} = \sum c_k \psi_k^{(0)}$$

and thus

$$\int \psi_j^{(0)} E_i^{(0)}\psi_i^{(1)} \, d\tau = \int \psi_j^{(0)} E_i^{(0)} \sum c_k \psi_k^{(0)} \, d\tau$$

and the latter is simply equal to $E_i^{(0)}c_j$, for the integral is zero for all ψ_k except when $k = j$. The second term may be evaluated in a similar manner, giving

$$\int \psi_j^{(0)} H^{(0)}\psi_i^{(1)} \, d\tau = \int \psi_j^{(0)} H^{(0)} \sum c_k \psi_k^{(0)} \, d\tau = E_j^{(0)}c_j$$

If we designate the first term as $H_{ij}^{(1)}$, the entire expression then becomes

$$c_j(E_j^{(0)} - E_i^{(0)}) = -H_{ij}^{(1)}$$

or

$$c_j = -\frac{H_{ij}^{(1)}}{E_j^{(0)} - E_i^{(0)}}$$

But, since

$$\psi_i^{(1)} = \sum c_k \psi_k^{(0)}$$

the final expression becomes

$$\psi_i^{(1)} = -\sum \frac{H_{ij}^{(1)}}{E_j^{(0)} - E_i^{(0)}} \psi_j^{(0)}$$

which is evaluated for all values of j except i. It can be seen that as j becomes large compared to i (i.e., where the state j is of much higher energy than the state i), the denominator becomes large, and the contribution by that term becomes quite small. Thus it is usually satisfactory to consider only a few terms in the summation.

We may now consider the application of this result to the problem of the box with a stepped well. If we use the first wave functions for the unperturbed case,

$$\psi_0^{(0)} = \sqrt{\frac{2}{a}} \sin\left(\frac{\pi x}{a}\right) \qquad \psi_1^{(0)} = \sqrt{\frac{2}{a}} \sin\left(\frac{2\pi x}{a}\right)$$

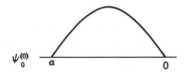
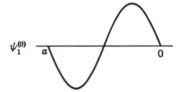

The perturbed wave function is as before

$$\psi_i = \psi_i^{(0)} + \lambda\psi_i^{(1)} + \lambda^2\psi_i^{(2)} + \cdots$$

Using only the first order terms, we have

$$\psi_i = \psi_i^{(0)} - \lambda \sum \frac{H_{ij}^{(1)}}{E_j^{(0)} - E_i^{(0)}} \psi_j^{(0)}$$

The integral $H_{ij}^{(1)}$ for i corresponding to the ground state and j corresponding to the first excited state is given by

$$H_{01}^{(1)} = \int_0^{a/2} \psi_0^{(0)} H^{(1)} \psi_1^{(0)} = \frac{2}{a} \int_0^{a/2} \sin\left(\frac{\pi x}{a}\right) E_0 \sin\left(\frac{2\pi x}{a}\right)$$

$$= 0.4246 E_0$$

and λ is as before equal to $\frac{1}{3}$. Thus the wave function for the ground state of the perturbed case is

$$\psi = \psi_0^{(0)} - \frac{1}{3}\frac{0.4246E_0}{4E_0 - E_0}\psi_1^{(0)} = \psi_0^{(0)} - 0.0472\psi_1^{(0)}$$

The accuracy of the result could, of course, be improved by the use of additional terms in the above summation. However, this result is adequate for the present purpose.

The resultant wave function will have a shape which is shifted to the left or lower potential part of the box. Since the square of the wave function is a probability, it can be seen that the wave function predicts that the electron will spend relatively more of its time in the lower potential part of the box, which is in agreement with one's expectations.

In some cases two or more states will have the same energy (usually called degenerate states). Then the approach described above is not applicable. This can easily be seen by considering the expression for $\psi_i^{(1)}$ in which the denominator is $E_j^{(0)} - E_i^{(0)}$. If these two energies are the same, the denominator is zero and the value of $\psi_i^{(1)}$ is indeterminate.

This case may be treated by using the variation method and setting up the secular determinant

$$\begin{vmatrix} H_{11} - \Delta_{11}E & H_{12} - \Delta_{12}E \\ H_{21} - \Delta_{21}E & H_{22} - \Delta_{22}E \end{vmatrix} = 0$$

where $H = H^{(0)} + H^{(1)}$. By using the normalized, unperturbed wave functions $\psi_a^{(0)}$ and $\psi_b^{(0)}$ (both corresponding to states having the energy E^0), $\Delta_{11} = \Delta_{22} = 1$ and $\Delta_{21} = \Delta_{12} = 0$. Similarly,

$$H_{11} = H_{22} = E^{(0)} + \int \psi_a^{(0)} H^{(1)} \psi_a^{(0)} \, d\tau = E^{(0)} + V_{11}$$

$$H_{21} = H_{12} = 0 \quad + \int \psi_a^{(0)} H^{(1)} \psi_b^{(0)} \, d\tau = V_{12}$$

Thus

$$\begin{vmatrix} E^{(0)} + V_{11} - E & V_{12} \\ V_{12} & E^{(0)} + V_{11} - E \end{vmatrix} = 0$$

and

$$E - E^{(0)} = V_{11} \pm V_{12}$$

Since we have energies, the wave functions may be obtained as described previously.

An interesting example of the use of perturbation theory for degenerate states is found in a treatment of benzene by Simpson.[16] Let us represent

[16] W. T. Simpson, *J. Am. Chem. Soc.*, **75**, 597 (1953).

one of the Kekule structures (with unequal bond lengths) as $\psi_I{}^2$ and the other as $\psi_{II}{}^2$. These will be set up as orthogonal functions. Then the

$$\bigcirc = \psi_I{}^2 \qquad\qquad \bigcirc = \psi_{II}{}^2$$

energy of the Kekule structures will be given by

$$E_I \psi_I = H^0 \psi_I \qquad\qquad E_{II} \psi_{II} = H^0 \psi_{II}$$

where H^0 is the appropriate Hamiltonian operator. If we are to consider benzene, the bonds in the Kekule structures must be made of equal length, and the operation of changing the bond lengths may be considered perturbation. Thus

$$H = H^0 + V$$

where V is the perturbation operator.

We may use the unperturbed wave functions ψ_I and ψ_{II} with the perturbed Hamiltonian operator in order to get the energy for benzene. However, since $E_I = E_{II}$, we must set up the secular equation in order to obtain the energies.

The secular determinant is

$$\begin{vmatrix} H_{11} - \Delta_{11}E & H_{12} - \Delta_{12}E \\ H_{21} - \Delta_{21}E & H_{22} - \Delta_{22}E \end{vmatrix} = 0$$

where H_{11} (the energy of one of the cannonical structures for benzene) is given by

$$H_{22} = H_{11} = \int \psi_I H^0 \psi_I \, d\tau + \int \psi_I V \psi_I \, d\tau = E_I + V_{11}$$

Here V_{11} is the compression energy involved in changing the bond lengths from those in the Kekule structures to that in benzene. H_{12} is given by

$$H_{21} = H_{12} = \int \psi_I H^0 \psi_{II} \, d\tau + \int \psi_I V \psi_{II} \, d\tau = 0 + V_{12}$$

Since the wave functions were normalized and orthogonal, $\Delta_{11} = \Delta_{22} = 1$, and $\Delta_{12} = \Delta_{21} = 0$. Thus

$$\begin{vmatrix} E_I + V_{11} - E & V_{12} \\ V_{12} & E_I + V_{11} - E \end{vmatrix} = 0$$

And

$$E = E_I + V_{11} \pm V_{12}$$

The relationship between these quantities is best seen by considering an energy diagram (Fig. 1-19).

It can be seen that the perturbation has caused the energy levels to split, giving two new levels which differ in energy by $2V_{12}$. The ground state will correspond to the lower level, and the excited state has a symmetry corresponding to that required for the state which leads to the 2600 Å adsorption band of benzene. The energy corresponding to this transition is 110 kcal/mole; therefore V_{12} is equal to 55 kcal/mole.

The difference in energy between the ground state and one of the cannonical structures for benzene is commonly called the delocalization energy and can be seen to be equal to V_{12} or 55 kcal/mole. This is a "vertical" delocalization energy, for it corresponds to the difference in energy between two species having the same bond lengths. The quantity which is measured thermochemically is the difference in energy between a Kekule structure (having different bond lengths) and the ground state. In order to obtain the thermochemical delocalization energy, we must subtract the compression energy from the vertical delocalization energy.

We may estimate the compression energy by using the Hooke's law equation

$$V = \tfrac{1}{2}kx^2$$

where k is the force constant for the bond in question and x is the displacement. The bond distance in benzene is 1.40 Å, whereas that for a single bond is 1.54 Å and that for a double bond is 1.34 Å. The force

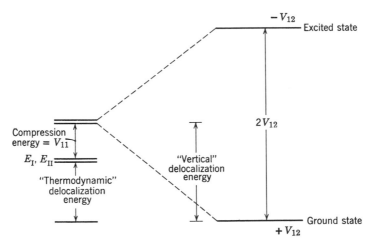

Fig. 1-19. Energy levels for hypothetical and real benzene molecules.

constant for a single bond is about 5×10^5 dynes/cm and that for a double bond is about 9×10^5 dynes/cm. The compression energy is then

$$V = \tfrac{3}{2}((0.14)^2 \times 10^{-16} \times 5 \times 10^5 \times 1.44 \times 10^{13} + (0.06)^2 \times 10^{-16}$$
$$\times 9 \times 10^5 \times 1.44 \times 10^{13})$$
$$= 19.5 \text{ kcal/mole}$$

The thermodynamic delocalization energy is now found to be $55 - 19.5 = 35$ kcal/mole, in remarkably good agreement with the observed value of 36 kcal/mole. This method may be applied to a number of other molecules, and the original reference should be consulted for details.

We may also obtain the wave functions for the ground and excited states. When $E = E_I + V_{11} + V_{12}$, $c_1 = c_2$, and

$$\psi_g = \frac{1}{\sqrt{2}} (\psi_I + \psi_{II})$$

Similarly, when $E = E_I + V_{11} - V_{12}$, $c_1 = -c_2$ and

$$\psi_e = \frac{1}{\sqrt{2}} (\psi_I - \psi_{II})$$

The structures are given by the squares of the ψ's, thus

$$\psi_g{}^2 = \frac{1}{2} (\psi_I{}^2 + \psi_{II}{}^2 + 2\psi_I\psi_{II})$$

$$\psi_e{}^2 = \frac{1}{2} (\psi_I{}^2 + \psi_{II}{}^2 - 2\psi_I\psi_{II})$$

It can be seen that the ground state corresponds to the average of the two Kekule structures plus an attractive term ($\psi_I\psi_{II}$). Thus it should have equal bond distances which are somewhat smaller than the average of those in the Kekule structures [$(1.54 + 1.34)/2 = 1.44$]. Similarly, the excited state should have equal bond distances which are somewhat larger than the average of those in the Kekule structures, since $-\psi_I\psi_{II}$ corresponds to repulsion. It is interesting to note that the excited state has been shown to have longer equilibrium bond distances than the ground state.[16a]

1-10 The Molecular Orbital Approach for the Hydrogen Molecule-Ion

The simplest molecular system is the hydrogen molecule-ion, for here the only Coulombic terms in the operator are the attraction of the electron

[16a] D. P. Craig, *J. Chem. Soc.*, 2146 (1950).

for each of the two protons and the repulsion of the two protons. The problem may be greatly simplified if one uses the Born-Oppenheimer[17] approximation, which treats motion of the relatively massive nuclei separately from that of the electron. Thus we may take a fixed internuclear distance and calculate the energy of the system. This process may be repeated for other distances, and finally one may construct a plot of energy against internuclear distance. The point having the lowest energy will correspond to the equilibrium internuclear distance, and the lowest energy plus the zero-point energy of the vibration of the two nuclei will give the ground state energy level.

The Hamiltonian operator for this case is

$$H = T_1 - \frac{e^2}{r_{1a}} - \frac{e^2}{r_{1b}} + \frac{e^2}{r_{ab}}$$

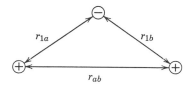

where T_1 is the kinetic energy operator which we have written previously for the hydrogen atom, the next two terms refer to the attraction of the electron for the nuclei, and the last term corresponds to the repulsion of the two nuclei. The wave equation is as before

$$H\psi = E\psi$$

It is possible to solve the wave equation for this case.[18] However, it is the only molecular system for which the wave equation may be solved, and thus the details of the solution are of little value in a general consideration of molecular systems. Hence we shall consider approximate methods for treating such systems, and we shall compare the wave functions which result with the true wave functions.

One of the general ways in which to consider the bonding in molecular systems is the LCAO-MO (linear combination of atomic orbitals, molecular orbital) method. Here one constructs molecular orbitals using linear combinations of atomic orbitals centered on the atoms involved, and one adjusts the coefficients associated with the atomic orbitals so as to minimize the total energy.

[17] M. Born and J. R. Oppenheimer, *Ann. Physik.*, **84,** 457 (1927).
[18] D. R. Bates, K. Ledsham, and A. L. Stewart, *Trans. Roy. Soc. London*, **A246,** 215 (1953).

For the hydrogen molecule-ion we will take linear combinations of $1s$ orbitals, which will be designated as ϕ. The subscripts a and b refer to the

$$\psi = c_1\phi_a + c_2\phi_b$$

two nuclei as before. In order to determine the coefficients of the atomic orbitals and the energies of the molecular orbitals formed from them, it is necessary to set up the secular determinant, which will be

$$\begin{vmatrix} H_{11} - \Delta_{11}E & H_{12} - \Delta_{12}E \\ H_{21} - \Delta_{21}E & H_{22} - \Delta_{22}E \end{vmatrix} = 0$$

Remembering that the wave functions for atomic orbitals are normalized, we can see that $\Delta_{11} = \Delta_{22} = 1$. The integrals $\Delta_{12} = \Delta_{21}$, will be abbreviated as s, the overlap integral. Since the atomic orbital wave functions ϕ_a and ϕ_b are the same, $H_{11} = H_{22}$ and $H_{12} = H_{21}$. The solutions of the secular determinant are

$$E_+ = \frac{H_{11} + H_{12}}{1 + s} \qquad E_- = \frac{H_{11} - H_{12}}{1 - s}$$

If one substitutes these values into the simultaneous equations which led to the secular determinant

$$c_1(H_{11} - \Delta_{11}E) + c_2(H_{12} - \Delta_{12}E) = 0$$

$$c_1(H_{21} - \Delta_{21}E) + c_2(H_{22} - \Delta_{22}E) = 0$$

one finds that for E_+, $c_1 = c_2$ and for E_-, $c_1 = -c_2$. The wave functions are then

$$\psi_+ = \frac{1}{\sqrt{2 + 2s}}(\phi_a + \phi_b)$$

$$\psi_- = \frac{1}{\sqrt{2 - 2s}}(\phi_a - \phi_b)$$

where $1/\sqrt{2 \pm 2s}$ is the normalization factor.

It is now necessary to evaluate the integrals H_{11} and H_{12}.

$$H_{11} = \int \phi_a \left(T_1 - \frac{e^2}{r_{1a}} - \frac{e^2}{r_{1b}} + \frac{e^2}{r_{ab}}\right)\phi_a \, d\tau$$

We have seen the integral $\int\phi_a(T_1 - e^2/r_{1a})\phi_a \, d\tau$ before when we considered the hydrogen atom. With ϕ_a a $1s$ wave function, this is simply the energy of an electron in a $1s$ orbital, or E_{1s}. The last term in the Hamiltonian is a constant and may be taken out from the integral. The other term, $\int\phi_a(-e^2/r_{1b})\phi_a \, d\tau$, represents the pull of the nucleus b on an electron in the atomic orbital on nucleus a. We shall designate this as J. The entire integral may then be written as

$$H_{11} = E_{1s} + \frac{e^2}{r_{ab}} + J$$

J is commonly known as the Coulombic integral and is given by

$$J = \frac{e^2}{a_0}\left[-\frac{1}{x} + e^{-2x}\left(1 + \frac{1}{x}\right)\right]$$

where $a_0 = 0.529$ Å and $x = r_{ab}/a_0$.

For the integral H_{12},

$$H_{12} = \int \phi_b\left(T_1 - \frac{e^2}{r_{1a}} - \frac{e^2}{r_{1b}} + \frac{e^2}{r_{ab}}\right)\phi_a \, d\tau$$

the function $(T_1 - e^2/r_{1a})$ operating on ϕ_a will give $E_{1s}\phi_a$. However, $\int \phi_a \phi_b \, d\tau$ is equal to s, and this part of the integral will therefore give sE_{1s}. Similarly, the constant term will give se^2/r_{ab}. The remaining term, $\int \phi_b(-e^2/r_{1b})\phi_a \, d\tau$, may be considered the pull of the nucleus b on the electron density distribution given by $\int \phi_a \phi_b \, d\tau$ and will be called K, the exchange integral. This may be visualized as

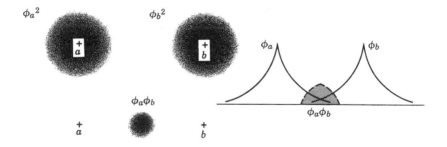

The integral may now be written as

$$H_{12} = sE_{1s} + \frac{se^2}{r_{ab}} + K$$

and if K is evaluated, it is found to be

$$K = -\frac{e^2}{a_0}e^{-x}(1 + x)$$

Similarly, s is found to be given by

$$s = (\tfrac{1}{3}x^2 + x + 1)e^{-x}$$

In terms of these expressions, the energies are

$$E_+ = E_{1s} + \frac{e^2}{r_{ab}} + \frac{J + K}{1 + s}$$

$$E_- = E_{1s} + \frac{e^2}{r_{ab}} + \frac{J - K}{1 - s}$$

The values of J, K, e^2/r_{ab}, and s are plotted in Fig. 1-20 as a function of internuclear distance. It can be seen that J and e^2/r_{ab} are approximately equal and of opposite sign at distances greater than the normal bond distance. Therefore, in a sense, the exchange term is the one which leads to the formation of a stable bond. The values of E_+ and E_- are plotted in Fig. 1-21. The equilibrium distance thus obtained is 1.32 Å, and the binding energy is 40.8 kcal/mole. These values may be compared with the

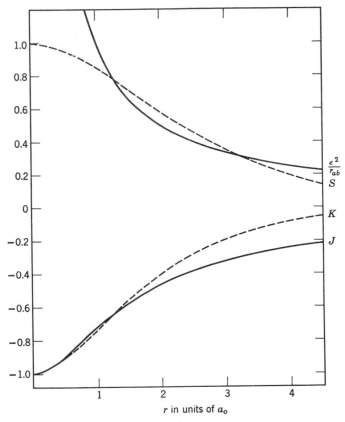

Fig. 1-20. Values of integrals for the hydrogen molecule ion. Values of J, K, and e^2/r_{ab} are in units of e^2/a_0; values of S are dimensionless.

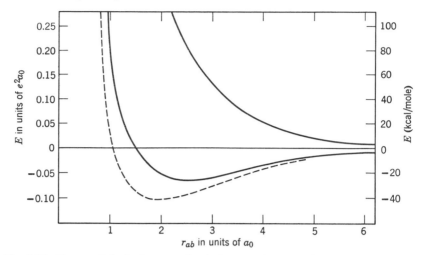

Fig. 1-21. Energy of the hydrogen molecule ion as a function of internuclear distance. The dotted line is the true value, and the solid line gives the calculated value.

true values, 1.06 Å and 64.1 kcal/mole. Although the calculated values are in reasonable agreement with the true values, they are far from being entirely satisfactory.

Before considering how the wave function may be improved, let us examine the electron density distribution which is given by each of the two wave functions. This is obtained by squaring the wave function, and for the bonding wave function we have

$$\psi^2 = \frac{1}{2 + 2s}(\phi_a{}^2 + \phi_b{}^2 + 2\phi_a\phi_b)$$

which may be represented as

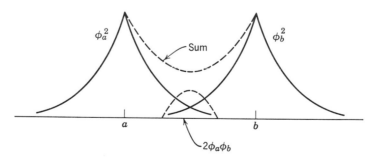

It can be seen that this wave function introduces more electron density between the nuclei than would be obtained from just the two atomic orbital wave functions. The attraction of the electrons in this region by the nuclei results in the formation of a stable bond.

With the antibonding wave function, the electron density distribution is given by

$$\psi^2 = \frac{1}{2 - 2s} (\phi_a{}^2 + \phi_b{}^2 - 2\phi_a\phi_b)$$

which may be represented by

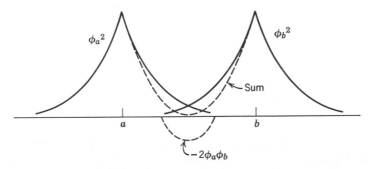

Here electron density is removed from between the nuclei, and the increased repulsion of the nuclei results in the formation of an unstable (antibonding) state.

Although, as indicated above, the bonding wave function leads to a state which is more stable than the separated atoms because the electron density between the atoms is increased over that for the separated atoms at the same internuclear distance, a comparison with the true wave function (Fig. 1-22) shows that the simple molecular orbital wave function does not increase the electron density sufficiently. Thus one must look for modifications of the wave function or for new wave functions which will increase the electron density between the nuclei.

In trying to see how the wave functions may be improved, let us consider a nucleus formed by coalescing two hydrogen nuclei on the one hand, and, on the other, the two nuclei separated by a large distance. In the first case an electron would experience a nuclear charge of two, whereas in the latter it would experience a charge of unity. At intermediate distances the effective charge experienced by an electron should be between the two extremes. Thus it would seem reasonable to vary the value of Z (the nuclear charge) in the hydrogenlike wave functions (p. 19) so as to minimize the energy. The variation theorem still applies; the lowest energy thus calculated should be the best approximation to the true energy, and it cannot be less than the latter. When this is done, the calculated binding energy is 51.9 kcal/mole, and the equilibrium internuclear distance

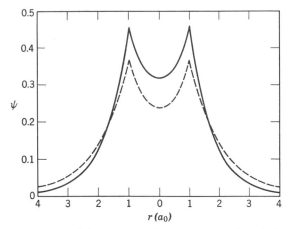

Fig. 1-22. A comparison of the true wave function (solid line) with the simple molecular orbital wave function (broken line) for the hydrogen molecule ion.

is 1.06 Å.[19]   This is a considerable improvement over the original result, but the binding energy is still in error by 19%. (Note, however, that the error in the *total* energy is quite small (3%). The error appears large only because we are only interested in the difference between the total energy of the molecule ion and of the two nuclei separated at a large distance.)

When we considered the variation method, we saw that the true energy and wave functions should be obtained if one set the unknown wave function equal to the sum of a *complete set* of wave functions, each weighted by a coefficient which was determined so as to minimize the total energy. If one uses atomic orbital wave functions in the summation, then one should use the complete set of these functions, that is, $1s$, $2s$, $2p_x$, $2p_y$, $2p_z$, $3s$, ... Clearly it is impractical to use the complete set of these functions, but in many cases it is possible to choose certain ones which would probably contribute more than others.   Up till now we have only used the $1s$ wave functions, which is the simplest possible approximation.   Since this wave function does not introduce sufficient electron density between the nuclei, the type of wave function which should next be used in the summation is a $2p$ wave function whose direction lies along the axis of the bond. As we saw when considering hybrid orbitals, the addition of a p wave function, having different signs on opposite sides of the nucleus, to an s wave function leads to a new wave function which gives an electron density distribution that is greater on one side of the nucleus than the other.

$$\psi = c_1\phi_{1s_a} + c_2\phi_{2p_a} + c_3\phi_{1s_b} + c_4\phi_{2p_b}$$

[19] B. N. Finkelstein and G. E. Horowitz, *Z. physik.*, **48**, 118 (1928).

A calculation using wave functions of this form[20] led to a binding energy of 61.2 kcal/mole and an internuclear distance of 1.06 Å. Thus the inclusion of more terms in the summation led to a considerable improvement in the calculated values.

Before closing this discussion it should be remarked that the concept of an exchange integral arises only because of the form of the mathematical treatment used. For example, the simple wave function

$$\psi = \frac{1}{\sqrt{N}} e^{-Z(r_a + r_b)}$$

gave a binding energy of 49.8 kcal/mole[21] and an internuclear distance of 1.06 Å. This result is a significant improvement over that obtained using the $1s$ hydrogen wave functions. A small modification of this expression

$$\psi = \frac{1}{\sqrt{N}} e^{-Z(r_a + r_b)} [1 + a(r_a - r_b)^2]$$

leads to a binding energy which differs from the true value by only 1%. In neither case does an integral similar to an exchange integral appear. Although functions of this type can lead to very good results for simple cases, it is difficult to use then for more complex ones. Therefore the following discussion will continue to use the LCAO-MO approach because of its inherent simplicity and general applicability.

Problem

1. Obtain the energy levels in terms of H_{11} and H_{12}, and the wave functions for the ion H_3^{+2} using the LCAO-MO method. Assume (a) that it is a linear ion for which $H_{12} = H_{23}$, $H_{13} = 0$, $\Delta_{12} = \Delta_{23}$, $\Delta_{13} = 0$ and (b) that it is in the form of an equilateral triangle for which $H_{12} = H_{13} = H_{23}$ and $\Delta_{12} = \Delta_{13} = \Delta_{23}$.

1-11 The Simple Molecular Orbital Approach for Conjugated Systems

The conjugated unsaturated hydrocarbons are of particular interest because they provide a relatively simple system to which quantum chemical ideas may be applied. The electrons in these compounds are normally divided into two types: those forming the σ bonds, which are the framework of the molecule, are oriented directly between two nuclei, and are usually in sp^2 hybrid orbitals; and those forming the π bonds which are

[20] B. N. Dickenson, *J. Chem. Phys.* **1**, 317 (1933).
[21] H. M. James, *J. Chem. Phys.*, **3**, 9 (1935).

derived from p atomic orbitals perpendicular to the sp^2 hybrid on a given atom. In trying to estimate the energy of these compounds, one commonly uses the "π-electron approximation"[22] in which the π-electron system is assumed not to interact with the σ electrons. With the planar hydrocarbons, this will be a good approximation, for the σ electrons will be in the nodal plane of the π electrons. However, it is *not* valid for the nonplanar hydrocarbons, such as cyclooctatetrene, in which case there will be overlap between the two types of orbitals. Using this method, we shall take linear combinations of the p atomic orbitals and construct molecular orbitals into which the unsaturation electrons may be placed.[23]

Let us first consider the allyl radical.

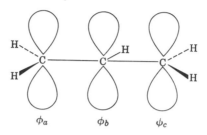

ϕ_a ϕ_b ψ_c

[22] E. Huckel, *Z. Physik*, **70**, 204 (1931); **76**, 628 (1932).

[23] Although the separation of orbitals into σ and π types and the statement that the "resonance" energy in benzene is 36 kcal/mole are commonly accepted, the last word has yet to be said. To encourage a healthy scepticism about the usual theoretical deductions, I wish to present the following quotations from the recent literature.

"There may be chemists who would contend that one innovation of great significance has been made—the introduction of the σ, π description of the double bond and the triple bond and of conjugated systems, in place of the bent bond description. I contend that the σ, π description is less satisfactory than the bent bond description, that this innovation is only ephemeral, and that the use of the σ, π description will die out before long." L. Pauling, in *Theoretical Organic Chemistry, The Kekule Symposium*, Butterworths Scientific Publications, London, 1959, p. 1.

"Consequently, the real resonance energy of benzene, due to a decrease in total π-energy is 12.8 kcal/mole. In other words, only about a quarter of the 'observed resonance energy' of benzene is due to resonance; half is due to changes in bond energy of carbon bonds with hybridization, and a quarter to the relief of σ-bond strain." M. J. S. Dewar and H. N. Schmeising, *Tetrahedron*, **5**, 166 (1959).

". . . that the π electrons are not the major source of stability for the regular hexagon, and that in fact the π electrons might well have a lower energy if the rings approached 'cyclohexatriene' like shapes. This would imply that the π electrons are largely responsible for the ease of distortion, and that the σ electrons determine the regular hexagon structure. Snyder has carried out Hückel model calculations of π and σ contributions to the energy of the B_{2u} distortion of benzene and concludes that this is indeed the case. The numerical values of the contributions are sensitive to the exact form of the potential. Nonetheless, two rather different potentials . . . both show the π electrons to be contributing to the *instability* of the regular hexagon of benzene, and therefore to the large amplitude motion." R. S. Berry, *J. Chem. Phys.*, **35**, 2253 (1961).

It is desired to obtain three wave functions which are linear combinations of the $2p_z$ atomic wave functions, ϕ_a, ϕ_b, and ϕ_c, and which will minimize the energy of the π electronic system.

$$\psi = c_1\phi_a + c_2\phi_b + c_3\phi_c$$

To do this it is necessary to set up the secular determinant and thereby determine the energies and the coefficients of the atomic orbitals. As shown previously, the secular determinant will be

$$\begin{vmatrix} H_{11} - \Delta_{11}E & H_{12} - \Delta_{12}E & H_{13} - \Delta_{13}E \\ H_{21} - \Delta_{21}E & H_{22} - \Delta_{22}E & H_{23} - \Delta_{23}E \\ H_{31} - \Delta_{31}E & H_{32} - \Delta_{32}E & H_{33} - \Delta_{33}E \end{vmatrix} = 0$$

In order to obtain the values of the quantities which are contained in the secular determinant, it would be necessary to integrate expressions of the type:

$$H_{12} = \int \psi_1 (T_1 + T_2 + T_3 - e^2/r_{1a} - e^2/r_{1b} - e^2/r_{1c}$$
$$- e^2/r_{2a} - e^2/r_{2b} - e^2/r_{2c} - e^2/r_{3a} - e^2/r_{3b}$$
$$- e^2/r_{3c} + e^2/r_{12} + e^2/r_{13} + e^2 r_{23})\psi_2 \, d\tau$$

where T_1, T_2, and T_3 are the kinetic energy operators for the three electrons, the next nine terms represent the attractions between electrons 1, 2, and 3 and the nuclei a, b, and c, and the last three terms represent the repulsion between the electrons. Without the last three terms the evaluation of the integrals would be tedious but not impractical. However, the last three terms, since they contain the coordinates of two electrons simultaneously, do not readily lead to a solution. Therefore a semi-empirical approach to the solution of the secular equation has been developed.

The integrals H_{11}, H_{22}, and H_{33} represent the energy of an electron when it is in the atomic orbital on the given atom. This represents a nonbonding state, and it is this state which is usually taken as the standard state. Thus the value of the integral is of relatively little importance in problems in which the net stabilization (or destabilization) is to be calculated. Integrals of this type will be designated as α. The integrals H_{12} and H_{23}, give a measure of the energy of an electron when it is between two nuclei and are similar to the exchange integrals which we considered when discussing the hydrogen molecule-ion. These integrals will be designated as γ. The integrals, Δ_{11}, Δ_{22}, and Δ_{33}, are unity, for the atomic orbitals are normalized, and the integrals Δ_{12} and Δ_{23} are the overlap integrals which will again be designated as s. In terms of these quantities the secular determinant becomes (assuming interactions between nonadjacent atoms to be so small that they may be considered as negligible):[24]

$$\begin{vmatrix} \alpha - E & \gamma - sE & 0 \\ \gamma - sE & \alpha - E & \gamma - sE \\ 0 & \gamma - sE & \alpha - E \end{vmatrix} = 0$$

If we write $(\alpha - E)$ as E' and $(\gamma - sE)$ as q, the solutions of the secular determinant are

$$(E')^3 - 2q^2 E' = 0$$

$$E' = 0, \sqrt{2}q, -\sqrt{2}q$$

Introducing the values of E' and q, we get

$$E = \alpha, \quad \frac{\alpha - \sqrt{2}\gamma}{1 - \sqrt{2}s}, \quad \frac{\alpha + \sqrt{2}\gamma}{1 + \sqrt{2}s}$$

as the three values of the energy. Now, it can be shown that not only is the lowest energy calculated by this variation method equal to or greater than the lowest energy but, also, each of the other energies is equal to or greater than the corresponding higher energies. Thus the energies calculated in this way are approximations to the energies of all the levels.

We are particularly interested in the energies above and below the nonbonding level, which has the energy α. Thus we shall set $\alpha = 0$; this being defined as the standard state, giving the energies as

$$E = 0, \quad \frac{\sqrt{2}\gamma}{1 - \sqrt{2}s}, \quad -\frac{\sqrt{2}\gamma}{1 + \sqrt{2}s}$$

The values of s for two $2p_z$ orbitals at a distance of 1.40 Å (as found in benzene) is 0.25,[25] and thus the numerical values of the energies are $+1.04\gamma, 0, -2.19\gamma$.

[24] These calculations are often made neglecting overlap (i.e., setting $s = 0$). The results obtained in this way, as far as a correlation of structure with π-electron delocalization energy is concerned, are the same as those obtained including overlap even though the spacing of the energy levels is quite different. However, it is theoretically more sound to include overlap, and this will be done throughout.

It may be noted that the energies which would be obtained neglecting overlap are obtained by setting q, which is used in the following calculations, equal to $-\beta$, the usual designation for the exchange integral when overlap is neglected. Similarly, the wave functions which would be obtained neglecting overlap are obtained by setting $s = 0$ in the normalization factor for the following wave functions.

[25] R. S. Mulliken, C. A. Rieke, D. Orloff, and H. Orloff, *J. Chem. Phys*, **17**, 1248 (1949).

Now, let us determine the coefficients for the atomic orbitals for each energy level. The equations which gave the secular determinant are (in terms of E' and q)

$$c_1E' + c_2q \qquad\quad = 0$$
$$c_1a + c_2E' + c_3q = 0$$
$$c_2q + c_3E' = 0$$

Substituting $E' = 0$, we find from the first equation that $c_2 = 0$ and, from the second equation, that $c_1 = -c_3$. If we call $c_1 = 1$, then the values of c_2 and c_3 are 0 and -1, respectively. The values must be normalized so that $\int \psi^2 \, d\tau = 1$, and this requires that $c_1{}^2 + c_2{}^2 + c_3{}^2 + 2c_1c_2s + 2c_2c_3s = 1$. Substituting the above values of c_1, c_2, and c_3, it is found that each value must be divided by $\sqrt{2}$, giving $1/\sqrt{2}$, 0, and $-1/\sqrt{2}$ as the coefficients.

In a similar fashion, the coefficients for the other energy levels may be evaluated, giving

$$E' = -\sqrt{2}q \quad E = 1.04\gamma \quad \psi_1 = \frac{1}{\sqrt{4 + 4\sqrt{2}s}}(\phi_a + \sqrt{2}\phi_b + \phi_c)$$

$$E' = 0 \qquad\quad E = 0 \qquad\quad \psi_2 = \frac{1}{\sqrt{2}}(\phi_a - \phi_c)$$

$$E' = \sqrt{2}q \quad E = -2.19\gamma \quad \psi_3 = \frac{1}{\sqrt{4 - 4\sqrt{2}s}}(-\phi_a + \sqrt{2}\phi_b - \phi_c)$$

If we plot these values and extend the curves, using a little imagination, we obtain curves strikingly similar to those obtained previously for the case of a particle in a one-dimensional box, and, accordingly, the one with no nodes has the lowest energy, that with one node has the intermediate energy, and the one with two nodes has the highest energy.

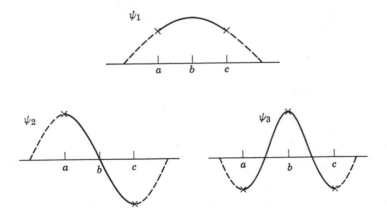

The relationship between the wave functions and the energies may perhaps be best seen by considering the squares of wave functions.

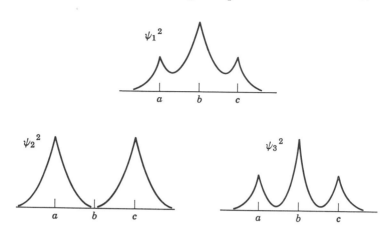

It can be seen that the lowest energy corresponds to the bonding case for the hydrogen molecule-ion, that the second is nonbonding (and should have an energy of zero), since the two regions of electron density are separated from each other by the central carbon, and that the third corresponds to the antibonding case for the hydrogen molecule-ion.

It may be noted that the value of γ has not been considered in this discussion. For reasons which will become clear later, it seems preferable to postpone a consideration of this point until after the application of this method to the case of benzene. The energy levels of the allyl carbonium ion, carbanion, and radical may nevertheless be indicated schematically as (neglecting interelectronic repulsion):

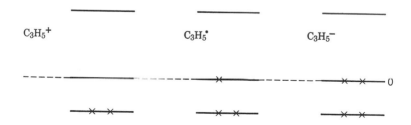

According to this scheme, all three should have the same energy, for the extra electrons go into a nonbonding orbital, and, neglecting electrostatic effects, this is approximately true.

The case of benzene will now be considered. The secular determinant, neglecting interaction between nonadjacent atoms, is

$$
\begin{array}{c|cccccc}
 & 1 & 2 & 3 & 4 & 5 & 6 \\
\hline
1 & \alpha - E & \gamma - sE & 0 & 0 & 0 & \gamma - sE \\
2 & \gamma - sE & \alpha - E & \gamma - sE & 0 & 0 & 0 \\
3 & 0 & \gamma - sE & \alpha - E & \gamma - sE & 0 & 0 \\
4 & 0 & 0 & \gamma - sE & \alpha - E & \gamma - sE & 0 \\
5 & 0 & 0 & 0 & \gamma - sE & \alpha - E & \gamma - sE \\
6 & \gamma - sE & 0 & 0 & 0 & \gamma - sE & \alpha - E
\end{array} = 0
$$

Making the substitutions, $(\alpha - E) = E'$ and $(\gamma - sE) = q$, it becomes

$$
\begin{vmatrix}
E' & q & 0 & 0 & 0 & q \\
q & E' & q & 0 & 0 & 0 \\
0 & q & E' & q & 0 & 0 \\
0 & 0 & q & E' & q & 0 \\
0 & 0 & 0 & q & E' & q \\
q & 0 & 0 & 0 & q & E'
\end{vmatrix} = 0
$$

This represents an equation of the sixth order, which is tedious to solve. The determinant is usually factored using group theory,[26] but for present purposes it does not seem appropriate to go into the details of this method. Therefore we shall use a method of factoring which is directly related to the use of group theory but which may be applied very simply. For any molecule, we shall look for reflection planes of symmetry which are perpendicular to the ring. Although there are several such reflection planes in benzene, we shall choose two which are mutually perpendicular.

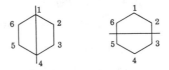

We shall now construct four diagrams which contain these planes of symmetry and take all combinations of positive and negative signs for the

[26] A good description of the method and its application in solving secular determinants is given in H. Margenau and G. Murphy, *The Mathematics of Physics and Chemistry*, D. Van Nostrand, Princeton, N.J., 1956.

quadrants thus formed (neglecting those formed by simply interchanging all the + and − signs in the diagrams shown).

+ +	+ +	+ −	+ −
+ +	− −	+ −	− +

The symmetry properties of the wave functions must correspond to the symmetry properties of the molecule, for there is a direct relationship between the location of the p_z atomic orbitals and the atoms in the molecule. Therefore the diagrams also correspond to the symmetry properties of the wave functions. Thus, considering the coefficients of the atomic orbitals in the wave equations,

$$\psi = c_1\phi_1 + c_2\phi_2 + c_3\phi_3 + c_4\phi_4 + c_5\phi_5 + c_6\phi_6$$

and remembering the numbering of the p_z atomic orbitals for benzene given above, the first diagram requires that

$$c_2 = c_3 = c_5 = c_6, \quad \text{and} \quad c_1 = c_4.$$

The second diagram requires

$$c_2 = -c_3 = -c_5 = c_6 \quad \text{and} \quad c_1 = -c_4.$$

The third requires

$$c_2 = c_3 = -c_5 = -c_6 \quad \text{and} \quad c_1 = c_4 = 0,$$

and the fourth requires

$$c_2 = -c_3 = c_5 = -c_6 \quad \text{and} \quad c_1 = c_4 = 0.$$

The first two equations which gave the secular determinant are (in terms of E' and q)

$$c_1E' + c_2q + c_6q = 0$$
$$c_1q + c_2E' + c_3q = 0$$

Substituting the values of c_3 and c_6 which correspond to the first diagram in terms of c_2,

$$c_1E' + 2c_2q = 0$$
$$c_1q + c_2(q + E) = 0$$

The determinant of the coefficients is

$$\begin{vmatrix} E' & 2q \\ q & q + E' \end{vmatrix} = 0$$

which gives the energies

$$E' = -2q, +q$$

or

$$E = \frac{2\gamma}{1 + 2s}, \frac{-\gamma}{1 - s}$$

Similarly, the values for the coefficients derived from the second diagram give $E' = 2q$ and $-q$ or $E = -2\gamma/(1 - 2s)$ and $\gamma/(1 + s)$. The third diagram gives $E' = -q$ ($E = \gamma/(1 + s)$), and the fourth diagram gives $E' = q$ ($E = -\gamma/(1 - s)$). Thus the original sixth order determinant has been factored into two second order determinants and two first order determinants, and the energies have been obtained. The energy level diagram is then

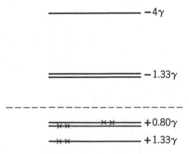

Let us now consider the question of the value of γ. If we assume that the value of γ is obtained using the full Hamiltonian operator, then it will contain within it the effect of interelectronic repulsion (actually, this will be counted twice, for if we consider the repulsion between electron 1 and electron 2 and then the repulsion between electron 2 and electron 1, we have counted the same quantity twice). Thus we may place the unsaturation electrons in the levels, starting at the lowest and placing two in each level in accordance with the Pauli exclusion principle. The electrons are shown as crosses in the energy level diagram. The total π-electronic energy will be $2(1.33\gamma) + 4(0.80\gamma)$ or 5.87γ. A corresponding calculation for ethylene would give

$$\frac{-\gamma}{1-s} = -1.33\gamma$$

$$\frac{\gamma}{1+s} = 0.80\gamma$$

and the π-electronic energy for three ethylenic double bonds would be $3 \times 2 \times 0.80\gamma = 4.80\gamma$. The net stabilization of benzene compared to ethylene would be 1.07γ. This should be equated to the vertical resonance energy—that determined using models having the same bond length as benzene. This is not directly available (although it may be approximated), and thus a further assumption is commonly made, that the compression energy involved in changing the bond lengths of the model compounds to those found in benzene may be included in the value of γ while still retaining it as a useful quantity. If we do this, 1.07γ will be equated to the thermochemically determined delocalization energy (36 kcal/mole) giving $\gamma = -33.5$ kcal/mole.

If we now repeat the calculations for some other cyclic aromatic hydrocarbon, we may use the value of γ obtained above in order to estimate the "thermochemical delocalization energy." This should give fairly good results if similar compounds are compared, for here the errors due to the approximations made will for the most part cancel out. The same value of γ cannot however be used for ions, radicals, or linear systems, for here the interelectronic repulsions and compression energies per bond will not be the same as with the cyclic aromatic hydrocarbons. Thus different values must be obtained for these compounds.

A comparison of calculated and observed values of the delocalization energy for a number of cyclic hydrocarbons is shown in Table 1-5. It can be seen that the results are in remarkably good agreement with the observed values, considering the approximations made. Thus the method described above has proved to be a valuable one for the theoretical study of unsaturated compounds.

Having the energies, it is now possible to evaluate the coefficients of the atomic orbitals in the wave functions corresponding to each of the energy levels. For example, the value $E' = -2q$ $[E = 2\gamma/(1 + 2s)]$ came from the equations

$$c_1 E' + 2c_2 q = 0$$
$$c_1 q + c_2(q + E') = 0$$

Substituting the value of E' and setting $c_1 = 1$, we have

$$-2q + 2c_2 q = 0$$
$$q + c_2(-q) = 0$$

or $c_2 = 1$. This indicates that $c_1 = c_2 = c_3 = c_4 = c_5 = c_6 = 1$ (remembering that this energy value arose from the first symmetry diagram). But now the coefficients must be normalized so that $\int \psi^2 \, d\tau = 1$. This requires that $c_1^2 + c_2^2 + c_3^2 + c_4^2 + c_5^2 + c_6^2 + 2c_1 c_2 s + 2c_2 c_3 s + 2c_3 c_4 s + 2c_4 c_5 s + 2c_5 c_6 s + 2c_6 c_1 s = 1$ (the other terms being zero, for they correspond to nonadjacent atomic orbitals). The required factor is seen to be

Table 1-5   A Comparison of Observed and Calculated Delocalization Energies

No. of Electrons		Observed D.E.[a]	Calculated D.E.
4	Butadiene[c]	3.5	3.5
6	Hexatriene[c]		7.7
8	Octatetraene[c]		12.2
10	Decapentaene[c]		17
6	Benzene	36	36
10	Naphthalene	61	63
14	Anthracene	84	88
18	Naphthacene	110	113
22	Pentacene		137
26	Hexacene		161
14	Phenanthrene	91	92
16	Pyrene	109	108
18	Chrysene	117	121
18	Perylene	126	136
18	Benz[a]anthracene	112	111
18	Benz[c]phenanthrene	110	121
18	Triphenylene	118	124
24	Coronene		176
8	Styrene	37	41
12	Diphenyl	71	76
12	Diphenylene[b]	10	72
14	Stilbene	77	82
10	Azulene[d]	32	54
12	Acenaphthalene[d]		77
14	Pyracylene[d]		86
14	Cyclohept(f)indene[d]		76
14	Dihydroacepleiadylene		62
14	Pleiadiene[d]		82
16	Acepleiadylene[d]	77	101
18	Pleiadene[d]		106
6	Fulvene[d]	11	22
8	Pentalene[d]		37
8	Heptafulvene[d]	14	26
10	Fulvalene[d]	20	41
12	Heptalene[d]		49
12	Cyclopentadienylidenecycloheptatriene[d]		63
14	Heptafulvalene[d]	29	50

[a] The values of the observed delocalization energy were taken from G. W. Wheland, *Resonance in Organic Chemistry*, J. Wiley and Sons, New York, 1955,

$\sqrt{6 + 12s}$, and so the wave function for the lowest energy level becomes

$$\psi_1 = \frac{1}{\sqrt{6 + 12s}}(\phi_a + \phi_b + \phi_c + \phi_d + \phi_e + \phi_f)$$

The other energy level which came from these equations is $E' = q\,(E = -\gamma/(1 - \gamma))$. Setting $c_1 = 1$ again, we find

$$q + 2c_2q = 0$$

and $c_2 = -\frac{1}{2}$. Remembering that $c_2 = c_3 = c_5 = c_6$ and $c_1 = c_4$ were the conditions for obtaining this energy level, we find that

$$c_1 = c_4 = 1$$

$$c_2 = c_3 = c_5 = c_6 = -\tfrac{1}{2}$$

Here the normalization factor is $1/\sqrt{3}$, and the wave function becomes

$$\psi = \frac{1}{\sqrt{3}}(\phi_a - \tfrac{1}{2}\phi_b - \tfrac{1}{2}\phi_c + \phi_d - \tfrac{1}{2}\phi_e - \tfrac{1}{2}\phi_f)$$

The entire set of wave functions evaluated in this way is

$$\psi_1 = \frac{1}{\sqrt{6 + 12s}}(\phi_a + \phi_b + \phi_c + \phi_d + \phi_e + \phi_f)\quad E = 1.33\gamma$$

$$\psi_2 = \frac{1}{\sqrt{4 + 4s}}(\phi_b + \phi_c - \phi_e - \phi_f)$$

$$\left.\begin{array}{l} \\ \psi_3 = \frac{1}{\sqrt{3}}(\phi_a + \tfrac{1}{2}\phi_b - \tfrac{1}{2}\phi_c - \phi_d - \tfrac{1}{2}\phi_e + \tfrac{1}{2}\phi_f)\end{array}\right\}\quad E = 0.80\gamma$$

$$\psi_4 = \frac{1}{\sqrt{4 - 4s}}(\phi_b - \phi_c + \phi_e - \phi_f)$$

$$\left.\begin{array}{l} \\ \psi_5 = \frac{1}{\sqrt{3}}(\phi_a - \tfrac{1}{2}\phi_b - \tfrac{1}{2}\phi_c + \phi_d - \tfrac{1}{2}\phi_e - \tfrac{1}{2}\phi_f)\end{array}\right\}\quad E = -1.33\gamma$$

$$\psi_6 = \frac{1}{\sqrt{6 - 12s}}(\phi_a - \phi_b + \phi_c - \phi_d + \phi_e - \phi_f)\quad E = -4\gamma$$

---

pp. 80, 98, and A. Streitwieser, Jr., *Molecular Orbital Theory for Organic Chemists*, John Wiley and Sons, 1961, p. 244.

[b] The large difference found in this case is probably due to the strain energy associated with the formation of the four-membered ring: H. J. Dauben, Jr., quoted in A Streitwieser, Jr., *ibid.* p. 244.

[c] The value of γ used for these compounds was 20, whereas the value of γ used for the other compounds was 33.5 kcal/mole.

[d] Indicates a nonalternate hydrocarbon.

and they may be represented symbolically as

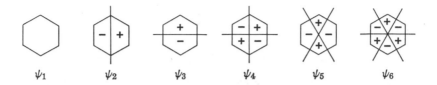

ψ_1 ψ_2 ψ_3 ψ_4 ψ_5 ψ_6

The above have a marked resemblance to the wave functions for a particle on a circle, and it may be remembered that benzene was treated using the latter model with considerable success.

Before considering the possible applications of the wave functions obtained by this method, two subjects must be considered. The first is the distinction between alternate and nonalternate hydrocarbons, and the second is the modification of the method described above which is required when treating heterocyclic compounds.

In connection with the first of these, let us consider the isomeric compounds, naphthalene and azulene. The spin of electrons on adjacent atoms should preferably be of opposite sign in order to minimize repulsions. Let us designate one sign of spin by *, and then star alternate carbons.

It can be seen that there are no adjacent starred atoms in naphthalene, and compounds of this type are known as alternate hydrocarbons.[27] Azulene, on the other hand, does have two adjacent starred (or unstarred) atoms and is known as a nonalternate hydrocarbon. The interelectronic repulsions would be expected to be different for the two types of hydrocarbons. It is generally observed that the simple LCAO-MO method gives the better results with the alternate hydrocarbons. However the results are often reasonably good with the nonalternate hydrocarbons also (cf. Table 1-5).

Pyridine is an example of the second type. Here the energy of an electron localized on nitrogen will be different from that of an electron localized on carbon. Since the electron withdrawing power of nitrogen is greater than that of carbon, due to the higher effective nuclear charge, the energy of an electron on nitrogen should be lower than that on a carbon. The

[27] C. A. Coulson and H. C. Longuet-Higgins, *Proc. Roy. Soc. London*, **A192**, 16 (1947).

secular determinant is then

$$
\begin{vmatrix}
\alpha_N - E & \gamma_{CN} - sE & 0 & 0 & 0 & \gamma_{CN} - sE \\
\gamma_{CN} - sE & \alpha_C - E & \gamma_{CC} - sE & \gamma_{CC}0 & 0 & 0 \\
0 & \gamma_{CC} - sE & \alpha_C - E & \gamma_{CC} - sE & 0 & 0 \\
0 & 0 & \gamma_{CC} - sE & \alpha_C - E & \gamma_{CC} - sE & 0 \\
0 & 0 & 0 & \gamma_{CC} - sE & \alpha_C - E & \gamma_{CC} - sE \\
\gamma_{CN} - sE & 0 & 0 & 0 & \gamma_{CC} - sE & \alpha_C - E
\end{vmatrix} = 0
$$

The exchange integral is usually taken to be equal to γ_{CC}. The Coulombic integral, α_N, may be written as $\alpha_C + \xi\gamma$, where ξ gives the difference between α_C and α_N in units of γ. When overlap is neglected, a value $\xi = 0.58$ gives a result which is in good agreement with the observed dipole moment, and the corresponding value when overlap is included is 0.535.[28] The nitrogen will also affect the Coulombic integral at the adjacent carbon, and this is commonly taken as $\alpha_C + \tfrac{1}{8}\xi\gamma$ or $\alpha_C + 0.068\gamma$. The secular equation is then

$$
\begin{vmatrix}
0.54\gamma - E & \gamma - 0.25E & 0 & 0 & 0 & \gamma - 0.25E \\
\gamma - 0.25E & 0.07\gamma - E & \gamma - 0.25E & 0 & 0 & 0 \\
0 & \gamma - 0.25E & -E & \gamma - 0.25E & 0 & 0 \\
0 & 0 & \gamma - 0.25E & -E & \gamma - 0.25E & 0 \\
0 & 0 & 0 & \gamma - 0.25E & -E & \gamma - 0.25E \\
\gamma - 0.25E & 0 & 0 & 0 & \gamma - 0.25E & 0.07\gamma - E
\end{vmatrix} = 0
$$

By using the vertical plane of symmetry in pyridine, the secular determinant may be factored into a 2×2 determinant ($c_2 = -c_6$, $c_3 = -c_5$, $c_1 = c_4 = 0$) and a 4×4 determinant ($c_2 = c_6$, $c_3 = c_5$).[29] The energies and wave functions thereby obtained are

$$E_1 = 1.44\gamma \qquad \psi_1 = \frac{1}{N_1}(.60\phi_1 + .43\phi_2 + .31\phi_3 + .28\phi_4 + .31\phi_5 + .43\phi_6)$$

$$E_2 = 0.94\gamma \qquad \psi_2 = \frac{1}{N_2}(.55\phi_1 + .15\phi_2 - .38\phi_3 - .61\phi_4 + .38\phi_5 + .15\phi_6)$$

[28] D. W. Davies, *Trans. Faraday Soc.*, **51**, 449 (1955).
[29] The values are more simply obtained using the method described in Appendix 2.

$$E_3 = 0.83\gamma \qquad \psi_3 = \frac{1}{N_3}(\qquad .50\phi_2 + .50\phi_3 \qquad - .50\phi_5 - .50\phi_6)$$

$$E_4 = -1.08\gamma \qquad \psi_4 = \frac{1}{N_4}(.56\phi_1 - .36\phi_2 - .24\phi_3 + .56\phi_4 - .24\phi_5 - .36\phi_6)$$

$$E_5 = -1.29\gamma \qquad \psi_5 = \frac{1}{N_5}(\qquad .50\phi_2 - .50\phi_3 \qquad + .50\phi_5 - .50\phi_6)$$

$$E_6 = -3.80\gamma \qquad \psi_6 = \frac{1}{N_6}(.36\phi_1 - .40\phi_2 + .43\phi_3 - .44\phi_4 + .43\phi_5 - .40\phi_6)$$

The N's in the wave functions are normalization factors, and the functions are written so that the sum of the squares of the coefficients is equal to unity and the N's contain only the effect due to the overlap of the atomic wave functions.

It can be seen that the effect of including α_N is to decrease the energies of most of the levels, the effect being the least for the levels in which a node goes through the nitrogen. Also, the coefficient of ϕ_1 is increased in most of the wave functions, indicating an increased probability of finding an electron near that atom. The same procedure may be used with thiophene or furan (except that $\alpha_O \sim \alpha_S \sim 1.0\gamma + \alpha_C$) and also with some substituted aromatic compounds, such as the phenyl trimethylammonium ion, in which the substituent may be considered to have changed the electron attracting power of the carbon to which it is attracted.

Having the energy levels given above, we are in a position to calculate the delocalization energy of pyridine. The total π energy will be 2 × $1.44\gamma + 2 \times 0.94\gamma + 2 \times 0.83\gamma$ or 6.40γ. From this we must subtract twice the energy of a C$=$N bond, twice the energy of a N—C$=$C—C bond, and twice the energy of a C—C$=$C—C bond. The last was evaluated previously and was found to be 0.8γ. The others may be obtained as follows:

C$=$N
$$\begin{vmatrix} 0.54 - E & \gamma - 0.25E \\ \gamma - 0.25E & 0.07 - E \end{vmatrix} = 0$$

$$E = +0.961, \ -1.070$$

N—C$=$C—N
$$\begin{vmatrix} 0.07 - E & \gamma - 0.25E \\ \gamma - 0.25E & 0.00 - E \end{vmatrix} = 0$$

$$E = +0.828, \ -1.289$$

The delocalization energy of pyridine is therefore calculated to be 1.22γ. The thermodynamically determined delocalization energy is essentially the same as that of benzene, and the calculated value is in good agreement with this observation.

Before continuing, one particular weakness of this one-electron approach must be mentioned. Consider a long polyene. The foregoing method of calculation would predict that there is considerable electron delocalization in the ground state. The calculated delocalization energies are

Butadiene	0.175γ
Hexatriene	0.387γ
Octatetraene	0.612γ
Decapentaene	0.843γ

The difficulty with such an interpretation may be seen in the following example. Suppose we were to write resonance structures involving charge separation:

$$-CH=CH-CH=CH-CH=CH-CH=CH-$$

$$-CH=CH-CH=CH\overset{\updownarrow}{-}\overset{+}{CH}=CH-\overset{+}{CH}-\overset{-}{CH}-$$

$$-CH=CH-CH=CH\overset{\updownarrow}{-}\overset{+}{CH}-CH=CH-\overset{-}{CH}-$$

$$-CH=CH-\overset{+}{CH}-CH\overset{\updownarrow}{=}CH-CH=CH-\overset{-}{CH}-$$

The first of these does not involve delocalization of the double bond and could be written for a monoene. The second involves considerable separation of charge and consequently has a high energy and will contribute little to the stabilization of the polyene. The last involves even a larger degree of charge separation and consequently contributes even less. Thus the extent of delocalization in the ground state will be small.

In terms of molecular orbitals, the same idea may be expressed by a consideration of electron correlation. Consider the case of butadiene.[30] We may represent the molecular orbitals simply as two lobes in which we will place the four electrons. Mutual repulsion of the electrons will place, at any one time, two electrons in the upper node and two electrons in the lower node. In each of the nodes the electrons will tend to repel each other; at the same time they will try to remain in the region between nuclei where the nuclear field is strongest. Thus the preferred arrangement will be

and the electron correlation will accentuate fixation of the double bonds in the 1,2 and 3,4 positions. An explicit calculation for butadiene is in

[30] M. J. S. Dewar and H. N. Schmeising, *Tetrahedron*, **5**, 166 (1959); **11**, 96 (1960); M. J. S. Dewar and C. E. Wulfman, *J. Chem. Phys*, **29**, 158 (1958).

agreement with this qualitative view.[31]   The apparent delocalization energies for linear polyenes (estimated from heats of hydrogenation or combustion) may arise in large part from a poor choice of reference compounds[30] and in part from interaction between two double bonds not involving charge transfer.[31,32]

Either point of view leads to the conclusion that there will not be significant electron delocalization in any compound or ion for which one may write only one classical structure.[33]   However, if more than one may be written, delocalization would be expected.   For example, in the pentadienyl cation, one may write the following resonance structures:

$$CH_2{=}CH{-}CH{=}CH{-}\overset{+}{C}H_2$$
$$CH_2{=}CH{-}\overset{+}{C}H{-}CH{=}CH_2$$
$$\overset{+}{C}H_2{-}CH{=}CH{-}CH{=}CH_2$$

These structures involve only the distribution of a charge and do not involve charge separation.   Thus all are of comparable energy and will contribute to the stabilization of the ion, leading to considerable delocalization energy.   Similarly, if we treat this ion by the molecular orbital approach, the preferred electron distribution will be

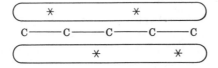

which involves distributing one electron per bond, again leading to considerable delocalization energy.

Finally, it must be stressed that although the simple LCAO-MO method is quite successful in predicting the π-electron delocalization energy for a large number of compounds, it is only a low-order approximation. It is successful because it, in principle, involves the perturbation of an experimental quantity (such as the "thermodynamic" delocalization energy of benzene) using a theoretical model and because the delocalization energy, the compression energy, and other factors are apparently roughly

[31] R. S. Berry, *J. Chem. Phys.*, **26**, 1660 (1957).
[32] W. T. Simpson, *J. Am. Chem. Soc.*, **73**, 5363 (1951).
[33] Electron delocalization will, however, be important in the electronically excited states of these compounds. This can be seen qualitatively by considering that excitation to a singlet (electron paired) state will normally involve charge separation. The charges thus produced may be delocalized over the π-electron system. It can also be seen by applying Dewar and Schmeising's argument to the excited states.

proportional. Thus one must be careful to use the relationship only for a series of compounds having similar structural features. When a different structural feature is present (such as bond angle deformation, or the extra electron repulsion in nonalternate hydrocarbons), one must take this into account.

It should further be noted that the simple LCAO-MO method does not necessarily have anything to do with π-electron delocalization. The quantum mechanical operator is, in effect, not specified because of the semiempirical approach. Thus all quantum chemical energy terms which may be described by an operator operating on wave functions centered on the nuclei will be calculated by the foregoing treatment.

References

Calculation of Delocalization Energies of Conjugated Systems from Heats of Combustion and Heats of Hydrogenation:

G. W. Wheland, *Resonance in Organic Chemistry*, John Wiley and Sons, New York, 1955, pp. 75–128.

A. Streitwieser, Jr., *Molecular Orbital Theory for Organic Chemists*, John Wiley and Sons, New York, 1962, pp. 237–247.

Discussion of Reference Compounds for the Above Calculations:

M. J. S. Dewar and H. N. Schmeising, *Tetrahedron*, **5**, 166 (1959); **11**, 96 (1960).

R. S. Mulliken, *Tetrahedron*, **6**, 68 (1959).

W. F. Yates, *J. Phys. Chem.*, **65**, 185 (1961).

Compression Energies and Vertical Resonance Energies:

C. A. Coulson and S. L. Altman, *Trans. Faraday Soc.*, **48**, 293 (1952).

R. G. Parr, *J. Chem. Phys.*, **19**, 799 (1951).

R. S. Mulliken and R. G. Parr, *J. Chem. Phys.*, **19**, 1271 (1951).

Effect of Inclusion of Strain Energies in Molecular Orbital Calculations:

H. J. Dauben, Jr., quoted in A. Streitwieser, Jr., *Molecular Orbital Theory for Organic Chemists*, pp. 243–244.

On the Question of Electron Delocalization in Linear Polyenes:

M. J. S. Dewar and H. N. Schmeising, *Tetrahedron*, **5**, 166 (1959); **11**, 96 (1960).

R. S. Mulliken, *Tetrahedron*, **6**, 68 (1959).

W. T. Simpson, *J. Am. Chem. Soc.*, **73**, 5363 (1951).

Application of Group Theory in Factoring Secular Equations:

A. Streitwieser, Jr., *Molecular Orbital Theory for Organic Chemists*, pp. 63–96.

R. Daudel, R. Lefebvre, and C. Moser, *Quantum Chemistry*, Interscience Publishers, New York, 1959.

H. Margenau and G. M. Murphy, *The Mathematics of Chemistry and Physics*, D. Van Nostrand Co., Princeton, N.J., 1956.

F. Cotton, *Chemical Applications of Group Theory*, John Wiley and Sons, New York, 1963.

The Valence-Bond (Resonance) Approach to Electron Delocalization:

G. W. Wheland, *Resonance in Organic Chemistry*, John Wiley and Sons, New York, 1955.

On the Question of Inclusion of the Overlap Integral in Molecular Orbital Calculations:

C. A. Coulson and L. J. Schaad, *J. Chem. Phys.*, **35**, 294 (1961).

Problems

1. Using the argument of Dewar and Schmeising, decide whether or not the allyl cation, radical, and anion should have the same delocalization energy.

2. (a) Obtain the energies and wave functions for cyclobutadiene. Bearing in mind how orbitals with the same energy are filled, what may one predict about the nature of the ground state of cyclobutadiene (based on this calculation)? What is the delocalization energy?

(b) Suppose cyclobutadiene were rectangular rather than square. Assuming that γ is proportional to the overlap integral (R. S. Mulliken, C. Rieke, and W. G. Brown, *J. Am. Chem. Soc.* **63**, 48 (1941)), and using $r_{C=C} = 1.33$ Å, and $r_{C-C} = 1.50$ Å, obtain the wave functions and energy levels. What prediction is now made about the ground state of the molecule? What is the delocalization energy?

3. Obtain the wave functions and energy levels for the cyclic 5 and 7 p-orbital systems. Calculate the delocalization energy (based on the one electron approximation) of the cyclopentadienyl anion, radical, and cation and the cycloheptatrienyl anion, radical, and cation. Which is the more favored species in each case? How do the results compare with the experimental data?

4. The π-electron approximation has been used in calculating the wave functions and energy levels for the homoallylic cations

$$\begin{array}{c} \diagdown \quad | \quad | \quad | \\ C{=}C{-}C{-}C{+} \\ \diagup \quad | \quad | \end{array}$$

(S. Winstein and M. Simonetti, *J. Am. Chem. Soc.*, **76**, 18 (1954), W. G. Woods, R. A. Carboni, and J. D. Roberts, *J. Am. Chem. Soc.*, **78**, 5653 (1956)). Make a drawing showing the geometrical arrangement of the orbitals in this case. Is it reasonable to use the π-electron approximation in this case?

5. Calculate the delocalization energy of a Kekule structure of benzene using the bond lengths and overlap integrals of problem 2(b). Compare the result with that for benzene.

1-12 Ground State Properties of Conjugated Systems

A number of ground state properties of conjugated systems are of interest. These include the electron density per carbon, the bond lengths, and the dipole moment. In this section these and other related properties will be considered. Because of its symmetry, benzene is an uninteresting example to use as the model compound. Therefore we shall start by considering butadiene.[34] The energy levels and wave functions are given below, where the ϕ's again represent the atomic orbitals on the respective carbons.

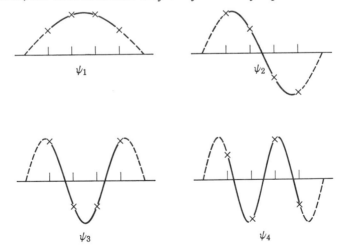

$$\psi_1 = \frac{1}{\sqrt{1 + 1.61s}}(0.37\phi_1 + 0.60\phi_2 + 0.60\phi_3 + 0.37\phi_4)$$

$$E' = -1.62q \qquad E = 1.15\gamma$$

$$\psi_2 = \frac{1}{\sqrt{1 + 0.61s}}(0.60\phi_1 + 0.37\phi_2 - 0.37\phi_3 - 0.60\phi_4)$$

$$E' = -0.62q \qquad E = 0.54\gamma$$

$$\psi_3 = \frac{1}{\sqrt{1 - 0.61s}}(0.60\phi_1 - 0.37\phi_2 - 0.37\phi_3 + 0.60\phi_4)$$

$$E' = 0.62q \qquad E = -0.73\gamma$$

$$\psi_4 = \frac{1}{\sqrt{1 - 1.61s}}(0.37\phi_1 - 0.60\phi_2 + 0.60\phi_3 - 0.37\phi_4)$$

$$E' = 1.62q \qquad E = -2.72\gamma$$

As before, the wave functions may be symbolically represented as

$$\psi_1 \qquad \psi_2$$

$$\psi_3 \qquad \psi_4$$

[34] This compound is used as the example because of its simplicity. However, as was indicated previously, the simple molecular orbital method probably exaggerates the amount of delocalization, and leads to incorrect wave functions, because of neglect of electron correlation terms. The method is, however, satisfactory for most compounds having two or more classical resonance structures.

which may be seen to be quite similar to the wave functions previously derived for a particle in a box.

In using these wave functions, one simplification may be made. It can be shown that the properties calculated using the wave functions for aromatic hydrocarbons are the same regardless of whether overlap is included or neglected,[35] provided that proper definitions are used throughout. Therefore in the following discussion, we shall set $s = 0$ in the normalization factor of the wave functions.

The probability of finding an electron at an atom is given by the square of the wave function at that atom. Thus, for ψ_1, the probability of finding an electron on carbon 1 would be

$$\int (0.37\phi_1)(0.37\phi_1)\, d\tau = (0.37)^2 \int \phi_1 \phi_1\, d\tau = 0.37^2$$

since the wave functions have been normalized. For the total electron density on carbon 1, we must remember that there are four electrons in the system and that they will be in the lowest energy levels, ψ_1 and ψ_2. Thus the total electron density on carbon 1 would be given by

$$2\int (0.37\phi_1)(0.37\phi_1)\, d\tau + 2\int (0.60\phi_1)(0.60\phi_1)\, d\tau = 1.00$$

Similarly, the electron density at each of the carbons will be found to be unity.

This result is always obtained with alternate hydrocarbons, in agreement with the observation that the dipole moments are always zero. The nonalternate hydrocarbons, on the other hand, do not have equal electron densities on the various atoms. Some typical values, obtained by the method described above, are

[35] B. H. Chirgwin and C. A. Coulson, *Proc. Roy. Soc. London* **A201**, 196 (1950). This does not, however, apply to heterocyclic molecules.

On this basis, azulene would be expected to have a dipole moment, and this has been observed to be $1.0D$.[36] Using the above charges, the charge on an electron (4.8×10^{-10} esu) and the bond distances for azulene, the dipole moment may be calculated as the vector sum of individual dipoles. The value thus obtained is $6D$.[37] We may now consider the reason why azulene has a dipole moment and then the reason for the difference between the observed and calculated values.

Suppose we consider azulene as two separate rings. The seven-membered ring would prefer to have six electrons, for then all would be in bonding orbitals. Similarly, the five-membered ring could accommodate six electrons in bonding orbitals. Thus each ring will have a tendency to have six electrons, which results in a positive charge in the seven-membered ring and a negative charge in the five-membered ring. The direction of the dipole in many nonalternate hydrocarbons may be predicted by considerations of this type.

If a carbon acquires a positive charge, the Coulombic attraction for an electron in its vicinity will be increased, and this will tend to oppose the development of charge. If the wave functions are recalculated, using values of the Coulombic integrals which are modified in accordance to the charges calculated above, a new set of electron densities may be calculated, and these will lead to a smaller and more realistic value of the dipole moment.[36,38]

The simple molecular orbital method may also be applied to ions, and if the conjugate acid of benzene is taken, the results are

Thus the positive charge is predicted to be distributed between the para and two ortho positions. Even the more sophisticated treatments lead to approximately the same result. The electron density at each position may

[36] G. W. Wheland and D. E. Mann, *J. Chem. Phys.*, **17**, 264 (1949).

[37] C. A. Coulson and H. C. Longuet-Higgins, *Rev. Sci.* **85**, 929 (1947).

[38] Another reason for the large calculated dipole moment of azulene is that the exchange integral (γ) was taken as the same for all bonds. The value for the central bond will be lower than that for the others because it is relatively long (1.483 Å) as would be expected for a nonalternate hydrocarbon. If the value $\gamma = 0$ were used, the results would be the same as for the alternate hydrocarbon cyclodecapentaene and the dipole moment would be zero. The observed dipole moment may be reproduced if one uses a small value of γ. (E. Sparatore, *Gazz. chim. ital.*, **88**, 671 (1958).)

be determined from the nmr spectra of the ion and from the corresponding ion derived from hexamethylbenzene.[39] The result is

It can be seen that the charge density is much more evenly distributed than would be predicted by the molecular orbital approach.

The reason for this is easily seen.[39] A C-C bond has a reasonable polarizability. Thus when a charge is developed on one carbon atom, the charge is distributed to the adjacent carbons via the inductive effect. The electron density at the *m*-position will then be decreased by electron withdrawal from carbons in the ortho and para positions. This is a type of indirect σ-π interaction which does not involve overlap of the σ and π orbitals. It is interesting to note that the Wheland-Mann approach[36] for obtaining the wave functions for nonalternate hydrocarbons takes the polarization of C-C bonds into account[39] although it was not designed for this purpose.

The leveling of charge density is an important concept in the chemistry of electron-rich and electron-deficient compounds and intermediates. It, for example, accounts for the electron releasing character of a *m*-amino group, whereas it is electron withdrawing via the inductive effect.

The π bond order may be considered next. This is an index of the amount of double bond character between two atoms and is defined as zero for a single bond and unity for a double bond. The bonding between two adjacent atoms is given by the product of the wave functions at each of the two atoms.

$$\int (c_a\phi_a)(c_b\phi_b)\,d\tau = c_a c_b \int \phi_a\phi_b\,d\tau = c_a c_b s$$

Thus the coefficient of s (i.e., $c_a c_b$) is the bond order if the number of electrons is considered, and if it is summed over all of the occupied energy levels, considering only the interaction of adjacent atoms. Therefore, for the C_1-C_2 bond in butadiene, the π bond order is given by

$$2\int (0.37\phi_1)(0.60\phi_2)\,d\tau + 2\int (0.60\phi_1)(0.37\phi_2)\,d\tau$$
$$= 2(0.37)(0.60)s + 2(0.60)(0.37)s = 0.88s$$

and so the bond order is 0.88.

[39] J. P. Colpa, C. Maclean, and E. L. Mackor, *Tetrahedron*, **19**, Suppl. 2, 65 (1963).

For the C_2-C_3 bond, the bond order is

$$2\int (0.60\phi_2)(0.60\phi_3)\, d\tau + 2\int (0.37\phi_2)(-0.37\phi_3)\, d\tau = 0.44s$$

Qualitatively, this says that the C_1-C_2 and C_3-C_4 bonds should have twice as much double bond character as the C_2-C_3 bond.

It should be noted that the value of the mobile bond order at a carbon may be estimated to within about 10% by the use of the Vroelant-Daudel approximation.[40] This is based on the Slater method of spin states and depends only on the nature of bonds adjacent to the bond in question. As an example, let us consider the case of naphthalene.

One first determines the "order" of the bonds in the conjugated system, that is, the number of other bonds to carbon made by the carbon atoms in the bond in question. The orders for the bonds in naphthalene would then be

It is, of course, assumed that the compound is a completely conjugated hydrocarbon so that all the bonds considered are to carbons bearing a p_z atomic orbital. A designation is now determined for each bond by the "order" of the adjacent bonds. For example, in naphthalene the α-β bond is a (2,3) bond, the β-β bond is a (2,2) bond, and the central bond is a (3,3,3,3) bond. The value of the mobile bond order is then found in Table 1-6. A comparison of the results obtained using this approximation with those obtained using the LCAO-MO wave functions is given in Table 1-7.

Since it is known that double bonds are shorter than single bonds, it is tempting to try to correlate the mobile bond orders calculated above with the observed bond lengths. This approach was first suggested by Pauling.[41] The correlation has commonly been made by taking three fixed points, namely, ethylene (1.33 Å) with a bond order of 1, benzene (1.40 Å) with a bond order of 0.667, and a value of about 1.50 Å for a bond order of zero. The last is somewhat shorter than the C—C bond length in ethane (1.55 Å) because the bonds in question are between sp^2 hybrid orbitals rather than sp^3 orbitals as in ethane. It would be expected that the former would give a somewhat shorter bond than the latter.[42]

[40] C. Vroelant and R. Daudel, *Compt. rend.*, **228**, 399 (1949); *Bull. Soc. Chim. France*, **16**, 217 (1949).

[41] L. Pauling, L. O. Brockway, and J. Y. Beach, *J. Am. Chem. Soc.*, **57**, 2705 (1935); L. Pauling and L. O. Brockway, *ibid.*, **59**, 1223 (1937).

[42] A. D. Walsh, *Disc. Faraday Soc.*, **2**, 18 (1947).

Table 1-6 Determination of the Mobile Bond Order by Vroelant-Daudel Approximation[a]

Designation of Bond	Mobile Bond Order	Designation of Bond	Mobile Bond Order
(2)	0.827	(2,3,3)	0.493
(3)	0.873	(2,3,4)	0.508
(1,1)	0.437	(2,4,4)	0.537
(1,2)	0.424	(3,3,3)	0.537
(1,3)	0.566	(3,3,4)	0.556
(2,2)	0.612	(3,4,4)	0.578
(2,3)	0.652	(2,2,3,3)	0.324
(2,4)	0.676	(2,2,3,4)	0.346
(3,3)	0.692	(2,2,4,4)	0.367
(3,4)	0.714	(2,3,3,3)	0.367
(4,4)	0.735	(2,3,3,4)	0.387
(1,2,3)	0.367	(2,3,4,4)	0.407
(1,2,4)	0.387	(2,4,4,4)	0.428
(1,3,3)	0.407	(3,3,3,3)	0.407
(1,3,4)	0.428	(3,3,3,4)	0.428
(1,4,4)	0.440	(3,3,4,4)	0.440
(2,2,2)	0.412	(3,4,4,4)	0.469
(2,2,3)	0.452	(4,4,4,4)	0.489
(2,2,4)	0.472		

[a] C. Vroelant and R. Daudel, *Compt. rend.*, **228**, 399 (1949); *Bull. Soc. Chim. France*, **16**, 217 (1949).

Table 1-7 A Comparison of Bond Orders Calculated by the Vroelant-Daudel Method and by the Simple LCAO-MO Method

Compound	Bond	Bond Order		Ratio
		V-D Method	LCAO-MO	
Benzene	all	0.612	0.667	1.09
Naphthalene	1,2	0.652	0.725	1.11
	2,3	0.612	0.603	0.99
	1,9	0.508	0.555	1.09
	9,10	0.402	0.518	1.29
Anthracene	1,2	0.652	0.737	1.13
	2,3	0.612	0.586	0.96
	1,11	0.508	0.535	1.05
	9,11	0.556	0.606	1.09
	11,12	0.402	0.485	1.21
Phenanthrene	1,2	0.652	0.707	1.08
	2,3	0.612	0.623	1.02
	3,4	0.652	0.702	1.08
	1,11	0.508	0.575	1.13
	9,10	0.692	0.775	1.12
	11,12	0.407	0.542	1.33
			Average	1.11 ± 0.07

Table 1-8   Bond Lengths and Bond Orders

Compound	Bond	Bond Order	Bond Length Obs.	Bond Length Calc.[d]
Benzene[a]	all	0.667	1.397	1.386
Naphthalene[b]	A	0.725	1.365	1.376
	B	0.555	1.425	1.416
	C	0.518	1.393	1.429
	D	0.603	1.404	1.401
Anthracene[b]	A	0.737	1.370	1.396
	B	0.535	1.423	1.423
	C	0.606	1.396	1.400
	D	0.485	1.436	1.442
	E	0.586	1.408	1.406
Pyrene[b]	A	0.536	1.45	1.422
	B	0.523	1.39	1.427
	C	0.594	1.42	1.404
	D	0.670	1.39	1.385
	E	0.504	1.45	1.435
	F	0.777	1.39	1.372
Perylene[b]	A	0.707	1.38	1.372
	B	0.552	1.38	1.417
	C	0.526	1.45	1.426
	D	0.629	1.45	1.394
	E	0.644	1.38	1.392
	F	0.529	1.45	1.425
	G	0.414	1.50	1.475
Coronene[b]	A	0.538	1.415	1.422
	B	0.745	1.385	1.373
	C	0.538	1.430	1.422
	D	0.522	1.430	1.428

Table 1-8 (Cont.)

Compound	*Bond*	*Bond Order*	*Bond Length* *Obs.*	*Calc.*[d]
Ovalene[c]	A	0.557	1.407	1.415
	B	0.519	1.416	1.429
	C	0.764	1.355	1.372
	D	0.511	1.438	1.432
	E	0.508	1.432	1.433
	F	0.526	1.431	1.426
	G	0.604	1.396	1.401
	H	0.541	1.427	1.421
	I	0.535	1.413	1.422
	J	0.497	1.428	1.437
	K	0.521	1.410	1.428
	L	0.726	1.386	1.375

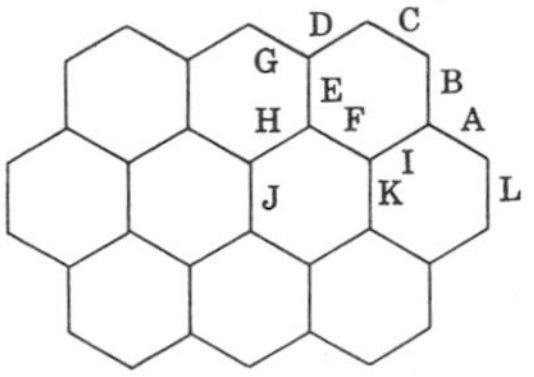

[a] B. P. Stoicheff, *Can. J. Phys.*, **32**, 339 (1954).
[b] J. M. Robertson, *Organic Crystals and Molecules*, Cornell University Press, Ithaca, New York, 1953.
[c] D. M. Donaldson and J. M. Robertson, *Proc. Roy. Soc.*, **A220**, 157 (1953).
[d] Calculated using the relationship:

$$\text{length} = 1.37 + 0.04(0.8 - \text{b.o.}) + 0.6(0.8 - \text{b.o.})^2.$$

A somewhat different approach will be used here. Table 1-8 gives bond distances and bond orders for some aromatic hydrocarbons. A plot of these data is shown in Fig. 1-23. The central line is an approximation to a "best fit," and the outside lines are drawn at a distance of 0.01 Å on each side of the central line. It can be seen that most of the points fall within the two outside lines—and that if the outside lines were moved to ±0.02 Å, nearly all the points would be included. Since the accuracy of the data in Table 1-8 given to four significant figures is ±0.01, and for that given to three significant figures is between ±0.02 to ±0.03 Å, it can be seen that the correlation is formally rather satisfactory.

However, it may be noted that most of the bond lengths lie between 1.38 to 1.45 Å, a spread of only 0.07 Å. Thus the deviations are a very large fraction of the total distance. It may also be noted that a large proportion of the points correspond to bond orders between 0.51 to 0.53 regardless of bond length. These considerations make the correlation lose some of its luster, although it is often useful in a qualitative sense. More sophisticated treatments appear to be no more satisfactory in this type of a correlation.[43]

[43] H. O. Pritchard and F. H. Sumner, *Proc. Roy. Soc., London,* **A226,** 128 (1954).

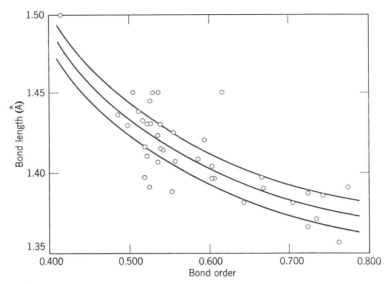

Fig. 1-23. Correlation of bond orders with bond lengths.

Another ground state quantity of interest is the free valence (F_r).[44] It bears a close resemblance to Thiele's idea of "residual affinity," which in the case of butadiene would be represented as

$$H_2C = C\underset{H}{-}C = CH_2$$

Here Thiele suggested that there was a tendency for some double bond character between the central carbons, leaving some residual, unused bonding capacity at the terminal carbons. In this way he explained the 1,4-addition of halogens to butadiene.

In considering free valence, we must first determine the total bonding to a given atom. Let us take the α-carbon of naphthalene as an example:

$$\underset{C_9 \qquad C_2}{\overset{\overset{\displaystyle H}{\displaystyle |}}{0.555 \ C_1 \ 0.725}}$$

The carbon forms three σ bonds and two π bonds which have orders of 0.725 and 0.555, respectively. The sum of the σ bonds and bond orders is

[44] C. A. Coulson, *Disc. Faraday Soc.*, **2**, 9 (1947).

then 4.280. Similarly, for the β-carbon:

$$
\begin{array}{c}
C_1 \ 0.725 \ H \\
\diagdown \qquad \diagup \\
C_2 \\
| \ 0.603 \\
C_3
\end{array}
$$

The total bonding is 4.328. The maximum value which is possible is $3 + \sqrt{3}$ or 4.732.[44] The free valence is then defined as 4.732 — the total bonding, which is 0.452 and 0.404 for the α- and β-positions, respectively.

The free valence has commonly, been used as an index to reactivity[45] in aromatic compounds; the position with the highest free valence is assumed to be the most reactive. This type of ground state reasoning is, of course, fundamentally unsound unless a relationship exists between the effect of structural change on the ground state property and on the activation energy for the given reaction.

Let us consider aromatic electrophilic substitution.

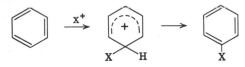

For a number of these reactions, one does not know whether step 1 or step 2 is rate controlling. However, a good argument may be made that the activated complexes for both steps have structures and energies similar to that of the intermediate.[46] Thus if we were to calculate the difference in energy between the hydrocarbon and the intermediate, we should have a quantity which is proportional to the activation energy. The energy of the intermediate may be calculated using the procedure previously employed for the hydrocarbons themselves, except that here the number of electrons is one less than the number of orbitals. The carbon bearing the —X group is simply left out of the calculation. The values thus obtained are given in Table 1-9 (consider the —X group in place of the extra proton in the compounds listed) as well as the difference in energy between the calculated values and that of the parent hydrocarbon. The fact that some of the differences are negative (corresponding to an apparent greater delocalization energy in the intermediate as compared to the hydrocarbon) is of little consequence. It arises because of the

[45] See B. Pullman and A. Pullman, in *Progress in Organic Chemistry*, Academic Press, New York, 1958 vol. 4.

[46] G. Hammond, *J. Am. Chem. Soc.*, **77**, 334 (1955).

Compounds Listed in Table 1-9 to 1-11
(The asterisks indicate the positions having the lowest electron localization energies and the highest values of free valence.)

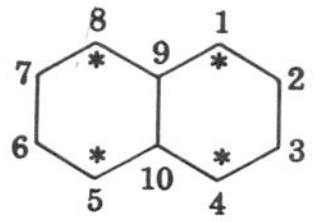

Naphthalene

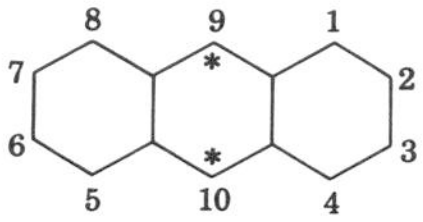

Anthracene

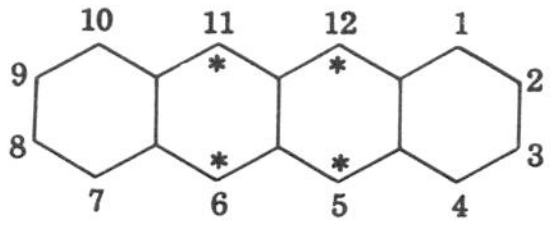

Naphthacene

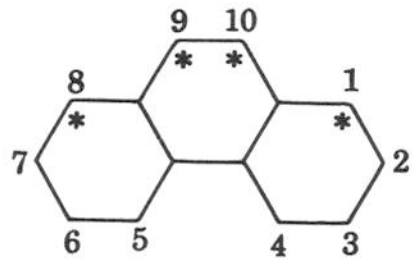

Phenanthrene

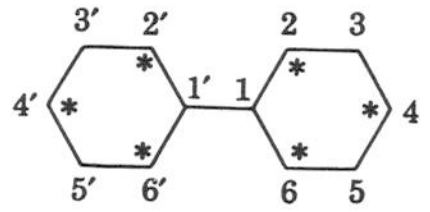

Diphenyl

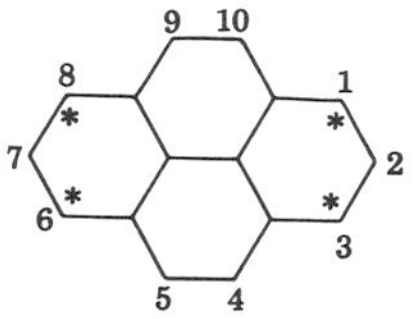

Pyrene

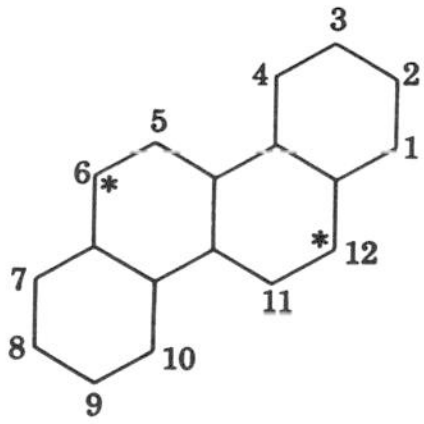

Chrysene

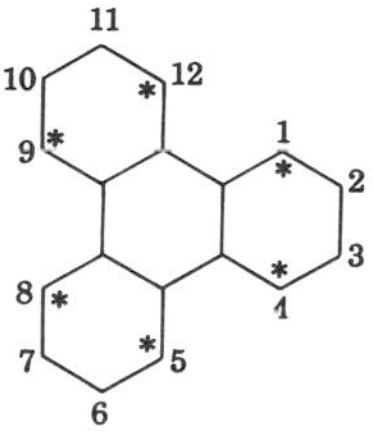

Triphenylene

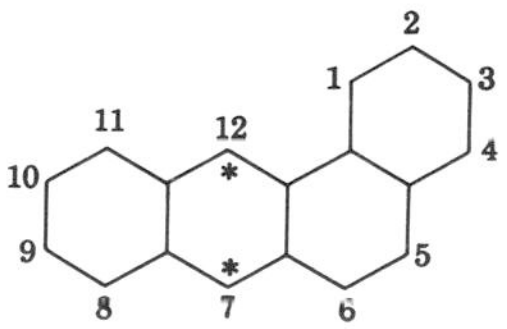

Benz [a] anthracene

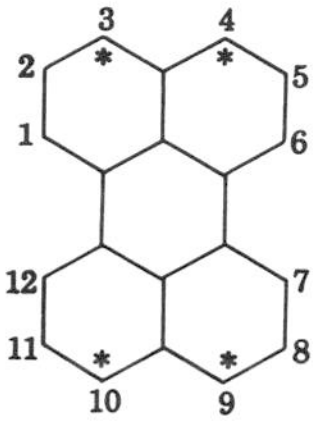

Perylene

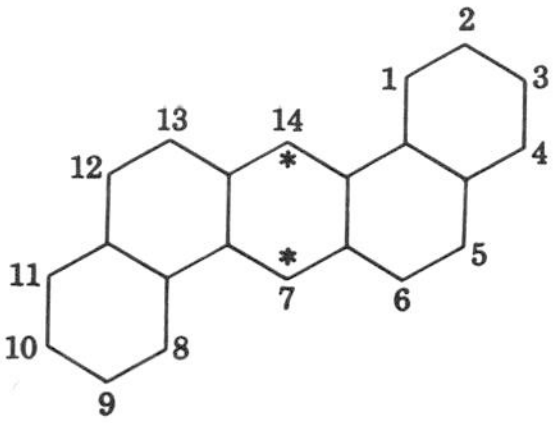

Dibenz [a, j] anthracene

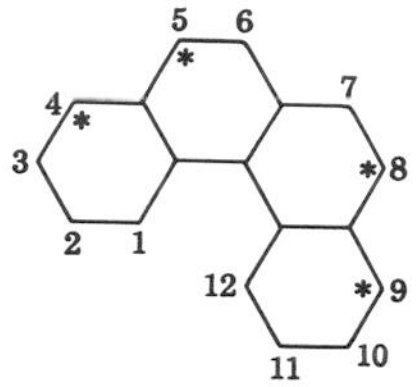

Benzo [c] phenanthrene

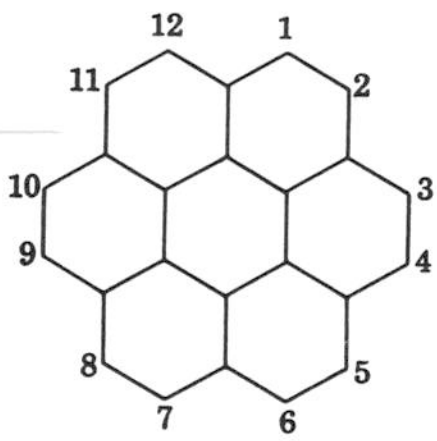

Coronene

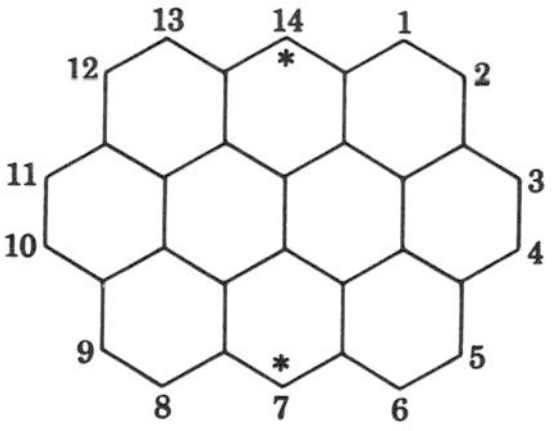

Ovalene

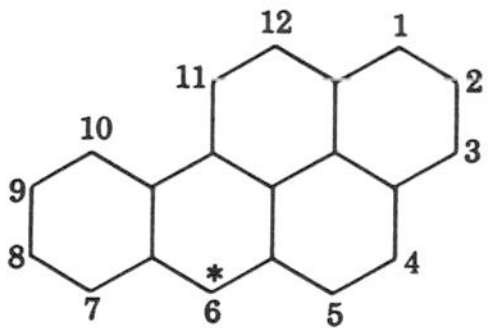

Benzo [a] pyrene

Table 1-9   Free Valence and Electron Location Energies

Compound	E	E^{ref}	ΔE^a	Fr^b
Protiobenzene	0.817	1.067	0.250	0.399
1-Protionaphthalene	1.823	1.863	0.040	0.452
2-Protionaphthalene	1.668	1.863	0.195	0.404
1-Protioanthracene	2.634	2.608	−0.016	0.459
2-Protioanthracene	2.469	2.608	0.139	0.409
9-Protioanthracene	2.825	2.608	−0.217	0.520
1-Protiophenanthrene	2.678	2.736	0.068	0.450
2-Protiophenanthrene	2.525	2.736	0.211	0.403
3-Protiophenanthrene	2.567	2.736	0.169	0.408
4-Protiophenanthrene	2.634	2.736	0.102	0.440
9-Protiophenanthrene	2.698	2.736	0.038	0.451
1-Protiobenz[a]anthracene	3.396	3.503	0.107	0.440
2-Protiobenz[a]anthracene	3.350	3.503	0.153	0.409
3-Protiobenz[a]anthracene	3.301	3.503	0.202	0.403
4-Protiobenz[a]anthracene	3.448	3.503	0.055	0.450
5-Protiobenz[a]anthracene	3.502	3.503	0.001	0.455
6-Protiobenz[a]anthracene	3.501	3.503	0.002	0.455
7-Protiobenz[a]anthracene	3.685	3.503	−0.182	0.514
8-Protiobenz[a]anthracene	3.515	3.503	−0.012	0.459
9-Protiobenz[a]anthracene	3.343	3.503	0.160	0.408
10-Protiobenz[a]anthracene	3.357	3.503	0.146	0.408
11-Protiobenz[a]anthracene	3.503	3.503	0.000	0.457
12-Protiobenz[a]anthracene	3.637	3.503	−0.134	0.502
1-Protiopyrene	3.276	3.212	−0.064	0.468
2-Protiopyrene	2.953	3.212	0.259	0.393
4-Protiopyrene	3.198	3.212	0.004	0.455
1-Protioperylene	4.112	4.058	−0.054	0.459
2-Protioperylene	3.837	4.058	0.221	0.400
3-Protioperylene	4.172	4.058	−0.114	0.472

[a] π-electron energies in units of γ.
[b] Free valence for the hydrocarbon for the position at which the proton was placed.

difference in the electronic repulsion terms and the neglect of the change in the values of the integrals used when going from the hydrocarbon to the ion.

A comparison of the values of free valence and the corresponding electron localization energies (as the energies calculated above are commonly called) is made in Fig. 1-24. The shape of the curve has no physical significance; it only serves to show that the values of free valence

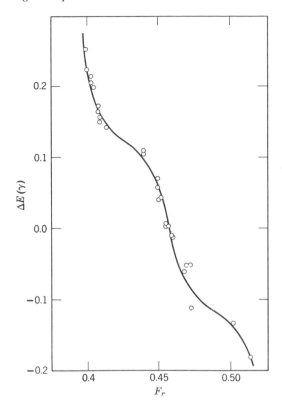

Fig. 1-24. *A comparison of electron localization energies with free valence.*

tend to come in groups. Although the correlation is not linear, it is apparent that higher values of free valence do indeed correspond to lower electron localization energies. Wheland[47] has shown that with alternate hydrocarbons, the lowest unfilled level of the ions discussed above is nonbonding. Thus one or two electrons may be added without changing the value of the energy (in the LCAO-MO approximation). For these hydrocarbons, the effect of adding a cation, a free radical, or an anion will be the same, and all three species should attack in the same position. This is, however, *not* the case with nonalternate hydrocarbons or with most substituted derivatives of the alternate hydrocarbons.

Many studies have been made on the correlation between the values of free valence or the electron localization energy and the reactivity in

[47] G. W. Wheland, *J. Am. Chem. Soc.*, **64**, 900 (1942).

electrophilic and free radical substitution reactions and in similar processes.[48] These correlations are often quite good.

In examining the experimental data, let us first consider the relatively straightforward process of the protonation of aromatic hydrocarbons. The equilibrium constants have been measured using anhydrous hydrogen fluoride as both the solvent and the acid.[49] The data are given in Table 1-10 and have been corrected for the number of positions which have equally high probability for accepting a proton (i.e., 6 for benzene and 4

Table 1-10   Basicities of Aromatic Hydrocarbons[a]

	Z^b	$\log K'^c$	$\Delta E(LCAO)^d$	$\Delta E(SCF)$
1. Benzene	6	−10.2	0.250	0.95
2. Diphenyl	6	−6.3	0.142	0.59
3. Triphenylene	6	−5.4	0.114	
4. Naphthalene	4	−4.6	0.040	0.50
5. Phenanthrene	4	−4.1	0.038	0.45
6. Chrysene	2	−2.0	−0.065	
7. Pyrene	4	1.5	−0.064	0.15
8. Dibenzanthracene	2	1.9	−0.144	
9. Benz[a]anthracene	2	2.0	−0.182	0.01
10. Anthracene	2	3.5	−0.217	0.01
11. Perylene	4	3.8	−0.114	0.03
12. Naphthacene	4	5.2	−0.298	

[a] The data are from E. L. Mackor, A. Hofstra, and J. H. van der Waals, *Trans. Faraday Soc.*, **54**, 66 (1958); A. A. Verrijn Stuart and J. H. Kruizinga, *Quantum Chemistry Symposium*, Paris, Sept. 1957, p. 229.
[b] Z is the statistical factor used in correcting the equilibrium constants and corresponds to the number of positions having approximately equal basicity.
[c] K' is the corrected equilibrium constant given by

$$\log K' = \log K - \log Z$$

[d] The energies are given in units of γ.

for naphthalene). The data are plotted against the electron localization energies in Fig. 1-25. With the exception of pyrene and perylene, a rather good correlation is found. If the more refined self-consistent field approach is used, even these compounds have their points fall on the line.[50] The

[48] A summary of these data may be found in A. Streitwieser, Jr., *Molecular Orbital Theory for Organic Chemists*, John Wiley and Sons, New York, 1961, pp. 307–356.
[49] E. L. Mackor, A. Hofstra, and J. H. van der Waals, *Trans. Faraday Soc.*, **54**, 66 (1958).
[50] A. A. Verrijn Stuart and J. H. Kruizinga, Quantum Chemistry Symposium, Paris, Sept. 1957, p. 229.

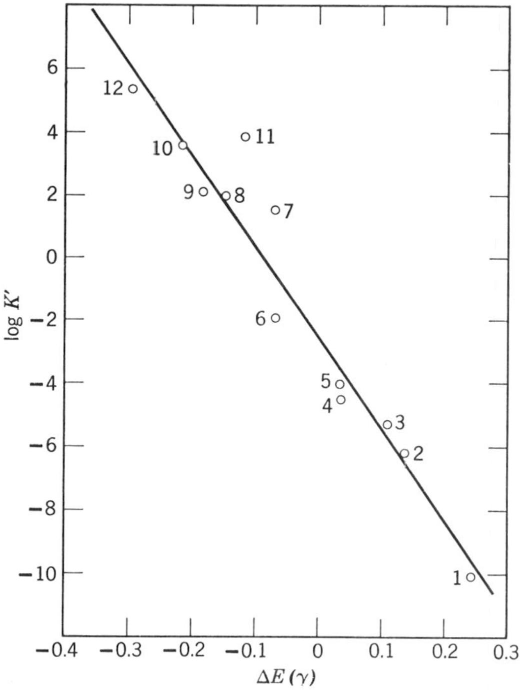

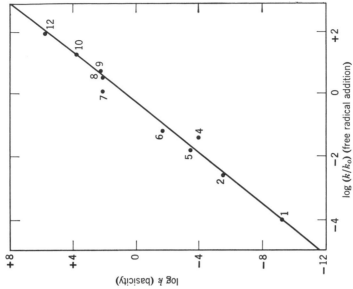

Fig. 1-26. Correlation between the basicity of hydrocarbons and the rate of reaction with trichloromethyl and methyl radicals. (E. L. Mackor, A. Hofstra and J. H. van der Waals, Trans. Faraday Soc., **54**, *66 (1958). The numbering is the same as in Table 1-10.*

Fig. 1-25. Correlation of basicity of hydrocarbons with electron localization energies.

correlation with the free valence is fair but not as good as with the localization energy.

The good correlation observed in this case suggests that the basicities are proportional to the true localization energies and can be used as a measure of these quantities. It is generally observed that there is a good linear relationship between the logarithms of the rates of electrophilic substitution reactions and the logarithms of the basicity constants for the hydrocarbons.[48] This approach is particularly useful in that the slope of the line (for comparable solvents) is a measure of the amount of cationic character developed in the ring of the activated complex.

In order to test the idea that the electron localization energies may also be used as an index to reactivity in free radical reactions, we may consider the reaction of aromatic hydrocarbons with trichloromethyl radicals.[51] A plot of the logarithms of the relative reactivities against the logarithms of the basicity constants of the hydrocarbons is shown in Fig. 1-26.[49] Again, the correlation is quite good and significantly better than the correlation found with the free valence.

One other type of localization energy—the bond localization energy— must be considered. The bond localization energy is the loss in delocalization energy resulting from the addition of hydrogen (or some other reagent) across a double bond. The values of the localization energy for several alternate hydrocarbons are given in Table 1-11. The bond order is a measure of the double bond character of a bond, and it might be expected that the bond having the highest bond order would have the lowest bond localization energy.[52] Figure 1-27 shows that the correlation is remarkably good.

One of the most extensively studied double bond reagents is osmium tetroxide. This reacts to form an osmate ester which on hydrolysis gives a diol. Many polycyclic aromatic hydrocarbons have been found to undergo this reaction, and it has been observed that the bond localization energies give a good index as to which bond will be the more reactive and

[51] E. C. Kooyman and E. Farenhorst, *Trans. Faraday Soc.*, **49**, 58 (1953).
[52] R. D. Brown, *Australian J. Sci. Research*, **2A**, 564 (1949); *J. Chem. Soc.*, 3249 (1950); 1950 (1951).

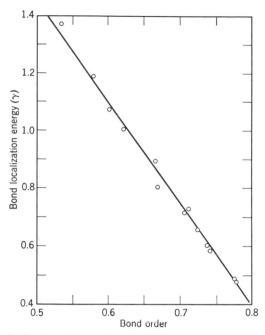

Fig. 1-27. Correlation of bond localization energies with bond orders.

Table 1-11   Bond Localization Energies for Alternate Hydrocarbons

Compound	Bond	Bond Order	Bond Localization Energy[a]
Benzene	all	0.667	0.892
Naphthalene	1,2	0.725	0.652
	2,3	0.603	1.085
Anthracene	1,2	0.737	0.598
	2,3	0.586	1.139
	9,10	—	0.474
Phenanthrene	1,2	0.707	0.711
	2,3	0.623	1.003
	3,4	0.702	0.726
	9,10	0.775	0.484
Pyrene	1,2	0.670	0.803
	4,5	0.777	0.476
	internal	0.536	1.372
Naphthacene	1,2	0.741	0.581
	2,3	0.581	1.191
	5,12	—	0.410

[a] In units of γ.

100

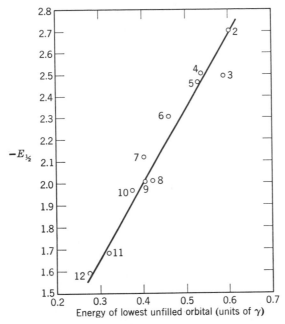

Fig. 1-28. Correlation of polarographic half-wave potentials with energies of lowest unfilled molecular orbitals. The numbers are those given in Table 1-10.

will semiquantitatively account for the relative rate of reactions of a number of unsaturated hydrocarbons.[53]

Ozone is another double bond reagent which has received considerable study. It is not practical to measure rates of reaction in this case, but it is again observed that the positions of attack are well correlated with the bond localization energies.[54]

A final quantity of interest with the alternate hydrocarbons is the polarographic reduction potential. Suppose one were to add an electron to an unsaturated hydrocarbon. The electron will be added to the lowest energy unfilled level. Thus there should be a relationship between the polarographic half-wave potential (which is proportional to the energy required to add an electron), and the energy of the lowest unfilled level.[55] The available data[56] are shown diagrammatically in Fig. 1-28. Again, a good correlation is observed.

[53] R. D. Brown, *Quart. Revs.*, **6**, 63 (1952).

[54] Ref. 48, pp. 441–442.

[55] A. Maccoll, *Nature*, **163**, 178 (1949).

[56] P. L. Elving and B. Pullman in I. Prigogine, ed., *Advances in Chemical Physics*, Interscience Publishers, New York, 1961, vol. III, p. 1.

Throughout we have seen that the simple molecular orbital method gives results which are usually in very good agreement with the experimental results. This arises in part from the semiempirical nature of the treatment and from the fact that rather similar compounds are usually compared.

Problems

1. Calculate the bond orders and electron densities for naphthalene, and see if your results agree with those in Table 1–7.

2. For the compounds in Table 1–9, calculate the bond orders by the Vroelant-Daudel method, and from this obtain the values of free valence. Plot these latter values against the localization energies which are given. Is the Vroelant-Daudel method useful in determining the position having the highest reactivity in alternate hydrocarbons?

3. Calculate the localization energies involved in the addition of a cation, a free radical, and an anion to the 1, 2, 4, 5, and 6 positions of azulene. Compare

these results with the values of the free valence, and with the experimental observations (E. Heilbronner in *Non-Benzenoid Aromatic Compounds*, D. Ginsberg (ed.), Interscience Publishers, New York, 1959, ch. 5). This calculation requires the use of a digital computor for diagonalizing the secular determinant (cf. Appendix 2). If this is not available, the same principle may be seen in the corresponding calculation for fulvene.

4. Based on the localization energies, determine the position of attack on the phenyltrimethylammonium ion by electrophilic and nucleophilic reagents. Make the simple assumption that the trimethylammonium group affects only the Coulombic integral at the carbon to which it is attached and that $\alpha = \alpha_C + 1.0\gamma$.

5. Wheland and Mann (*J. Chem. Phys.*, **17**, 264 (1949)) have suggested the use of a relationship between the Coulombic integral and the charge density which may be written in the form

$$\alpha_r = \alpha_C + (1 - p_{rr})\omega q$$

where p_{rr} is the charge density on the rth atom, ω is a proportionality constant ($\sim$1.4), and $q = \gamma - sE$. Using this relationship, calculate the charge density distribution in fulvene, and compare the results with those obtained from the simple molecular orbital theory. (Note that the values of p_{rr} must first be obtained from the latter.) Calculate the dipole moments derived from both sets of charge densities, and compare with the experimental value of $1.2D$.

6. Show whether or not there is a relationship between bond order and bond localization energies in nonalternate hydrocarbons.

7. Apply Dewar and Schmeising's arguments concerning butadiene (p. 80) to the four nonalternate hydrocarbons shown on p. 85. What does this imply concerning the electron delocalization in each?

8. Dewar (*J. Am. Chem. Soc.*, **74**, 3341 (1952)) has suggested a simple approximation method (NBMO—nonbonding molecular orbitals) which may be applied to the calculation of the properties of aromatic systems. Using his method, calculate the various functions for naphthalene, and compare the results with those obtained by the simple molecular orbital method.

References

Charge Densities in Aromatic Compounds and Ions:
  J. P. Colpa, C. Maclean, and E. L. Mackor, *Tetrahedron*, in press.
  A. Streitwieser, Jr., *Molecular Orbital Theory for Organic Chemists*, John Wiley and Sons, New York, 1961, pp. 139–147, 357–362.
  G. W. Wheland and D. E. Mann, *J. Chem. Phys.* **17**, 264 (1949).
Bond Orders and Bond Lengths:
  A. Streitwieser Jr., *Molecular Orbital Theory for Organic Chemists*, pp. 165–172.
  M. J. S. Dewar and H. N. Schmeising, *Tetrahedron*, **5**, 166 (1959); **11**, 96 (1960).
  R. S. Mulliken, *Tetrahedron*, **6**, 68 (1959).
  B. Bak and L. Hansen-Nygaard, *J. Chem. Phys.*, **33**, 418 (1960).
  T. H. Goodwin, *J. Chem. Soc.*, 4851 (1960).
Free Valence:
  B. Pullman and A. Pullman in *Progress in Organic Chemistry*, Academic Press, New York, 1958, vol. 4.
Electron and Bond Localization Energies:
  G. W. Wheland, *J. Am. Chem. Soc.*, **64**, 900 (1942).
  A. Streitwieser, Jr., *Molecular Orbital Theory for Organic Chemists*, pp. 335–356, 398–407.
  R. D. Brown, *J. Chem. Soc.*, 3249 (1950); 1950 (1951).

1-13 The Hydrogen Molecule

We have treated a number of molecular systems using one-electron wave functions, and the difficulties inherent in this approach have been considered. The principal difficulty was that the interaction between electrons was not explicitly considered. The following discussion will outline some of the ways in which this problem has been treated, and in order to keep the system as simple as possible, the hydrogen molecule will be used as the example throughout. Later the application of some of these ideas to systems of more general interest to organic chemists will be considered.

The exact form of the Hamiltonian operator for this case is easily written, and we will make the usual assumption that the motion of the nuclei may be treated separately.

$$H = -\frac{h^2}{8m\pi^2}\left(\frac{\partial^2}{\partial x_1^2} + \frac{\partial^2}{\partial y_1^2} + \frac{\partial^2}{\partial z_1^2}\right) - \frac{h^2}{8m\pi^2}\left(\frac{\partial^2}{\partial x_2^2} + \frac{\partial^2}{\partial y_2^2} + \frac{\partial^2}{\partial z_2^2}\right)$$

$$- \frac{e^2}{r_{1a}} - \frac{e^2}{r_{1b}} - \frac{e^2}{r_{2a}} - \frac{e^2}{r_{2b}} + \frac{e^2}{r_{12}} + \frac{e^2}{r_{ab}}$$

If the solution of the wave equation using this operator could be obtained, a plot of the energy against the value of r_{ab} which led to it would result in the dissociation curve for the hydrogen molecule. However, because of the e^2/r_{12} term, which represents the repulsion between the two electrons, it is not possible to separate the variables in the differential equation, and it is not as yet possible to solve it directly. Therefore it is necessary to rely on an approximation method.

Using the molecular orbital approach, the trial wave function which might appropriately be chosen would be that for the hydrogen molecule-ion, which was (p. 59)

$$\psi = \frac{1}{\sqrt{2 + 2s}}(\phi_a + \phi_b)$$

Since there are two electrons, the corresponding hydrogen molecule wave functions would be the product of a wave function of the above type for electron 1 and for electron 2:

$$\Psi = \psi(1)\psi(2) = N[\phi_a(1) + \phi_b(1)][\phi_a(2) + \phi_b(2)]$$

where N is the normalization factor. The energy may then be found from

$$E = \int \Psi H \Psi \, d\tau$$

The integrals are not easily evaluated, and, in particular, the e^2/r_{12} term gives trouble, for it involves simultaneously the coordinates of the two electrons. The integral containing this term is evaluated as the repulsion between one electron and the average distribution of the other. The value thus obtained will be too large because there is a correlation between the motion of the two electrons. As a result of the repulsion between them, they tend to stay as far from each other as possible, thus minimizing the value of the repulsion term.

The integrals have been evaluated and the energy has been determined as a function of r_{ab}.[57] The calculated equilibrium internuclear distance was 0.850 Å with a corresponding bond dissociation energy of 61.8 kcal/mole. These may be compared with the observed values, 0.740 Å and 109.5 kcal/mole.

Just as with the hydrogen molecule-ion, the introduction of a scale factor into the hydrogen atomic wave functions from which the molecular orbital wave functions are formed will improve the result. With $Z = 1.197$, the internuclear distance was calculated to be 0.732 Å and the energy, 80.0 kcal/mole.[57]

Another type of simple wave function is that suggested by Heitler and London.[58] They considered that two reasonable wave functions would be

$$\psi_1 = N[\phi_a(1)\phi_b(2)]$$

and

$$\psi_2 = N[\phi_a(2)\phi_b(1)]$$

In the first, electron 1 is in the $1s$ atomic orbital ϕ_a and electron 2 is in ϕ_b. In the second, the positions of the electrons are reversed. The two wave functions, when considered separately, both lead to the same energy. If we wish to consider mixing of the wave functions, we must obtain the energies and coefficients from the secular determinant:

$$\begin{vmatrix} H_{11} - \Delta_{11}E & H_{12} - \Delta_{12}E \\ H_{21} - \Delta_{21}E & H_{22} - \Delta_{22}E \end{vmatrix} = 0$$

where

$$\Delta_{12} = \Delta_{21} = N^2 \int [\phi_a(1)\phi_b(2)][\phi_a(2)\phi_b(1)]\, d\tau = s^2$$

and where s is the overlap integral between ϕ_a and ϕ_b. The energies are then

$$E_+ = \frac{H_{11} + H_{12}}{1 + s^2}$$

$$E_- = \frac{H_{11} - H_{12}}{1 - s^2}$$

[57] C. A. Coulson, *Trans. Faraday Soc.*, **33**, 1479 (1937).
[58] W. Heitler and F. London, *Z. Physik*. **44**, 455 (1927).

In this (Valence-Bond) treatment, the integral H_{11} is commonly called a Coulombic integral (J) and H_{12} is designated as an exchange integral (K). The corresponding wave functions are

$$\psi_+ = N[\phi_a(1)\phi_b(2) + \phi_a(2)\phi_b(1)]$$

$$\psi_- = N[\phi_a(1)\phi_b(2) - \phi_a(2)\phi_b(1)]$$

where the first is for the bonding state and the second is for the antibonding state.

Let us first compare ψ_+ with that obtained in the molecular orbital method. Multiplying out the latter, we get

$$\psi = N[\phi_a(1)\phi_b(2) + \phi_a(2)\phi_b(1) + \phi_a(1)\phi_a(2) + \phi_b(1)\phi_b(2)]$$

It can be seen that the two wave functions are the same for the first two terms and that the difference lies in the fact that there are two additional terms in the wave functions obtained by the molecular orbital method. Let us consider the physical significance of the term $\phi_a(1)\phi_a(2)$. This corresponds to both electrons being in the $1s$ atomic orbital ϕ_a and corresponds to the structure H^-H^+. Similarly, the last term corresponds to H^+H^-, and these two terms are commonly referred to as "ionic" terms. The molecular orbital method includes these terms in equal proportion to the nonionic terms, whereas the Heitler-London (Valence Bond) wave function leaves them out completely.

The required integrals have been evaluated,[57,59] and the energy and equilibrium internuclear distance have been calculated to be 72.4 kcal/mole and 0.869 Å. Again, an improvement might be expected if a scale factor were included in the original atomic orbitals, and the values thus obtained are 86.7 kcal/mole and 0.743 Å.[60] The energies calculated by the Heitler-London approach are somewhat better than those obtained by the molecular orbital method. Both functions lead to reasonable estimates of the energy and of the bond distance, but neither can be said to be outstanding in its ability to reproduce the experimental data.

The fundamental difficulty with the molecular orbital wave function is that the correlation of the motions of the electrons is not taken into account. The "ionic" terms in the wave function are given equal importance with the nonionic terms, even though the repulsion of the electrons should make these terms have less importance. The Heitler-London wave function is better than the molecular orbital function because the former

[59] Y. Sigiura, *Z. Physik.*, **45**, 484 (1927). See L. Pauling and E. B. Wilson, Jr., *Introduction to Quantum Mechanics*, McGraw-Hill Book Co., New York, 1935, pp. 340–343.
[60] S. C. Wang, *Phys. Rev.*, **31**, 579 (1928).

does not include terms in which both electrons are on the same nucleus and thus introduces correlation. However, some contribution of the ionic terms is probably involved, and the Heitler-London wave function has gone too far in the other direction.

One rather satisfactory way in which to introduce correlation of electronic motion in the molecular orbital approach is to use configurational interaction. Suppose a fraction of the first excited state wave function is added to the original wave function. The new wave function is then (neglecting the normalization factor)

$$\psi = [\phi_a(1) + \phi_b(1)][\phi_a(2) + \phi_b(2)] + a[\phi_a(1) - \phi_b(1)][\phi_a(2) - \phi_b(2)]$$

The effect of introducing the second term can best be seen by multiplying out the wave function, giving

$$\psi = (1 + a)[\phi_a(1)\phi_a(2) + \phi_b(1)\phi_b(2)] + (1 - a)[\phi_a(1)\phi_b(2) + \phi_a(2)\phi_b(1)]$$

It can be seen that if $a = 0$, this is simply the molecular orbital type wave function, and that if $a = -1$, it is the Heitler-London wave function. Thus configurational interaction provides a method for obtaining the most satisfactory contribution of ionic terms.

The bond energy of the hydrogen molecule calculated in this way is 74 kcal with an equilibrium bond length of 0.884 Å. The value of a was found to be -0.727. If a scale factor, Z, is introduced into the $1s$ atomic orbitals, and the energy is minimized with respect to both a and Z, the calculated values are 92 kcal/mole, 0.748 Å, with $a = -0.591$ and $Z = 1.193$. The result thus obtained differs from the observed value by only 15%.[61] This indicates that configurational interaction provides a satisfactory method for taking correlation energy into account.

In principle, it should be possible to expand the arbitrary ψ used in the calculation in terms of the wave functions for the successively higher energy states of a hydrogen molecule-ion (i.e., including p orbitals, etc.). If a complete set of these wave functions were taken, we could have confidence that the variation method would allow us to obtain the true energy and the true wave function. However, the labor involved in including even a moderately large number of terms is prohibitive, and usually two or, at most, three or four configurations are considered to interact. In the foregoing example a considerable improvement was made by including the first excited state, and a further improvement could be made by including the first π-electronic state.

[61] S. Weinbaum, *J. Chem. Phys.*, **1**, 593 (1933).

1-14 The Treatment of Aromatic Compounds Including Electron Repulsion Terms

We have previously considered the simple Hückel one-electron treatment of aromatic compounds. Although it did not use the correct Hamiltonian operator for a many electron case, it was a useful method in that various properties of aromatic compounds could be reasonably well correlated with the results of the treatment, provided that some empirically determined parameters were employed. We have also briefly considered the case of the hydrogen molecule, including electron repulsion terms. The extension of the latter to the case of the aromatic hydrocarbons will now be considered. The following will still be an approximation because the correlation of the movement of electrons is not properly taken into account in calculating the electron repulsion terms and because the wave functions used are not entirely satisfactory. The inclusion of electron correlation and the use of better wave functions (such as the inclusion of contribution from d and f states) are more difficult and beyond the scope of this work.

Let us first consider ethylene, while still retaining the π-electron approximation. The justification for this approximation was given previously (p. 66). The Hamiltonian operator for the two-electron system, neglecting the nuclear repulsion term, will be

$$H = T_1 + V_{a1} + V_{b1} + T_2 + V_{a2} + V_{b2} + \frac{e^2}{r_{12}}$$

where T_1 is the kinetic energy operator for electron 1, V_{a1} is the potential energy operator between nucleus a and electron 1, and e^2/r_{12} is the electron repulsion term. This is commonly abbreviated as

$$H = H_1^{\text{core}} + H_2^{\text{core}} + \frac{e^2}{r_{12}}$$

where H_1^{core} represents the kinetic energy operator for electron 1 plus its potential energy operator in the field of the nuclear core of the molecule.

In the case of ethylene, the molecular orbital wave functions are

$$\psi_+ = \frac{1}{\sqrt{2 + 2s}}(\phi_a + \phi_b) = N(a + b)$$

$$\psi_- = \frac{1}{\sqrt{2 - 2s}}(\phi_a - \phi_b) = N'(a - b)$$

and it will be convenient to use these functions as starting points. The ground state of ethylene has two electrons in ψ_+ (both in the bonding molecular orbital). The energy obtained from the core Hamiltonian for electron 1 is the same as that obtained from electron 2, and thus the expression will be written for one electron and multiplied by two

$$E^{\text{core}} = 2N^2 \int (a + b)(T_1 + V_{a1} + V_{b1})(a + b) \, d\tau$$

Furthermore, a and b are identical wave functions, and thus only one need be used in the right-hand part, and the expression will again be multiplied by two, giving

$$E^{\text{core}} = 4N^2 \int (a + b)(T_1 + V_{a1} + V_{b1})a \, d\tau$$

$$= 4N^2 \left[\int a(T_1 + V_{a1})a \, d\tau + \int b(T_1 + v_{a1})a \, d\tau \right.$$

$$\left. + \int a(V_{b1})a \, d\tau + \int b(V_{b1})a \, d\tau \right]$$

The first term is simply $E_{2p} \int a^2 \, d\tau = E_{2p}$, the energy of an electron in a $2p$ atomic orbital. The second term is $E_{2p} \int ab \, d\tau = sE_{2p}$, where s is the overlap integral between the $2p$ atomic orbitals ϕ_a and ϕ_b. The third term, $\int a(V_{b1})a \, d\tau$, may be considered as the attraction between a carbon atom at b which has lost a π-electron and an electron at a. It is evaluated by expanding the V_{b1} part of the Hamiltonian as follows:[62]

$$V_{b1} = V_{b1}{}^* - \int b_2{}^2 \frac{e^2}{r_{12}} \, d\tau_2$$

Here, $V_{b1}{}^*$ refers to the potential due to a neutral carbon atom, and the last term is a correction term corresponding to the loss of a π-electron from the carbon. The integral then becomes

$$\int a(V_{b1})a \, d\tau_1 = \int a(V_{b1}{}^*)a \, d\tau_1 - \iint a^2 b^2 \frac{e^2}{r_{12}} \, d\tau_1 \, d\tau_2$$

In order to be able to refer to these integrals in a convenient fashion, a special notation will be used. For those integrals involving $V_b{}^*$ the notation will be

$$-\int a V_b{}^* a \, d\tau = (1 \,|\, 22) = -\int b V_a{}^* b \, d\tau$$

$$-\int b V_b{}^* a \, d\tau = (1 \,|\, 12) = -\int a V_a{}^* b \, d\tau$$

[62] M. Goeppert-Mayer and A. L. Sklar, *J. Chem. Phys.*, **6**, 645 (1938).

The number 1 in this notation refers to the nucleus involved in the V^* function and the numbers following the vertical line refer to the atomic orbitals involved in the integral, the number 1 being given if the orbital is on the nucleus being considered, and the number 2 being given if it is on an adjacent nucleus. For those integrals involving the correction term, the following notation will be used:

$$\iint a_1{}^2 b_2{}^2 \frac{e^2}{r_{12}} d\tau_1 d\tau_2 = (11 \mid 22)$$

$$\iint a_1 b_1 b_2{}^2 \frac{e^2}{r_{12}} d\tau_1 d\tau_2 = (12 \mid 22)$$

$$\iint a_1 b_1 a_2 b_2 \frac{e^2}{r_{12}} d\tau_1 d\tau_2 = (12 \mid 12)$$

$$\iint a_1{}^2 a_2{}^2 \frac{e^2}{r_{12}} d\tau_1 d\tau_2 = (11 \mid 11)$$

where the terms on one side of the vertical line refer to the orbitals for electron 1 and those on the other side refer to electron 2. It makes no difference in which order the terms are taken, so that, for example, $(12 \mid 22) = (22 \mid 12)$. Furthermore, since ϕ_a and ϕ_b are identical wave functions in space, $(12 \mid 22) = (12 \mid 11)$. In terms of this notation, the third term is equal to $-(1 \mid 22) - (11 \mid 22)$.

The last term, $\int b(V_{b1})a\, d\tau$, is one we have encountered previously and have termed the exchange integral γ. In terms of the above notation, this is $-(1 \mid 12) - (12 \mid 22)$. Thus the entire core integral becomes

$$E^{\text{core}} = 4N^2[(1 + s)E_{2p} - (1 \mid 22) - (11 \mid 22) + \gamma_{12}]$$

If the interelectronic repulsion term is taken as the interaction of one electron with the smeared-out distribution of the other, the electron repulsion ("two-electron") part of the wave function will be

$$E^{\text{rep.}} = \int \psi_1 \left(\int \psi_2{}^2 \frac{e^2}{r_{12}} \right) \psi_1 \, d\tau_1 \, d\tau_2$$

where ψ_1 is the wave function for electron 1 and ψ_2 is the wave function for electron 2. Replacing ψ_1 and ψ_2 by their atomic orbital equivalents, we have

$$E^{\text{rep.}} = N^4 \iint (a + b)_1 (a + b)_1 \frac{e^2}{r_{12}} (a + b)_2 (a + b)_2 \, d\tau_1 \, d\tau_2$$

$$= N^4 \iint (a^2 + 2ab + b^2)_1 \frac{e^2}{r_{12}} (a^2 + 2ab + b^2)_2 \, d\tau_1 \, d\tau_2$$

If this integral is taken term by term, the values may be given using the above notation

$$E^{rep.} = N^4[2(11 \mid 11) + 2(11 \mid 22) + 8(11 \mid 12) + 4(12 \mid 12)]$$

When we sum the core and repulsion terms and then correct for the repulsion of the two positively charged nuclei to which the electrons were added (equal to $(11 \mid 22)$), we will obtain the π-electronic energy. All these integrals have been evaluated and tabulated (cf. Appendix 4), and those required here are listed in Table 1-12.

Table 1-12   Values of Atomic Integrals for Ethylene[a]

$$s = 0.277$$
$$(11 \mid 11) = 16.93 \text{ ev}$$
$$(11 \mid 22) = 9.26$$
$$(12 \mid 12) = 1.08$$
$$(11 \mid 12) = 3.58$$
$$(1 \mid 22) = 0.99$$
$$(1 \mid 12) = 2.06$$

[a] R. G. Parr and B. L. Crawford, *J. Chem. Phys.*, **16**, 526 (1948).

By using these values of the integrals, the π-electronic energy is found to be $2E_{2p} - 24.87 + 13.09 + 9.26$ or $2E_{2p} - 2.52$ ev. Since $2E_{2p}$ is simply the energy of two electrons in isolated $2p$ orbitals, we shall set this as the zero of energy, and thus the calculated π-electronic energy is -2.52 ev or -58 kcal/mole. This may be compared with the experimental value of -64 kcal/mole, and thus this gives a rather good result. Unfortunately, the calculation of the energy of the excited states in the same fashion does not give as good agreement with the observed ultraviolet spectrum. The reason for this difficulty is at least partly due to the way in which the integrals were evaluated, that is, without taking electron correlation into account. The integral $(11 \mid 11)$, for example, was evaluated as the repulsion between one electron and the smeared out distribution of another, both being in the same orbital. In actuality, the electronic repulsion will keep the electrons as far from each other as possible, and this will reduce the calculated repulsion term.

If we wish to extend this treatment to the conjugated unsaturated compounds, it is possible to simplify matters by using slightly modified atomic orbitals. Along the axis of a bond, two $2p\pi$ atomic orbitals may be

represented by

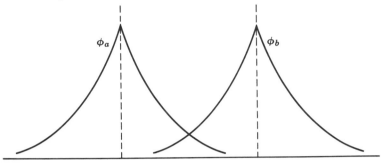

and it is clear that these wave functions are not orthonormal (i.e., $s_{ab} \neq 0$). However, they may be modified and made orthonormal by writing them as

$$\phi_a' = a\phi_a + b\phi_b$$
$$\phi_b' = c\phi_a + d\phi_b$$

and setting the values of a, b, c, and d so that ϕ_a' and ϕ_b' are orthonormal.[63] This requires that $a = d$ and $b = c$, and the values are then

$$a = \frac{1}{2}\left[\frac{1}{\sqrt{1+s}} - \frac{1}{\sqrt{1-s}}\right]$$

$$b = \frac{1}{2}\left[\frac{1}{\sqrt{1+s}} - \frac{1}{\sqrt{1-s}}\right]$$

The orbitals which result are

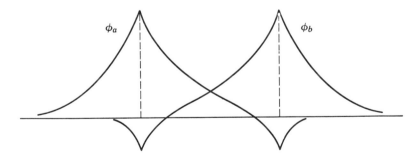

Using these orbitals, the wave functions for ethylene would become

$$\psi_+ = \frac{1}{\sqrt{2}}(\phi_a' + \phi_b')$$

$$\psi_- = \frac{1}{\sqrt{2}}(\phi_a' - \phi_b')$$

[63] P. O. Löwdin, *J. Chem. Phys.*, **18**, 365 (1950).

Corresponding orbitals may be written for the conjugated unsaturated compounds, and this will permit us to set $s = 0$ for neighboring carbons. The required integrals should then be calculated using these modified orbitals. However, it can be shown[64] that the terms which must be included to correct the integrals essentially cancel. Furthermore, the theoretically calculated integrals are not satisfactory because they do not take electron correlation properly into account.[65] For example, the integral $(11 \mid 11)$ is calculated to have the value 16.93 ev. A good argument can be made that the integral should be the difference between the ionization potential and the electron affinity of the atom, and for carbon this is 10.96 ev.[65] In a similar fashion, the other integrals may be corrected semiempirically, and to a certain extent this correction will take into account the use of orthonormal orbitals.

The question of appropriate values of the integrals has been examined by Pariser and Parr,[65] who have also considered the spectra and other properties of aromatic and heterocyclic compounds by a procedure similar to that given above for ethylene. The values they have assigned to the integrals are given in Appendix 4.

We shall now consider the application of this type of treatment to the determination of delocalization energies, charge densities, and bond orders. In doing this we shall follow the self-consistent field procedure (SCF) so that it will be applicable to the nonalternate hydrocarbons, such as azulene.[66]

For any π-electronic system, the Hamiltonian operator may be written as

$$H = \sum_i H_i^{\text{core}} + \sum_{i<j} \frac{e^2}{r_{ij}}$$

The second term which involves simultaneously the coordinates of two electrons is the one that is difficult to evaluate. Following the method of Hartree,[67] we will replace this term by an electrostatic term involving one electron in the average field of the other. The average field of an electron is given by $\int \psi^2 \, d\tau$, and thus this part of the operator becomes

$$\int \psi(2)^2 \frac{e^2}{r_{12}} \, d\tau_2 = J$$

[64] R. Daudel, R. Lefebvre, and C. Moser, *Quantum Chemistry*, Interscience Publishers, New York, 1959, pp. 502–504.
[65] R. Pariser and R. G. Parr, *J. Chem. Phys.*, **21**, 466, 767 (1953); R. G. Parr and R. Pariser, *J. Chem. Phys.*, **23**, 711 (1955); R. Pariser, *J. Chem. Phys.*, **24**, 250 (1956); M. J. S. Dewar and N. L. Hojvat, *J. Chem. Phys.*, **34**, 1232 (1961).
[66] It should be mentioned that approximately the same results may be obtained using the Pariser-Parr method if configurational interaction (cf. the discussion of the hydrogen molecule, p. 107) is included. See the discussion at the end of this section.
[67] D. R. Hartree, *Proc. Cambridge Phil. Soc.*, **24**, 89, 111, 426 (1928).

where the operation is on the wave function $\psi(1)$. As stated above, this will give too large a value for the repulsion term. However, it is the only convenient approximation we can use, and following Pariser and Parr,[65] we may modify the value semiempirically.

The foregoing operator also neglects the possibility of electron exchange between orbitals, and this requires an additional term, usually designated as K, which has the form

$$K_j \psi_i(1) = \left[\int \psi_j(2) \psi_i(2) \frac{e^2}{r_{12}} d\tau_2 \right] \psi_j(1)$$

where again the numbers 1 and 2 refer to the two electrons, and the subscripts i and j refer to orbitals. The wave equation written in this way is usually known as the Hartree-Fock equation

$$\left\{ \sum H^{\text{core}} + \sum_j \left[\int \psi_j(2)^2 \frac{e^2}{r_{12}} d\tau_2 \right] \right\} \psi_i(1)$$

$$- \sum_j \left[\psi_j(2) \psi_i(2) \frac{e^2}{r_{12}} d\tau_2 \right] \psi_j(1) = E_i \psi_i(1)$$

or

$$\left(\sum H^{\text{core}} + \sum_j J_j - \sum_j{}' K_j \right) \psi_i(1) = E_i \psi_i(1)$$

The prime on the third summation indicates that it is to be taken over orbitals having the same spin.

For hydrocarbons each level will be doubly occupied, and the terms J_j will come in pairs. However, in evaluating K_j we must take the spin of the electrons into account. If we consider the exchange of one electron with the electrons in another orbital, only one exchange is possible, for the two which are exchanged must have the same spin. Thus there will be half as many K terms as there are J terms. If the summation is taken over the occupied orbitals, of which there are n, the wave equation takes the form[68]

$$\left[\sum H^{\text{core}} + \sum_{j=1}^{n} (2J_j - K_j) \right] \psi_i(1) = E_i \psi_i(1)$$

The operator given above is usually known as the self-consistent field operator and will be abbreviated as H^{SCF}. Thus we have the usual equation

$$H^{\text{SCF}} \psi_i = E_i \psi_i$$

[68] This is commonly known as Roothaan's equation (C. C. Roothaan, *Rev. Mod. Phys.*, **23**, 69 (1951)). In the form given here it applies only to cases in which each occupied level is completely filled. For other cases it is necessary to consider electrons with different spin states separately.

In order to apply this formulation, we must have a set of molecular orbital wave functions, ψ_i, with which to begin. The obvious ones are those derived from the simple one-electron treatment of aromatic compounds. Thus

$$\psi_i = \sum_k c_{ik}\phi_k$$

where the ϕ_k's are $2p_\pi$ atomic orbitals. The energies are then given by

$$H^{\mathrm{SCF}} \sum_i c_{ik}\phi_k = E_i \sum_k c_{ik}\phi_k$$

or

$$\sum_i c_{ik}H^{\mathrm{SCF}}\phi_k = E_i \sum_k c_{ik}\phi_k$$

Now, if we multiply both sides by ϕ_l and integrate, we obtain

$$\sum_i c_{ik} \int \phi_l H^{\mathrm{SCF}}\phi_k \, d\tau = E_i \sum_k c_{ik} \int \phi_l\phi_k \, d\tau$$

As before, we may abbreviate

$$\int \phi_l H^{\mathrm{SCF}}\phi_k \, d\tau = H^{\mathrm{SCF}}_{lk}$$

$$\int \phi_l\phi_k \, d\tau = \Delta_{lk}$$

and thus

$$\sum_i c_{ik}(H^{\mathrm{SCF}}_{lk} - E_i \Delta_{lk}) = 0$$

This would be the same as the familiar set of secular equations we discussed previously (p. 46) if it were not for the fact that H^{SCF}_{lk} depends on the c_{ik}'s (note that ψ appears in the operators J and K, which are part of H^{SCF}). Thus this case must be treated by an iterative procedure in which one starts with a set of molecular orbitals, proceeds through the calculation, and obtains the c_{ik}'s of the new orbitals. This is done as before by obtaining the eigenvectors of the secular determinant

$$|H^{\mathrm{SCF}}_{lk} - E \Delta_{lk}| = 0$$

(cf. the determination of the c_{ik}'s for the Hückel treatment of benzene, p. 74, and also Appendix 2).

The set of molecular orbitals which are determined by this procedure are used to obtain another new set of c_{ik}'s using the procedure outlined above, and this process is continued until the molecular orbitals used in calculating the H^{SCF}_{lk} terms are the same as those which are obtained from a solution of the secular determinant. The orbitals thus obtained are then said to be those for a self-consistent field (SCF).

It is now necessary to show how the H_{lk}^{SCF} terms are to be evaluated. In the following, we shall use the procedure suggested by Pople,[69] which involves basically the same approximations as those suggested by Pariser and Parr.

Let us first consider the diagonal terms of the secular determinant, H_{kk}^{SCF}. This is given by

$$H_{kk}^{\text{SCF}} = \int \phi_k \left[\sum H^{\text{core}} + \sum_{j=1}^{n} (2J_j - K_j) \right] \phi_k \, d\tau$$

The first term, involving H^{core}, has been evaluated previously in considering ethylene (p. 109) and is given by

$$\int \phi_k \sum H^{\text{core}} \phi_k \, d\tau = E_{2p} - \sum_{p \neq k} (pp \mid kk) - \sum_{q \neq k} (q \mid kk)$$

Thus for ethylene, which has only two electrons, this term was given by

$$H_{11}^{\text{core}} = H_{22}^{\text{core}} = E_{2p} - (11 \mid 22) - (1 \mid 22)$$

The second part of the diagonal term is given by

$$\int \phi_k \left[\sum_{j=1}^{n} (2J_j - K_j) \right] \phi_k \, d\tau$$

In expanded form, the J part is

$$2 \int \phi_k \left[\sum_{j=1}^{n} \int \sum c_{jm} \phi_m(2) \sum c_{jn} \phi_n(2) \frac{e^2}{r_{12}} \, d\tau_2 \right] \phi_k \, d\tau$$

or

$$2 \sum_{j=1}^{n} \sum_{m,n} c_{jm} c_{jn} \int \phi_m(2) \phi_n(2) \frac{e^2}{r_{12}} \phi_k(1) \phi_k(1) \, d\tau_1 \, d\tau_2$$

In the notation which we have given previously, this is

$$2 \sum_{j=1}^{n} \sum_{p,q} c_{jp} c_{jq} (pq \mid kk)$$

The K part may be evaluated in a similar fashion, giving

$$- \sum_{j=1}^{n} \sum_{p,q} c_{jp} c_{jq} (kp \mid kq)$$

If we use orthonormal orbitals, the integrals such as $(11 \mid 12)$ will be zero, and the diagonal term will be given by

$$H_{kk}^{\text{SCF}} = E_{2p} + \sum_{p \neq k} (p_{kk} - 1)(pp \mid kk)$$
$$+ \tfrac{1}{2} p_{kk}(kk \mid kk) - \sum_{q \neq k} (q \mid kk)$$

[69] J. A. Pople, *Trans. Faraday Soc.*, **49**, 1375 (1953); **50**, 901 (1954); *J. Phys. Chem.*, **61**, 6 (1957). In his papers he symbolizes H_{lk}^{SCF} as F_{lk}, $(11 \mid 11)$ as γ_{11}, $(11 \mid 22)$ as γ_{12}, and $E_{2p} - \Sigma(q \mid kk)$ as U.

where $p_{kk} = \sum\limits_{j} 2c_{jk}c_{jk}$, the electron density on atom j. The last term would be expected to be small and roughly constant in any comparison and therefore is usually included in the constant E_{2p}.

The off-diagonal terms must now be evaluated. As before,

$$\int \phi_k H^{core} \phi_l \, d\tau = \beta_{kl}$$

and commonly, β_{kl} is assumed to be zero for non-neighbor centers, although this is not necessary. The integral

$$\int \phi_k \sum_{j=1}^{n} (2J_j - K_j) \phi_l \, d\tau$$

may be evaluated in the same way as for the diagonal term and will be found to be

$$\sum_{j=1}^{n} \sum_{p,q} c_{jp}c_{jq}[2(kl \mid pq) - (kp \mid lq)]$$

Assuming the use of orthonormal orbitals, the terms $(kl \mid pq)$ will be zero, since $k \neq l$. Similarly, of the terms $(kp \mid lq)$, only those having $p = k$ and $q = l$ will be nonzero. Thus the off-diagonal term will be

$$H_{kl}^{SCF} = \beta_{kl} - \tfrac{1}{2}p_{kl}(kk \mid ll)$$

where $p_{kl} = 2 \sum\limits_{j} c_{jk}c_{jl}$, the bond order between atoms k and l.

Starting with a set of Hückel molecular orbitals, one then calculates the values of the bond order and the electron density per carbon. This allows one to evaluate the H_{kl}^{SCF} terms, and since $\Delta_{jk} = 0$ unless $j = k$ (using orthonormal orbitals), the diagonalization of the H_{lk}^{SCF} matrix will give the required eigenvalues, and the corresponding eigenvectors will be the c_{ij}'s required for the next iteration (cf. Appendix 2).

The c_{ij}'s are then used to calculate a new set of bond orders and electron densities, and from this set one calculates a new H_{lk}^{SCF} matrix. One repeats this calculation until the c_{ij}'s attain constant values.

As an example, let us consider the case of benzene. The eigenvectors are given by

0.408	0.408	0.408	0.408	0.408	0.408	(ψ_1)
0.000	0.500	0.500	0.000	−0.500	−0.500	(ψ_2)
0.577	0.289	0.289	−0.577	−0.289	−0.289	(ψ_3)
0.000	0.500	−0.500	0.000	0.500	−0.500	(ψ_4)
0.577	−0.289	−0.289	0.577	−0.289	−0.289	(ψ_5)
0.408	−0.408	0.408	−0.408	0.408	−0.408	(ψ_6)

Thus $p_{11} = p_{22} = p_{33} = p_{44} = p_{55} = p_{66} = 1.00$, $p_{12} = p_{23} = p_{34} = p_{45} = p_{56} = p_{16} = 0.667$, $p_{14} = p_{25} = p_{36} = -0.333$ whereas all the other p's are zero. The values of the repulsion integrals used by Pople are $(11 \mid 11) = 10.53$, $(11 \mid 22) = 7.30$, $(11 \mid 33) = 5.46$ and $(11 \mid 44) = 4.90$ ev. The value of β which appears to be commonly used is -2.06 ev. Setting $E_{2p} + \Sigma (q \mid kk) = 0.0$ as the standard state, the H_{kl}^{SCF} matrix thus becomes

$$
\begin{vmatrix}
5.27 & -4.49 & 0.00 & 0.82 & 0.00 & -4.49 \\
-4.49 & 5.27 & -4.49 & 0.00 & 0.82 & 0.00 \\
0.00 & -4.49 & 5.27 & -4.49 & 0.00 & 0.82 \\
0.82 & 0.00 & -4.49 & 5.27 & -4.49 & 0.00 \\
0.00 & 0.82 & 0.00 & -4.49 & 5.27 & -4.49 \\
-4.49 & 0.00 & 0.82 & 0.00 & -4.49 & 5.27
\end{vmatrix}
$$

The solution of the equation

$$
|H_{lk}^{\text{SCF}} - E \, \Delta_{lk}| = 0
$$

(i.e., the determinant in which E is subtracted from all the diagonal elements of the H^{SCF} matrix) leads to the same eigenvectors as originally used. Thus these are the SCF eigenvectors. This is generally true only with monocyclic conjugated unsaturated hydrocarbons, and normally the values change but converge on the SCF solution. Thus one ordinarily computes a new set of charge densities and bond orders and repeats the calculation until no further change is found.

Having the eigenvectors, we may calculate the π-electronic energy. In the case of ethylene we saw previously that it was given by

$$
E_\pi = 4N^2[(1 + s)E_{2p} - (1 \mid 22) - (11 \mid 22) + \gamma_{12}]
$$
$$
+ N^4[2(11 \mid 11) + 2(11 \mid 22) + 8(11 \mid 12) + 4(12 \mid 12)]
$$

Using the present approximation that $\Delta_{lk} = 0$ when $l \neq k$, and setting $E_{2p} - (1 \mid 22)$ as the zero of energy, this becomes

$$
E_\pi = 2\beta_{12} + \tfrac{1}{2}(11 \mid 11) - \tfrac{1}{2}(11 \mid 22)
$$

If the treatment were carried out for a general case, the result would have been

$$
E_\pi = \sum_l \tfrac{1}{4}p_{ll}(11 \mid 11) + 2 \sum_{l<k} p_{lk}\beta_{lk} + \sum_{l<k} [(p_{ll} - 1)(p_{kk} - 1) - \tfrac{1}{2}p_{lk}^2](ll \mid kk)
$$

where the summation is over the total number of π-electrons. For benzene this becomes

$$
E_\pi = \tfrac{3}{2}(11 \mid 11) + 8\beta_{12} - \tfrac{4}{3}(11 \mid 22) - \tfrac{1}{6}(11 \mid 44)
$$

For three ethylene units this would have been

$$3E_\pi^{\text{ethylene}} = \tfrac{3}{2}(11 \mid 11) + 6\beta_{12} - \tfrac{3}{2}(11 \mid 22)$$

Thus the delocalization energy of benzene will be

$$E_\pi = 2\beta_{12} + \tfrac{1}{6}(11 \mid 12) - \tfrac{1}{6}(11 \mid 44)$$

The value obtained in the simple Hückel treatment would have been $2\beta_{12}$, and the other terms represent the change in energy due to the electron repulsion terms, which are neglected in the simple treatment. It can be shown that for the ground state, the sum of the electron repulsion terms is always small and the results of this more detailed treatment are about the same as those obtained for the simple method.[69] This is partly the reason for the success of the latter method.

The π-electron energy calculated in this way is that obtained by a comparison of the energy of benzene with a nonconjugated cyclohexatriene having the same bond distances. The value of the π-electron energy has been estimated by a number of workers giving values which range from 5[30] to 112 kcal/mole.[70] Therefore we shall not consider this question further.

The results which have been obtained with naphthalene and azulene are interesting. Pople[69] has applied his method to naphthalene and has obtained the bond orders given in Table 1-13. It can be seen that there is a

Table 1-13   Bond Orders and Bond Lengths for Naphthalene[a]

Method	Bond			
	1,2	2,3	1,9	9,10
Simple molecular orbital bond orders	0.725	0.603	0.555	0.518
Calculated bond lengths	1.376	1.401	1.416	1.429
SCF bond orders	0.78	0.54	0.50	0.60
Calculated bond lengths	1.373	1.421	1.436	1.402
SCF bond lengths less 0.01 Å	1.363	1.411	1.425	1.392
Observed bond lengths	1.365	1.404	1.425	1.393

[a] The bond lengths were calculated using the relationship given on p. 91; the SCF data are from J. A. Pople, *Trans. Faraday Soc.*, **49**, 1375 (1953).

significant improvement in the correlation of bond length with bond order, and, particularly, if 0.01 Å is subtracted from the calculated bond lengths, the results are excellent. It should not be surprising that a different correlation curve is required for the SCF bond orders than for

[70] G. Glockler, *J. Chem. Phys.*, **21**, 1249 (1953).

Table 1-14 Results of Different Theoretical Treatments of Azulene

Method	$\mu(D)$	$d_{2,2}$	$d_{3,3}$	$d_{10,10}$	$d_{4,4}$	$d_{5,5}$	$d_{6,6}$	$b_{2,3}$	$b_{3,10}$	$b_{4,10}$	$b_{4,5}$	$b_{5,6}$	$b_{9,10}$
Perimeter[a] M.O., no C.I.	0.00	1.000	1.000	1.000	1.000	1.000	1.000	0.674	0.674	0.674	0.674	0.674	0.000
Hückel M.O.,[a] no C.I.	6.40	1.047	1.173	1.027	0.855	0.986	0.870	0.656	0.596	0.586	0.664	0.639	0.401
SCF[b]	1.7	0.997	1.049	1.042	0.908	1.034	0.938	—	—	—	—	—	—
Perimeter[a] M.O. with C.I.	3.36	1.001	1.118	1.016	0.886	1.015	0.930	0.662	0.610	0.592	0.657	0.648	0.288
Hückel M.O.[a] with C.I.	1.88	0.979	1.096	1.013	0.879	1.049	0.948	0.660	0.610	0.611	0.651	0.648	0.288
Wheland-Mann[c]		1.048	1.118	1.020	0.905	0.975	0.916						
Variable Electronegativity[d]		1.004	1.061	1.009	0.937	1.009	0.961						

a R. Pariser, *J. Chem. Phys.*, **25**, 1112 (1956).
b A. Julg, *J. chim. phys.*, **52**, 377 (1955).
c G. Wheland and D. E. Mann, *J. Chem. Phys.*, **17**, 264 (1949).
d R. D. Brown and M. L. Heffernan, *Australian J. Chem.*, **13**, 38 (1960).

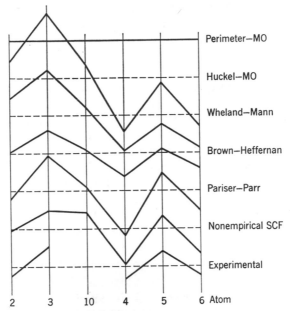

Fig. 1-29. Electron densities for azulene derived from different approximations. The horizontal lines give the origins for unit electron densities and the lines are spaced 0.1 unit apart.

the simple molecular orbital bond orders. Unfortunately, it has been reported that this improvement does not carry over to larger aromatic systems.[43] It is possible that some of the difference may be due to distortion of the molecules due to H-H repulsion in some of the more compact polycyclic compounds.

The bond order and charge densities for azulene have been obtained by a number of investigators and are summarized in Table 1-14. The perimeter molecular orbital method is basically the Hückel method, leaving out the exchange integral for the 9,10 bond. The calculation is then for an alternate hydrocarbon, and all charge densities are unity. The Variable-Electronegativity method is one developed by Brown and Heffernan[71] which includes non-neighbor β's and the variation of α with p_{rr}.

The results for the electron densities are presented graphically in Fig. 1-29, and the experimental results obtained from an analysis of the hydrogen and carbon-13 chemical shifts in the nuclear magnetic resonance spectrum of azulene[72] are also given. It can be seen that the SCF procedure gives a reasonable agreement with the observed electron densities

[71] R. D. Brown and M. L. Heffernan, *Trans. Faraday Soc.*, **54**, 757 (1958); *Australian J. Chem.*, **13**, 38 (1960).
[72] H. Spiesecke and W. G. Schneider, *Tetrahedron, Letters*, 468 (1961).

(probably within the experimental error in the latter), whereas the Hückel or perimeter molecular orbitals give electron densities which are far from correct. Part of the improvement comes from a reduction of the 9,10 bond order, and the rest comes from taking the electron repulsion terms properly into account.

It is important to note that the Hückel molecular orbitals may be used in the Pariser-Parr method and lead to a much improved electron density distribution when configurational interaction (C.I.) is included. Even the perimeter molecular orbitals lead to an improved electron density distribution when configurational interaction is used. Thus one has a choice of trying to obtain the best molecular orbitals to start with (the idea of the SCF method), or one can use a set of molecular orbitals and correct them by using configurational interaction. Even here, however, reasonably good molecular orbitals are needed if one is to use only a reasonable number of configurations. On the whole, it would seem that the self-consistent field approach is the more satisfactory for use by the organic chemist, particularly if reasonable computing facilities are available.

The results which have been given above are a distinct improvement over those obtained neglecting the electron repulsion terms. An even more striking improvement is found in the correlation with ultraviolet spectra, and this will be discussed subsequently.

References

General Theory:
> C. C. Roothaan, *Rev. Mod. Phys.*, **23**, 69 (1951).
> R. Daudel, R. Lefebvre, and C. Moser, *Quantum Chemistry*, Interscience Publishers, New York, 1959, Part II.

Pariser-Parr Method:
> R. Pariser and R. G. Parr, *J. Chem. Phys.*, **21**, 466, 767 (1953); R. Pariser, *J. Chem. Phys.*, **24**, 250 (1956).

Semiempirical SCF Method:
> J. A. Pople, *Trans. Faraday Soc.*, **49**, 1375 (1953); **50**, 901 (1954); *J. Chem. Phys.*, **61**, 6 (1957).

Variable Electronegativity SCF:
> R. D. Brown and M. L. Heffernan, *Trans. Faraday Soc.*, **54**, 757 (1958).

Split p-Orbital (SPO) Method:
> M. J. S. Dewar and N. L. Hojvat, *J. Chem. Phys.*, **34**, 1232 (1961).

Problems

1. If a computor is available, apply the Pople method to the calculation of the electron densities and bond orders for azulene, and compare the results with those obtained by the other methods. Do the Pople simplifications lead to a satisfactory treatment of azulene?

2. If a computor is available, calculate the bond orders for the various bonds of the compounds given in Table 1–8, and plot the bond lengths against the bond orders. Has there been a significant improvement over the results obtained by the simple molecular orbital method? (In problem 1 and 2, the computor is needed mainly in diagonalizing the H_{kk}^{SCF} matrix. A program for this purpose is available in most computor laboratories. With a large computor, all the compounds could readily be studied. With a smaller computor, such as an IBM 650, the time for the last two compounds in problem 2 would probably be excessive, especially since about 10 iterations are needed before the values become reasonably constant. The results of the last few iterations may be extrapolated to the values to which they are approaching asymptotically.)

1-15 The Quantum Chemical Treatment of Saturated Compounds; Hyperconjugation

The quantum chemical treatment of saturated compounds is not too far developed. The inherent simplicity of the aromatic compounds is based on the π-electron approximation which permits one to consider one small group of electrons separately from all other electrons. No such simple and convenient approximation is available for saturated compounds. In this section, methods of studying the latter will be introduced by considering two cases of special interest, the strain energy of cyclopropane and the question of hyperconjugation.

First, let us consider some possible orbital representations of the cyclopropane ring. If sp^3 orbitals were used in forming the framework of the ring (Fig. 1-30a), then the orbitals would not be directed between the carbons but, rather, would point outward from the ring. The angle between the direction of the orbitals and the direction of the next carbon would be 24.7°, a very considerable deviation. If pure p orbitals were used (Fig. 1-30b; only one half of each orbital is shown), then the angle would be reduced to 15°, but at the same time the external bonds would involve sp hybrids giving a H-C-H angle of 180°. Finally, a quite different representation is shown in Fig. 1-30c.[73] Here an sp^2 orbital is directed from each carbon to the center of the ring, and the remaining bonds are made by π-type overlap of another p orbital at each carbon. Although this may appear at first to be very different from the bent bond descriptions (as the first two models are commonly called), such is not the case. Both models are built up as linear combinations of the same basis functions (s and p atomic orbitals) and thus may be considered as equivalent

[73] A. D. Walsh, *Nature*, **159**, 165, 712 (1947).

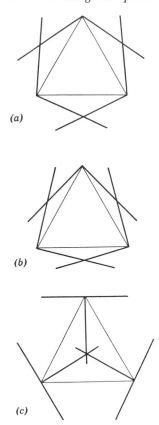

(a)

(b)

(c)

Fig. 1-30. Three orbital representations for a cyclopropane ring. (a) sp^3 orbitals (b) p-orbitals (only one-half of each is shown), (c) sp^2-orbitals directed toward the center of the ring and p-orbitals at each carbon.

representations. The important point is how the s character is distributed between the ring bonds and the external bonds.

The observed H-C-H bond angle is 114°,[74] considerably larger than tetrahedral (109.5°) but still much smaller than 180°. Thus it appears that the true picture involves ring bonds formed using orbitals with more p character than sp^3 but still being far from pure p.

In order to arrive at a description of the bonding in cyclopropane, two factors must be balanced—the improvement of the directional characteristics of the hybrid orbitals as the amount of p character increases and the decrease in bond strength with increasing p character as a result of the orbital being less concentrated in the direction of bonding. This was first recognized by Kilpatrick and Spitzer[75] and was developed independently and in greater detail by Coulson and Moffitt.[76]

In this case the arrangement of orbitals about a carbon atom may be taken as shown in Fig. 1-31 (cf. the discussion of hybridization in water in Section 1-7). The four orbitals have the directions Oa, Ob, Oc, and Od and come in pairs, Oa-Ob and Oc-Od. The first two make an angle of $\pi/2 - \xi$ with the twofold axis of symmetry (Oz). The other two make an angle of $\pi/2 - \eta$ with the downward direction of Oz. The planes Oab and Ocd are perpendicular and may be taken as the yz and zx planes, respectively.

For simplicity we may use orbitals formed from a $2s$ atomic wave function and $2p$ atomic wave functions which are directed along Oa, Ob, Oc, and Od. The latter will be linear combinations of the basic $2p$ orbitals.

[74] O. Bastiansen, and P. N. Skancke, in I. Prigogine, ed., *Advances in Chem. Phys.*, Interscience Publishers, New York, 1961, vol. III, p. 323.

[75] J. E. Kilpatrick and R. Spitzer, *J. Chem. Phys.*, **14**, 463 (1946).

[76] C. A. Coulson and W. Moffitt, *J. Chem. Phys.*, **15**, 151 (1947); *Phil. Mag.*, **40**, 1 (1949).

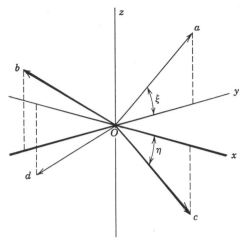

Fig. 1-31. Coordinates and directions for bonds from a tetrahedral carbon.

The four hybrid orbitals may then be written

$$\psi_a = l\{\psi(2s) + \lambda\psi(2p\sigma_a)\}$$
$$\psi_b = l\{\psi(2s) + \lambda\psi(2p\sigma_b)\}$$
$$\psi_c = m\{\psi(2s) + \mu\psi(2p\sigma_c)\}$$
$$\psi_d = m\{\psi(2s) + \mu\psi(2p\sigma_d)\}$$

The quantities λ and μ are related to ξ and η by the conditions for orthogonality and normalization:

$$0 = 1 - \mu^2 \cos 2\eta = 1 - \lambda^2 \cos 2\xi = 1 - \lambda\mu \sin \xi \sin \eta$$

$$l^2(1 + \lambda^2) = 1 = m^2(1 + \mu^2) \qquad |\xi| \geqslant 0 \quad |\eta| \leqslant \frac{\pi}{4}$$

If we examine these relationships, it can be seen that only one independent choice of parameters can be made. Suppose we choose to vary ξ; then the other parameters would be given by

$$\lambda = \sqrt{\sec^2 \xi} \qquad\qquad l = \frac{1}{\sqrt{2}} \sec \xi \sqrt{\cos 2\xi}$$

$$\mu = A \operatorname{cosec} \xi \qquad\qquad m = \frac{1}{\sqrt{2}} \tan \xi$$

$$\eta = \sec^{-1}(A \sec \xi) \qquad A = \sqrt{\cos^2 \xi + \cos 2\xi}$$

If $\xi = \eta = \sin^{-1}(1/\sqrt{2})$, all the orbitals would be equivalent and would be the familiar tetrahedral orbitals. If $\xi = \pi/4$ and $\eta = 0$, the bonds would be $2p$. Thus the hybridization may be varied by varying the angle ξ. The amount of p character in one set of orbitals would be given by $\lambda^2/(1 + \lambda^2)$ and, for the other, by $\mu^2/(1 + \mu^2)$.

The calculation of the energy of a system of three carbons and six hydrogens as a function of the angle ξ by the molecular orbital method is difficult because it involves integrals which have not been evaluated. The Valence-Bond method may be applied more simply in this case, and thus Coulson and Moffitt used this method for determining the values of the parameters which would lead to the lowest energy for the system. The details of the calculation cannot be given without first presenting sufficient background material on the Valence-Bond method. Hence only the results will be given here.

The total energy was evaluated for a number of values of the angle ξ, and the value which led to the lowest energy of the system was determined graphically. For cyclopropane, ξ was found to be 38°, which leads to a H-C-H angle of 116°, in good agreement with experiment. The values of the parameters for cyclopropane, and also for cyclobutane and cyclopentane, are given in Table 1-15. The energy which is calculated is in good agreement with the thermochemically determined strain energy.

Table 1-15   Calculated Parameters for Some Cyclic Compounds[a]

Compound	ξ	η	θ[b]	H—C—H angle	λ	μ
Cyclopropane	38°	32°	22°	116°	2.03	1.51
Cyclobutane	36°	34.5	9	111	1.80	1.67
Cyclopentane	35.25	35.25	0	109.5	1.73	1.73

[a] C. A. Coulson and W. Moffitt, *Phil. Mag.*, **40**, 1 (1949).
[b] θ is the angle between the direction of the orbital and the line joining the carbon atoms.

Several results of this treatment should be noted. First, we may obtain the amount of s and p character for the bonds of each compound. For cyclopropane the ring orbitals are calculated to be $0.80p$ and $0.20s$, whereas the external orbitals are $0.70p$ and $0.30s$. The orbitals for cyclobutane are calculated to be $0.76p$ and $0.24s$ (ring) and $0.74p$ and $0.26s$ (external). All the orbitals of cyclopentane are calculated to be $0.75p$ and $0.25s$ (tetrahedral). The greater s character in the external bonds of cyclopropane is experimentally observed in the lower dipole moment of cyclopropyl chloride as compared with cyclopentyl chloride ($1.76D$ vs. $2.08D$).[77] A $2s$ orbital on carbon is more electron attracting than a $2p$

[77] M. T. Rogers and J. D. Roberts, *J. Am. Chem. Soc.*, **68**, 843 (1946).

orbital.[78] Thus as the amount of s character increases, the electron-attracting ability of carbon approaches that of chlorine, leading to a reduced dipole moment.

The cyclopropane ring is known to interact with double bonds, leading to shifts in the positions of ultraviolet absorption bands.[79] The ring orbitals of cyclopropane, because of their "bent" character, are able to interact with double bonds in much the same fashion as p orbitals. There is probably little, if any, electron delocalization in the ground state of the compounds, but in the excited state, where charges are developed, electron delocalization involving the ring would be expected. The bonds of cyclobutane and the higher cycloalkanes are negligibly bent, and thus it is not surprising that these compounds do not interact with double bonds.

The effect of bond bending on the electron density distribution is easily calculated from the wave functions and is shown in Fig. 1-32. In cyclopropane, the electron density distribution would then be expected to lie largely outside the ring, and this is apparent in the results of the calculation (Fig. 1-33).

Although the calculation is still somewhat crude, it may be seen to give results which are in very good agreement with the observations concerning the cycloalkanes.

Let us now consider the question of "hyperconjugation."[80] If we compare the bromination of benzene with that of the alkyl substituted benzenes, we find that the rates of reaction are[81]

	CH_3	CH_2CH_3	$CH(CH_3)_2$	$C(CH_3)_3$
1	340	290	180	110

Similarly, in the solvolysis of benzhydryl chlorides in 80% acetone, the relative rates for p-substituted derivatives were[82]

$-H$	$-CH_3$	$-C_2H_5$	$-CH(CH_3)_2$	$-C(CH_3)_3$
1	21.4	17.3	13.8	10.9

[78] A. D. Walsh, *Trans. Faraday Soc.*, **43**, 60 (1947).
[79] See N. H. Cromwell and M. A. Graff, *J. Org. Chem.*, **17**, 414 (1952).
[80] R. S. Mulliken, *J. Chem. Phys.*, **7**, 339 (1939); R. S. Mulliken, C. A. Rieke, and W. G. Brown, *J. Am. Chem. Soc.*, **63**, 41 (1941).
[81] P. W. Robertson, P. B. D. de la Mare, and B. E. Swedlund, *J. Chem. Soc.*, 782 (1953).
[82] E. D. Hughes, C. K. Ingold, and N. A. Taher, *J. Chem. Soc.*, 949 (1940).

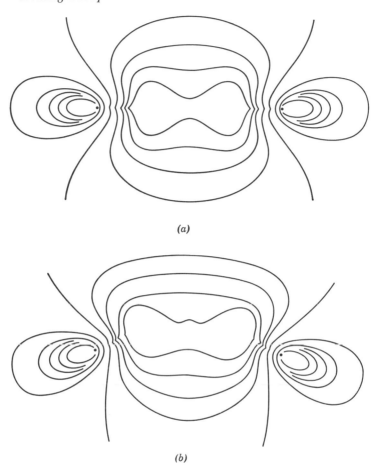

(a)

(b)

Fig. 1-32. (a) *Electron density contours for an unstrained carbon-carbon bond*, (b) *electron density contours for a strained carbon-carbon bond* (C. A. Coulson and W. Moffitt, Phil. Mag., **40**, *1* (1949)).

Results of this type have been obtained in many systems in which a positive charge is developed either at or adjacent to an aromatic ring.[83]

These data pose two different questions: first, why do alkyl groups stabilize a positive charge; and second, why is a *t*-butyl group apparently less electron releasing than methyl in many of these reactions? The answer to the second will not be easy to give, for a number of factors are probably involved. One rather satisfying hypothesis is that much of the

[83] J. W. Baker, *Hyperconjugation*, Oxford University Press, Oxford 1952; E. Berliner, *Tetrahedron*, **5**, 202 (1959).

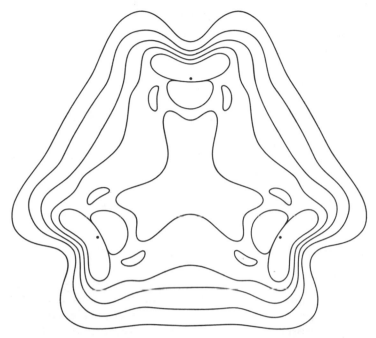

Fig. 1-33. Electron density contours for cyclopropane (C. A. Coulson and W. Moffitt, Phil. Mag., **40,** *1 (1949)).*

change in rate between methyl and *t*-butyl derivatives is due to steric hindrance of solvation of the activated complex when the larger group is present.[84] This is supported by the observation that a *t*-butyl group appears to be more electron releasing than methyl in the gas phase where there are no solvent interactions.[84]

Now, let us concentrate on the major question of the increased reactivity of toluene as compared with benzene, or of *p*-methylbenzhydryl chloride as compared to benzhydryl chloride. One possible explanation is that the methyl group will stabilize the positive charge which is developed in the activated complexes for these reactions via an inductive effect.[85] The ring carbons will become more electron attracting than the methyl group as a result of the positive charge in the ring, and thus the electrons forming the bond between the methyl carbon and a ring carbon will tend to spend more time near the latter, resulting in a shift in electron density from the methyl group to the ring. This inductive model successfully correlates the

[84] W. M. Schubert, J. M. Craven, R. G. Minton, and R. B. Murphy, *Tetrahedron,* **5,** 194 (1959).

[85] G. W. Wheland and L. Pauling, *J. Am. Chem. Soc.,* **57,** 2086 (1935); H. C. Longuet-Higgins, *J. Chem. Phys.,* **18,** 283 (1950); *Proc. Roy. Soc.,* **207,** 121 (1951).

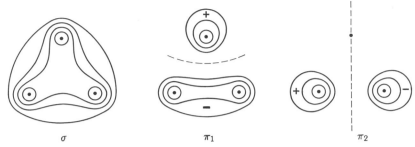

Fig. 1-34. Linear combination of 1s orbitals for the hydrogens of a methyl group (C. A. Coulson, Valence, Oxford University Press, London, 1952, p. 312).

effect of methyl groups on the basicities of aromatic hydrocarbons[86] and gives fairly good agreement with the observed ionization potentials of a series of alkenes, aromatic hydrocarbons, and radicals.[87]

The inductive effect could also explain the small dipole moment of toluene (0.4D), which appears to involve a positive methyl group and a negative ring. The ring carbons use sp^2 hybrid orbitals, whereas the methyl carbon uses an sp^3 orbital. The former is more electron withdrawing than the latter[78] (cf. the acidity order of ethane, ethylene, and acetylene); consequently there will be an electron drift from the methyl group to the ring here also. Of course, the amount of electron displacement will be much less than in an electrophilic substitution reaction in which a positive charge has been developed.

Another model for explaining the electron releasing property of a methyl group has been suggested; it is known as the "hyperconjugation" model.[80] Here it is assumed that the methyl group gives only a small electron release via an inductive effect and that a special type of conjugation is operative.

If we take the three hydrogen atoms of the methyl group and designate the corresponding 1s orbitals as a, b, and c, we may form the following linear combinations.

$$\sigma = N_1(a + b + c)$$
$$\pi_1 = N_2(a - \tfrac{1}{2}b - \tfrac{1}{2}c)$$
$$\pi_2 = N_3(b - c)$$

These linear combinations are satisfactory descriptions of the wave functions for the three hydrogen atoms and may be used in the treatment

[86] E. L. Mackor, G. Dallinga, J. H. Kruizinga, and A. Hofstra, *Rec. trav. chim.*, **75**, 836 (1956); E. L. Mackor, A. Hofstra, and J. H. van der Waals, *Trans. Faraday Soc.*, **54**, 186 (1958).
[87] A. Streitwieser, Jr. and P. M. Nair, *Tetrahedron*, **5**, 149 (1959).

of the bonding of the hydrogens with other atoms. The first is a completely symmetric combination resembling that of an ordinary σ orbital (Fig. 1-34). The second and third have symmetries resembling that of π orbitals.

The atomic orbitals of the methyl carbon may be taken as an sp hybrid and two p orbitals. One of the hybrid orbitals may form a bond with σ (above) and the other with the aromatic ring. The two p orbitals may form bonds with π_1 and π_2. At the same time one of the two p orbitals on the carbon may interact with the π-electronic system of the aromatic ring. Thus, in effect, the methyl group is considered to have two localized bonds (σ_H-σ_C, π_H-π_C in the plane of the aromatic ring) and one delocalized bond (π_H-π_C perpendicular to the aromatic ring). We may represent this as

$$\langle\!\!\!\langle\ \rangle\!\!\!\rangle\!=\!\!=\!\!\!C\!\equiv\!H_3$$

One consequence of this formulation is that there should not be a stereochemical requirement for hyperconjugation in that the two perpendicular π orbitals on the methyl carbon give in effect a cylindrically symmetrical wave function for interaction with the ring π orbital.

If one knew the appropriate values of the required Coulombic and exchange integrals, one could then obtain an approximation to the energy and electronic charge distribution, using the LCAO-MO treatment (for an eight electron system in the case of toluene). Coulson and Crawford[88] have suggested the following as reasonable values:

$$\beta_{12} = 2.5\beta_{CC}$$
$$\beta_{23} = 0.7\beta_{CC}$$
$$\alpha_1 = \alpha_C - 0.5\beta \quad \alpha_2 = \alpha_C - 0.1\beta \quad \alpha_3 = \alpha_C$$

(with ring labeled positions 3, 2, 1 on $-\overset{2}{C}-H_3$)

Using these values, the electron density distribution is found to be

$$
\begin{array}{c}
1.000 \quad 1.005 \\
1.076 \ 0.915 \\
1.004 \ \langle\!\!\!\langle\ \rangle\!\!\!\rangle - C - H_3 \\
0.996
\end{array}
$$

which is in good agreement with the observed dipole moment of 0.4. However, if one remembers that the molecular orbital method exaggerates the electron density differences (cf. the discussion of azulene, p. 85), it will be seen that the apparent charge displacements are too small to account for the dipole moment. This should be the case, for electron

---

[88] C. A. Coulson and V. A. Crawford, *J. Chem. Soc.*, 2052 (1953). β is the designation for the exchange integral when overlap is neglected.

delocalization involving charge separation is normally not very important, and hence if hyperconjugation is a real phenomenon, it should not be observed in the neutral ground states of molecules.

A more reasonable place in which to apply this concept is in the study of rates of reactions which involve the development of a positive charge in the activated complex and in the study of electronic transitions leading to dipolar excited states. A calculation of the energy of the activated complex for electrophilic substitution (by deleting the carbon which is attacked and placing the positive charge in the remaining π-electron system) for this case predicts a lowering of the activation energy and a consequent increase in the rate, of reaction, as has been observed.[83] However, a more definitive test is found in studies of methyl-substituted carbonium ions, and here the results are less satisfactory than with the simple inductive model.[89]

It is interesting that the model which appears to be the most satisfactory (at least in the simple molecular orbital method) is one which considers the methyl group as equivalent to a single atom having a single electron pair.[90] This seems like a strange model for a methyl group, and it will be interesting to see what further developments may result from this model.

In summary, it appears that the hyperconjugation model, at least in the framework of the simple molecular orbital theory, is not too successful in correlating experimental results.[90a] Conjugation (of any kind) involving alkyl groups is probably minimal in the ground states of neutral molecules. In excited states, carbonium ions and radicals, alkyl groups are electron releasing, although the role of the inductive effect and of conjugation has not been clearly differentiated. Finally, the nature of the electron delocalization due to the alkyl groups has not been established.

References

Quantum Chemical Treatment of Methane and Related Saturated Compounds:
    J. H. Van Vleck, *J. Chem. Phys.*, **1**, 177, 219 (1933); **2**, 20 (1934).
    I. Mills, *Mol. Phys.*, **1**, 99 (1958).
    W. G. Penney, *Trans. Faraday Soc.*, **31**, 734 (1935).
    G. Del Re, *J. Chem. Soc.*, 4031 (1958).

[89] E. L. Mackor, G. D. Dallinga, J. H. Kruizinga, and A. Hofstra, *Rec. trav. Chim.*, **75**, 836 (1956); E. L. Mackor, A. Hofstra, and J. H. van der Waals, *Trans. Faraday Soc.*, **54**, 186 (1958); A. Streitwieser, Jr, and P. M. Nair, *Tetrahedron*, **5**, 149 (1959).
[90] F. A. Matsen, *J. Am. Chem. Soc.*, **72**, 5243 (1950); A. Streitwieser, Jr. and P. M. Nair, *Tetrahedron*, **5**, 149 (1959).
[90a] A semiempirical SCF treatment of hyperconjugation has, however, given results which are in good agreement with the basicities of methyl substituted benzenes: S. Ehrenson, *J. Am. Chem. Soc.*, **83**, 4493 (1961).

Quantum Chemical Treatment of Bond Deformation:
C. A. Coulson and W. Moffitt, *Phil. Mag.*, **40**, 1 (1949).
Hyperconjugation:
R. S. Mulliken, *J. Chem. Phys.*, **7**, 339 (1939).
R. S. Mulliken, C. A. Rieke, and W. G. Brown, *J. Am. Chem. Soc.* **63**, 41 (1941).
V. A. Crawford, *Quart. Revs.* **3**, 226 (1949).
J. W. Baker, *Hyperconjugation*, Oxford University Press, Oxford, 1952.
F. A. Matsen, *J. Am. Chem. Soc.*, **72**, 5243 (1950).
C. A. Coulson and V. A. Crawford, *J. Chem. Soc.*, 2052, (1953).
M. M. Kreevoy and H. Eyring, *J. Am. Chem. Soc.*, **79**, 5121 (1957).
Indiana University Conference on Hyperconjugation (*Tetrahedron*, **5**, pp. 105–274 (1959)).
S. Ehrenson, *J. Am. Chem. Soc.*, **83**, 4493 (1961).

1-16 Dispersion Forces

Up until now we have considered only ordinary bonding, which involves the sharing of electrons between two atoms. However, it is readily apparent that there are other forces of attraction between molecules. These are the forces which make the liquid state stable in spite of the loss of translational energy of the molecules in going from the gas to the liquid phase and which are responsible for much of the deviation from perfect gas behavior. In general, they are known as van der Waal's forces. These are short-range forces which decrease in intensity as the inverse sixth power of the distance between the atoms.[91]

They are of several types. The best known is probably the dipole-dipole interaction, as typified by a hydrogen bond.

$$-H \overset{\delta+}{} \quad \overset{\delta+}{H}$$

The second involves the interaction between a dipole and a molecule into which it induces a dipole. This is known as an induction or Debye force. These two attractive forces are not additive.

However, it is observed for some molecules, and, in particular, for rare gas atoms, that the van der Waal's force is additive and cannot be "saturated." Thus, for example, the energy of three neon atoms is the sum of

[91] A good review of this subject is found in H. Margenau, *Rev. Mod. Phys.*, **11**, 1 (1939).

the attraction between Ne(1) and Ne(2), between Ne(2) and Ne(3), and between Ne(1) and Ne(3), in each case not considering the third atom. Since this behavior cannot be interpreted in terms of the dipole orientation force or the induction force, and since these forces cannot operate between two rare gas atoms, London[92] was led to look for another factor leading to an additive force.

In order to obtain an understanding of the origin of the three types of attractive forces, let us first consider the interaction of two dipoles in a one-dimensional case. Let us consider the dipoles to be made up of two point charges + and − at a distance X_L for the left-hand dipole and X_R

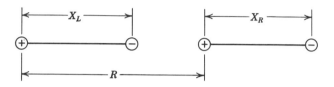

for the right-hand dipole. We must calculate the potential energy resulting from the interaction of a point charge in the left-hand system with a point charge in the right-hand system, as, for example, − of the former and + of the latter. This is given by Coulomb's law as e^2/r; thus

$$\frac{V}{e^2} = \frac{1}{R - X_L} = \frac{1}{R}\left(1 - \frac{X_L}{R}\right)^{-1}$$

Let us call $X_L/R = \epsilon$. Then

$$\frac{V}{e^2} = \frac{1}{R}(1 - \epsilon)^{-1} = \frac{1}{R}(1 + \epsilon + \epsilon^2 + \epsilon^3 + \cdots)$$

We shall assume that ϵ is small, which is experimentally known to be the case. Therefore only the first three terms of the expansion will be used. At the same time, we may note that the expansion of $(1 + \epsilon)^{-1}$ is $1 - \epsilon + \epsilon^2 - \epsilon^3 + \dots$.

For the whole system, we must consider the attraction between the unlike charges (two pairs) and the repulsion between the two positive charges and between the two negative charges. This gives

$$\frac{V}{e^2} = \frac{1}{R} - \frac{1}{R - X_L} - \frac{1}{R + X_R} + \frac{1}{R + X_R - X_L}$$

| Repulsion between positive charges | Attraction | Repulsion between negative charges |

[92] F. London, *Trans. Faraday Soc.*, **33**, 8 (1937).

If we call $X_R/R = \delta$, we have

$$\frac{V}{e^2} = \frac{1}{R} - \frac{1}{R}(1 + \epsilon + \epsilon^2) - \frac{1}{R}(1 - \delta + \delta^2) + \frac{1}{R}(1 + (\epsilon - \delta) + (\epsilon - \delta)^2)$$

$$= -2\frac{\delta\epsilon}{R}$$

Thus

$$\frac{V}{e^2} = -\frac{2X_L X_R}{R^3}$$

which is the classical interaction between two dipoles for a one-dimensional case. This corresponds to the dipoles being most stable when oriented

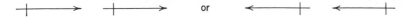

For the three-dimensional case, the expression becomes

$$\frac{V}{e^2} = \frac{X_L X_R + Y_L Y_R - 2Z_L Z_R}{R^3}$$

where a line between the positive centers defines the Z direction.

Let us now consider each of the components of the total van der Waal's attraction.

1. Dipole Orientation Force. If the two dipoles were optimally oriented with respect to each other, the attraction would be proportional to the inverse third power of the distance between them. However, these forces are relatively weak and the dipoles will not be optimally oriented because the thermal energy of the molecules ($\approx kT$) is greater than the potential energy due to attraction (V). If all orientations were equally probable, the net energy would be zero. However, as we shall see when we consider equilibria, the probability of an orientation is given by

$$\frac{n_i}{n_0} = P_i = e^{-V_i/kT}$$

where n_i is the number of dipoles having an orientation with $V = V_i$, and n_0 is the number of dipoles having an orientation giving no interaction between the dipoles (i.e., oriented at right angles to each other). The orientations leading to an attractive potential (giving a negative value of V) will be relatively more probable, and if the interaction is averaged over all orientations, taking into account the relative probabilities, one finds that the average potential energy is given approximately by

$$\bar{V} = -\frac{2\mu_1^2\mu_2^2}{3kTR^6}$$

where μ_1 and μ_2 are the dipole moments for the two dipoles. It is important to note that the dipole orientation force is temperature dependent. This results from the increased disorder, and consequent smaller attraction, at higher temperatures.

2. Induction Force. The electric dipole of a molecule possessing a permanent dipole moment may induce a redistribution of electron density in another molecule, leading to an induced dipole. Here the important factor is the polarizability, which is defined as the electric moment induced per unit electric field. The higher the polarizability of the second molecule, the larger will be the induced dipole and, consequently, the larger will be the energy of interaction of a dipole with the polarizable molecule. Again the interaction energy must be averaged over all orientations of the permanent dipole, giving as the net interaction

$$\bar{V} = -\frac{\alpha\mu^2}{R^6}$$

where α is the polarizability. It should be noted that this force is temperature independent.

3. Dispersion or London Force. Before considering the dispersion force, it will be convenient to evaluate the polarizability in terms of the molecular wave functions. The effect of an electric field on the electron distribution in a molecule may be considered by using perturbation theory. The Hamiltonian operator will be written as

$$H = H^{(0)} + H^{(1)}$$

where, in this case, the perturbation is given by

$$H^{(1)} = \mathscr{E}ex$$

Here $\mathscr{E}$ is the electric field potential, and ex is the induced moment (the displacement multiplied by the electronic charge). We will consider an electron in a molecule to have the following ground state and first excited state wave functions:

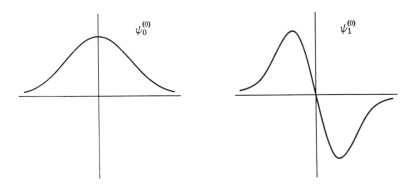

According to the perturbation theory, we add a small amount of $\psi_1^{(0)}$ to $\psi_0^{(0)}$ to get the perturbed wave function ψ_0, which has a lopsided distribution leading to an electric moment:

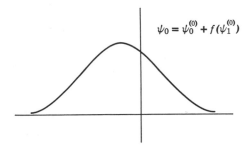

$$\psi_0 = \psi_0^{(0)} + f(\psi_1^{(0)})$$

The major contribution will be made by the ground state and the first excited state, for here $E_i - E_0$ will be a minimum. Thus

$$\psi_0 = \psi_0^{(0)} - \frac{H_{01}^{(1)}}{E_1 - E_0}\,\psi_1^{(0)}$$

The quantity, $H_{01}^{(1)}$, may be evaluated as

$$H_{01}^{(1)} = \int \psi_0^{(0)} \mathscr{E} ex\psi_1^{(0)}\, dx = \mathscr{E}\int \psi_0^{(0)} ex\psi_1^{(0)}\, dx$$

The quantity under the integral is the change in dipole moment in going from the ground state to the excited state and will be designated as m, the transition moment. Thus

$$H_{01}^{(1)} = \mathscr{E} m$$

and the perturbed wave function is

$$\psi_0 = \psi_0^{(0)} - \frac{\mathscr{E} m}{\Delta E}\,\psi_1^{(0)}$$

We must now obtain the electric moment, which will be given by

$$\int \psi_0 ex\psi_0\, dx$$

where ex is the electric moment operator. This may be evaluated as follows:

$$\int \psi_0 ex\psi_0\, dx = \int \left(\psi_0^{(0)} - \frac{\mathscr{E} m}{\Delta E}\,\psi_1^{(0)}\right) ex \left(\psi_0^{(0)} - \frac{\mathscr{E} m}{\Delta E}\,\psi_1^{(0)}\right) dx$$

$$= \int \psi_0^{(0)} ex\psi_0^{(0)}\, dx + \frac{\mathscr{E}^2 m^2}{\Delta E^2}\int \psi_1^{(0)} ex\psi_1^{(0)}\, dx$$

$$- \frac{2\mathscr{E} m}{\Delta E}\int \psi_0^{(0)} ex\psi_1^{(0)}\, dx$$

The first two terms are zero, since, for example, x operating on $\psi_0^{(0)}$ gives

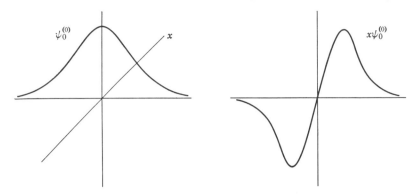

and the area under the product of $x\psi_0^{(0)}$ with $\psi_0^{(0)}$ will be zero. The integral in the third term gives m, and the induced electric moment will be

$$-\frac{2\mathscr{E}m^2}{\Delta E}$$

This is the product of the moment per unit field (α, the polarizability) and the magnitude of the field. Thus the polarizability is given by

$$\alpha = -\frac{2m^2}{\Delta E}$$

For the three-dimensional case, and considering all excited states, the result would have been

$$\alpha = \frac{2}{3}\sum_n \frac{(m_x)_{n0}{}^2 + (m_y)_{n0}{}^2 + (m_z)_{n0}{}^2}{E_n{}^0 - E_0{}^0}$$

In terms of experimentally measured quantities, the polarizability is commonly evaluated using the Lorenz-Lorentz equation

$$\alpha = \frac{n^2 - 1}{n^2 + 2}\cdot\frac{M}{d}$$

where n is the refractive index, M is the molecular weight, and d is the density. The latter is, of course, the value arising from all the electrons, whereas in the above calculation we were concerned with the behavior of one electron.

Now in order to obtain the energy of interaction between two atoms, let us take two nuclei and consider the motion of an electron about each nucleus as that of a harmonic oscillator. This is reasonable if we consider the Coulombic interaction between the electron and nucleus as the restoring force to a displacement and if we consider the components of motion in all directions. For simplicity we shall consider the case of two one-dimensional oscillators:

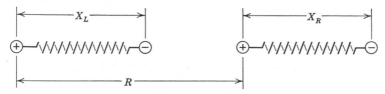

From before, we have that

$$\frac{V}{e^2} = -\frac{2X_L X_R}{R^3}$$

and, using perturbation theory,

$$H = H^{(0)} + H^{(1)} = H_L^{(0)} + H_R^{(0)} - \frac{2e^2 X_L X_R}{R^3}$$

The ground state perturbation energy is given by

$$E' = \int \psi_0 H^{(1)} \psi_0 \, dx$$

but in the absence of a permanent field, $\psi_0 = \psi_0^{(0)}$ and thus $E' = 0$. In order to find an interaction it is necessary to use the second-order perturbation expression, which is obtained from the terms containing λ^2 on p. 50.

$$E'' = \sum_i \frac{H_{0i}^{(1)} H_{i0}^{(1)}}{E_0 - E_i}$$

$$H_{0i}^{(1)} = H_{i0}^{(1)} = \int \psi_0^{(0)} H^{(1)} \psi_i^{(0)} \, dx$$

For a harmonic oscillator, the $H_{0i}^{(1)}$ term is nonzero only when $i = 1$. Therefore

$$H_{01}^{(1)} = \int \psi_{L_0}^{(0)} \psi_{R_0}^{(0)} \left(-\frac{2e^2 X_L X_R}{R^3} \right) \psi_{L_1}^{(0)} \psi_{R_1}^{(0)} \, dx$$

where the wave functions are those given before (p. 13) at each of the two centers. Evaluating the quantity

$$H_{01}^{(1)} = -\frac{2}{R^3} \left(\int \psi_{L_0}^{(0)} e X_L \psi_{L_1}^{(0)} \int \psi_{R_0}^{(0)} e X_R \psi_{R_1}^{(0)} \, dx \right)$$

$$= -\frac{2m^2}{R^3}$$

we find that the interaction energy is given by

$$E'' = \frac{(-2m^2/R^3)^2}{\Delta E}$$

For two harmonic oscillators, the ground state energy is $h\nu$ and that for the first excited state is $3h\nu$. Thus, in terms of the oscillator frequency, the energy is

$$E'' = \frac{2m^4}{h\nu} \cdot \frac{1}{R^6}$$

or in terms of the polarizability (replacing ΔE by $h\nu$)

$$E'' = -\alpha^2 \frac{h\nu}{2R^6}$$

Thus the more polarizable the molecule, the larger will be the interaction, and the negative sign indicates that it is an attractive interaction.

In physical terms the foregoing results say that the instantaneous dipoles in molecules which are created by the motion of electrons will tend to be synchronized so that a net attractive potential is found. The perturbation is a small one, which accounts for the additive character of this force.

The above expression was derived for a one-dimensional case. For the three-dimensional case, the result is

$$E'' = -\alpha^2 \frac{3h\nu}{4R^6}$$

The motion of an electron in a molecule cannot be described by a single frequency; rather, it involves the summation of a series of frequencies, each weighted by a suitable coefficient. Thus the above expression is not in a useful form for molecules of interest to organic chemists. It has, however, been found that the appropriate factor $h\nu$ may be reasonably well represented by the ionization potential (I).[92] The latter may be measured, and the polarizability may be determined from the refractive index allowing the interaction energy for two identical molecules to be calculated from

$$E'' = -\frac{3}{4} \frac{\alpha^2 I}{R^6}$$

The equivalent form for two different molecules is

$$E'' \cong \frac{\alpha_a \alpha_b}{R^6} \frac{3 I_a I_b}{2(I_a + I_b)}$$

where the last term is the reduced ionization potential.

London and Margenau have made comparisons of the magnitudes of the three attractive forces for a number of molecules, and the results are shown in Table 1-16. It can be seen that except for water and ammonia, which form particularly good hydrogen bonds, the dispersion force is the largest component. Even for ammonia the dispersion force is nearly as large as the orientation force. From this it would appear that the dispersion force is the main component of the van der Waal's type attraction for larger molecules in which the dipole orientation force cannot be as important as for water and ammonia.

Table 1-16   Comparison of Different Types of van der Waal's Forces[a]

Substance	*Polarizability* $cm^3 \times 10^{24}$	*Dipole Moment* (esu $\times 10^{18}$)	*Interaction Energy*[b] (ergs $\times 10^{12}$)		
			Orientation	*Induction*	*Dispersion*
H_2O	1.48	1.84	190	10	47
NH_3	2.24	1.5	84	10	70
HI	5.4	0.38	0.35	1.68	370
HBr	3.58	0.78	6.2	4.05	185
HCl	2.63	1.03	18.6	5.4	111
CO	1.99	0.1	0.003	0.057	67.5
Cl_2	4.60	0	0	0	321
O_2	1.57	0	0	0	39.8
N_2	1.74	0	0	0	57.2
H_2	0.81	0	0	0	11.4
Xe	4.0	0	0	0	273
Kr	2.46	0	0	0	129
A	1.63	0	0	0	69.5
Ne	0.39	0	0	0	7.97
He	0.205	0	0	0	1.49

[a] F. London, *Trans. Faraday Soc.*, **33**, 8 (1937); H. Margenau, *Revs. Mod. Phys.*, **11**, 1 (1939).
[b] Coefficient K of $E = -K/R^6$ when R is in Å and E is in ergs.

References

Hydrogen Bonds:
  G. C. Pimentel and A. L. McClellan, *The Hydrogen Bond*, W. H. Freeman and Co., San Francisco, 1960.
van der Waals Forces:
  H. Margenau, *Rev. Mod. Phys.*, **11**, 1 (1939).

1-17 Vibrational Spectra

The use of infrared spectra by organic chemists is commonly limited to structure determination using empirically determined characteristic frequencies for various functional groups. More information may often be obtained from a detailed analysis of the spectra, and certain aspects of such an analysis which will be of value in the later considerations of the calculations of thermodynamic properties of molecules and of the absolute rate theory will be presented here.

We have previously obtained the energy levels for a harmonic oscillator in terms of the force constant and masses involved:

$$E = h\nu(n + \tfrac{1}{2}) \qquad n = 1, 2, 3, \ldots$$

$$\nu = \frac{1}{2\pi} \sqrt{k/\mu} = 1303 \sqrt{k/\mu} \ \mathrm{cm}^{-1}$$

where the force constant, k, is given in units of 10^5 dynes/cm in the last expression and where μ is the reduced mass

$$\mu = \frac{m_1 m_2}{m_1 + m_2}$$

It should be noted that the reduced mass is approximately equal to the mass of the lighter component if the difference in mass is large. Although the vibration of molecules does not follow a simple parabolic potential law (Fig. 1-35), the latter is a reasonable approximation for small vibrations. Thus we shall use this approximation throughout the following section.

It is interesting to note that most single bonds have about the same force constant ($\sim$5 $\times$ 10^5 dynes/cm = 5 md/Å) (Table 1-17). Similarly,

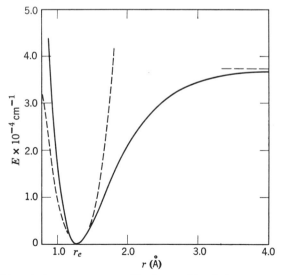

Fig. 1-35. Dissociation energy curve of hydrogen chloride (solid line) and the parabolic representation appropriate for small displacements (dotted line).

it is found that most double bonds have a force constant of about 9×10^5 dynes/cm, and most triple bonds have a constant of about 16×10^5 dynes/cm. This relative constancy of the force constant for a given type of bond permits the use of infrared spectra for the identification of various structural units which may be present in molecules.

Table 1-17a   Approximate Stretching Force Constants[a]

Bond	Molecule	$\dfrac{k}{(md/\text{Å})^b}$	Bond	k
H—F	HF	9.7	C—C	4.5–5.6
H—Cl	HCl	5.2	C=C	9.5–9.9
H—Br	HBr	4.1	C≡C	15.6–17.0
H—I	HI	3.2	N—N	3.5–5.5
H—O	H_2O	7.8	N=N	13.0–13.5
H—S	H_2S	4.3	N≡N	23
H—N	NH_3	6.5	O—O	3.5–5.0
H—C	CH_3X	4.7–5.0	C—N	4.9–5.6
H—C	C_2H_4	5.1	C=N	10–11
H—C	C_6H_6	5.1	C≡N	16.2–18.2
H—C	C_2H_2	5.9	C—O	5.0–5.8
F—C	CH_3F	5.6	C=O	11.8–13.4
Cl—C	CH_3Cl	3.4		
Br—C	CH_3Br	2.8		
I—C	CH_3I	2.3		

[a] Adapted from E. B. Wilson, Jr., J. C. Decius, and P. C. Cross, *Molecular Vibrations*, McGraw-Hill Book Co., New York, 1955, p. 175.
[b] The units millidynes per Angstrom and 10^5 dynes per centimeter are equivalent.

The infrared spectrum, of course, represents the transitions between the possible vibrational energy levels in molecules. Thus it is important to consider the case of several coupled harmonic oscillators and to obtain the energy levels for such a system. Consider the case of carbon dioxide. Each of the atoms in the molecule has three degrees of freedom (i.e., movement along the x, y, and z axes). A molecule of carbon dioxide, having three atoms, then has 3×3 or 9 degrees of freedom. Three of these are translation along the x, y, and z axes, respectively, and two refer to rotation in the xz plane and in the xy plane, where the x axis coincides with the axis of the molecule.[93] Four degrees of freedom remain

[93] It should be noted that there are, in general, three rotational degrees of freedom, rotation about each of the three axes. However, with linear molecules rotation about the x axis has no meaning, and there are but two rotational degrees of freedom.

Table 1–17b   **Approximate Bond Bending Force Constants**[a]

Angle	Molecule	k/r_1r_2 (md/Å)[b]
HOH	H_2O	0.69
HSH	H_2S	0.43
HNH	NH_3	0.4–0.6
HCH	CH_4	0.46
HCH	C_2H_4	0.30
FCF	CF_4	0.71
ClCCl	CCl_4	0.33
BrCBr	CBr_4	0.24
HCF	CH_3F	0.57
HCCl	CH_3Cl	0.36
HCBr	CH_3Br	0.30
HCI	CH_3I	0.23
OCO	CO_2	0.57
SCS	CS_2	0.23
HCC	C_2H_2	0.12
HCN	HCN	0.20

[a] *Source:* same as for Table 1-17a.
[b] The values r_1 and r_2 are the equilibrium lengths of the bonds forming the angle. This gives the force constant in the same dimensions as the stretching force constant.

unaccounted for, and these must be vibrations. The four possible normal modes of vibration are

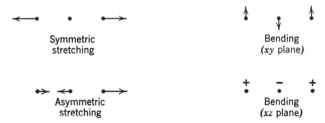

Symmetric
stretching

Bending
(*xy* plane)

Asymmetric
stretching

Bending
(*xz* plane)

The relationship between the frequencies of these vibrations and the force constants and masses is usually determined following a procedure described by Wilson.[94] However, for the present purpose it is more instructive to consider only the two stretching frequencies and to do this by a simple, direct procedure.

[94] See E. B. Wilson, Jr., J. C. Decius, and P. C. Cross, *Molecular Vibrations*, McGraw-Hill Book Co., New York, 1955, ch. 5.

Let us consider the case of three masses, m_1, m_2, and m_3, which are constrained to move along the x axis and which are connected by springs having the force constants k_1 and k_2.

The displacement of mass 1 from its equilibrium position will be designated as x_1, and similar displacements are considered for the other two masses. The potential energy resulting from the displacement x_1 with m_2 and m_3 remaining fixed is given by

$$V = \tfrac{1}{2}kx_1{}^2$$

We can then write the potential energy of the system of three masses as a function of the three displacements as

$$V = \tfrac{1}{2}k_1(x_2 - x_1)^2 + \tfrac{1}{2}k_2(x_3 - x_2)^2$$

The quantity of interest is not the potential energy but rather the force involved. However, since the derivative of the potential energy with respect to the coordinate gives the force, we have

$$\left(\frac{\partial V}{\partial x_1}\right)_{x_2, x_3} = -F_1 = -k_1(x_2 - x_1)$$

$$\left(\frac{\partial V}{\partial x_2}\right)_{x_1, x_3} = -F_2 = k_1(x_2 - x_1) - k_2(x_3 - x_2)$$

$$\left(\frac{\partial V}{\partial x_3}\right)_{x_1, x_2} = -F_3 = k_2(x_3 - x_2)$$

The forces will be considered to be classical and therefore will be given by the familiar expression

$$F = ma = m\frac{d^2x}{dt^2}$$

The assumption of simple harmonic motion permits us to obtain a relationship between the displacement and time which will be that of a sine wave:

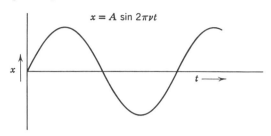

$$x = A \sin 2\pi\nu t$$

Differentiating with respect to time,

$$\frac{dx}{dt} = 2\pi\nu A \cos 2\pi\nu t$$

$$\frac{d^2x}{dt^2} = -4\pi^2\nu^2 A \sin 2\pi\nu t$$

But since

$$x = A \sin 2\pi\nu t$$

$$\frac{d^2x_1}{dt^2} = \frac{F_1}{m_1} = -4\pi^2\nu^2 x_1 = -\lambda x_1$$

where

$$\lambda = +4\pi^2\nu^2$$

we obtain

$$F_1 = -\lambda x_1 m_1$$
$$F_2 = -\lambda x_2 m_2$$
$$F_3 = -\lambda x_3 m_3$$

Substituting the values of F obtained previously,

$$-m_1\lambda x_1 - k_1(x_2 - x_1) = 0$$
$$-m_2\lambda x_2 + k_1(x_2 - x_1) - k_2(x_3 - x_2) = 0$$
$$-m_3\lambda x_3 + k_2(x_3 - x_2) = 0$$

As we have seen before, a set of simultaneous equations of this type can be solved by setting the determinant of the coefficients of x_1, x_2, and x_3 equal to zero. Consequently

$$\begin{vmatrix} k_1 - m_1\lambda & -k_1 & 0 \\ -k_1 & k_1 + k_2 - m_2\lambda & -k_2 \\ 0 & -k_2 & k_2 - m_3\lambda \end{vmatrix} = 0$$

Multiplying this out, we obtain

$$-m_1 m_2 m_3 \lambda^3 + (k_1 m_2 m_3 + k_1 m_1 m_3 + k_2 m_1 m_2 + k_2 m_1 m_3)\lambda^2$$
$$+ (-k_1 k_2 m_1 - k_1 k_2 m_2 - k_1 k_2 m_3)\lambda = 0$$

From this there may be factored out a λ which is then equal to zero. This corresponds to the translation of the whole molecule and is not of interest to us (i.e., this mode is one in which all the nuclei move in the same direction at the same time). After factoring the last term, this then becomes

$$-m_1 m_2 m_3 \lambda^2 + (k_1 m_2 m_3 + k_1 m_1 m_3 + k_2 m_1 m_2 + k_2 m_1 m_3)\lambda$$
$$- (m_1 + m_2 + m_3)(k_1 k_2) = 0$$

The equation may be more conveniently expressed in the form

$$\lambda_1 + \lambda_2 = \left(\frac{1}{m_1} + \frac{1}{m_2}\right)k_1 + \left(\frac{1}{m_2} + \frac{1}{m_3}\right)k_2$$

$$\lambda_1 \lambda_2 = \left(\frac{1}{m_1 m_2} + \frac{1}{m_1 m_3} + \frac{1}{m_2 m_3}\right)k_1 k_2$$

For the particular case in question, it may be simplified if one remembers that $m_1 = m_3$ and $k_1 = k_2$. Then

$$\lambda_1 + \lambda_2 = 2k\left(\frac{1}{m_1} + \frac{1}{m_2}\right) = k\left(\frac{1}{m_1} + \frac{2m_1 + m_2}{m_1 m_2}\right)$$

$$\lambda_1 \lambda_2 = k^2\left(\frac{2}{m_1 m_2} + \frac{1}{m_1^2}\right) = \frac{k^2}{m_1}\left(\frac{2m_1 + m_2}{m_1 m_2}\right)$$

and it is apparent that

$$\lambda_1 = \frac{k}{m_1}$$

$$\lambda_2 = \frac{k(2m_1 + m_2)}{m_1 m_2} = \frac{k}{\mu}$$

The first of these equations corresponds to the symmetrical stretching frequency and the second to the asymmetric frequency. Thus the asymmetric vibration of the two harmonic oscillators will be coupled so long as m_1 and m_2 are comparable. If, however, m_2 is much larger than m_1, the difference between the frequencies will be small, m_2 acting as sort of an insulator between the two oscillators.

Since the expression for the frequencies in terms of the force constant has been obtained, we may substitute the observed values for these frequencies and obtain the force constant. The symmetrical frequency is 1337 cm^{-1} and the asymmetric frequency is 2349 cm^{-1}.[95] Substituting

[95] Vibrational frequencies are usually given in cm^{-1} rather than in cycles per second because the numbers are then of a more convenient magnitude. The frequency in cm^{-1} (or wave numbers) multiplied by the velocity of light ($3.0 \times 10^{10} \text{ cm/sec}$) gives the frequency in cycles per sec. Also $\lambda = (\nu/1303)^2$ when k is in units of 10^5 dynes/cm, and ν is given in cm^{-1}.

these values into the expressions given above results in values of $k = 16.8$ and 14.2×10^5 dynes/cm for the two vibrations, respectively. If no other factors were operative, the two values for the force constant should, of course, be the same.

Consider what happens in the asymmetric stretching mode as one C-O bond begins to lengthen and the other begins to contract.[96] The π overlap for the former bond will decrease, and the bond order might be expected to decrease. The bond order for the other C-O bond might also be expected to increase since the bond length decreases. Expressed in another way, we may consider the contributing Valence-Bond structures for carbon dioxide

$$^-O—C{=}O^+ \leftrightarrow O{=}C{=}O \leftrightarrow \overset{+}{O}{=}C—O^-$$

In the absence of vibrational excitation, the first and third structures should contribute equally. However, if the left C-O bond were elongated and the right bond were shortened, the first structure would contribute more than the third, and whereas the bond order for the left C-O bond will have decreased, that for the right bond will have increased. Thus during the vibration, the two force constants do not remain equal but are so only on a time average.

This phenomenon may be measured in terms of an interaction constant between the first and third atoms. This process requires the insertion of an additional term in the secular equation. If the interaction constant is called k_{12}, the equation relating the potential energy to the force constant becomes

$$V = \tfrac{1}{2}k_1(x_2 - x_1)^2 + \tfrac{1}{2}k_2(x_3 - x_2)^2 + k_{12}(x_2 - x_1)(x_3 - x_2)$$

Following the procedure outlined above, the secular determinant now becomes

$$\begin{vmatrix} k_1 - m_1\lambda & k_{12} - k_1 & -k_{12} \\ k_{12} - k_1 & k_1 + k_2 - m_2\lambda - 2k_{12} & k_{12} - k_2 \\ -k_{12} & k_{12} - k_2 & k_2 - m_1\lambda \end{vmatrix} = 0$$

The solution of the determinant is then

$$\lambda_1 + \lambda_2 = \left(\frac{1}{m_1} + \frac{1}{m_2}\right)k_1 + \left(\frac{1}{m_2} + \frac{1}{m_3}\right)k_2 - \frac{2k_{12}}{m_2}$$

$$\lambda_1\lambda_2 = \left(\frac{1}{m_1 m_2} + \frac{1}{m_1 m_3} + \frac{1}{m_2 m_3}\right)(k_1 k_2 - k_{12}^2)$$

[96] H. W. Thompson and J. W. Linnett, *J. Chem. Soc.*, 1384 (1937).

which differs from that previously obtained only by the addition of terms in k_{12}. Substituting the values of λ_1 and λ_2, k is found to be 15.5×10^5 dynes/cm, and k_{12} is 1.3×10^5 dynes/cm. As might be expected, the force constant thus obtained is the average of the two force constants calculated without including the interaction term.

The coupling of vibration illustrated above is a very common occurrence. For example, the two vinyl hydrogens of propylene represent a similar case. There are a symmetrical and an asymmetric frequency (2976 and 3077 cm^{-1}, respectively).

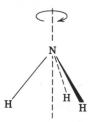

The two frequencies differ by a much smaller factor than in the case of carbon dioxide because here the central atom has a mass twelve times as great as that for the end atoms. The coupling of the C-H vibrations with that of the C-C double bond is small because of the large difference in frequency between these vibrations.

In considering equilibria it would be useful to be able to make vibrational frequency assignments for molecules. This is often a difficult problem, but it may be illustrated by a relatively simple example.[97] Before proceeding, it is first necessary to consider the symmetry elements which molecules may possess.

One of the common symmetry elements is an axis of symmetry, which is designated as C_n for an n-fold axis of symmetry. If we consider ammonia and draw a line through the nitrogen to a point equidistant from the three hydrogens, then rotation by 120° about this axis will bring the molecule to

[97] Other examples, including a complete vibrational analysis for benzene, will be found in E. B. Wilson, Jr., J. C. Decius, and P. C. Cross, *Molecular Vibrations*, McGraw-Hill Book Co., New York, 1955.

a position which is indistinguishable from its original position. Since this occurs three times during a rotation through 360°, it is described as a threefold axis of symmetry. Water has a twofold axis of symmetry; carbonate ion, boron trifluoride, and methane have threefold axes of symmetry, whereas benzene has a sixfold axis of symmetry.

Corresponding to the symmetry element—the axis of symmetry—there is a symmetry operation, rotation about the axis of symmetry. This operation is designated as $C_n{}^k$, which indicates a rotation of $360k/n$ degrees about the n-fold axis. It should also be noted that many molecules have more than one axis of symmetry. For example, benzene has six twofold axes along with the sixfold axis. The axis having the largest value of n is usually referred to as the principal axis.

Another symmetry element is the plane of symmetry. As an example, the water molecule has two planes of symmetry, one of which passes through all of the atoms, whereas the second is perpendicular to the first and passes through the oxygen.

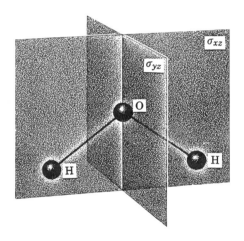

The planes of symmetry are denoted as σ. If a plane is parallel to the principal axis of symmetry, it is designated as σ_v; if it is perpendicular to this axis, it is designated as σ_h; and if it bisects the angle between the twofold axes of symmetry, it is designated as σ_d. The symmetry operation which corresponds to this symmetry element is reflection through the plane of symmetry.

If a molecule has a point which is located so that a straight line drawn from any atom through that point will also pass through an equivalent atom on the other side, and if each pair of two atoms is equidistant from this point, the latter is known as a center of symmetry. Compounds which possess a center of symmetry include ethylene, benzene, and cyclohexane. The highly symmetrical molecule, methane, however, does not possess a center of symmetry. The corresponding operation is known as inversion through the center of symmetry and is designated as i.

The remaining symmetry element is an alternating axis of symmetry. The corresponding operation consists of a rotation followed by a reflection through a plane perpendicular to the rotational axis. A good example is methane. Consider the arrangement in which two hydrogens lie in one plane and the other two hydrogens lie in a plane perpendicular to the first. The intersection of these planes corresponds to a twofold axis of symmetry.

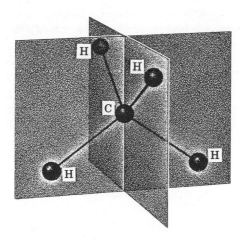

If the molecule is rotated through 90° and then reflected through a plane perpendicular to the original planes and passing through the carbon, the original arrangement of the atoms will be reproduced. The alternating axis of symmetry is designated as S_n for an n-fold axis, and thus in the above case it would be designated as S_4. The corresponding operation is denoted as S_n^k, corresponding to a rotation through $360k/n$ degrees about the n-fold axis followed by a reflection. If k is even, $S_n^k = C_n^k$.

A final symmetry operation is the trivial one of leaving the molecule alone. It is designated as E.

Only certain groups of symmetry elements are possible in molecules, and for each possible set of elements there is a corresponding point group. The simplest of these is that for a compound having no element of symmetry, and this is designated as $\mathscr{C}_1$. If there is an n-fold axis of symmetry, the compound is in group $\mathscr{C}_n$. If there are also n twofold axes of symmetry perpendicular to the principal axis, the compound is in group $\mathscr{D}_n$. The presence of a plane of symmetry perpendicular to the principal axis in addition to the above places a compound in group $\mathscr{D}_{nh}$. If the plane had been diagonal (σ_d), the compound would have been in group $\mathscr{D}_{nd}$.

Starting again with a compound having an n-fold axis of symmetry, but without n additional twofold axes, there may be a plane of symmetry perpendicular to the rotational axis. In this case the compound is in group $\mathscr{C}_{nh}$. If, instead, there is a plane of symmetry parallel to the principal axis, the compound is in group $\mathscr{C}_{nv}$. The other common groups are $\mathscr{T}$, $\mathscr{T}_d$, $\mathscr{O}$, and $\mathscr{O}_h$. The group $\mathscr{T}$ contains all the rotational axes possessed by a regular tetrahedron, whereas $\mathscr{T}_d$ contains the planes of symmetry as well. Similarly, $\mathscr{O}$ contains the rotations, and $\mathscr{O}_h$ contains all the elements of symmetry possessed by a cube.

The point groups are best understood by considering some examples. Ammonia has a threefold axis of symmetry and three planes of symmetry parallel to the principal axis (each passes through the nitrogen and one of the hydrogens). Therefore ammonia is in group $\mathscr{C}_{3v}$. In ethylene, there is a twofold axis of symmetry passing through the two carbons (C_2^x). In addition, there are two twofold axes of symmetry (C_2^y and C_2^z) perpendicular to the principal axis. There is also a plane of symmetry (σ_h) passing through all the atoms. Thus ethylene is in group $\mathscr{D}_{2h}$. The other symmetry elements are a center of symmetry and two other planes of symmetry.

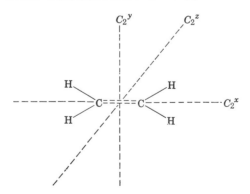

Allene has a twofold axis of symmetry (C_2) and a fourfold alternating axis of symmetry passing through all three carbons. In addition, there are two twofold axes (C_2' and C_2'') perpendicular to the principal axis (each bisecting the angle between the z and y axes), and there are two diagonal planes of symmetry (σ_d). Each of the latter passes through all three carbons and one pair of hydrogens. Therefore allene is in group $\mathscr{D}_{2d}$.

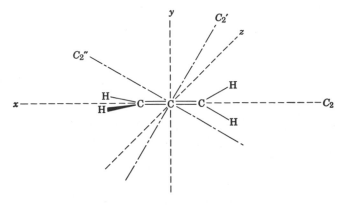

Benzene has a sixfold axis of symmetry passing through the center of the molecule. There are six twofold axes of symmetry perpendicular to this ($3C_2'$ and $3C_2''$), and there is a plane of symmetry (σ_h) passing through all the atoms. Thus it is in class $\mathscr{D}_{6h}$. The other symmetry elements present in this group are a center of symmetry, six planes of symmetry perpendicular to σ_h ($3\sigma_v'$ and $3\sigma_v''$), and a sixfold alternating axis of symmetry. These symmetry elements generate the following symmetry operations: rotation about the principal axis by $60°(C_6)$, $120°(C_3)$, $180°(C_2)$, $240°(C_3)$, $300°(C_6)$ (i.e., rotation by $60°$ in the reverse direction), and $360°(E)$; rotation by $180°$ about the axes C_2' and C_2'' ($3C_2'$, $3C_2''$); inversion through the center of symmetry (i); rotation by 60 or $300°$ followed by a reflection through σ_h ($2S_3$) (note that rotation through $180°$ followed by reflection through σ_h is equivalent to i); reflection through σ_h; reflection through σ_v'; and reflection through σ_v'' (see Fig. 1-36).

The operations which are possible for a given point group are listed in the headings of the group character tables given in Appendix 3. For example, the heading for $\mathscr{D}_{6h}$ is E, $2C_6$, $2C_3$, $3C_2'$, $3C_2''$, i, $2S_3$, $2S_6$, σ_h, $3\sigma_v'$, $3\sigma_v''$ corresponding to those found above. The character tables also contain information about the nature of the species of the group. Considering the vibrations of benzene as a particular case, the vibrations which leave the symmetry of the molecule unchanged (such as ring breathing) belong to the species A_{1g}. It will be noted in the character table (p. 136) that a + 1 is listed under all the symmetry operations of that species, which means that each of the symmetry operations are unchanged as a result of an A_{1g} type vibration.

The classification of the species is as follows: The A species are symmetric with respect to rotation about the principal axis, whereas the B species are antisymmetric with respect to such a rotation. The E species correspond to doubly degenerate vibrations and the T species correspond

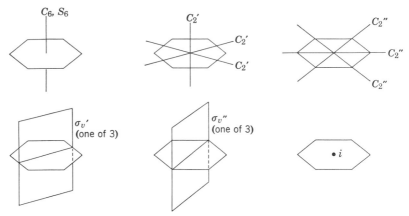

Fig. 1-36. Symmetry elements for benzene. The remaining symmetry element is σ_h, a plane which includes all the atoms of the ring.

to triply degenerate vibrations. The subscripts 1 and 2 are used with A and B to indicate the species which are symmetrical or antisymmetric with respect to rotation about one of the twofold axes perpendicular to the principal axis in group $\mathscr{D}_n$ or with respect to reflection through a vertical plane, σ_v, in group $\mathscr{C}_{nv}$. The other subscripts, g and u, indicate species which are symmetrical or antisymmetric with respect to inversion through a center of symmetry.

Several important pieces of information may be derived in terms of the species of each group. Let us consider translation and rotation of ethylene ($\mathscr{D}_{2h}$) as an example. Suppose a translation occurred along the x axis. The resultant molecule would still be symmetrical with respect to rotation about the x axis but would be antisymmetric with respect to rotation about the *original* y or z axes, and with respect to inversion through the original center of symmetry. The species which has -1 for these operations is B_{3u}, and the translation belongs to this species. A rotation about the x axis will lead to the same results as above, except that the molecule will still be symmetrical with respect to inversion through the original center of symmetry. Rotation about the x axis therefore belongs to the species B_{3g}. The species corresponding to the translational and rotational modes are summarized at the left of each character table in Appendix 3.

The selection rules for infrared and Raman spectra may be obtained in the same way. In order for infrared light to interact with a molecule and cause a transition from one vibrational state to another, the transition must involve a change in dipole moment. The transition moment (proportional to the intensity of the band) is given by

$$m_x = \int \psi_g e x \psi_e \, d\tau$$

for the x direction, and corresponding equations may be written for the y and z directions. In order for the integral to have a value other than zero, the product of the ground state wave function (ψ_g), the coordinate (x), and the excited state wave function (ψ_e) must be an even function. The ground state wave function is symmetric and consequently is an even function. The coordinate is antisymmetric (i.e., is $+$ on one side of the origin and $-$ on the other side) and is an odd function. The excited state wave function must then be an odd function with respect to the coordinate in question. Wave functions belonging to the species B_{3u} are antisymmetric with respect to the yz plane and fill the requirement.

A detailed discussion of the selection rules may be found elsewhere.[98] The results of such considerations are shown on the right of each of the character tables. The notation IR indicates species whose vibrations will be infrared active. It may be noted that the totally symmetric vibration in each case (corresponding to the first species in any character table) is always infrared inactive. This arises because a change in dipole moment during the vibration is required in order for absorption of infrared radiation to occur, and this condition is not met in a totally symmetric vibration. The notations $R(p)$ and $R(dp)$ refer to Raman active species. The subscript p refers to a polarized band and dp refers to a depolarized band. To determine this, polarized light is used in obtaining the Raman spectrum, and the polarization (if any) of the Raman line is determined. Only the totally symmetric vibration can give a polarized Raman line.

Let us now take ethylene as a specific example and try to assign all the vibrations. Ethylene has six atoms, and each atom has 3 degrees of freedom, making a total of 18 degrees of freedom for the molecule. Of these, 3 are translations, and 3 are rotations, leaving 12 vibrational degrees of freedom. The observed frequencies for ethylene are given in Table 1-18, and the problem is to assign these frequencies to the various vibrational modes.[99]

[98] E. B. Wilson, Jr., J. C. Decius, and P. C. Cross, *Molecular Vibrations*, McGraw-Hill Book Co., New York, 1955, ch. 7 and appendix 16.
[99] The problem is oversimplified here because the observed spectrum also contains a number of combination bands and overtone bands. The sorting out of the fundamental vibrations from the others involves considerable trial and error manipulations of the sums and multiples of frequencies. The problem can often be considerably simplified if the spectra of a number of isotopically substituted derivatives are available. See the discussion of the vibrational spectrum of benzene and of other compounds in ref. 97.

The procedure used in determining the number of vibrations belonging to each species of a point group will be given below without proof. A

Table 1-18   **Fundamental Vibrational Frequencies for Ethylene**[a]

Vibration	Class	Infrared	Raman
1	A_{1g}		3019 (p)
2	A_{1g}		1623 (p)
3	A_{1g}		1342 (p)
4	A_{1u}		
5	B_{1g}		3272 (dp)
6	B_{1g}		
7	B_{1u}	949 ($\parallel$)	
8	B_{2g}		943 (dp)
9	B_{2u}	3106 ($\parallel$)	
10	B_{2u}	995	
11	B_{3u}	2990 ($\perp$)	
12	B_{3u}	1444 ($\perp$)	

[a] These data are taken from G. Herzberg, *Infrared and Raman Spectra*, D. Van Nostrand Co., New York, 1945, p. 325.

detailed discussion will be found elsewhere.[97] Ethylene is in group $\mathscr{D}_{2h}$, and therefore the character table is as shown.

$\mathscr{D}_{2h}$	E	$C_2{}^z$	$C_2{}^y$	$C_2{}^x$	i	σ_{xy}	σ_{xz}	σ_{yz}		
A_{1g}	1	1	1	1	1	1	1	1	$R(p)$	
A_{1u}	1	1	1	1	-1	-1	-1	-1		
B_{1g}	1	1	-1	-1	1	1	-1	-1	$R(dp)$	R_z
B_{1u}	1	1	-1	-1	-1	-1	1	1	$IR(\parallel)$	T_z
B_{2g}	1	-1	1	-1	1	-1	1	-1	$R(dp)$	R_y
B_{2u}	1	-1	1	-1	-1	1	-1	1	$IR(\parallel)$	T_y
B_{3g}	1	-1	-1	1	1	-1	-1	1	$R(dp)$	R_x
B_{3u}	1	-1	-1	1	-1	1	1	-1	$IR(\perp)$	T_x

For each operation we shall look for the number of atoms which are unshifted as a result of the operation. Further, we shall treat the carbons and hydrogens separately for convenience. For example, with ethylene, the operation E leaves two carbons and four hydrogens unshifted; the operation $C_2{}^z$ (where z is the axis perpendicular to the plane of the molecule) leaves no carbons or hydrogens unshifted; the operation $C_2{}^y$ leaves no carbons or hydrogens unshifted; the operation $C_2{}^x$ (where x is the axis passing through the two carbons) leaves two carbons and no hydrogens unshifted; the operation i leaves no carbons or hydrogens unshifted; the operation σ_{xy} leaves the two carbon and four hydrogens unshifted; the operation σ_{xz} leaves two carbons and no hydrogens unshifted; and the operation σ_{yz} leaves no carbons or hydrogens unshifted. For each operation the number of unshifted atoms is multiplied by a factor appropriate to that operation (Table 1-19). Thus

$$\chi^C(E) = 3 \times 2 = 6 \qquad \chi^H(E) = 3 \times 4 = 12$$
$$\chi^C(C_2{}^z) = -1 \times 0 = 0 \qquad \chi^H(C_2{}^z) = -1 \times 0 = 0$$
$$\chi^C(C_2{}^y) = -1 \times 0 = 0 \qquad \chi^H(C_2{}^y) = -1 \times 0 = 0$$
$$\chi^C(C_2{}^x) = -1 \times 2 = -2 \qquad \chi^H(C_2{}^x) = -1 \times 0 = 0$$
$$\chi^C(i) = -3 \times 0 = 0 \qquad \chi^H(i) = -3 \times 0 = 0$$
$$\chi^C(\sigma_{xy}) = 1 \times 2 = 2 \qquad \chi^H(\sigma_{xy}) = 1 \times 4 = 4$$
$$\chi^C(\sigma_{xz}) = 1 \times 2 = 2 \qquad \chi^H(\sigma_{xz}) = 1 \times 0 = 0$$
$$\chi^C(\sigma_{yz}) = 1 \times 0 = 0 \qquad \chi^H(\sigma_{yz}) = 1 \times 0 = 0$$

Table 1-19   Contribution per Unshifted Atom

Operation	Factor	Operation	Factor
$C_n{}^k$	$1 + 2\cos(360k/n)$	$S_n{}^k$	$-1 + 2\cos(360k/n)$
$E = C_1{}^k$	3	$\sigma = S_1{}^1$	1
$C_2{}^1$	-1	$i = S_2{}^1$	-3
$C_3{}^1, C_3{}^2$	0	$S_3{}^1, S_3{}^2$	-2
$C_4{}^1, C_4{}^3$	1	$S_4{}^1, S_4{}^3$	-1
$C_6{}^1, C_6{}^5$	2	$S_6{}^1, S_6{}^5$	0

The total number of symmetry operations for group $\mathscr{D}_{2h}$ is 8. For each species of the group, we multiply each χ by the value in the character table under the appropriate operation. Then the sum of these values is divided by the total number of operations, which is 8. The number thus obtained is the number of degrees of freedom belonging to that species.

$$N^C_{A_{1g}} = \tfrac{1}{8}(6 - 2 + 2 + 2) = 1 \qquad N^H_{A_{1g}} = \tfrac{1}{8}(12 + 4) = 2$$
$$N^C_{A_{1u}} = \tfrac{1}{8}(6 - 2 - 2 - 2) = 0 \qquad N^H_{A_{1u}} = \tfrac{1}{8}(12 - 4) = 1$$
$$N^C_{B_{1g}} = \tfrac{1}{8}(6 + 2 + 2 - 2) = 1 \qquad N^H_{B_{1g}} = \tfrac{1}{8}(12 + 4) = 2$$
$$N^C_{B_{1u}} = \tfrac{1}{8}(6 + 2 - 2 + 2) = 1 \qquad N^H_{B_{1u}} = \tfrac{1}{8}(12 - 4) = 1$$
$$N^C_{B_{2g}} = \tfrac{1}{8}(6 + 2 - 2 + 2) = 1 \qquad N^H_{B_{2g}} = \tfrac{1}{8}(12 - 4) = 1$$
$$N^C_{B_{2u}} = \tfrac{1}{8}(6 + 2 + 2 - 2) = 1 \qquad N^H_{B_{2u}} = \tfrac{1}{8}(12 + 4) = 2$$
$$N^C_{B_{3g}} = \tfrac{1}{8}(6 - 2 - 2 - 2) = 0 \qquad N^H_{B_{3g}} = \tfrac{1}{8}(12 - 4) = 1$$
$$N^C_{B_{3u}} = \tfrac{1}{8}(6 - 2 + 2 + 2) = 1 \qquad N^H_{B_{3u}} = \tfrac{1}{8}(12 + 4) = 2$$

We may see from the character table that translational modes belong to the species B_{1u}, B_{2u}, and B_{3u}. These may be subtracted from the number of carbon degrees of freedom to get the number of carbon vibrations. Similarly, the rotational modes belong to the species B_{1g}, B_{2g}, and B_{3g}. Rotation about the x axis (B_{3g}) does not effect the carbons, and so this rotation must be subtracted from the hydrogen degrees of freedom. The other two rotations are subtracted from the carbon degrees of freedom. The number of vibrational modes of each type are then

Symmetry Type	Skeletal Modes	H Modes	Total Modes	Selection Rules
A_{1g}	1	2	3	$R(p)$
A_{1u}	0	1	1	inactive
B_{1g}	0	2	2	$R(dp)$
B_{1u}	0	1	1	IR
B_{2g}	0	1	1	$R(dp)$
B_{2u}	0	2	2	IR
B_{3g}	0	0	0	$R(dp)$
B_{3u}	0	2	2	IR

Having the number of vibrations belonging to each species, we may now try to determine which vibration belongs to each species. For example, a vibration such as

will retain the original symmetry of the compound and therefore will belong to the species A_{1g}. A vibration such as

where a plus sign indicates that the atom is moving toward the reader and a minus sign indicates that the atom is moving away from the reader is still symmetrical with respect to any of the rotational operations but is antisymmetric with respect to inversion through the center of symmetry and reflection through any of the original planes of symmetry. Therefore it is in group A_{1u} (+ signs for the first four operations and − signs for the rest). Also, a vibration such as

will be symmetrical with respect to rotation about the y axis, reflection through the xz plane, and inversion through the center of symmetry. It is antisymmetric with respect to rotation about the x or z axes, and reflection through the xy or yz planes, and therefore belongs to the species B_{2g}.

In a similar fashion, one may consider all twelve possible vibrations, and the results are summarized in Fig. 1-37.

We saw above that there should be a total of $3A_{1g}$ vibrations. All should be Raman active and give polarized lines. (Note that there are no coincidences between the Raman and infrared bands; this is a property of molecules possessing a center of symmetry.) It may be seen from Table 1-18 that there are three Raman lines which fit this description, at 3019, 1623, and 1342 cm^{-1}. The high frequency for the first of these indicates that it is a C-H bond stretching mode which should therefore correspond to ν_1. All the vibrations of ν_3 are coupled, and it is essentially a C-H bending mode, and therefore it should have the lowest frequency, 1342 cm^{-1}. The other one is essentially a C-C double bond stretching mode and therefore corresponds to ν_2 (and has a typical frequency for such a vibration).

The torsional vibration ν_4 is inactive in both the infrared and Raman spectra (although its frequency may be deduced from an overtone in the spectrum). The remaining two Raman lines at 3272 and 943 cm^{-1}, along with some other not observed line, must correspond to ν_5, ν_6, and ν_8. The first of these is a C-H stretching mode and presumably corresponds to the 3272 cm^{-1} line. The bending mode, ν_8 would be expected to have a low frequency because bending force constants are much lower than stretching force constants. Therefore it probably corresponds to the 943 cm^{-1} band.

There are two perpendicular type infrared bands (this refers to the shape of the band), and they must correspond to the species B_{3u}, and ν_{11} and ν_{12}. The first is a stretching vibration and therefore corresponds to the higher frequency 2990 cm^{-1} band. The second is a bending vibration for which the value 1444 cm^{-1} appears reasonable. The remaining parallel bands at 949, 3106 and 955 cm^{-1} must correspond to ν_7, ν_9, and ν_{10}. The second of these is a stretching vibration and therefore leads to the

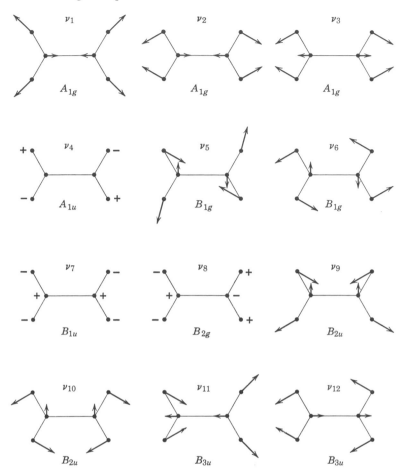

Fig. 1-37. *Normal vibrational modes for ethylene (G. Herzberg, Infrared and Raman Spectra, D. Van Nostrand Co., New York, 1945).*

3106 cm^{-1} band. The other two are bending vibrations for which 949 and 995 cm^{-1} appear to be reasonable values.

By an analysis of the combination and overtone bands, the frequencies corresponding to ν_4 and ν_6 have been determined. The former is 825 cm^{-1} and the latter 1050 cm^{-1}. Thus these vibrations have low frequencies, as might be expected. The torsional mode, such as ν_4, is often the lowest frequency made in a molecule.

Although the foregoing discussion has been somewhat simplified, it illustrates the method used in treating vibrational spectra. It must be noted that if one considers compounds which have degenerate (E or T)

vibrational modes, the number of vibrations corresponding to these modes which are calculated by the method given above must be doubled (E) or tripled (T) in order to get the total number of vibrations.

Finally, it should be noted that the secular equation concerned with the energies of the normal modes of vibration (cf. p. 146) may be factored in accordance with the symmetry properties of the molecule. Vibrations belonging to one symmetry species (such as A_{1g}) will form a submatrix which will not be coupled to one of the other submatrices. Thus, for the case of ethylene, the secular equation may be factored into a 3 × 3 submatrix (A_{1g}), three 2 × 2 submatrices (B_{1g}, B_{2u}, B_{3u}), and three 1 × 1 submatrices (A_{1u}, B_{1u}, B_{2g}).

References

General Theory:
  E. B. Wilson, Jr., J. C. Decius, and P. C. Cross, *Molecular Vibrations*, McGraw-Hill Book Co., New York, 1955.
  A. B. F. Duncan, in *Chemical Applications of Spectroscopy*, Interscience Publishers, New York, 1956, pp. 187 ff.
Empirical Applications to Organic Chemistry:
  L. M. Bellamy, *The Infrared Spectra of Complex Molecules*, John Wiley and Sons, New York, 1954.
  R. N. Jones and C. Sandorfy in *Chemical Applications of Spectroscopy*, Interscience Publishers, New York, 1956, pp. 247 ff.

Problems

1. Give the symmetry classes for each of the following compounds:

2. Determine the number of vibrations of each species of the group $\mathscr{D}_{3h}$ which should be found in cyclopropane. Separate the frequencies into hydrogen and carbon modes, and state whether the vibration should be infrared or Raman active. Give a pictorial representation of each of the vibrational modes.

3. The vibrational spectrum of cyclobutene (R. C. Lord and D. G. Rea, *J. Am. Chem. Soc.* **79**, 2401 (1957) is:

Raman Lines: 3126(*dp*), 3058(*p*), 2933(*p*), 2916(?), 1566(*p*), 1444(*p*), 1429(*dp*), 1276(?), 1182(*p*), 1113(*p*), 986(?), 325(?), 875(*dp*), 850(?).

Infrared Bands: 3126(B), 3058(A), 2933(A), 2955(C), 1566(?), 1444(?), 1429(B), 1288(B), 1210(B), 1182(?), 1113(?), 1074(C), 986(?), 850(B), 846(C), 635(C). [A bands belong to A_1, B to B_1 and C to B_2].

Frequencies deduced from combination bands (Infrared inactive): 2955, 1100, 800, 640.

(a) Determine the number of vibrational modes of each type which the molecule may have. Divide the modes into those which involve predominantly carbons and those which involve predominantly the hydrogens.

(b) Assign the observed vibrational frequencies to the various symmetry species determined in part a.

(c) As far as possible, give a representation of the vibrational modes in a fashion similar to that given in Fig. 1-37 for ethylene.

1-18 Electronic Spectra

INTRODUCTION

The previous discussion of the energy levels of molecules now permits us to consider electronic spectra. The subject of the mechanism of the interaction of compounds with light will not be considered, and the assumption will be made that light will be absorbed only when its energy is equal to the energy of one of the possible electronic transitions.[99a]

Let us first consider the case of benzene. Using the simple molecular orbital method, the orbital energies were found to be

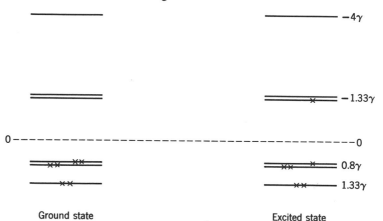

Ground state   Excited state

[99a] A good discussion of this subject will be found in W. Kauzmann, *Quantum Chemistry*, Academic Press, New York, 1957, chs. 15 and 16.

The lowest energy electronic transition would correspond to the excitation of an electron from the highest filled level to the lowest unfilled level. Calling the higher energy bonding orbitals ψ_2 and ψ_3, and the lower energy antibonding orbitals ψ_4 and ψ_5, we can see that there are four ways in which this excitation could occur, and each would lead to the same energy for the transition.

$$\psi_2 \rightarrow \psi_4$$
$$\psi_2 \rightarrow \psi_5$$
$$\psi_2 \rightarrow \psi_4$$
$$\psi_3 \rightarrow \psi_5$$

Thus there should be four excited states having the same energy. However, the ultraviolet spectrum shows that this is not the case and that these energy levels are split as follows.

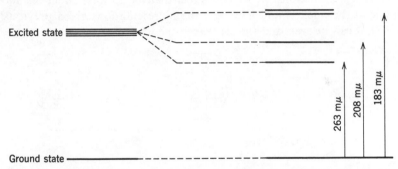

As we have seen previously (p. 54), two or more states having the same energy[100] will interact in the presence of a perturbation to give a new set of levels. In the present case the perturbation is the electron repulsion term. This may be seen as follows. Suppose we had a core of 6 empty p orbitals (as in benzene) and only one electron. Then the levels would be given correctly by the simple molecular orbital method. If we considered an excitation of the electron from ψ_2 or ψ_3 to ψ_4 or ψ_5, we might write the secular determinant

$$\begin{vmatrix} H_{11} - \Delta_{11}E & H_{12} - \Delta_{12}E & H_{13} - \Delta_{13}E & H_{14} - \Delta_{14}E \\ H_{21} - \Delta_{21}E & H_{22} - \Delta_{22}E & H_{23} - \Delta_{23}E & H_{24} - \Delta_{24}E \\ H_{31} - \Delta_{31}E & H_{32} - \Delta_{32}E & H_{33} - \Delta_{33}E & H_{34} - \Delta_{34}E \\ H_{41} - \Delta_{41}E & H_{42} - \Delta_{42}E & H_{43} - \Delta_{43}E & H_{44} - \Delta_{44}E \end{vmatrix} = 0$$

[100] More correctly, any set of states whose energy difference is not large compared to the perturbation energy.

The quantity H_{11} will simply be the transition energy for $\psi_2 \to \psi_4$, H_{22} will be that for $\psi_3 \to \psi_4$, and so on. All the off-diagonal terms would be zero, for there is no way in which the states may interact with each other. The energies will simply be the values of the diagonal elements.

In the case of benzene, with six π-electrons, the terms such as H_{12} will be reasonably large compared to H_{11}, as a result of interelectronic repulsion. According to perturbation theory, we may still use the unperturbed wave functions, and we will write the operator as

$$H = H^{(0)} + H^{(1)}$$

where $H^{(1)}$ is the electron repulsion operator. All the H_{ij} terms are then evaluated using this new operator, and the solution of the secular determinant will give the transition energies. These will be different than the unperturbed transition energies.

Before proceeding, let us examine the symmetry properties of the benzene wave functions. If we remember that the $2p$ wave functions have a node at the nucleus and if we use the representations given previously (p. 77), it can be seen that the six wave functions are

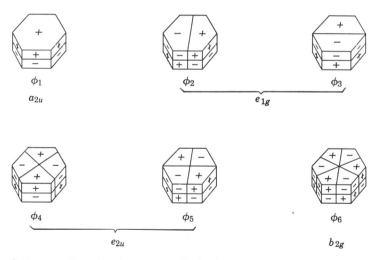

The first wave function is symmetrical with respect to rotation about the principal axis and is in class a. It is antisymmetric with respect to rotation about one of the twofold axes, and therefore it is in class a_2. Finally, it is antisymmetric with respect to inversion through the center of symmetry, and it is therefore in class a_{2u}. The symmetry classes of the others are derived in the same fashion (e representing a doubly degenerate level). The general types of eigenfunctions for the symmetry operators for the $\mathscr{D}_{6h}$ case are shown in Fig. 1-38.

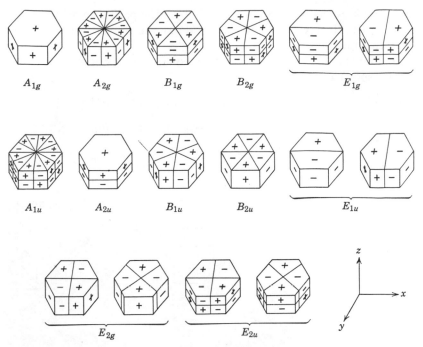

Fig. 1-38. Representation of the eigenfunctions of the symmetry operator for a regular hexagon.

If we place two electrons into any of these orbitals, a totally symmetric state (A_{1g}) results. This can be seen by taking ψ_1 as an example. The first electron will go in with the signs shown, and the second (with opposite spin) will go in with the signs reversed. The total wave function is the product of the wave functions for the two electrons, giving

In a similar fashion, it can be seen that any state multiplied by an A_{1g} state will give a new state having the symmetry properties of the first.

The ground state of benzene has the total wave function

$$\psi_g = |\phi_1{}^+(1)\phi_1{}^-(2)\phi_2{}^+(3)\phi_2{}^-(4)\phi_3{}^+(5)\phi_3{}^-(6)|$$

where the signs give the spin of the electron (α or β) and the numbers in parentheses correspond to electrons. Each of the three molecular orbital wave functions has two electrons and is A_{1g}. The product must then also be A_{1g}. This is a general conclusion about the ground state of most unsaturated hydrocarbons.

The four singlet excited states (having equal numbers of electrons with α and β spins) are[101]

$$\psi_e{}^1 = |\phi_1{}^+(1)\phi_1{}^-(2)\phi_2{}^+(3)\phi_2{}^-(4)\phi_3{}^+(5)\phi_5{}^-(6)|$$

$$\psi_e{}^2 = |\phi_1{}^+(1)\phi_1{}^-(2)\phi_2{}^+(3)\phi_3{}^+(4)\phi_3{}^-(5)\phi_5{}^-(6)|$$

$$\psi_e{}^3 = |\phi_1{}^+(1)\phi_1{}^-(2)\phi_2{}^+(3)\phi_2{}^-(4)\phi_3{}^+(5)\phi_4{}^-(6)|$$

$$\psi_e{}^4 = |\phi_1{}^+(1)\phi_1{}^-(2)\phi_2{}^+(3)\phi_3{}^+(4)\phi_3{}^-(5)\phi_4{}^-(6)|$$

In $\psi_e{}^1$, ϕ_1 and ϕ_2 are filled, and the symmetry is determined by ϕ_3 and ϕ_5

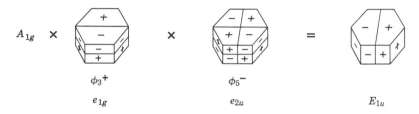

and it is in class E_{1u}. In the same way we may try to determine the symmetry classes of the other total wave functions (see top of page 167). In the last two cases the results obtained using this simple pictorial representation do not have the requisite symmetry properties for a regular hexagon. In these cases it is necessary to use linear combinations of $\psi_e{}^3$ and $\psi_e{}^4$, which are

$$\psi^+ = \frac{1}{\sqrt{2}}(\psi_e{}^3 + \psi_e{}^4)$$

and

$$\psi^- = \frac{1}{\sqrt{2}}(\psi_e{}^3 - \psi_e{}^4)$$

These wave functions have the representations B_{1u} and B_{2u}. Thus there will be two nondegenerate levels and one doubly degenerate level, and there will be three different singlet-singlet transition frequencies (as observed).

---

[101] Properly, one should take into account the wave functions in which the spins of the electrons are interchanged. This is essential if one is to consider triplet states also but will not be necessary in the following discussion, which is concerned only with singlet (electron spin paired) states. For a good discussion, see R. Daudel, R. Lefebvre, and C. Moser, *Quantum Chemistry*, Interscience Publishers, New York, 1959, ch. 19.

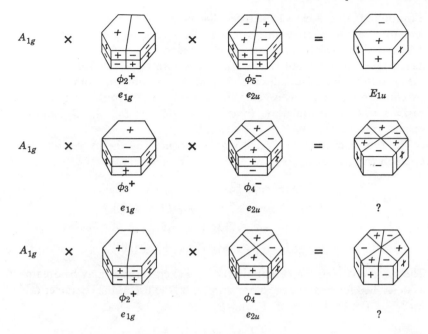

The conclusions for other molecules having $\mathcal{D}_3$ or $\mathcal{D}_6$ symmetry (e.g., coronene and triphenylene) are similar. All will have a degenerate excited state and two other levels which will be described by wave functions like ψ^+ and ψ^-.[102]

Let us now consider naphthalene, which is typical of a large group of aromatic hydrocarbons in class $\mathcal{D}_{2h}$ (i.e., anthracene, naphthacene, pyrene, etc.) The two highest filled and two lowest unfilled wave functions are

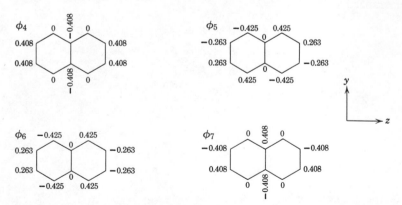

[102] M. J. S. Dewar and H. C. Longuet-Higgins, *Proc. Phys. Soc.*, **67A**, 795 (1954); R. Pariser, *J. Chem. Phys.*, **24**, 250 (1956).

Compounds in this class have a peculiarity in that they have three equivalent principal axes of symmetry. The long axis is usually taken as z. The B species which is symmetric with respect to rotation about the z axis is given the subscript 1, that symmetric with respect to rotation about the y axis is given the subscript 2, and that symmetric with respect to rotation about the x axis is given the subscript 3. With this in mind, it is easily seen that the four wave functions are of class B_{3u}, A_u, B_{2g}, and B_{1g}, respectively.

The four excited states which may be formed by the excitation of an electron from ϕ_4 or ϕ_5 to ϕ_6 or ϕ_7 may be represented as

$$\psi_e{}^1 = |\text{———}\phi_4{}^+(7)\phi_4{}^-(8)\phi_5{}^+(9)\phi_6{}^-(10)|$$
$$\psi_e{}^2 = |\text{———}\phi_4{}^+(7)\phi_5{}^+(8)\phi_5{}^-(9)\phi_6{}^-(10)|$$
$$\psi_e{}^3 = |\text{———}\phi_4{}^+(7)\phi_4{}^-(8)\phi_5{}^+(9)\phi_7{}^-(10)|$$
$$\psi_e{}^4 = |\text{———}\phi_4{}^+(7)\phi_5{}^+(8)\phi_5{}^-(9)\phi_7{}^-(10)|$$

The symmetry class (representation) of the excited states may be obtained as described for benzene or, more simply, by the use of the character table for $\mathscr{D}_{2h}$. The characters of A_u and B_{2g} are

$$A_u(1 \quad 1 \quad 1 \quad 1 \quad -1 \quad -1 \quad -1 \quad -1)$$
$$B_{2g}(1 \quad -1 \quad 1 \quad -1 \quad 1 \quad -1 \quad 1 \quad -1)$$

and the product is $(1 \quad -1 \quad 1 \quad -1 \quad -1 \quad 1 \quad -1 \quad 1)$, which are the characters of B_{2u}. Thus the excited state formed by a transition of an electron from $\phi_5(A_u)$ to $\phi_6(B_{2g})$ is B_{2u}.

One need not go through the operation for each case because the product of multiplying the characters of two representations may be generalized as follows:

$$
\begin{array}{lll}
A \times A = A & B \times B = A & A \times B = B \\
A \times E = E & B \times E = E & \\
A \times F = F & B \times F = F & \\
g \times g = g & {}' \times {}' = {}' & 1 \times 1 = 1 \\
u \times u = g & {}'' \times {}'' = {}' & 2 \times 2 = 1 \\
u \times g = u & {}' \times {}'' = {}'' & 1 \times 2 = 2 \\
\end{array}
$$

$$A \times E_1 = E_1 \qquad A \times E_2 = E_2$$
$$B \times E_1 = E_2 \qquad B \times E_2 = E_1$$

For the B species of $\mathscr{D}_2$ and $\mathscr{D}_{2h}$,

$$B_1 \times B_2 = B_3 \qquad B_2 \times B_3 = B_1 \qquad B_1 \times B_3 = B_2$$

For doubly degenerate cases,

$$E_1 \times E_1 = E_2 \times E_2 = A_1 + A_2 + E_2$$
$$E_1 \times E_2 = B_1 + B_2 + E_1$$

The representations of the four excited states are then

$$\psi_e^1 \quad A_u \times B_{2g} = B_{2u}$$
$$\psi_e^2 \quad B_{3u} \times B_{2g} = B_{1u}$$
$$\psi_e^3 \quad A_u \times B_{1g} = B_{1u}$$
$$\psi_e^4 \quad B_{3u} \times B_{1g} = B_{2u}$$

The transition energies for $\psi_g \rightarrow \psi_e^1$ and for $\psi_g \rightarrow \psi_e^4$ would be expected to be rather different, and as a result the energy levels would be expected to be affected relatively little by interelectronic repulsion. However, the transition energies for $\psi_g \rightarrow \psi_e^2$ and $\psi_g \rightarrow \psi_e^3$ will be quite similar, leading to a strong interaction. The wave functions of the resultant states will be approximately[102]

$$\psi^+ = \frac{1}{\sqrt{2}} (\psi_e^2 + \psi_e^3)$$

$$\psi^- = \frac{1}{\sqrt{2}} (\psi_e^2 - \psi_e^3)$$

The compounds in this group will then have four transitions, which may be described as

$$\psi_g \rightarrow \psi_e^1$$
$$\psi_g \rightarrow \psi_e^+$$
$$\psi_g \rightarrow \psi_e^-$$
$$\psi_g \rightarrow \psi_e^4$$

The case is quite similar to that for benzene, except that for the latter the equivalents of ψ_e^1 and ψ_e^4 give a degenerate level. If we continue this analysis, we find that the above description fits a large number of aromatic compounds. For the larger molecules, the energy levels will be close enough for other transitions to be observed, and thus the complexity of the spectrum increases with the size of the conjugated system.

BAND SHAPES, INTENSITIES, AND POLARIZATIONS

Before comparing the theoretical conclusions with the observed spectra, it is necessary to consider band shapes, intensities, and polarizations. If the transitions were simply as described earlier, we should expect to find a

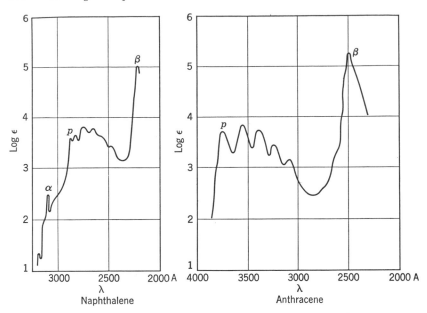

Fig. 1-39. Ultraviolet spectra of naphthalene and anthracene (E. Clar, Aromatische Kohlenwasserstoffe, Springer-Verlag, Berlin, Göttingen, Heidelberg, 1952).

series of relatively sharp lines, as in atomic spectra. The observed spectra are relatively broad and often have considerable structure, as in the spectrum of anthracene (Fig. 1-39).

Let us consider the ground and excited states in somewhat more detail, and for simplicity let us consider a diatomic molecule. The case of a polyatomic molecule is similar, except that only vibrations with the proper symmetry may couple with a given electronic transition. The equilibrium internuclear distance is probably greater in the excited state than in the ground state giving the potential curves shown in Fig. 1-40. In each of the states, the vibrational levels and wave functions are shown.

If the vibrational frequency is reasonably high, essentially all the molecules will be in the vibrational ground state. Excitation can occur to any of the excited state vibrational levels giving a series of lines as shown in Fig. 1-41, all of which will be on the blue (high energy) side of the band origin. In the gas phase each of the lines will be broadened by the rotational fine structure, and in solution they will be broadened by other effects.

We may now consider the band intensity and shape. The beam of light used in exciting the electron from its ground state to the excited state has associated with it an electric and a magnetic field. Since the charge on an

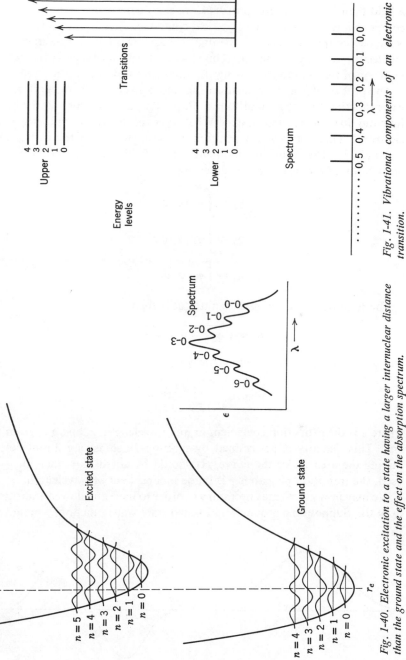

Fig. 1-41. Vibrational components of an electronic transition.

Fig. 1-40. Electronic excitation to a state having a larger internuclear distance than the ground state and the effect on the absorption spectrum.

electron is much more important in determining its interaction with such a field than is its magnetic property, we shall consider only the electrical component of the field. The electrical component may be considered as a wave having the frequency of the light being used. This can interact with an electron only by moving it. Thus there must be a change in the dipole moment of the compound during the transition if it is to be allowed.

The probability of the transition should be given by the integral of the wave function for the ground state multiplied by an operator and the wave function for the excited state. What type of operator will move an electron? This would be the position operator, which for the x direction is simply x. The transition moment length (which is a function of the probability of the transition) is given by

$$\mathbf{q}_x = \int \psi_g x \psi_e \, dx$$

$$\mathbf{q}_y = \int \psi_g y \psi_e \, dy$$

$$\mathbf{q}_z = \int \psi_g z \psi_e \, dz$$

The total transition moment length ($\mathbf{q}$) is then

$$\mathbf{q} = \sqrt{\mathbf{q}_x{}^2 + \mathbf{q}_y{}^2 + \mathbf{q}_z{}^2}$$

and it can be shown to be numerically equal to

$$\mathbf{q} = \sqrt{\frac{\int \epsilon \, d \log \lambda}{1.09 \times 10^{19}}}$$

where ϵ is the extinction coefficient at any wavelength, λ, and $\mathbf{q}$ is given in cm. This quantity is determined by plotting ϵ against $\log \lambda$ and determining the area under the curve. It should be noted that since $\log \lambda$ is used, the transition probability is made independent of wavelength.

We may now ask what is necessary in order to have an allowed transition ($\mathbf{q} \neq 0$). Suppose the ground and excited state wave functions were given by

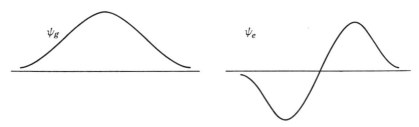

The product of ψ_e and x will be

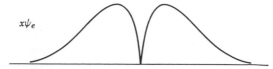

and this multiplied by ψ_g will give a finite area. Thus the requirement is that ψ_e is an odd function (i.e., antisymmetric) with respect to the coordinate being considered. This can be stated in general terms. The representation of the excited state must be that corresponding to translation along the x, y, or z directions (T_x, T_y, or T_z in the character tables), and the transition will be allowed only in that direction.

The foregoing relationship applies also to the vibrational levels. For an allowed transition, the excited state vibrational wave function which gives the largest integrated product with the ground state vibrational wave function gives the highest transition probability.[103] Thus over the coordinate range of the lowest vibrational level of the ground state, the vibrational wave function in the excited state must be an even function. (Note that the total wave function—electronic and vibrational—must have only one odd part which is converted to even by the position operator.)

If we examine Fig. 1-40 again, it can be seen that the maximum overlap of vibrational wave functions occurs for the excitation to the vibrational state $n = 3$. This will have the highest intensity, and all other transitions will be less probable giving the spectrum shown.[104]

Another possibility is that the ground and excited states have the same internuclear distance. In this case (Fig. 1-42) it can be seen that only the excited state vibrational levels with even quantum numbers will give a nonzero integrated product with the ground state vibrational wave function, and thus only transitions to the even-numbered levels are possible. The spectrum which results is also shown in Fig. 1-42. Here, the 0-0 transition has the highest intensity.

Before closing this brief discussion of band shapes, it should be mentioned that the vibrational levels are usually much better resolved at low

[103] This assumes that essentially all the ground state molecules are in the lowest vibrational state. If there is a significant population in the first excited state, then there will also be a transition from this level to an excited state vibrational level which has the proper symmetry.

[104] These conclusions apply only if nuclear motion is negligible during the electronic transition. The large difference in mass between the electron and the nucleus assures that this will be the case. This conclusion about the absence of nuclear motion during an electronic transition is usually known as the Franck-Condon principle: J.Franck, *Trans. Faraday Soc.*, **21**, 536 (1926); E. U. Condon, *Phys. Rev.*, **28**, 1182 (1926); **32**, 858 (1928).

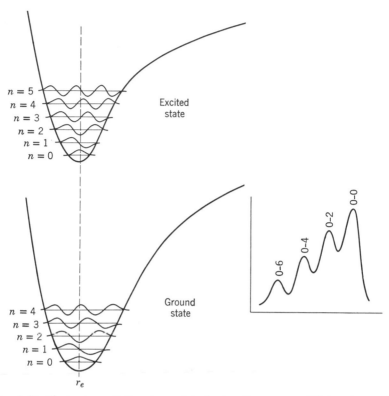

Fig. 1-42. Electronic excitation to a state having the same equilibrium internuclear distance as the ground state and the effect on the spectrum.

temperatures than at room temperature. It is often desirable to obtain spectra in a "glass" formed by cooling the solvent to liquid nitrogen temperature.

THE SPECTRA OF UNSATURATED HYDROCARBONS

The spectra of naphthalene and anthracene (Fig. 1-39) are useful in initiating this discussion. It is evident that there are three different transitions (labeled p, α, and β).[105] We must now relate these transitions to the theoretically deduced excited states.

The excited states of naphthalene had two representations, B_{1u} and B_{2u}. An examination of the character table for $\mathscr{D}_{2h}$ shows that the first

[105] The nomenclature for the bands is that of Clar, *Aromatische Kohlenwasserstoffe*, 2nd ed., Springer-Verlag, Berlin, 1952. A more systematic and generally accepted nomenclature is that of J. Platt, *Ann. Rev. Phys. Chem.*, **10**, 354 (1959).

should lead to an allowed, z polarized transition and the second should lead to an allowed, y polarized transition. The polarization of the bands may often be measured by examining the spectrum of a single properly oriented crystal using plane polarized light. One will observe strong absorption when the plane of polarization of the light coincides with the allowed direction for the transition and a very low absorption at right angles to this.

The polarization of the bands in naphthalene and anthracene has been determined,[106] and it has been found that the p band has a y polarization and thus arises from a transition to a B_{2u} excited state. The α band has been found to have a z polarization, and it is believed that the β band is also polarized in this direction. Thus these transitions arise from excitation to B_{1u} excited states.

The p band is then considered as a transition from $\psi_g \rightarrow \psi_e^1$, and the other B_{2u} state presumably leads to a much higher energy transition. We must now determine which of the pair α, β corresponds to $\psi_g \rightarrow \psi_e^+$ and to $\psi_g \rightarrow \psi_e^-$.

We may recall that

$$\psi_e^+ = \frac{1}{\sqrt{2}}(\psi_e^2 + \psi_e^3)$$

and that ψ_e^2 for naphthalene is the product of a totally symmetric wave function with $\phi_4 \times \phi_6$, and ψ_e^3 is the product of a totally symmetric wave function with $\phi_5 \times \phi_7$. If we take the products of the wave functions at each center, we find

$$\phi_4 \times \phi_6 \qquad\qquad \phi_5 \times \phi_7$$

The transition moment length for $\psi_g \rightarrow \psi_e^+$ in the allowed (z) direction will be

$$\mathbf{q}_z = \frac{1}{\sqrt{2}} \int \psi_g z(\psi_e^2 + \psi_e^3)\, dz$$

Now, ψ_e^2 and ψ_e^3 are both odd functions with respect to the z coordinate, and the transition moment lengths associated with

$$\int \psi_g z \psi_e^2\, dz$$

[106] D. S. McClure, *J. Chem. Phys.*, **22**, 1256, 1668 (1954); J. W. Sidman, *J. Chem. Phys.*, **25**, 115, 122 (1956).

and with

$$\int \psi_g z \psi_e^{\,3}\, dz$$

will reinforce each other, leading to a relatively intense transition. (Note also that transitions in the z direction are normally more intense than those in the y direction, for the transition moment length can never exceed half the length of the molecule in the given direction.)

Table 1-20   Electronic Spectra of Alternate Hydrocarbons[a]

Compound	α Band[b]	p Band	β Band
Benzene	38000	48050	54500
Naphthalene	32000	34600	45400
Anthracene		26400	39000
Naphthacene		21100	36700
Pentancene	24000	17100	32300
Phenanthrene	28300	33000	39400
Chrysene	27500	30200	37200
1,2-Benzanthracene	26700	27300	34800
3,4-Benzphenanthrene	26700	30300	35600
Triphenylene	29200	33200	38900

[a] H. B. Klevens and J. R. Platt, *J. Chem. Phys.*, **17**, 470 (1949).
[b] Frequencies are given in cm^{-1}.

For the transition $\psi_g \rightarrow \psi_e^-$, the transition moment length will be

$$\mathbf{q}_z = \frac{1}{\sqrt{2}} \int \psi_g z (\psi_e^{\,2} - \psi_e^{\,3})\, dz$$

But since $\psi_e^{\,2}$ and $\psi_e^{\,3}$ are very similar wave functions, the component due to the latter will cancel that due to the former, leading to a very weak transition. It is clear that the transition to ψ_e^+ leads to the β band and that the α band arises from a transition to the ψ_e^- wave function.

In the same way the bands for related compounds may be assigned, and some typical values obtained in hexane solution are given in Table 1-20.[107] In the case of the α and p bands, the wavelength given is that for the 0-0 vibrational component. This is the quantity which should be compared in theoretical treatments of spectra. For the β band, however, the vibrational structure is not very evident, and one must be satisfied with taking the wavelength of maximum absorbance.

[107] More extensive lists may be found in ref. 105, and in E. M. Layton, Jr., *J. Mol. Spect.*, **5**, 181 (1960).

We may now compare the experimental spectra with the theoretical deductions. This may be done on two levels—the application of the simple molecular orbital method and the application of methods which include the effects of interelectronic repulsion.

In the simple theory, the p band of alternate hydrocarbons arises from the lowest energy transition from a filled to an unfilled orbital. If compounds of the same type are compared, one might expect that a plot of the observed transition energies against those derived from the molecular orbitals would lead to a linear correlation. It seems reasonable to exclude benzene and other compounds which have degenerate levels and for which the electron repulsion terms might be expected to be different than for the other compounds. The data are presented in Fig. 1-43 and indicate a fairly good linear relationship. The slope of the line is given by

$$\nu(\text{cm}^{-1}) = 9000 + 1.96(\Delta E) \times 10^4$$

The slope is equivalent to $\gamma = 56$ kcal/mole, which is a quite reasonable value.[108]

The α and β band transition energies should be related to the second and third excitation energies between the Hückel molecular orbitals.

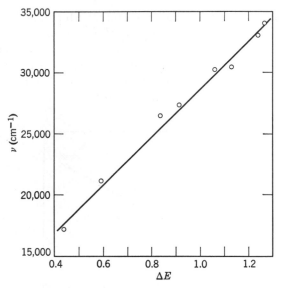

Fig. 1-43. Correlation of the p-band of alternate hydrocarbons with the energy difference between the highest filled level and the lowest unfilled level.

[108] This correlation has been examined with a wider range of compounds by A. Streitwieser, Jr., *Molecular Orbital Theory for Organic Chemists*, John Wiley and Sons, New York, 1961, pp. 220–222, with equivalent results.

Specifically, the observed transition energies should be correlated with the eigenvalues of the determinant

$$\begin{vmatrix} H_{11} - \Delta_{11}E & H_{12} - \Delta_{12}E \\ H_{21} - \Delta_{21}E & H_{22} - \Delta_{22}E \end{vmatrix} = 0$$

where H_{11} is the second excitation energy, H_{22} is the third excitation energy, and $H_{12} = H_{21}$ is the electron repulsion term. Since $E_2 \sim E_3$, we may approximate the two values by their average, which we may call E'. The two energies are then $E' + H_{12}$ and $E' - H_{12}$.

In the simple treatment, we have no way of estimating H_{12}, but we might hope that it is roughly proportional to E'. Then a plot of the observed transition energies against E' would give a linear relationship. This is roughly the case, as can be seen in Fig. 1-44 and 1-45. However, as might be expected, the correlation is not as good as with the p band. The deficiency of the treatment is further indicated by the fact that the slope for neither the α or β bands is as great as for the p bands, although we would expect one to have a slope which is greater as a result of the term H_{12} and that the other should have a smaller slope for the same reason.

The simple molecular orbital method is useful for estimating the location of absorption bands for alternate hydrocarbons using the empirical relationships between band positions and calculated energy levels. It is not satisfactory from a theoretical point of view, and it is quite unsatisfactory for nonalternate hydrocarbons, predicting an α band for azulene at about 380 mμ, whereas it is found at 690 mμ!

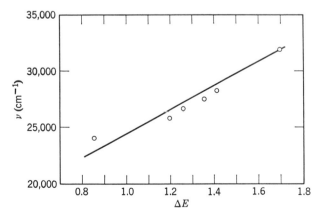

Fig. 1-44. Correlation of the α-band of alternate hydrocarbons with the average of the second and third excitation energies.

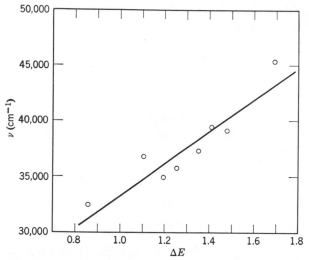

Fig. 1-45. *Correlation of the β-band of alternate hydrocarbons with the average of the second and third excitation energies.*

Let us now consider the more detailed theory, and as the first example, let us calculate the energy of the excited states of ethylene. The two molecular orbital wave functions were

$$\phi_1 = \frac{1}{\sqrt{2}}(a + b)$$

$$\phi_2 = \frac{1}{\sqrt{2}}(a - b)$$

where a and b are the two $2p$ atomic wave functions. From these we can form the ground state and five excited states

$$^1\psi_1 = |\phi_1^+(1)\phi_1^-(2)|$$

$$^1\psi_2 = |\phi_2^+(1)\phi_2^-(2)|$$

$$^1\psi_3 = \frac{1}{\sqrt{2}}|\phi_1^+(1)\phi_2^-(2) + \phi_2^+(1)\phi_1^-(2)|$$

$$^3\psi_4 = \frac{1}{\sqrt{2}}|\phi_1^+(1)\phi_2^-(2) - \phi_2^+(1)\phi_1^-(2)|$$

$$^3\psi_5 = |\phi_1^+(1)\phi_2^+(2)|$$

$$^3\psi_6 = |\phi_1^-(1)\phi_2^-(2)|$$

where the sign indicates the spin of the electron and the numbers in parentheses refer to the two electrons. The last three wave functions lead to the same energy and therefore are a degenerate set, corresponding to the triplet state in which the spins of the electrons are the same.

In order to get the best estimates of the energies, we should allow for mixing of the wave functions (configurational interaction), and we will write

$$\psi = c_1 \psi_1 + c_2 \psi_2 + c_3 \psi_3$$

The triplet state need not be included, for there will be no mixing of singlet and triplet states. The energies and coefficients for the singlet states will be given by the solution of the determinant

$$\begin{vmatrix} H_{11} - \Delta_{11}E & H_{12} - \Delta_{12}E & H_{13} - \Delta_{13}E \\ H_{21} - \Delta_{21}E & H_{22} - \Delta_{22}E & H_{23} - \Delta_{23}E \\ H_{31} - \Delta_{31}E & H_{32} - \Delta_{32}E & H_{33} - \Delta_{33}E \end{vmatrix} = 0$$

To simplify the problem, we may use the Pariser-Parr method,[65] and set $\Delta_{ij} = 0$ $(i \neq j)$. The operator is

$$H = H_1^{\text{core}} + H_2^{\text{core}} + \frac{e^2}{r_{12}}$$

In evaluating the integrals, it will be convenient to define α and β as follows:

$$\int a H^{\text{core}} a \, d\tau = \int b H^{\text{core}} b \, d\tau = \alpha$$

$$\int a H^{\text{core}} b \, d\tau = \beta$$

The integral H_{11} is now given by

$$H_{11} = \frac{2}{2} \int (a + b) H^{\text{core}}(a + b) \, d\tau$$

$$+ \frac{1}{4} \iint (a + b)_1 (a + b)_1 \frac{e^2}{r_{12}} (a + b)_2 (a + b)_2 \, d\tau_1 \, d\tau_2$$

$$= 2\alpha + 2\beta + \frac{1}{2}(11 \mid 11) + \frac{1}{2}(11 \mid 22)$$

The two-electron part was evaluated previously (p. 110), and integrals such as $(12 \mid 12)$ are neglected as a result of setting $\Delta_{ij} = 0$. The integral H_{22} may be evaluated in the same way, but because of the negative sign in the wave function, the β term comes in with a negative sign. Thus

$$H_{22} = 2\alpha - 2\beta + \frac{1}{2}(11 \mid 11) + \frac{1}{2}(11 \mid 22)$$

The interaction integral between ψ_1 and ψ_2 will be given by

$$H_{12} = \frac{2}{2} \int (a+b) H^{\text{core}} (a-b) \, d\tau$$

$$+ \frac{1}{4} \iint (a+b)_1 (a-b)_1 \frac{e^2}{r_{12}} (a+b)_2 (a-b)_2 \, d\tau_1 \, d\tau_2$$

In the first integral all the quantities cancel, and the value is zero. In general, the core integral between two orthogonal orbitals will be zero. If we multiply out the second integral, remembering that subscript 1 refers to electron 1 and subscript 2 refers to electron 2, we obtain

$$\frac{1}{4} \left(\iint a_1{}^2 \frac{e^2}{r_{12}} a_2{}^2 \, d\tau_1 \, d\tau_2 + \iint b_1{}^2 \frac{e^2}{r_{12}} b_2{}^2 \, d\tau_1 \, d\tau_2 \right.$$

$$\left. - \iint a_1{}^2 \frac{e^2}{r_{12}} b_2{}^2 \, d\tau_1 \, d\tau_2 - \iint b_1{}^2 \frac{e^2}{r_{12}} a_2{}^2 \, d\tau_1 \, d\tau_2 \right)$$

In terms of the symbolism given before, this is

$$\tfrac{1}{4}[2(11\,|\,11) - 2(11\,|\,22)] = H_{12}$$

The simple approach given above for the evaluation of H_{11}, H_{22} and H_{12} is not applicable for the evaluation of the other integrals because the spin of the electron must be taken into account. Each wave function must be antisymmetric, and this may be ensured by writing them in the form of a determinant (usually known as a Slater determinant). Thus for ψ_1 we should have written

$$\psi_1 = \frac{1}{\sqrt{N}} \begin{vmatrix} (\phi_1 \alpha)^1 & (\alpha_1 \beta)^1 \\ (\phi_1 \alpha)^2 & (\phi_1 \beta)^2 \end{vmatrix}$$

where α and β are the spin quantum numbers, and the superscripts refer to the two electrons.

If the integrals are evaluated using the properly written wave functions, we find that the one electron part gives only 2α, and that the two electron part gives $(11\,|\,11)$. In order to make a later substitution we may write the integral in the form:

$$H_{33} = 2\alpha + \tfrac{1}{2}[(11\,|\,11) + (11\,|\,22)] + \tfrac{1}{2}[(11\,|\,11) - (11\,|\,22)]$$

In the same way, the interaction integral H_{13} may be shown to be zero.[109]

[109] It is generally true that the interaction integral between the ground state and a singly excited state will be zero if SCF orbitals are used: L. Brillouin, *Les champs Self Consistents de Hartree et de Fock*, Hermann et Cie., Paris, 1934, p. 19.

If we make the following abbreviations:

$$J = \tfrac{1}{2}[(11 \mid 11) + (11 \mid 22)]$$
$$K = \tfrac{1}{2}[(11 \mid 11) - (11 \mid 22)]$$

the determinant becomes

$$\begin{vmatrix} 2\alpha + 2\beta + J - E & K & 0 \\ K & 2\alpha - 2\beta + J - E & 0 \\ 0 & 0 & 2\alpha + J + K - E \end{vmatrix} = 0$$

and the solutions are

$$E_1 = 2\alpha + J + \sqrt{4\beta^2 + K^2}$$
$$E_2 = 2\alpha + J - \sqrt{4\beta^2 + K^2}$$
$$E_3 = 2\alpha + J + K$$

Using the values of the integrals suggested by Pariser and Parr[65] ($\beta = 2.92$ ev, $(11 \mid 11) = 10.53$, $(11 \mid 22) = 7.38$), we find that configurational interaction has stabilized the ground state by 0.2 ev (4.6 kcal/mole) and that the lowest singlet-singlet transition should occur at 7.60 ev (163 mμ), which is the observed value. This should not be surprising, for the value of β was taken as that which would correctly give the energy of this transition. However, the value is very close to the theoretical value. More important is the location of the triplet state. If we evaluate H_{44} using the first of the three wave functions given, we find the same result as for H_{33}, except that the sign of K is reversed.[110] Thus

$$H_{44} = 2\alpha + J - K = E_4$$

The excitation energy from the ground state to the triplet state is calculated to be 4.5 ev compared to an observed value of 4.6 ev.[111] This is a major improvement over the simple molecular orbital treatment, which places the singlet and triplet levels at the same energy.

The application of this method to the study of larger molecules requires the formulation of the wave functions as sums of Slater determinants in order to take the spin functions properly into account.[112] It does not

[110] The evaluation of the integrals for ethylene using antisymmetrized wave functions is discussed by R. G. Parr and B. Crawford, *J. Chem. Phys.*, **16**, 526 (1948); R. G. Parr and R. Pariser, *J. Chem. Phys.*, **23**, 711 (1955); and R. Daudel, R. Lefebvre and C. Moser, *Quantum Chemistry*, Interscience Publishers, New York, 1959, ch. 19.
[111] D. F. Evans, *J. Chem. Soc.*, 1735 (1960).
[112] A good discussion of this subject and the application to the spectra of alternate hydrocarbons is found in R. Pariser, *J. Chem. Phys.*, **24**, 250 (1956).

seem profitable to go into a detailed discussion of this subject here, and only some typical results will be presented.

The stabilization of the ground state of the hydrocarbons by configurational interaction is small if SCF orbitals are used and will be zero if only singly excited states are considered. If configurational interaction among the singly excited states is included in the calculation of the energy of these states for benzene (as must be done because of the degeneracy of the levels), the Pariser-Parr treatment gives the energies listed in Table 1-21.[112] It can be seen that the values are in good accord with the experimental ones and give the proper splitting of the levels. This is in marked contrast to the results of the simple molecular orbital treatment, in which all of the singlet and triplet transitions were given the same energy.

Table 1-21   Energies of Excited States of Benzene

State	Calcd. Energy (ev)	Obs. Energy (ev)
$^1A_{1g}$	(0.000)	(0.000)
$^1B_{2u}$	4.71	4.71
$^1B_{1u}$	5.96	5.96
$^1E_{1u}$	6.55	6.76
$^3B_{1u}$	3.59	3.59

One may well ask, "Are good results obtained because one is using a multiparameter equation and has arbitrarily adjusted the parameters to give a fit, or is this a genuinely useful method employing reasonable values of the integrals?" For benzene, the energy terms depend on the following integrals, β, $(11 \mid 11)$, $(11 \mid 22)$, $(11 \mid 33)$, and $(11 \mid 44)$. The last two were taken as the theoretical values. The integral $(11 \mid 11)$ was taken as the difference between the ionization potential and the electron affinity of the carbon atom using a $2p$ orbital. The integral $(11 \mid 22)$ was adjusted downward from its theoretical value to be in accord with $(11 \mid 11)$ and $(11 \mid 33)$. Finally, β was chosen as the value which gave a good fit to the spectrum. The value used was -2.371 ev, whereas the theoretical value is -2.477 ev. It can be seen that all the numbers have reasonable values.

The method has been applied to a number of benzenoid alternate hydrocarbons, and using the same values of the integrals, the spectra have been fit quite well. More important, the method has been applied to a non-alternate hydrocarbon, azulene, giving the results listed in Table 1-22.[113] Although the integrals were those derived from the benzene spectrum, a very good fit of the observed spectrum was obtained. This indicates the general usefulness and validity of the procedure.

[113] R. Pariser, *J. Chem. Phys.*, **25**, 1112 (1956).

It should be mentioned that Pople's modification of the SCF treatment leads to a fairly simple formulation for the main transitions of the alternate hydrocarbons.[114] For these compounds, three features of the simple

Table 1-22   Energies of Excited States of Azulene

State	Calcd. Energy (ev)	Obs. Energy (ev)
$^1A_1$	(0.000)	(0.000)
$^1B_1$	1.732	1.79
$^1A_1$	3.084	3.50
$^1B_1$	4.112	4.05 (?)
$^1A_1$	4.692	4.52
$^1B_1$	5.604	5.24

molecular orbital treatment (neglecting overlap) carry over to the SCF method.

1. The electron density at each carbon is unity.
2. The eigenvalues of the F matrix (E_i) are symmetrically arranged about the value $\frac{1}{2}(11 \mid 11)$. Thus if $\frac{1}{2}(11 \mid 11) + \epsilon$ is an eigenvalue, so is $\frac{1}{2}(11 \mid 11) - \epsilon$.
3. The coefficients of the orbitals are paired.

If alternate carbons are starred, the pair of molecular orbitals with energies $\frac{1}{2}(11 \mid 11) \pm \epsilon$ can be written

$$\psi^+ = \sum{}^* c_i \phi_i + \sum{}^0 c_i \phi_i$$
$$\psi^- = \sum{}^* c_i \phi_i - \sum{}^0 c_i \phi_i$$

Here the first term in the summation is over all starred atoms, and the second summation is over all unstarred atoms.

If the highest filled orbital is designated as ψ_m, the wave functions for the two highest filled and two lowest unfilled orbitals are

$$\psi_{m-1} = \sum{}^* b_i \phi_i + \sum{}^0 b_i \phi_i$$
$$\psi_m = \sum{}^* a_i \phi_i + \sum{}^0 a_i \phi_i$$
$$\psi_{m+1} = \sum{}^* a_i \phi_i - \sum{}^0 a_i \phi_i$$
$$\psi_{m+2} = \sum{}^* b_i \phi_i - \sum{}^0 b_i \phi_i$$

For the compounds having $\mathcal{D}_2$ or lower symmetry, the excited states were

[114] J. A. Pople, *Proc. Phys. Soc.*, **A68**, 81 (1955).

formed by the following transitions:

$$p \quad \psi_m \rightarrow \psi_{m+1}$$

$$\beta' \quad \psi_{m+1} \rightarrow \psi_{m+2}$$

$$\alpha \quad \frac{1}{\sqrt{2}} [(\psi_{m-1} \rightarrow \psi_{m+1}) - (\psi_m \rightarrow \psi_{m+2})]$$

$$\beta \quad \frac{1}{\sqrt{2}} [(\psi_{m-1} \rightarrow \psi_{m+1}) + (\psi_m \rightarrow \psi_{m+2})]$$

The transition energies may now be given an explicit formulation as

p band

$$\Delta E = E_{m+1} - E_m + \left(\sum_i^* \sum_j^* + \sum_i^0 \sum_j^0 - 6 \sum_i^* \sum_j^0 \right) a_i^2 a_j^2 (ii \mid jj)$$

β′ band

$$\Delta E = E_{m+2} - E_{m-1} + \left(\sum_i^* \sum_j^* + \sum_i^0 \sum_j^0 - 6 \sum_i^* \sum_j^0 \right) b_i^2 b_j^2 (ii \mid jj)$$

α band

$$\Delta E = E_{m+1} - E_{m-1} - \sum_{ij} a_i^2 b_j^2 (ii \mid jj)$$

$$+ \left(\sum_i^* \sum_j^* + \sum_i^0 \sum_j^0 + 2 \sum_i^* \sum_j^0 \right) a_i b_i a_j b_j (ii \mid jj)$$

β band

$$\Delta E = E_{m+1} - E_{m-1} - \sum_{ij} a_i^2 b_j^2 (ii \mid jj)$$

$$+ \left(3 \sum_i^* \sum_j^* + 3 \sum_i^0 \sum_j^0 - 10 \sum_i^* \sum_j^0 \right) a_i b_i a_j b_j (ii \mid jj)$$

The values obtained for naphthalene are summarized in Table 1-23. It can be seen that there is fairly good agreement with all the bands except β'. It might be expected that a larger degree of configurational interaction might improve the results, and this is suggested by the values in the second column in Table 1-23. However, the values of the integrals used in the two

Table 1-23 Energies of Excited States of Naphthalene

State	Calcd. Freq.[a]	Calcd. Freq.[b]	Obs. Freq.
α	35500	32500	32000
p	37500	36300	34500
β	49500	48000	45500
β′	50000	51000	60000

[a] J. A. Pople, *Proc. Phys. Soc.*, **68A**, 81 (1955).
[b] R. Pariser, *J. Chem. Phys.*, **24**, 250 (1956).

cases were somewhat different, and we cannot compare them directly. The results given above indicate that the semiempirical approaches are capable of giving a good account of the shifts in spectral bands with changes in structure. It remains to provide a nonempirical procedure which will do as well. The main feature of such a procedure will be the proper evaluation of the electron repulsion integrals, and progress is being made in this direction.[115]

TYPES OF ELECTRONIC EXCITATION

Up until now we have considered only the excitation of an electron from one π-molecular orbital to another (commonly referred to as an $\pi \rightarrow \pi^*$ transition). Here there are two classes, those involving a singlet excited state and those involving a triplet excited state. Only the former gives bands of reasonable intensity; the excitation to a triplet state is formally forbidden and gives a very weak band. This does not mean that the triplet excited state is unimportant, for many singlet excited states decay to a lower energy triplet state. The latter has a reasonably long life time because the transition to the ground state is relatively improbable. Thus many photochemical reactions appear to involve the triplet state.[116]

Another important type of electronic transition involves the excitation of an electron of an unshared pair (say on nitrogen or oxygen) to an antibonding π-molecular orbital. This type of transition is a common feature of the spectra of unsaturated amines (such as pyridine), and of ketones and aldehydes, [117] and is referred to as an $n \rightarrow \pi^*$ transition.

It is often of importance to distinguish between the two types of transitions. For example, before the existence of $n \rightarrow \pi^*$ transitions was recognized, the low energy ($\sim$300 mμ) transition of the azines was attributed to a $\pi \rightarrow \pi^*$ transition, and this led to erroneous values of delocalization energies based on the Valence-Bond treatment. Similarly, much work has been done on the effect of small rings and other groups on the low energy ($\sim$260 mμ) transition of ketones, whereas a study of the higher energy $\pi \rightarrow \pi^*$ transition appears to be more valuable.[118] It is sometimes difficult to distinguish between the two types of transitions. The main tools are solvent effect, polarization of the bands, and the band intensities. The solvent effect will be discussed below. It is easily seen that

[115] See M. J. S. Dewar and N. L. Hojvat, *J. Chem. Phys.*, **34**, 1232 (1961); L. C. Snyder and R. G. Parr, *J. Chem. Phys.*, **34**, 1661 (1961).
[116] See G. S. Hammond, W. P. Baker, and W. M. Moore, *J. Am. Chem. Soc.*, **83**, 2795 (1961); H. E. Zimmerman and D. I. Schuster, *J. Am. Chem. Soc.*, **83**, 4486 (1961).
[117] A good review of this subject has been given by J. W. Sidman, *Chem. Revs.*, **58**, 689 (1958); see M. Kasha, *Discussions Faraday Soc.*, **9**, 14 (1950).
[118] E. M. Kosower, *J. Am. Chem. Soc.*, **80**, 3261 (1958).

the $n \rightarrow \pi^*$ transition will have a low intensity. The unshared pair may be considered to have sp^2 hybridization. The s component is an even function, and the integral of this times two odd functions (the coordinate and the π-wave function in the direction perpendicular to the δ bonds):

$$q = \int \psi_{2s} x \psi_\pi \, d\tau$$

will be nonzero. However, it will be small, for the distance from the center of the $2s$ orbital to the center of one of the π lobes is small. The p component of the unshared pair will give zero in the corresponding integral, since it is antisymmetric with respect to the direction of its major axis. Thus the total transition moment length will be one third (the contribution of the s part to the orbital) of the above integral, or about 0.2 Å. It can be seen that the transition is allowed only in the direction perpendicular to the σ framework of the molecule, and thus the $n–\pi^*$ transition is allowed in a direction different than the $\pi \rightarrow \pi^*$ transitions.

Finally, it should be emphasized that in the comparison of the spectra of related compounds, it is essential to compare the same transition for all compounds. One cannot always assume that the bands will appear in the same order from compound to compound. For example, the band in pentacene which corresponds to the 260 mμ band of benzene is at 417 mμ, whereas the band which corresponds to the 208 mμ band of benzene is at 580 mμ.

SOLVENT EFFECTS ON ELECTRONIC TRANSITIONS

In considering the change in wavelength of absorption in going from gas phase to a solution, one must consider both the change in excitation energy which is due to the dielectric constant of the solvent and specific solvation effects, such as hydrogen bonding. Aniline shows both effects clearly, as seen in the data of Table 1-24.

The band which is being considered may be roughly represented as resulting from the transition

The dipolar excited state will be stabilized by an increase in the dielectric constant more than the nonpolar ground state.[119] Thus, as the dielectric

[119] See N. S. Bayliss and E. G. McRae, *J. Phys. Chem.*, **58**, 1002 (1954).

constant of the solvent increases, the excitation energy should be reduced, leading to a red shift. This is observed in going from the gas phase to a solvent and also in going from a nonpolar solvent to a relatively polar one, such as acetonitrile or dioxane.

In considering the effect of such a solvent as ethanol or water, we must bear in mind the Franck-Condon principle[120] that electronic excitations occur much faster that the motion of nuclei. Thus during a spectral transition neither the positions of the nuclei in the compound nor the

Table 1-24 Effect of Solvent on the Ultraviolet Absorption Spectrum of Aniline[a]

Solvent	λ_{max} (mμ)
Gas phase	229.5
Heptane	234.0
Cyclohexane	234.5
Acetonitrile	238.5
Dioxane	240.0
Ethanol	235.0
Methanol	233.5
Water	229.5

[a] W. M. Schubert and J. M. Craven, *J. Am. Chem. Soc.*, **82**, 1357 (1960).

positions of the solvent molecules are changed. In ethanol, the aniline will be hydrogen bonded to the solvent protons, and this will lower the energy of the ground state as compared to the molecule in the vapor phase. However, hydrogen bonding will be less important in the excited state because of the positive charge on nitrogen. Some stabilization could be effected if the solvent molecules could move so as to be in a more favorable orientation for dipole-dipole interaction with the excited molecule. This is, however, not possible in the time required for the electronic transition. Dissolving aniline in ethanol will then lower the energy of the ground state more than that of the excited state, with a consequent increase in excitation energy and a blue shift. It can be seen from Table 1-24 that the red shift caused by the dielectric constant effect for water is just canceled by the blue shift due to the change in hydrogen bonding, and aniline has essentially the same absorption maximum in water as it has in the gas phase.

[120] J. Franck, *Trans. Faraday Soc.*, **21**, 536 (1926); E. U. Condon, *Phys. Rev.*, **28**, 1182 (1926); **32**, 858 (1928).

It is interesting to compare the effects observed with aniline with those for nitrobenzene. The data for the latter are given in Table 1-25. The transition may be represented as

in which the excited state is more polar than the ground state. Accordingly, it is observed that the excitation energy decreases in going from the gas

Table 1-25   Effect of Solvent on the
Ultraviolet Absorption
Spectrum of Nitrobenzene[a]

Solvent	λ_{max} (mμ)
Gas phase	239.0
i-Pentane	250.1
Cyclohexane	253.0
t-Butyl chloride	257.1
Acetonitrile	261.0
t-Butyl alcohol	257.7
95% Ethanol	259.7
Water	267.5

[a] W. M. Schubert and J. Robins, *J. Am. Chem. Soc.*, **80**, 559 (1958).

phase to a solvent and in going from a nonpolar solvent to a more polar one.

In this case hydrogen bonding would be expected to lower the energy of the excited state, for the molecule in the ground state will be hydrogen bonded to the protons of the solvent via the oxygens of the nitro group. In the excited state, the hydrogen bonding should become more important, for the negative charge on oxygen is increased over that in the ground state. Thus hydrogen bonding should decrease the energy of the excited state more than that of the ground state, leading to a red shift.

It might be mentioned that the excited state derived from an $n \rightarrow \pi^*$ transition has a considerable dipole, since an electron was taken from an oxygen or nitrogen (usually) and placed in a π orbital. As a result of the positive charge placed on the heteroatom, the absorption band arising from such a transition always shows a strong blue shift on going from a non-hydrogen bonding solvent to an alcohol or water. The shift is one of the criteria for this type of transition, although, as we have seen, aniline also gives this type of a shift for its $\pi \to \pi^*$ transition.

1-19 Nuclear Magnetic Resonance Spectra

The nuclear magnetic resonance spectrum arises from transitions between different energy states of nuclei. These transitions may be treated in a quantitative fashion using the ideas about quantum chemistry which we have developed, and since such a treatment is necessary for even a simple interpretation of the spectrum, it seems appropriate to consider this in some detail here. The case of the proton will be considered throughout, both for convenience and because the proton spectrum is by far the most commonly studied. The procedure is equally applicable to other nuclei if the appropriate values of the spin quantum number are used.

In the absence of an external magnetic field, a proton will have only one energy state. However, if a magnetic field is applied, it may assume two states—one in which its angular momentum vector lies in the direction of the applied field and the other in which it is opposed to the field. A classical analogy is that of a coil through which a current flows, leading to a magnetic field. In the absence of an external field, the energy of the coil is independent of its orientation. However, if an external field is applied, the magnetic field of the coil will be lined up with the external field in the lowest energy state and opposed to it in the highest energy state. The coil, of course, may have any intermediate orientation, but the proton will be subject to quantum restrictions and will have only certain permitted values. These values differ by one in the magnetic quantum number. Thus in the case of a proton and other nuclei having a spin quantum number of $\frac{1}{2}$, the magnetic quantum number may be $+\frac{1}{2}$ or $-\frac{1}{2}$. Similarly, with nuclei having spin quantum number of 1, the latter may assume values of $+1$, 0, and -1.

Let us first consider the case of a single proton in a magnetic field applied in the z direction. The spin wave function may be either α or β, the former corresponding to alignment with the field and the latter to alignment opposed to the external field. These two wave functions are normalized and orthogonal. The energy for either state will be given as usual by

$$E = \int \psi H \psi \, d\tau$$

and if E is to be obtained in units of cycles per second, the operator is

$$H = \frac{1}{2\pi} \sum_i \gamma \mathbf{H}_i I_z(i)$$

where γ is the magnetogyric ratio for a proton, $\mathbf{H}_i$ is the magnetic field at the ith proton, and I_z is the z component of the spin operator. This may be considered to be an empirically determined operator in which γ is a proportionality constant. For the present it may simply be noted that I_z operating on the wave function α gives $+\frac{1}{2}\alpha$, and operating on β it gives $-\frac{1}{2}\beta$.

We may now obtain the values of the energy for each of the two spin wave functions:

$$E_1 = \frac{1}{2\pi} \int \alpha(\gamma \mathbf{H} I_z)\alpha \, d\tau = \frac{1}{2 \cdot 2\pi} \gamma \mathbf{H} \int \alpha\alpha \, d\tau = \frac{1}{2 \cdot 2\pi} \gamma \mathbf{H}$$

$$E_2 = \frac{1}{2\pi} \int \beta(\gamma \mathbf{H} I_z)\beta \, d\tau = -\frac{1}{2 \cdot 2\pi} \gamma \mathbf{H} \int \beta\beta \, d\tau = -\frac{1}{2 \cdot 2\pi} \gamma \mathbf{H}$$

If we call $\dfrac{1}{2\pi} \gamma \mathbf{H}_i = \nu_i$, then the two energies are simply $\frac{1}{2}\nu$ and $-\frac{1}{2}\nu$ (the subscript i being dropped, for there is only one proton). A transition between the two states will then require an energy of ν. This energy is supplied by the radio frequency generator via a coil mounted perpendicular to the applied field, and in which the sample is placed. Absorption of rf power will occur when the radio frequency is equal to ν.

The case of two protons may now be considered. For convenience in presentation, the case in which there is no interaction between the protons will be considered first. There are four possible combinations of the spin wave functions on the two nuclei. They are

$$\psi_1 = \alpha(1)\alpha(2)$$
$$\psi_2 = \alpha(1)\beta(2)$$
$$\psi_3 = \beta(1)\alpha(2)$$
$$\psi_4 = \beta(1)\beta(2)$$

where the numbers in parentheses refer to the nucleus on which the given spin wave function is found. These wave functions are commonly abbreviated as $\alpha\alpha$, $\alpha\beta$, $\beta\alpha$, and $\beta\beta$. The energy for the first state is given by

$$E_1 = \frac{1}{2\pi} \int \alpha\alpha[\gamma \mathbf{H}_1 I_z(1) + \gamma \mathbf{H}_2 I_z(2)]\alpha\alpha \, d\tau$$

$$= \frac{1}{2\pi} \left\{ \int \alpha\alpha[\gamma \mathbf{H}_1 I_z(1)]\alpha\alpha \, d\tau + \int \alpha\alpha[\gamma \mathbf{H}_2 I_z(2)]\alpha\alpha \, d\tau \right\}$$

The operator $I_z(1)$ operating on the wave function $\alpha(1)\alpha(2)$ will give $+\frac{1}{2}\alpha\alpha$, for it affects only the wave function on the nucleus with which it is associated. Remembering that the wave functions are normalized and orthogonal, and the definition of ν_i, the energy becomes

$$E_1 = \frac{1}{2\pi}\left\{\tfrac{1}{2}\gamma H_1 \int (\alpha\alpha)(\alpha\alpha)\,d\tau + \tfrac{1}{2}\gamma H_2 \int (\alpha\alpha)(\alpha\alpha)\,d\tau\right\} = \tfrac{1}{2}(\nu_1 + \nu_2)$$

In the same way, the other wave functions are evaluated to be

$$E_2 = \frac{1}{2\pi}\int \alpha\beta[\gamma H_1 I_z(1) + \gamma H_2 I_z(2)]\alpha\beta\,d\tau = \tfrac{1}{2}(\nu_1 - \nu_2)$$

$$E_3 = \frac{1}{2\pi}\int \beta\alpha[\gamma H_1 I_z(1) + \gamma H_2 I_z(2)]\beta\alpha\,d\tau = \tfrac{1}{2}(-\nu_1 + \nu_2)$$

$$E_4 = \frac{1}{2\pi}\int \beta\beta[\gamma H_1 I_z(1) + \gamma H_2 I_z(2)]\beta\beta\,d\tau = \tfrac{1}{2}(-\nu_1 - \nu_2)$$

It can be shown that transitions may occur only between states having a net change of one spin. Thus the possible transitions are from states $2 \rightarrow 1$, $3 \rightarrow 1$, $4 \rightarrow 2$, and $4 \rightarrow 3$. The energies for these transitions will be

$$
\begin{array}{ll}
2 \rightarrow 1 & \Delta E = \nu_2 \\
3 \rightarrow 1 & \Delta E = \nu_1 \\
4 \rightarrow 2 & \Delta E = \nu_1 \\
4 \rightarrow 3 & \Delta E = \nu_2
\end{array}
$$

and thus two resonance bands should be seen, one at a frequency ν_1 and the other at a frequency ν_2.

On the basis of what has been said thus far, it is not apparent why ν_1 is not equal to ν_2. They should be equal if $H_1 = H_2$. It must be noted that the operator contained the magnitude of the field at the proton in question. If there were a system of bare protons, the field would be equal to the applied field. However, in molecules, the protons may be magnetically shielded by the associated electrons, and thus the local field is not equal to the applied field. Further, the shielding is not the same for all protons. It is this difference in shielding which leads to chemical shifts between differently situated nuclei in molecules.

The observed spectra are usually not as simple as would be expected on the basis of the foregoing treatment. For example, the spectrum of a two-spin case, such as the β-chloroacrylate ion, is usually found to have four bands rather than the expected two. For the case in which the difference between ν_1 and ν_2 is large compared to the splitting of the bands,

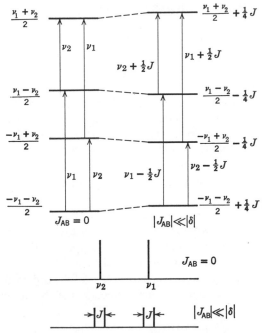

Fig. 1-46. Nuclear magnetic resonance spectrum for the simple AB *case.*

the effect may be considered in a simple, qualitative way. Consider the four possible wave functions again, symbolizing α by $\uparrow$ and β by $\downarrow$.

$$\begin{array}{cccc} \uparrow\uparrow & \uparrow\downarrow & \downarrow\uparrow & \downarrow\downarrow \\ 1 & 2 & 3 & 4 \end{array}$$

In the absence of an interaction between the protons, the energy levels will be as shown on the left of Fig. 1-46. If the field direction is from the bottom of the page to the top, the state corresponding to wave function 1 will have the lowest energy, that corresponding to wave function 4 will have the highest energy, for the magnetic moments will be opposed to the field, and the other two states will give intermediate energies, for one magnetic moment is in the direction of the field and the other is opposed to it. If the two nuclei were identical, levels 2 and 3 would coalesce into one, for it would make no difference which nucleus was aligned with the field. However, with two nuclei having different chemical shifts, one of the two arrangements will be more favorable than the other and the levels will shift up and down from the levels they would have if they were identical.

If the nuclei were coupled in such a way that they could "feel" each other's spin, then it is apparent that the arrangements $\uparrow\uparrow$ and $\downarrow\downarrow$ would be less favorable than in the absence of such coupling. Similarly, the arrangements ↑↓ and ↓↑ would be more favorable than before. Therefore the levels will shift as shown in the right of Fig. 1-46. There will result four transitions, the spacing within the band due to a given proton being twice the change in energy for any one of the states. For the simple case we have been considering here, it is found in general that the number of components in a given band is equal to the number of adjacent protons of a given type plus one. Thus for the ethoxy group, the methyl band will be split into three components and the methylene will be split into four components. If there is more than one type of adjacent proton, the splittings due to each must be considered separately.

When the bands associated with one proton are relatively far from the bands associated with the other, it is found that the difference between the centers of the bands is directly proportional to the magnitude of the magnetic field used, whereas the spacing of the components of each band remains constant (Fig. 1-47). It is thus apparent that the coupling constant, J, is independent of the applied field.

This is a case of a small perturbation (J is of the order of 0 to 15 cycles/sec for most cases) on a relatively large effect (ν is of the order of 30 to 60 mc), and therefore it may be treated with high accuracy using the perturbation method. Thus we shall write the operator as

$$H = H^{(0)} + H^{(1)}$$

where $H^{(0)}$ is the part of the operator for which the true wave functions

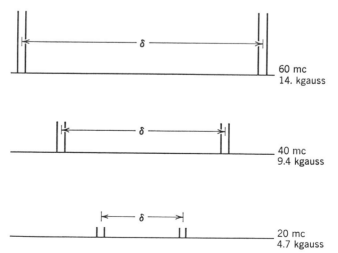

Fig. 1-47. Effect of the magnitude of the applied field on the appearance of the nmr spectrum.

are known, and $H^{(1)}$ is the perturbation operator. The operator written previously is, of course, $H^{(0)}$, and it has been found empirically that the perturbation operator is given by

$$H^{(1)} = \sum_{i<j} J_{i,j} I(i) \cdot I(j)$$

Under the influence of the perturbation operator, the wave functions may mix, and therefore a variation method treatment in which the appropriate secular equation is set up and solved must be used.

For any system of n protons, the number of states will be 2^n. Thus for a relatively simple case, such as that of three protons, there will be eight wave functions which must be considered, and an 8 by 8 determinant must be solved. Fortunately, the secular determinant is easily factored into smaller determinants, and this factoring will now be considered. Let us define a function, F_z, which will be the sum of the spin eigenvalues of the operator I_z for the given wave function. Thus this is simply the sum of $+\frac{1}{2}$ for each α and $-\frac{1}{2}$ for each β in a given wave function. For example, the possible wave functions for the three proton case and the associated values of F_z are

$$\psi_1 = \alpha\alpha\alpha \qquad F_z = +\tfrac{3}{2}$$
$$\psi_2 = \alpha\alpha\beta \qquad = +\tfrac{1}{2}$$
$$\psi_3 = \alpha\beta\alpha \qquad = +\tfrac{1}{2}$$
$$\psi_4 = \beta\alpha\alpha \qquad = +\tfrac{1}{2}$$
$$\psi_5 = \beta\beta\alpha \qquad = -\tfrac{1}{2}$$
$$\psi_6 = \beta\alpha\beta \qquad = -\tfrac{1}{2}$$
$$\psi_7 = \alpha\beta\beta \qquad = -\tfrac{1}{2}$$
$$\psi_8 = \beta\beta\beta \qquad = -\tfrac{3}{2}$$

It can be shown (cf., problem 1) that the only wave functions which mix are those with the same value of F_z. Thus the original 8 by 8 determinant may be factored into two 1 by 1 determinants (using ψ_1 and ψ_8, respectively), and two 3 by 3 determinants (using the set ψ_2, ψ_3, and ψ_4, and the set ψ_5, ψ_6, and ψ_7, respectively). It is this method of factoring which permits the solution of the secular equation for a number of many proton problems.

If we return to the two proton case, the secular determinant becomes

$$\begin{vmatrix} H_{11} - \Delta_{11}E & 0 & 0 & 0 \\ 0 & H_{22} - \Delta_{22}E & H_{23} - \Delta_{23}E & 0 \\ 0 & H_{32} - \Delta_{32}E & H_{33} - \Delta_{33}E & 0 \\ 0 & 0 & 0 & H_{44} - \Delta_{44}E \end{vmatrix} = 0$$

and we now must evaluate the integrals it contains. Let us first obtain the terms on the diagonal. As stated previously, the operator for this case will be

$$H = H^{(0)} + H^{(1)}$$

The integral H_{11} will then be

$$H_{11} = \int \alpha\alpha(\gamma H_1 I_z(1) + \gamma H_2 I_z(2))\alpha\alpha \, d\tau + \int \alpha\alpha(J_{12}I(1) \cdot I(2))\alpha\alpha \, d\tau$$

The first part, which contains $H^{(0)}$, has already been evaluated and was found to equal $\frac{1}{2}(\nu_1 + \nu_2)$. The part containing $H^{(1)}$ may be evaluated if I is expanded in terms of its components in the x, y, and z directions

$$I(1) = I_x(1) + I_y(1) + I_z(1)$$

The properties of I_z have already been mentioned, and the effects of I_x and I_y operating on the wave functions α and β are

$$I_x\alpha = \beta/2$$

$$I_x\beta = \alpha/2$$

$$I_y\alpha = -i\beta/2$$

$$I_y\beta = i\alpha/2$$

The difference between the operators I_x and I_y on one hand and I_z on the other is best seen by considering these operators as matrices:

$$I_x = \frac{1}{2}\begin{pmatrix} 0 & 1 \\ 1 & 0 \end{pmatrix} \qquad I_y = \frac{1}{2}\begin{pmatrix} 0 & i \\ -i & 0 \end{pmatrix} \qquad I_z = \frac{1}{2}\begin{pmatrix} 1 & 0 \\ 0 & -1 \end{pmatrix}$$

and the wave functions as vectors:

$$\alpha = \begin{pmatrix} 1 \\ 0 \end{pmatrix} \qquad \beta = \begin{pmatrix} 0 \\ 1 \end{pmatrix}$$

It can readily be seen that the spin operators are orthogonal, for any two multiplied together will give zero. The conclusions about the effect of I_x, I_y, and I_z operating on α and β are easily seen by multiplying the vectors by each of the matrices in turn. It should be noted that only the I_z operator is diagonal, and thus α and β are wave functions of this operator only.

The product $I(1) \cdot I(2)$ is then

$$I(1) \cdot I(2) = I_x(1)I_x(2) + I_y(1)I_y(2) + I_z(1)I_z(2)$$

and the cross terms, such as $I_x(1)I_y(2)$, drop out because of the orthogonality of the components of the spin operator. The integral may now be evaluated:

$$H_{11}^{(1)} = J_{12}\left(\int \alpha\alpha(I_x(1)I_x(2))\alpha\alpha \; d\tau + \int \alpha\alpha(I_y(1)I_y(2))\alpha\alpha \; d\tau \right.$$

$$\left. + \int \alpha\alpha(I_z(1)I_z(2))\alpha\alpha \; d\tau \right)$$

$$= J_{12}\left(\frac{1}{2}\cdot\frac{1}{2}\int(\alpha\alpha)(\beta\beta)\,d\tau - \frac{i}{2}\cdot\frac{i}{2}\int(\alpha\alpha)(\beta\beta)\,d\tau \right.$$

$$\left. + \frac{1}{2}\cdot\frac{1}{2}\int(\alpha\alpha)(\alpha\alpha)\,d\tau \right)$$

$$= J_{12}\left(0 + 0 + \frac{1}{4}\right) = \frac{1}{4}J_{12}$$

The terms containing I_x and I_y gave nothing because these operators change the spin wave function from α to β, leading to the integral of the product of two orthogonal wave functions, which is zero. Also, note that if the wave function used were $\alpha\beta$, the operator I_z would have given $-\frac{1}{4}J$. Thus this may be generalized

$$H_{mm}^{(1)} = \frac{1}{4}\sum_{i<j} J_{ij}T_{ij}$$

where $T_{ij} = 1$ or -1 according to whether the spin wave functions on nuclei i and j are the same or different. For example,

$$\int \alpha\alpha\beta(H^{(1)})\alpha\alpha\beta = \tfrac{1}{4}(J_{12} - J_{13} - J_{23})$$

The nondiagonal elements must now be considered. Let us consider the integral

$$\int \alpha\alpha\beta(H^{(0)} + H^{(1)})\alpha\beta\alpha \; d\tau = H_{mn}$$

The operator $H^{(0)}$ will not interchange the spin wave functions on any of the nuclei, and since $\alpha\alpha\beta$ is orthogonal to $\alpha\beta\alpha$, the term involving $H^{(0)}$ must be zero. The part involving $H^{(1)}$ may be expanded as

$$H_{mn}^{(1)} = \int \alpha\alpha\beta\left(\sum_{i<j} J_{ij}I(i)\cdot I(j)\right)\alpha\beta\alpha \; d\tau$$

$$= \left\{\int \alpha\alpha\beta(J_{12}I(1)\cdot I(2))\alpha\beta\alpha \; d\tau + \int \alpha\alpha\beta(J_{13}I(1)\cdot I(3))\alpha\beta\alpha \; d\tau \right.$$

$$\left. + \int \alpha\alpha\beta(J_{23}I(2)\cdot I(3))\alpha\beta\alpha \; d\tau\right\}$$

In the first term, the I_z component of the operator will give nothing because it cannot interchange the spin wave functions. The operators I_x and I_y will interchange the wave functions on nuclei 1 and 2. However, the resultant wave function is still orthogonal to $\alpha\alpha\beta$ and the term is zero. The same is true of the second term.

The last term may be further expanded as

$$\int \alpha\alpha\beta(J_{23}I(2) \cdot I(3))\alpha\beta\alpha \, d\tau = J_{23}\int \alpha\alpha\beta(I_x(2)I_x(3))\alpha\beta\alpha \, d\tau$$

$$+ J_{23}\int \alpha\alpha\beta(I_y(2)I_y(3))\alpha\beta\alpha \, d\tau + J_{23}\int \alpha\alpha\beta(I_z(2)I_z(3))\alpha\beta\alpha \, d\tau$$

$$= \tfrac{1}{4}J_{23}\int (\alpha\alpha\beta)(\alpha\alpha\beta) \, d\tau$$

$$+ \tfrac{1}{4}J_{23}\int (\alpha\alpha\beta)(\alpha\alpha\beta) \, d\tau - \tfrac{1}{4}J_{23}\int (\alpha\alpha\beta)(\alpha\beta\alpha) \, d\tau$$

$$= J_{23}(\tfrac{1}{4} + \tfrac{1}{4} - 0) = \tfrac{1}{2}J_{23}$$

Thus, in general, the only coupling constant which appears is that between the two nuclei which must be interchanged in order to make $\psi_n = \psi_m$, and the whole integral will equal $\tfrac{1}{2}$ that coupling constant. Thus, for the integral,

$$\int \alpha\alpha\beta\alpha\beta(H^{(1)})\alpha\beta\alpha\alpha\beta = \tfrac{1}{2}J_{23}$$

Note also that if ψ_n cannot be converted to ψ_m by a single exchange of spin wave functions between two nuclei, the integral will equal zero.

Returning to the two proton case, it can now be seen that the secular determinant will take the form:

$$\begin{vmatrix} \tfrac{1}{2}(\nu_1 + \nu_2) + \tfrac{1}{4}J_{12} - E & 0 & 0 & 0 \\ 0 & \tfrac{1}{2}(\nu_1 - \nu_2) - \tfrac{1}{4}J_{12} - E & \tfrac{1}{2}J_{12} & 0 \\ 0 & \tfrac{1}{2}J_{12} & \tfrac{1}{2}(-\nu_1 + \nu_2) - \tfrac{1}{4}J_{12} - E & 0 \\ 0 & 0 & 0 & \tfrac{1}{2}(-\nu_1 - \nu_2) + \tfrac{1}{4}J_{12} - E \end{vmatrix} = 0$$

It is immediately apparent that

$$E_1 = \tfrac{1}{2}(\nu_1 + \nu_2) + \tfrac{1}{4}J_{12}$$

$$E_4 = \tfrac{1}{2}(-\nu_1 - \nu_2) + \tfrac{1}{4}J_{12}$$

The 2 by 2 determinent which may be factored out is more easily solved if one makes the substitutions

$$C = \tfrac{1}{2}[(\delta^2 + J^2)^{\frac{1}{2}}]$$

where $\delta = \nu_1 - \nu_2$. The energies are then found to be

$$E_2 = -\tfrac{1}{4}J + C$$

$$E_3 = -\tfrac{1}{4}J - C$$

The change in energy for each of the four possible transitions will be

Transition	Energy
$3 \to 1$	$\frac{1}{2}(\nu_1 + \nu_2) + \frac{1}{2}J + C$
$4 \to 2$	$\frac{1}{2}(\nu_1 + \nu_2) - \frac{1}{2}J + C$
$2 \to 1$	$\frac{1}{2}(\nu_1 + \nu_2) + \frac{1}{2}J - C$
$4 \to 3$	$\frac{1}{2}(\nu_1 + \nu_2) - \frac{1}{2}J - C$

It can be seen that the appearance of the spectrum will depend only on the ratio of J to δ. The expected results for a number of values of this ratio are shown in Fig. 1-48. When J is relatively small, the spectrum has only two doublets. The spacing within the doublets gives J, and the spacing between the doublets gives δ. As J becomes larger, the doublets become unsymmetrical, although the spacing between the outside pairs of lines in this case is still equal to J. Finally, the two central lines merge into one, and the two outer lines become forbidden, so that there is but a single line. Since J is independent of the applied magnetic field, a case which has an unfavorable value of J/δ will give progressively more simple spectra as the magnitude of the applied field is increased. This is one reason for operating at 14.1 kgauss (resonance at about 60 mc) rather

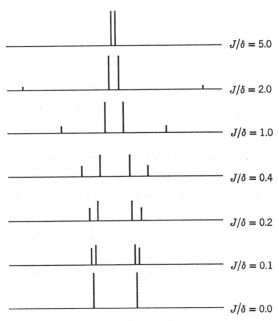

Fig. 1-48. Theoretical spectra for the AB *case.*

than at the lower field strengths which were common a few years ago and which are more easily obtained.

Although the relative intensities of the lines are shown in Fig. 1-48, we have not as yet considered the intensity of the lines. The quantity of interest here is the transition moment m, which is given by (cf. the discussion of ultraviolet spectra)

$$m = \int \psi_m \sum I_x(i) \psi_n \, d\tau$$

where ψ_m and ψ_n are the wave functions for the starting and final states, respectively. The spin operator I_x is used because the coil which supplies the rf power which induces the transition is mounted at right angles to the direction of the applied field, and thus the quantity of interest is the probability of inducing a transition in the x or y directions. The transition moment is evaluated at each nucleus, and the result is summed over all the nuclei. As before, the intensity of the transition is a function of m^2.

The wave functions for each of the states must then be evaluated. This is done, as before, by substituting the values of the energy into the equations which led to the secular determinant. The result, for the two proton case we have been considering, may be simplified by making the substitution

$$\sin 2\theta = \frac{J}{2C}$$

Then the wave functions are

$$\psi_1 = \alpha\alpha$$
$$\psi_2 = \cos \theta(\alpha\beta) + \sin \theta(\beta\alpha)$$
$$\psi_3 = -\sin \theta(\alpha\beta) + \cos \theta(\beta\alpha)$$
$$\psi_4 = \beta\beta$$

The relative intensity of a transition from $\psi_2 \rightarrow \psi_1$ is then

$$m^2 = \left\{ \int (\cos \theta(\alpha\beta) + \sin \theta(\beta\alpha))(I_x(1) + I_x(2))(\alpha\alpha) \, d\tau \right\}^2$$

$$= \left\{ \tfrac{1}{2} \cos \theta \int (\alpha\beta)(\beta\alpha) \, d\tau + \tfrac{1}{2} \cos \theta \int (\alpha\beta)(\alpha\beta) \, d\tau \right.$$

$$\left. + \tfrac{1}{2} \sin \theta \int (\beta\alpha)(\beta\alpha) \, d\tau + \tfrac{1}{2} \sin \theta \int (\beta\alpha)(\alpha\beta) \, d\tau \right\}^2$$

$$= \tfrac{1}{4}(\cos \theta + \sin \theta)^2$$

$$= \tfrac{1}{4}(1 + \sin 2\theta)$$

Thus the relative intensities of the four possible transitions are

$$3 \rightarrow 1 \quad 1 - \sin 2\theta$$
$$4 \rightarrow 2 \quad 1 + \sin 2\theta$$
$$2 \rightarrow 1 \quad 1 + \sin 2\theta$$
$$4 \rightarrow 3 \quad 1 - \sin 2\theta$$

The foregoing treatment may perhaps be made clearer by considering another example. As was mentioned, for the three proton case there are eight possible combinations of spin wave functions on the three nuclei:

$$\psi_1 = \alpha\alpha\alpha \quad F_z = +\tfrac{3}{2}$$
$$\psi_2 = \beta\alpha\alpha \quad = +\tfrac{1}{2}$$
$$\psi_3 = \alpha\beta\alpha \quad = +\tfrac{1}{2}$$
$$\psi_4 = \alpha\alpha\beta \quad = +\tfrac{1}{2}$$
$$\psi_5 = \beta\beta\alpha \quad = -\tfrac{1}{2}$$
$$\psi_6 = \beta\alpha\beta \quad = -\tfrac{1}{2}$$
$$\psi_7 = \alpha\beta\beta \quad = -\tfrac{1}{2}$$
$$\psi_8 = \beta\beta\beta \quad = -\tfrac{3}{2}$$

Let us consider the simple first order $(J_{AB} \ll \delta)$ spectrum which would be expected for the AB_2 case in which two of the protons are identical. In this simple case, the off-diagonal elements of the secular equation are close to zero, and so the diagonal elements give the energies directly. Symbolizing α as $\uparrow$ and β as $\downarrow$, the wave functions are the corresponding energies for the case in which $J_{AB} = 0$ are

	A	B	
ψ_1	$\uparrow$	$\uparrow\uparrow$	$E_1 = \tfrac{1}{2}(\nu_A + 2\nu_B)$
ψ_2	$\downarrow$	$\uparrow\uparrow$	$E_2 = \tfrac{1}{2}(-\nu_A + 2\nu_B)$
ψ_3	$\uparrow$	$\downarrow\uparrow$	$E_3 = \tfrac{1}{2}(\nu_A)$
ψ_4	$\uparrow$	$\uparrow\downarrow$	$E_4 = \tfrac{1}{2}(\nu_A)$
ψ_5	$\downarrow$	$\downarrow\uparrow$	$E_5 = \tfrac{1}{2}(-\nu_A)$
ψ_6	$\downarrow$	$\uparrow\downarrow$	$E_6 = \tfrac{1}{2}(-\nu_A)$
ψ_7	$\uparrow$	$\downarrow\downarrow$	$E_7 = \tfrac{1}{2}(\nu_A - 2\nu_B)$
ψ_8	$\downarrow$	$\downarrow\downarrow$	$E_8 = \tfrac{1}{2}(-\nu_A - 2\nu_B)$

These energies and the permitted transitions are diagrammed in Fig. 1-49, and the resultant spectrum is shown in Fig. 1-50. It should be noted that the transition $\psi_7 \rightarrow \psi_2$ is forbidden, for it involves the change of two B

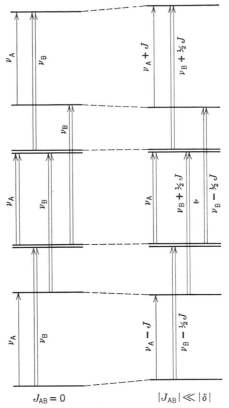

Fig. 1-49. Energy levels for the simple AB_2 case.

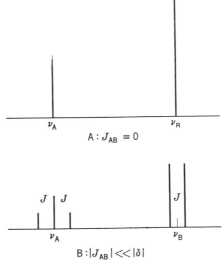

Fig. 1-50. Spectra for the simple AB_2 case.

spins simultaneously. Also, two of the four transitions expected between the two degenerate levels are forbidden. All the other transitions are equally probable, leading to a 2:1 ratio of intensities for the B and A resonance bands.

If the spins on nucleus A and the two B nuclei are coupled in some way, then one arrangement of spins will be more favorable than another. If we assume that they are coupled so that the arrangement $\uparrow\uparrow$ (or $\downarrow\downarrow$) is unfavorable, and the arrangement $\uparrow\downarrow$ (or $\downarrow\uparrow$) is favorable, then the effects of the coupling are easily seen. In ψ_1 (and ψ_8) there are two unfavorable arrangements of nucleus A with the B nuclei. The energy of the interaction will be called $\frac{1}{2}J$ ($\frac{1}{4}J$ each, as before). In ψ_2 (and ψ_7) there are two favorable interactions, and the energy of the interaction will be $-\frac{1}{2}J$. In ψ_3, ψ_4, ψ_5, and ψ_6 there are one favorable interaction and one unfavorable one, leading to no change in energy. The effect of the coupling is shown to the right of Fig. 1-49, and the resultant spectrum is shown in Fig. 1-50. Again, assuming that all the allowed transitions have the same probability, the relative intensities are as shown in the above figure.

For the general ABC case in which all three protons have different chemical shifts and there are three coupling constants, the foregoing treatment is not convenient. Further, when the coupling constants have a value greater than about 10% that of the chemical shifts, the above treatment is not adequate to explain the spectrum. This is illustrated for the AB_2 case in Fig. 1-51, and it can be seen that the value of J cannot be obtained directly from the spectrum. Thus we must again write the secular determinant for the problem and obtain the energies and the wave functions from it.

The energies corresponding to the first and eighth wave functions may be written down directly, for neither of these wave functions mixes with any others (i.e., each has a unique value of F_z):

$$E_1 = \tfrac{1}{2}(\nu_1 + \nu_2 + \nu_3) + \tfrac{1}{4}(J_{12} + J_{13} + J_{23})$$

$$E_2 = \tfrac{1}{2}(-\nu_1 - \nu_2 - \nu_3) + \tfrac{1}{4}(J_{12} + J_{13} + J_{23})$$

Let us now write the 3 by 3 determinant involving ψ_2, ψ_3, and ψ_4, which may be factored out from the secular determinant:

$$\begin{vmatrix} \tfrac{1}{2}(\nu_1 + \nu_2 - \nu_3) + \tfrac{1}{4}(J_{12} - J_{13} - J_{23}) - E & \tfrac{1}{2}J_{12} & \tfrac{1}{2}J_{13} \\ \tfrac{1}{2}J_{12} & \tfrac{1}{2}(\nu_1 - \nu_2 + \nu_3) + \tfrac{1}{4}(-J_{12} + J_{13} - J_{23}) - E & \tfrac{1}{2}J_{12} \\ \tfrac{1}{2}J_{13} & \tfrac{1}{2}J_{12} & \tfrac{1}{2}(-\nu_1 + \nu_2 + \nu_3) + \tfrac{1}{4}(-J_{12} - J_{13} + J_{23}) - E \end{vmatrix} = 0$$

It can be seen that the determinant gives a cubic equation, and thus the values of energy cannot readily be given in analytical form. However, if a

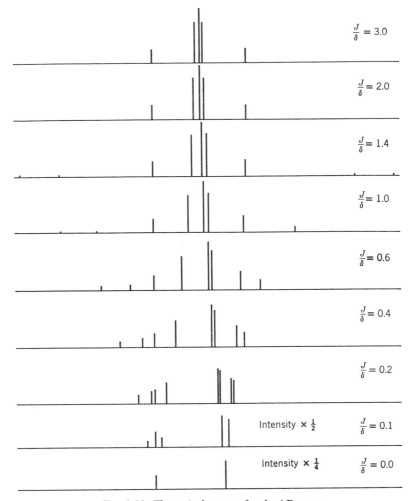

Fig. 1-51. Theoretical spectra for the AB_2 *case.*

set of values for the ν's and the J's were substituted into the determinant, it could easily be solved for the values of the energy. The same is true for the other 3 by 3 determinant. The calculated spectrum which is obtained using the assumed values may be modified until it is in agreement with the observed spectrum. The values of the parameters which give the best fit to the observed spectrum will then be the proper frequencies and coupling constants for the case in question.

Having the values of the energies, we may obtain the wave functions and also evaluate the intensities. This provides a second check on the correctness of the assigned values. In other than such simple cases as described above, the calculation of the theoretical spectrum derived from a set of assumed chemical shifts and spin coupling constants is time consuming and tedious. The calculations are, however, easily carried out using a digital computer, and such a procedure is described in Appendix 8.

The preceding pages have presented a scheme for interpreting nmr spectra and for obtaining the appropriate values of the chemical shifts and spin coupling constants. However, we have not yet considered the reasons for chemical shifts, nor for the magnitudes of the coupling constants. One of the principal causes of chemical shifts is the magnetic shielding of a nucleus by its associated electrons. An electron associated with a proton, when placed in a magnetic field, behaves in the same fashion as electrons in a moving coil of wire. Thus a force is exerted on the electron by the magnetic field, which causes the electrons to move around the nucleus predominantly in one direction. The movement of the electron produces a local magnetic field (usually called an induced magnetic field, for it arises as a result of the applied field). This local field has, at the nucleus, a direction which is opposed to that of the applied field.

The condition for observing an nmr signal is that the ratio of the field at the nucleus to the applied radio frequency must have a certain value. With a fixed radio frequency, the applied field must equal the required field at the nucleus plus the induced field. The magnitude of the induced field will be proportional to the electron density at the nucleus (since the induced field is caused by these electrons), and thus the chemical shift caused by this effect should be proportional to the electron density about the proton.

A common way in which to consider changes in electron density is to make use of the electronegativity difference between two atoms. Thus a comparison of the chemical shift for a proton with the electronegativity difference between the carbon to which it is attached and the group which is bonded to the carbon might give a linear relationship.[121] Figure 1-52 shows that the expected correlation is realized for a series of methyl derivatives, although the halogens and the other atoms do not fall on the same line.

There are many data showing that the electron density is not the only factor involved. The difference in slope between the two lines referred to above is one; the observation that the resonance band for aromatic protons appears at a lower field than that for olefinic protons is another.[122] The cause of the latter effect has been well studied.

[121] A. A. Bothner-By and C. Naar-Colin, *Ann. N.Y. Acad. Sci.*, **70**, 833 (1958).
[122] J. A. Pople, *J. Chem. Phys.*, **24**, 1111 (1956).

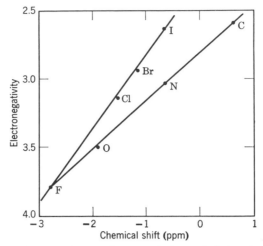

*Fig. 1-52. Relation between electron density and chemical shifts of methyl derivatives (A. A. Bothner-By and C. Naar-Colin, Ann. N.Y. Acad. Sci., **70**, 833 (1958).)*

Consider the case in which the direction of the applied field is perpendicular to the plane of the aromatic ring. This will induce a ring current into the π-electron system, again resulting in an induced magnetic field. (Fig. 1-53). At distances larger than the radius of the ring, the induced field will reinforce the applied field. Thus a lower applied field will be required for absorption of rf power, resulting in a downfield shift of the resonance band of the aromatic protons. The value of the chemical shift calculated using classical electromagnetic theory for a system of six electrons is -1.7 ppm,[122] whereas the observed difference between benzene and ethylene is 1.4 ppm. The agreement between these values indicates the validity of this treatment.

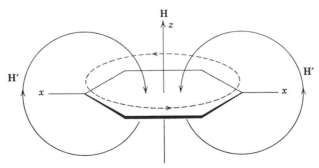

Fig. 1-53. Effect of a magnetic field on benzene. **H** *is the applied magnetic field, the dotted line indicates the induced ring current, and* **H′** *represents the magnetic field associated with the ring current.*

A particularly interesting confirmation of this treatment is found in the spectra of the annulenes[123] (i.e., conjugated cyclopolyolefins). In compounds such as these, there is a set of hydrogens directed toward the center of the ring. Within the radius of the aromatic ring, the induced magnetic field opposes the applied field, requiring a greater applied field to reach the resonance condition. The observed resonance band was at $\tau = 10 - 12$,[124] which is markedly higher than normal olefinic protons ($\tau = 4 - 5$), in agreement with the prediction.

Similar explanations have been proposed for the upfield shift of the resonance for acetylenic protons as compared with ethylenic protons, for the differences in chemical shifts between the cyclic hydrocarbons, and a number of other cases.[125]

We may now turn to the spin coupling constants. To a large extent the spin coupling is effected by the interaction of the magnetic moment of a proton with its associated electron. Since the electrons in adjacent bonds also interact, the electrons in effect transmit information concerning the magnetic moments of the two nuclei. The magnitude of the effect will be to a first approximation, proportional to the square of the overlap integral between the two C-H bond orbitals in question. Thus the effect should be small if the protons are separated by three or more carbons. Similarly, for protons on adjacent carbons, the spin coupling should be large when the two C-H bonds are either *cis-* or *trans-* to each other (cf. the sp^3 orbital, Fig. 1-10) and should be small when the bonds are at right angles to each other.

This has been confirmed by an investigation of a series of rigid systems for which the dihedral angle between two C-H bonds (i.e., the angle between the two bonds observed when sighting down the axis of the C-C bond) could be estimated from models and for which the spin coupling could be measured. The data are shown in Fig. 1-54.[126] To a first approximation, it would be expected that the interaction between the two bonds would fall off as the square of the cosine of the angle between

[123] F. Sondheimer, R. Wolovsky, Y. Gaoni, Y. Amiel, and D. A. Ben-Efraim, presented at the 139th Meeting, American Chemical Society, St. Louis, 1961; F. Sondheimer and R. Wolovsky, *Tetrahedron Letters*, No. 3, 3 (1959).
[124] The value τ is the observed chemical shift in ppm referred to tetramethylsilane (10.00) as the internal standard in dilute carbon tetrachloride solution. (G. V. Tiers, *J. Phys. Chem.*, **62**, 1151 (1958).
[125] See J. A. Pople, W. G. Schneider, and H. J. Bernstein, *High Resolution Nuclear Magnetic Resonance*, McGraw-Hill Book Co., New York, 1959, pp. 175–183; L. M. Jackman, *Nuclear Magnetic Resonance*, Pergamon Press, London, 1959, pp. 15–19, 112–129.
[126] H. Conroy, *Advances in Organic Chemistry*, Interscience Publishers, New York, 1960, vol. 2, p. 311.

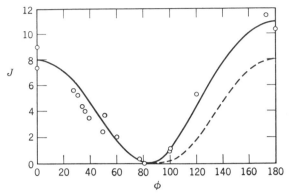

Fig. 1-54. Effect of dihedral angle on the magnitude of the coupling constant for protons on adjacent carbons. The dotted line and its solid extension are a $\cos^2 \phi$ curve.

them. The dotted line represents the $\cos^2 \phi$ curve, and it can be seen to fit the points from 0 to 90° fairly well. At angles larger than 90°, the predicted values are too small. However, a detailed theoretical treatment of this case shows that the *trans*-coupling should be larger than the *cis*-coupling, in agreement with experiment.[127]

The case of spin coupling of *gem*-protons has also been considered, but here the agreement between theory and experiment is rather poor, and except for epoxides and related compounds, the wrong sign of the coupling constant is predicted.[128]

It would appear from the preceding that the vicinal coupling constants might provide useful information about the geometry of molecules. Even here, however, there are difficulties in that large long-range coupling constants have been observed[129] and until these have been explained, our understanding of the magnitude of the coupling constants is not satisfactory.

References

General Theory and Calculation of Spin Coupling Constants and Chemical Shifts:
J. A. Pople, W. G. Schneider, and H. J. Bernstein, *High-resolution Nuclear Magnetic Resonance*, McGraw-Hill Book Co., New York, 1959.

[127] M. Karplus, *J. Chem. Phys.*, **30**, 11 (1959); M. Karplus and D. H. Anderson, *J. Chem. Phys.*, **30**, 6 (1959).

[128] R. L. Fraser, R. U. Lemieux and J. D. Stevens, *J. Am. Chem. Soc.*, **83**, 3901 (1961); F. Kaplan and J. D. Roberts, *J. Am. Chem. Soc.*, **83**, 4666 (1961); C. A. Reilly and J. D. Swalen, *J. Chem. Phys.*, **35**, 1522 (1961).

[129] J. Meinwald and A. Lewis, *J. Am. Chem. Soc.*, **83**, 2769 (1961); D. R. Davis, R. P. Lutz and J. D. Roberts, *J. Am. Chem. Soc.*, **83**, 246 (1961); K. B. Wiberg, B. R. Lowry and B. J. Nist, *J. Am. Chem. Soc.*, **84**, 1594 (1962).

J. D. Roberts, *An Introduction to Spin-Spin Splitting in High Resolution Nuclear Magnetic Resonance Spectra*, W. A. Benjamin, New York, 1961.
K. B. Wiberg and B. J. Nist, *Interpretation of NMR. Spectra*, W. A. Benjamin, New York, 1962.
Applications of NMR Spectroscopy in Organic Chemistry:
L. M. Jackman, *Applications of Nuclear Magnetic Resonance Spectroscopy in Organic Chemistry*, Pergamon Press, London, 1959.
H. Conroy, "Nuclear Magnetic Resonance in Organic Structure Elucidation," in vol. II, *Advances in Organic Chemistry*, Interscience Publishers, New York, 1960.

Problems

1. Evaluate the matrix element between wave functions ψ_1 and ψ_2 on p. 201. From this, can one see why the matrix elements between wave functions with different values of F_z are zero?

2. One of the two 3×3 determinants for the ABC case is given on p. 203. Evaluate the matrix elements for the other one. Having these determinants in hand, calculate the spectrum which should arise from the following set of parameters:

$$\nu_A = 15.0 \qquad \nu_B = 25.0 \qquad \nu_C = 50.0$$

$$J_{AB} = 7.5 \qquad J_{BC} = 4.5 \qquad J_{AC} = 2.0$$

3. A compound has the following spectrum which arises from the coupling of three protons. Obtain the set of spectral parameters which best fit the spectrum.

Freq.	Rel. Int.	Freq.	Rel. Int.
93.4	0.48	105.1	0.48
95.4	0.41	106.2	0.41
97.4	1.52	1098.5	1.00
99.4	1.59	1099.6	1.00
101.1	1.52	1100.4	1.00
102.2	1.59	1101.5	1.00

(*Note:* It might help to read through Appendix 5.)
4. Check your assignments in problem 3 by calculating the expected intensities and comparing them with the observed intensities.

PART TWO

Equilibria

2-1 Introduction

The study of equilibria is of importance for two reasons. First, many reactions involve equilibria in one or more steps, and others are entirely equilibrium controlled. Examples of the latter include some hydrocarbon isomerization reactions and the sulfonation of naphthalene at higher temperatures. Second, most kinetic processes may be thought of as involving an equilibrium between the reactants and a species called the activated complex. Thus a knowledge of the factors which influence the equilibrium constant will aid considerably in the later discussion of kinetics.

It is well recognized that two factors control the position of equilibrium in a reaction. The first is the intrinsic difference in energy between the reactants, that is, the difference in energy which would be observed at absolute zero. The second is that due to the increase in energy of the molecules as the temperature is raised from absolute zero to the reaction temperature. If this is not the same for the reactants and the products, the position of equilibrium will be a function of temperature.

This latter factor is often easily considered in a quantitative fashion and thus will be discussed first. Next, the difference in the intrinsic energy will be considered. After an examination of some reactions in which neither the reactants nor the products are ionic, the effect of solvents on ionic species will be discussed, and this will permit a treatment of equilibria involving ions, such as acid-base equilibria.

2-2 The Boltzmann Distribution Law

The energy levels for a molecule may be conveniently considered as a sum of several components—translational, vibrational, rotational, and electronic. The last of these involves such a large difference between energy levels that it is unlikely that a significant number of molecules will be in an electronically excited state (except in photochemical reactions). The energy levels for each of these components of the total energy may, in principle, be determined from the spectrum of the compound. The question is then, "How do the molecules distribute themselves between the available energy levels, and how does this distribution vary with temperature?"

Each molecule in the system which we might choose to study may be described by means of a wave function. If it were possible to obtain the wave function for each molecule in the system, we would potentially be able to specify all the properties of the system. However, in view of the large number of molecules in an ordinary chemical system, this would not be practical, and thus we must resort to a statistical treatment of the problem. In order to do this we must first obtain the distribution law which gives the population of molecules in each of the translational, vibrational, and rotational energy states of the system.

Let us consider the number of ways in which a given number of molecules may distribute themselves between the available energy states. Suppose, as an example, five molecules were to be distributed between two states. The molecules will be indicated by A, B, C, D, and E, and the two states will be represented by two boxes. Some of the possible distributions, leaving out those which simply permute the molecules within one state, are seen at the top of page 212.

If we take the case of four molecules in the first state, there are five possible arrangements. The total number of permutations of five molecules is 5!, but this has been reduced by the number of permutations of molecules within the first box (4!), which should not be counted. The total number is thus given by 5!/4!. Similarly, for the case in which there are three molecules in the first box and two in the other, the total number of permutations, 5!, is divided by the number of permutations in each box, or 3! 2!, giving the 10 arrangements shown below. In general,

$$t = \frac{N!}{n_1! \, n_2! \, n_3! \cdots}$$

A B C D E		A B C	D E
		A B D	C E
A B C D	E	A C D	B E
A B C E	D	B C D	A E
A B D E	C	A B E	C D
A C D E	B	A C E	B D
B C D E	A	B C E	A D
		A D E	B C
		B D E	A C
		C D E	A B

where t is the number of arrangements, N is the total number of molecules, n_1 is the number of molecules in the microscopic state 1, n_2 is the number in the microscopic state 2, and so on.

The equilibrium distribution of molecules among states will be the distribution which is associated with the largest number of different arrangements, for each arrangement having a given energy is equally probable. Thus it is necessary to determine what conditions will maximize t or, more conveniently, $\ln t$. This must be subject to two restrictions, for the total number of molecules must remain constant:

$$\sum n_i = N_{\text{total}}$$

and the total energy must remain constant:

$$\sum n_i \epsilon_i = E_{\text{total}}$$

If we take logarithms of both sides of the expression for t, we obtain

$$\ln t = \ln N! - \sum_i \ln n_i!$$

The last two terms may be evaluated as follows:

$$\ln N! = \ln 1 + \ln 2 + \ln 3 + \cdots + \ln N = \sum_{x=1}^{N} \ln x$$

If N is large, the summation may be replaced by an integration, giving

$$\ln N! \cong \int_1^N \ln x \, dx = N \ln N - N + 1 \cong N \ln N - N$$

since N is large compared to unity. This is known as Stirling's approximation.

Making the appropriate substitutions, we obtain

$$\ln t = N \ln N - N - \sum n_i \ln n_i + \sum n_i$$

In order to obtain the maximum value of $\ln t$, the derivative is set equal to zero:

$$\delta \ln t = - \sum \ln n_i \, \delta n_i = 0$$

It is now necessary to include the restrictions given above. To do this, let us first differentiate the equations describing the restrictions:

$$\sum \delta n_i = 0$$
$$\sum \epsilon_i \, \delta n_i = 0$$

Then let us multiply the first expression by a constant α, and the second by a constant β.

$$\sum \alpha \, \delta n_i = 0$$
$$\sum \beta \epsilon_i \, \delta n_i = 0$$

These expressions may be added to that for $\delta \ln t$, giving

$$\delta \ln t = \sum_{i=1}^{\infty} (-\ln n_i + \alpha + \beta \epsilon_i) \, \delta n_i = 0$$

Let us examine the first two expressions in the sum.

$$-\ln n_1 + \alpha + \beta \epsilon_1$$
$$-\ln n_2 + \alpha + \beta \epsilon_2$$

It is clear that values of α and β may be chosen which will make each of these expressions equal zero. The remaining equation then becomes

$$\delta \ln t = \sum_{i=3}^{\infty} (-\ln n_i + \alpha + \beta \epsilon_i) \, \delta n_i = 0$$

The two restrictions have been taken care of, and so the remaining values of δn_i may be chosen at will. Let us make the choice that $\delta n_i = 0$ with the exception of δn_k, which will be set equal to unity. Then for the latter,

$$-\ln n_k + \alpha + \beta \epsilon_k = 0$$

no matter what the choice of k was. Therefore for a maximum value of $\ln t$,

$$\ln n_i = \alpha + \beta \epsilon_i$$

or

$$n_i = e^\alpha \, e^{\beta \epsilon_i}$$

It can be shown that β is equal to $-1/kT$, where k is the Boltzmann constant (1.38×10^{-16} erg/deg or 1.99 cal/deg/mole), and thus

$$n_i = e^\alpha e^{-\epsilon_i/kT}$$

Similarly, for the ratio of molecules in two states,

$$\frac{n_i}{n_j} = e^{-(\epsilon_i - \epsilon_j)/kT}$$

The last two expressions are known as the Boltzmann distribution law.

As an example of the use of this relationship, let us calculate the population of the first excited vibrational level for some typical bonds at room temperature. The frequency for a C—H single bond is about 3000 cm^{-1}, which corresponds to an energy change of 8520 cal/mole in going from the ground state to the first vibrationally excited state. The ratio of molecules in the first excited state and the ground state is then

$$\frac{n_i}{n_0} = e^{-8520/593} = e^{-14.3} = 0$$

Thus a negligible number of the molecules will be in the excited state. For a C—O bond having a vibrational frequency of 950 cm^{-1} about 1 % of the molecules will be in the excited state, and with a low frequency skeletal vibration having a frequency of about 460 cm^{-1}, about 10% of the molecules will be in the excited state. Thus it may be seen that for most bonds the largest population of molecules will be in the ground vibrational state. But as we shall see, this is not true for rotation or translation.

2-3 *Isomerization Equilibria*

The Boltzmann distribution may be used in any case in which molecules are distributed between energy levels, and isomerization equilibria is one simple example. Consider the case of the gas phase reaction

$$\text{Keto} \rightleftharpoons \text{Enol}$$

For the equilibrium

$$K = \frac{N_E}{N_K}$$

the Boltzmann distribution may be written as

$$N_E = e^\alpha e^{-\epsilon^E/kT}$$
$$N_K = e^\alpha e^{-\epsilon^K/kT}$$

It can be shown that α is dependent only on the number and kind of atoms present in a molecule, and thus α will be the same for both components of an isomerization equilibrium. The equilibrium constant may then be written as

$$K = \frac{N_E}{N_K} = e^{-(\epsilon^E - \epsilon^K)/kT}$$

At a low temperature, all the molecules would be in the lowest energy level, $E_0{}^0$,[1] and the equilibrium constant would be (on a mole basis)

$$K = e^{-(E_0{}^{0E} - E_0{}^{0K})/RT}$$

or

$$\ln K = -\frac{\Delta E_0{}^0}{RT}$$

and

$$\Delta E_0{}^0 = -RT \ln K$$

It should be remembered that at absolute zero, $\Delta E_0{}^0 = \Delta H_0{}^0 = \Delta F_0{}^0$, and so this is a familiar thermodynamic expression.

At higher temperatures it is necessary to include vibrational, rotational, and translational energies (although in the particular case being considered, the change in translational energy must be the same for both species, for it depends only on the mass and the temperature). Thus we must sum over the number of molecules of each type in each of the available energy states:

$$N_E = n_0{}^E + n_1{}^E + n_2{}^E + n_3{}^E + \cdots$$
$$N_K = n_0{}^K + n_1{}^K + n_2{}^K + n_3{}^K + \cdots$$

where $n_0{}^E$ is the number of enol molecules in the lowest energy level, $n_1{}^E$ is the number in the next higher energy level, and so on.

Using the Boltzmann distribution, we find that

$$N_E = g_0 e^\alpha e^{-\epsilon_0{}^E/kT} + g_1 e^\alpha e^{-\epsilon_1{}^E/kT} + g_2 e^\alpha e^{-\epsilon_2{}^E/kT} + \cdots$$

[1] The subscript zero on the thermodynamic function refers to zero degrees Kelvin, and the superscript zero refers to standard quantities at the specified temperature.

where the g's are factors indicating the number of levels having the same energy. This eliminates the need for writing a term containing a given energy more than once. Dividing by $e^{\alpha}e^{-\epsilon_0 E/kT}$, we obtain

$$\frac{N_E}{e^{\alpha}e^{-\epsilon_0 E/kT}} = g_0 + g_1 e^{-(\epsilon_1 E - \epsilon_0 E)/kT} + g_2 e^{-(\epsilon_2 E - \epsilon_0 E)/kT} + \cdots$$

$$= \sum_i g_i e^{-(\epsilon_i E - \epsilon_0 E)/kT}$$

If we now define a new quantity, Q, the partition function, as $\sum_i g_i e^{-(\epsilon_i E - \epsilon_0)/kT}$, then

$$N_E = e^{\alpha}e^{-\epsilon_0 E/kT}Q_E$$

and the equilibrium constant may be written as

$$K = \frac{N_E}{N_K} = \frac{e^{\alpha}e^{-\epsilon_0 E/kT}Q_E}{e^{\alpha}e^{-\epsilon_0 K/kT}Q_K} = e^{-(\epsilon_0 E - \epsilon_0 K)/kT}\frac{Q_E}{Q_K}$$

and on a mole basis, for an isomerization equilibrium,

$$RT \ln K = -\Delta E_0^0 + RT \ln \left(\frac{Q_E}{Q_K}\right) = -\Delta F^0$$

Let us examine the partition function and determine what it is. Again, using the Boltzmann distribution,

$$\frac{n_i}{n_0} = \frac{g_i}{g_0} e^{-(\epsilon_i - \epsilon_0)/kT}$$

But since g_0 must equal unity, and

$$Q = \sum_i g_i e^{-(\epsilon_i - \epsilon_0)/kT}$$

therefore

$$Q = \sum_i \frac{n_i}{n_0} = \frac{1}{n_0} \sum_i n_i = \frac{N}{n_0}$$

where N is the total number of molecules and equal to $\sum_i n_i$. Thus the partition function is simply the ratio of the total number of molecules to the number in the lowest energy level. As the temperature approaches zero, n_0 approaches N and Q approaches unity.

We are now in a position to evaluate some of the common thermodynamic quantities relating to equilibria in terms of the partition functions. Let us first obtain the temperature coefficient for the equilibrium, and to do this, let us differentiate the partition function with respect to temperature.

$$Q = \sum g_i e^{-(\epsilon_i - \epsilon_0)/kT}$$

$$\frac{\partial Q}{\partial T} = \sum \frac{g_i(\epsilon_i - \epsilon_0)}{kT^2} e^{-(\epsilon_i - \epsilon_0)/kT}$$

Both sides are multiplied by kT^2/Q:

$$\frac{kT^2 \, \partial \ln Q}{\partial T} = \sum \frac{g_i(\epsilon_i - \epsilon_0)e^{-(\epsilon_i - \epsilon_0)/kT}}{Q}$$

and substituting n_i/n_0 for the Boltzmann factor in the numerator and substituting the expression for the partition function in terms of the number of molecules in the denominator, we get

$$\frac{kT^2 \, \partial \ln Q}{\partial T} = \sum \frac{(\epsilon_i - \epsilon_0)n_i/n_0}{N/n_0} = \sum \frac{(\epsilon_i - \epsilon_0)n_i}{N}$$

Now if both sides are multiplied by N, we obtain

$$\frac{RT^2 \, \partial \ln Q}{\partial T} = \sum (\epsilon_i - \epsilon_0)n_i = E^0 - E_0^{\ 0}$$

As was shown previously,

$$-RT \ln K = \Delta E_0^{\ 0} - RT \ln \frac{Q_E}{Q_K}$$

If this is differentiated with respect to temperature,

$$RT^2 \frac{\partial \ln K}{\partial T} = \Delta E_0^{\ 0} + RT^2 \frac{\partial \ln Q_E/Q_K}{\partial T}$$

and the above expression for the rate of change of the partition function with temperature is substituted, we get

$$RT^2 \frac{\partial \ln K}{\partial T} = \Delta E_0^{\ 0} + E^E - E_0^{\ 0E} - E^K + E_0^{\ 0K} = \Delta E^0$$

Since for an isomerization equilibrium there is no volume change, the change in energy is equal to the change in enthalpy. Therefore

$$RT^2 \frac{\partial \ln K}{\partial T} = \Delta H^0$$

and

$$\Delta H^0 = \Delta E_0^{\ 0} + RT^2 \frac{\partial \ln (Q_E/Q_K)}{\partial T}$$

If there is a change in the number of molecules involved, the quantity $\Delta(pV)$ must be added to the expressions for ΔF^0 and ΔH^0.

The entropy change may also be evaluated making use of the familiar thermodynamic expression

$$-T \Delta S^0 = \Delta F^0 - \Delta H^0$$

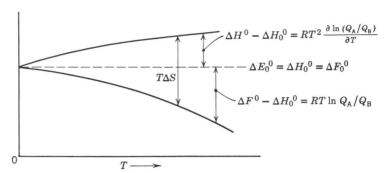

Fig. 2-1. Effect of temperature on the thermodynamic functions for an isomerization equilibrium.

Making the appropriate substitutions for ΔF and ΔH, we obtain[2]

$$-T\Delta S^0 = \Delta E_0{}^0 - RT\ln\left(\frac{Q_E}{Q_K}\right) - \Delta E_0{}^0 - RT^2\frac{\partial \ln (Q_E/Q_K)}{\partial T}$$

$$\Delta S^0 = R\ln\left(\frac{Q_E}{Q_K}\right) + RT\frac{\partial \ln (Q_E/Q_K)}{\partial T}$$

It should be noted that both ΔF^0 and ΔH^0 change with $\ln (Q_E/Q_K)$ but in opposite directions. Therefore the effect of temperature on these thermodynamic quantities is in the opposite direction, as illustrated in Fig. 2-1. This figure is drawn for the case in which the spacing of the energy levels in A is larger than that in B, and the diagram would be inverted if the opposite were true.

The evaluation of the partition functions must now be considered, and in order to do this it is necessary to make the simplifying assumption that the total partition function can be separated into the partition

[2] The thermodynamic quantities may also be written for a single compound. They may be derived by the procedure given above and are found to be

$$H_0{}^0 = E_0{}^0$$

$$H^0 = H_0{}^0 + RT + RT^2\frac{\partial \ln Q}{\partial T}$$

$$F^0 = H_0{}^0 + RT - RT\ln\frac{Q}{N}$$

$$S^0 = \frac{(H^0 - F^0)}{T} = R\ln\frac{Q}{N} + RT\frac{\partial \ln Q}{\partial T}$$

The RT factors in the H^0 and F^0 terms arise from the pV difference between E^0 and H^0 on one hand and between A^0 and F^0 on the other. The functions E^0 and A^0 are appropriate for reactions carried out at constant volume, and H^0 and F^0 refer to those carried out at constant pressure.

functions for vibration (Q_v), rotation (Q_r), translation (Q_{tr}), and electronic excitation (Q_{el}).

$$Q = Q_v Q_r Q_{tr} Q_{el}$$

Of these, the last may be neglected, for the energy levels are widely separated, and at a reasonable temperature essentially all the molecules will be in the ground electronic state. Thus for the electronic part, $N/n_0 = 1 = Q_{el}$.

The translational partition function will be considered first. There are three degrees of freedom for translation, in the x, y, and z directions. We have previously determined that the energy of a particle in a one-dimensional box, which corresponds to translational energy, is

$$E = \frac{n^2 h^2}{8ma^2}$$

and for a three-dimensional box, this becomes

$$E = \frac{h^2}{8m}\left(\frac{n_x^2}{a^2} + \frac{n_y^2}{b^2} + \frac{n_z^2}{c^2}\right)$$

where a is the length of the box in the x direction, b is the length in the y direction, and c is the length in the z direction. It can be seen that if $a = b = c$, the a^2 factor could be taken out from the sum and could be replaced by $V^{2/3}$, where V is the volume of the box, giving

$$E = \frac{h^2}{8mV^{2/3}}(n_x^2 + n_y^2 + n_z^2)$$

and this may be shown to be correct for any shape of box.

The translational energy of any state will then be

$$(\epsilon_i)_{tr} = (n_x^2 + n_y^2 + n_z^2)\frac{h^2}{8mV^{2/3}}$$

$$= (n_x^2 + n_y^2 + n_z^2)s^2$$

where

$$s^2 = \frac{h^2}{8mV^{2/3}}$$

and the n's refer to the quantum numbers for the ith state. The partition function Q is given by

$$Q_{tr} = \sum_i e^{-(\epsilon_i - \epsilon_0)/kT}$$

$$= \sum_i e^{-(n_x^2 + n_y^2 + n_z^2)s^2/kT}$$

$$= \sum_i e^{-n_x^2 s^2/kT} \sum_i e^{-n_y^2 s^2/kT} \sum_i e^{-n_z^2 s^2/kT}$$

Since the levels are closely spaced, each sum may be replaced by an integral:

$$\sum e^{-n^2 s^2/kT} \cong \int_0^\infty e^{-n^2 s^2/kT} \, dn$$

which is a well-known definite integral:

$$\int_0^\infty e^{-a^2 u^2} \, du = \frac{\sqrt{\pi}}{2a}$$

Therefore

$$\sum e^{-n^2 s^2/kT} = \frac{\sqrt{\pi}}{2(s^2/kT)^{1/2}} = (2\pi mkT)^{1/2} \frac{V^{1/3}}{h}$$

and

$$Q_{tr} = \left((2\pi mkT)^{1/2} \frac{V^{1/3}}{h} \right)^3 = \left(\frac{2\pi mkT}{h^2} \right)^{3/2} V = \left(\frac{2\pi mkT}{h^2} \right)^{3/2} \frac{RT}{P}$$

Now, let us evaluate the translational partition function and the related thermodynamic quantities for one mole of a typical compound ($m = 100$) at 25° and 1 atmosphere pressure. By substitution of the numerical values of the constants,

$$Q_{tr} = \left[\frac{2 \times 3.14 \times 100 \times 1.38 \times 10^{-16} \times 298}{6.02 \times 10^{23} \times (6.63)^2 \times 10^{-54}} \right] \cdot \frac{82.1 \times 298}{1.}$$

$$= 2.35 \times 10^{31}$$

If one remembers that the partition function is the ratio of the total number of molecules to the number in the ground state, it can be seen that a very large fraction of the molecules will be in translationally excited states. This is a consequence of the fact that the translational levels are very close to each other, and so there are many levels of approximately equal energy which a molecule may occupy.

If one substitutes the above expression for the translational partition function in the equations obtained previously for the free energy and enthalpy, one obtains

$$F^0 = H_0^0 - 6.864\, T \log M - 11.44 T \log T + 7.282 T$$

$$H^0 = H_0^0 + 4.968 T$$

$$S^0 = \frac{-(F^0 - H^0)}{T}$$

Using these expressions, the results for $T = 298$, $M = 100$, are

$$F^0 = H_0^0 - 10{,}430$$

$$H^0 = H_0^0 + 1480$$

$$S^0 = 39.9$$

It can be seen that the loss of translational energy by a molecule represents a change in free energy of about 10.5 kcal/mole. A process in which much of the translational energy is lost is a dimerization reaction, such as

$$2A \rightleftharpoons B$$

Suppose A has a mass of 50 and B has a mass of 100. Then for 2A,

$$F^0 = 2H_0^0(A) - 19{,}480 \text{ cal}$$
$$H^0 = 2H_0^0(A) + 2960 \quad \text{cal}$$
$$S^0 = 75.3 \qquad\qquad \text{eu}$$

and for B,

$$F^0 = H_0^0(B) - 10{,}350 \text{ cal}$$
$$H^0 = H_0^0(B) + 1480 \quad \text{cal}$$
$$S^0 = 39.9 \qquad\qquad \text{eu}$$

and the change in the thermodynamic functions due to translation alone would be

$$\Delta F^0 = H_0^0(B) - 2H_0^0(A) + 9130 \text{ cal}$$
$$\Delta H^0 = H_0^0(B) - 2H_0^0(A) - 1480 \text{ cal}$$
$$\Delta S^0 = -35.4 \text{ eu}$$

It can be seen that the loss of translational energy levels caused by dimerizing A leads to a large increase in free energy and a large decrease in entropy. Thus unless the bonding in the dimer is reasonably strong, the dimer will not be favored at equilibrium. As an example, consider the hydrogen bonding in acetic acid and in an alcohol. If a hydrogen bond is worth about 5000 cal/mole, then an alcohol should be in the monomeric form in the vapor. The acid, having two hydrogen bonds per dimer unit, has sufficiently strong hydrogen bonding to overcome the loss of translational energy levels in the dimer and is found to be dimeric in the vapor.

We may now consider the rotational partition functions. For a non-linear molecule there are three rotational degrees of freedom—about the x, y, and z axes. Usually the z axis is considered to coincide with the principal axis of symmetry of the molecule, and the x and y axes are taken so as to coincide, if possible, with the remaining symmetry axes.

When we considered a particle on a circle (p. 9), the energy was found to be given by

$$E = \frac{h^2 n^2}{8\pi^2 mr^2} \qquad n = 0, 1, 2, 3, \ldots$$

Rotation about an axis is a similar case, and one might expect a similar relationship to hold. If one considered the case of hydrogen bromide, the rotation would not involve a significant movement of the massive bromine, and the moment of inertia (I) would be simply mr^2 where m is the mass of the hydrogen. The additional quantum restrictions on rotation about an axis makes it necessary to replace n^2 by $j(j + 1)$, giving

$$E = \frac{j(j + 1)h^2}{8\pi^2 I} \qquad j = 0, 1, 2, 3, \ldots$$

where j is the rotational quantum number. The lowest energy is 0, and therefore the difference in energy between an excited state and the ground state would be given by

$$(\epsilon_i - \epsilon_0) = \frac{j(j + 1)h^2}{8\pi^2 I}$$

In the general case, one cannot assume that only one particle of a diatomic molecule moves during rotation. The general expression for the moment of inertia is

$$I = \sum mr^2 = m_1 r_1{}^2 + m_2 r_2{}^2$$

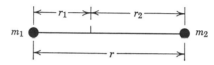

Let us multiply both sides by $m_1 + m_2$,

$$(m_1 + m_2)I = m_1{}^2 r_1{}^2 + m_2{}^2 r_2{}^2 + m_1 m_2 r_1{}^2 + m_1 m_2 r_2{}^2$$

A rotation will occur about a center of mass, and therefore

$$r_1 m_1 = r_2 m_2$$

Substituting this in the above expression, one obtains

$$(m_1 + m_2)I = 2m_1 m_2 r_1 r_2 + m_1 m_2 r_1{}^2 + m_1 m_2 r_2{}^2$$

$$= m_1 m_2 (2r_1 r_2 + r_1{}^2 + r_2{}^2)$$

$$= m_1 m_2 r^2$$

Therefore

$$I = \left(\frac{m_1 m_2}{m_1 + m_2}\right) r^2 = \mu r^2$$

For other than a diatomic molecule it is, of course, necessary to sum all the products of mass times distance squared, using the center of mass as the origin.

Let us designate $h^2/8\pi^2 I$ as b. Then, since it can be shown that g_i (the number of states having the same energy) is equal to $2j + 1$, the rotational partition function is evaluated as

$$(\epsilon_i - \epsilon_0) = j(j + 1)b$$

$$Q_r = \sum_j (2j + 1)e^{-j(j+1)b/kT}$$

Again, since the spacing of the energy levels is small with respect to kT, the sum may be replaced by an integral. Doing this, and evaluating the integral, gives

$$Q_r = \frac{8\pi^2 I k T}{h^2}$$

or, for a nonlinear polyatomic molecule which has three moments of inertia,

$$Q_r = \left(\frac{8\pi^2 kT}{h^2}\right)^{\!3/2} \frac{(\pi I_x I_y I_z)^{1/2}}{\sigma}$$

where σ is the symmetry number.

The symmetry number must be introduced in order to avoid counting interchanges of indistinguishable particles. In methane, for example, there are four threefold axes of symmetry and thus twelve ways in which indistinguishable particles (i.e., hydrogens) may be interchanged by rotation, and the symmetry number is 12. Similarly, the symmetry number of ethylene is 4 and that of ammonia is 3.

One may obtain expressions for the contribution of rotation to the change in free energy and enthalpy as before, giving

$$F^0 = H_0^0 - 2.289 T \log (I_x I_y I_z \times 10^{117}) - 6.864 T \log T + 4.576 T \log \sigma$$
$$+ 3.014 T$$

$$H^0 = H_0^0 + 2.980 T$$

$$S^0 = - \frac{(F^0 - H^0)}{T}$$

We may now calculate these quantities for water. Using $r_{\text{OH}} = 0.958 \times 10^{-8}$ cm, and $\not\!\!\sphericalangle$ (HOH) $= 104.27°$, one finds that

$$I_z = 1.024 \times 10^{-40} \text{ g cm}^2$$
$$I_x = 1.920 \times 10^{-40}$$
$$I_y = 2.947 \times 10^{-40}$$

Substituting these values, and $\sigma = 2$, into the above expressions gives at room temperature

$$F^0 = H_0^0 - 2225 \text{ cal/mole}$$
$$H^0 = H_0^0 + 888 \text{ cal/mole}$$
$$S^0 = 10.45 \text{ eu/mole}$$

It can be seen that these values are considerably smaller than those arising from the translational partition function for water (p. 228).

The importance of the rotational partition functions may be illustrated by considering the equilibrium between *n*-pentane and neopentane. Here the translational partition function will be the same for both, and this may be neglected. In the following, we shall consider only rotation about the center of mass, and we shall not include internal rotation of the alkyl groups.

In neopentane the center of mass coincides with the central carbon, and because of its spherical symmetry, the three moments of inertia must be the same. The easiest one to calculate is that about the z axis. Using the dimensions $r_{C-C} = 1.54$ Å, $r_{C-H} = 1.08$ Å and tetrahedral bond angles, the projected distances on the xy plane shown in Fig. 2-2 may be derived. It may be assumed that the hydrogens of the methyl group will act like a group of mass three whose distance from the central carbon is $(1.54 + 1.08 \cos 70.5°) \cos 19.5°$ or 1.80 Å. The moment of inertia will be

$$I = \sum mr^2 = \frac{3 \times 12(1.45)^2 + 9 \times 1(1.80)^2 + 3 \times 1(1.02)^2}{6.03 \times 10^{23} \times 10^{16}}$$

$$= 17.9 \times 10^{-39} \text{ g cm}^2$$

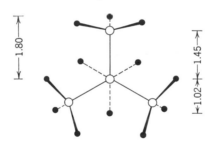

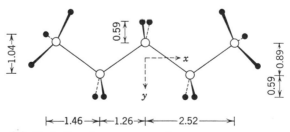

Fig. 2-2. Projection of neopentane and n-pentane on the xy plane.

Since the symmetry number is 12, the contribution of rotation to the thermodynamic functions for neopentane will be

$$F^0 = H_0{}^0 - 5260 \text{ cal/mole}$$

$$H^0 = H_0{}^0 + 888 \text{ cal/mole}$$

$$S^0 = 20.6 \text{ eu/mole}$$

If the contribution due to translation were added, these numbers would become

$$F^0 = H_0{}^0 - 15{,}320 \text{ cal}$$

$$H^0 = H_0{}^0 + 2370 \text{ cal}$$

$$S^0 = 59.3 \text{ eu}$$

The observed values are[3]

$$F^0 = H_0{}^0 - 16{,}800 \text{ cal}$$

$$H^0 = H_0{}^0 + 5040 \text{ cal}$$

$$S^0 = 73.23 \text{ eu}$$

It can be seen that although vibration and internal rotation have not as yet been included, the values calculated above are reasonably close to the observed values. The enthalpy term is the one having the largest deviation, and it is this term which is principally affected by the vibrational partition function and by internal rotation.

For the purpose of calculating the moments of inertia, *n*-pentane may be considered as a planar molecule having the geometry shown in Fig. 2-2. The center of mass lies 0.38 Å under the central carbon.[4] Using the

[3] American Petroleum Institute, Project 44, Carnegie Institute of Technology, Selected Values of Properties of Hydrocarbons."

[4] The center of mass need not be obtained, and the moment of inertia may be obtained by first evaluating

$$I_{xx} = \sum m_i(y_i{}^2 + z_i{}^2) - \frac{1}{M} \left(\sum m_i y_i \right)^2 - \frac{1}{M} \left(\sum m_i z_i \right)^2$$

$$I_{yy} = \sum m_i(x_i{}^2 + z_i{}^2) - \frac{1}{M} \left(\sum m_i x_i \right)^2 - \frac{1}{M} \left(\sum m_i z_i \right)^2$$

$$I_{zz} = \sum m_i(x_i{}^2 + y_i{}^2) - \frac{1}{M} \left(\sum m_i x_i \right)^2 - \frac{1}{M} \left(\sum m_i y_i \right)^2$$

$$I_{xy} = \sum m_i x_i y_i - \frac{1}{M} \left(\sum m_i x_i \right)\left(\sum m_i y_i \right)$$

$$I_{xy} = \sum m_i x_i z_i - \frac{1}{M} \left(\sum m_i x_i \right)\left(\sum m_i z_i \right)$$

$$I_{yz} = \sum m_i y_i z_i - \frac{1}{M} \left(\sum m_i y_i \right)\left(\sum m_i z_i \right)$$

where M is $\Sigma\, m_i$. The moments of inertia are then obtained by diagonalizing the

dimension given, the moments of inertia are found to be

$$I_x = 3.3 \times 10^{-39} \text{ g cm}^2$$
$$I_y = 43.3 \times 10^{-39}$$
$$I_z = 40.0 \times 10^{-39}$$

Since *n*-pentane is not a planar molecule, it has no rotational axis of symmetry, and therefore $\sigma = 1$. Using these values, the thermodynamic functions due to rotation are

$$F^0 = H_0{}^0 - 6730 \text{ cal/mole}$$
$$H^0 = H_0{}^0 + 888 \text{ cal/mole}$$
$$S^0 = 25.5 \text{ eu/mole}$$

The difference between these values and those for neopentane are

$$\Delta F^0 = \Delta H_0{}^0 - 1470 \text{ cal/mole}$$
$$\Delta H^0 = \Delta H_0{}^0$$
$$\Delta S^0 = 4.9 \text{ eu/mole}$$

whereas the observed values are

$$\Delta F^0 = \Delta H_0{}^0 - 1760 \text{ cal/mole}$$
$$\Delta H^0 = \Delta H_0{}^0 + 640 \text{ cal/mole}$$
$$\Delta S^0 = 10.0 \text{ eu/mole}$$

Again, the difference in free energy is close to the observed values because of the relative insensitivity of free energy to the vibrational partition function. Thus rotation alone accounts for about 80% of the free energy change. The products of the three moments of inertia for neopentane and for *n*-pentane are about the same, and the difference in free energy arises largely from the difference in symmetry number. This illustrates an important fact: the more symmetrical molecule will become increasingly less favored in an equilibrium as the temperature is increased because of the symmetry restriction on the availability of the rotational energy levels.

---

determinant

$$\begin{vmatrix} I_{xx} & -I_{xy} & -I_{xz} \\ -I_{xy} & I_{yy} & -I_{yz} \\ -I_{xz} & -I_{yz} & I_{zz} \end{vmatrix}$$

Also, the product of the three moments of inertia (which is usually the quantity of interest) is equal to the value of the determinant.

In considering the vibrational partition function it is convenient to first consider the case of a diatomic molecule using the harmonic oscillator approximation. The spacing of the energy levels will be $h\nu$, and the partition function will be given by

$$(\epsilon_i - \epsilon_0) = v_i h\nu \qquad v = 0, 1, 2, \ldots, \infty$$

$$Q_v = \sum_0^\infty e^{-v_i h\nu/kT}$$

but

$$\sum_0^\infty e^{-v_i x} = \frac{1}{1 - e^{-x}}$$

and therefore

$$Q_v = (1 - e^{-x})^{-1}$$

where $x = h\nu/kT$. For a polyatomic molecule, Q_v is evaluated for each vibrational degree of freedom, and the product is taken. Using the expressions previously obtained, and substituting the values of the partition function, one obtains

$$F^0 = H_0^{\ 0} + 1.987\, T \sum_j \ln\left(1 - e^{-x_j}\right)$$

$$H^0 = H_0^{\ 0} + 1.987\, T \sum_j \frac{x_j}{e^{x_j} - 1}$$

where j refers to the vibrational degrees of freedom.

For water, the vibrational frequencies are 1597, 3652, and 3756 cm^{-1}. The partition functions are

$$Q_1 = (1 - e^{-7.69})^{-1} = 1$$

$$Q_2 = (1 - e^{-17.61})^{-1} = 1$$

$$Q_3 = (1 - e^{-18.11})^{-1} = 1$$

and it can be seen that in each case Q is negligibly different from unity. Thus the contribution to F^0 and H^0 for these vibrations is essentially zero. It is readily seen that only the low frequency vibrations (< 1000 cm^{-1}) can affect the value of the partition function.

This being the case, the contributions due to rotation and translation given above should correspond to the observed values. A comparison is given in Table 2-1.

So long as the vibrational assignments are available, and the molecule is rigid, so that it has no internal rotations, the thermodynamic functions may be calculated with a high degree of precision, using the equations derived above. The case of internal rotation will be considered separately in Section 2-5.

The treatment described above has proved to be of great value in considering many equilibrium processes, for if the heats of combustion of all of the compounds are known, the equilibrium constant may be calculated as a function of temperature with an accuracy comparable to that of good experimental measurements. Although such calculations are not often made by organic chemists, some qualitative observations

Table 2-1   Thermodynamic Functions for Water at 25°C

	Translation	*Rotation*	*Total*	*Observed*
$F^0 - E_0$ (cal/mole)	-8839	-2228	$-11{,}067$	$-11{,}081$
$H^0 - E_0$ (cal/mole)	1480	888	2368	2368
S^0 (eu)	34.6	10.45	45.1	45.1

may be made. The first, which was mentioned previously, is that symmetrical molecules become less favored as the temperature increases, for the spacing of the rotational energy levels is greater for symmetrical molecules than for nonsymmetrical ones. The second is that an equilibrium of the type

$$2A \rightleftharpoons B$$

will not be favored by the translational partition function. An example of this was given on p. 221. These conclusions are not only of importance in considering equilibria but will also be important in our later discussion of kinetics.

2-4 Ground State Energies of Molecules

We saw in the preceding section that the change in equilibrium constant with temperature for a reaction carried out in the gas phase could be calculated if the required spectroscopic data were available. However, the evaluation of the equilibrium constant required a knowledge of the intrinsic energy of molecules—that which they would have at absolute zero. Actually, the true energy at any temperature would do as well, for it could be corrected to that for any other temperature if we know the change in the partition function with temperature.

The problem is then to obtain the heat of formation. This is defined as the change in heat content on going from the elements in their normal state to the compound in question. For some inorganic compounds this may be determined directly, as in the reaction of an element with oxygen or chlorine. In other cases it may be obtained from the heat of a reaction when the heats of formation of the other compounds are known, or from an equilibrium constant when the entropy change is known. However, for most organic compounds it must be determined indirectly from the heat of combustion.

The heat of combustion is the heat evolved in the reaction of the compound with oxygen. In principle, this is a simply determined quantity for compounds containing only carbon, hydrogen, and oxygen, for here the products are only carbon dioxide and water. The actual measurement of the heat of combustion is, however, not so simple, and it is only recently that data of high accuracy have been obtained. The difficulty is illustrated by cyclohexane, which has a heat of combustion of 944.79 kcal/mole, leading to a heat of formation of -29.43 kcal/mole. Although the latter quantity is much smaller than the former, it contains all the error associated with the heat of combustion. Thus in order to obtain the heat of formation with an accuracy of ± 0.1 kcal/mole, the heat of combustion must be measured with an accuracy of 0.01 %.

The conversion of the heat of combustion to the heat of formation may be considered in terms of the process

$$C_nH_mO_{l(g)} \rightarrow nC + \frac{m}{2} H_2 + \frac{l}{2} O_2 \xrightarrow{O_2} nCO_{2(g)+} \frac{m}{2} H_2O_{(l)}$$

The heat of combustion of graphite (the standard state for carbon) is 94.05 kcal/g atom and the heat of combustion of hydrogen to liquid water is 68.32 kcal/mole. Thus the heat of formation at 25°C (ΔH_f) is given by

$$\Delta H_f = \Delta H_{comb.} - n(94.05) - \frac{m}{2}(68.32)$$

The determination of the heat of combustion for compounds having other elements is a more difficult problem. With nitrogen containing compounds, the nitrogen may appear as nitrogen, or as one of the nitrogen oxides or their hydrates. Similarly, sulfur compounds may lead to sulfur dioxide, sulfur trioxide, and their hydration products. The analysis of the results in these cases may be rather difficult.

An example of the determination of the heat of formation from the heat of reaction is found in the hydrogenation of alkenes.[5] Knowing the heat of formation of cyclohexane and the heat change in the reaction

$$\text{benzene} + 3H_2 \rightarrow \text{cyclohexane}$$

we may calculate the heat of formation of benzene.

Although the heats of formation are extremely important in studying properties of compounds (i.e., changes in energy due to electron delocalization, to steric effects, and to bond angle deformation) and in interpreting kinetic and equilibrium data, the available data are very limited and the number of persons involved in making the necessary measurements is remarkably small.

Since approximate data are better than no data, we shall now consider one of the several attempts at providing data which will allow the prediction of heats of formation and also of the entropy. The original work along these lines was done by Parks and Huffman,[6] leading to constants describing the effect of introducing various substituents into a parent compound. The results obtained using this very simple method are not too satisfactory, and a number of improved methods have been developed. We shall describe only one of them, Franklin's method of group equivalents.[7]

The calculation of the thermodynamic properties of aliphatic hydrocarbons using the appropriate partition functions has been well developed.[8] It is found that the contributions to the thermodynamic functions may be expressed in terms of the groups present, with suitable correction for the symmetry number. The intrinsic energy is also a function of the groups present, with a correction for steric effects. Thus the heat of formation at any temperature may be expressed by the summation of the appropriate group constants (Table 2-2), followed by correction for the symmetry number and steric effects.

---

[5] The determination of heats of hydrogenation in solution has been discussed in detail by R. B. Williams, *J. Am. Chem. Soc.*, **64**, 1395 (1942); R. B. Turner, W. R. Meador, and R. E. Winkler, *J. Am. Chem. Soc.*, **79**, 4116 (1957). These papers also give descriptions of simple calorimeters which are suitable for determining heats of reaction in solution.

[6] G. S. Parks and H. M. Huffman, *The Free Energies of Some Organic Compounds*, Reinhold Publishing Co, New York, 1932.

[7] J. L. Franklin, *Ind. Eng. Chem.* **41**, 1070 (1949). See G. J. Janz, *Estimation of Thermodynamic Properties of Organic Compounds*, Academic Press, New York, 1958, who summarizes all the available methods for estimating thermodynamic properties.

[8] K. S. Pitzer, *J. Chem. Phys.*, **8**, 711 (1940), *Chem. Revs.*, **27**, 39 (1940).

As an example of the application of this method, we may consider the thermodynamic functions for *n*-pentane and neopentane.[9]

n-pentane	$\Delta H_f(298°)$	$H^0 - H_0^0(298°)$	$F^0 - H_0^0(298°)$
2 × CH_3	-20.24	2.86	-13.92
3 × CH_2	-14.78	3.07	-5.14
$RT \ln 2$			0.40
	$\overline{-35.02}$	$\overline{5.93}$	$\overline{-18.66}$

$$S^0 = (18.66 + 5.93)/298.2 = 82.4$$

neopentane			
4 × CH_3	-40.48	5.72	-27.84
1 × C	0.80	-0.68	9.53
$RT \ln 12$			1.47
	$\overline{-39.68}$	$\overline{5.04}$	$\overline{-16.84}$

$$S^0 = (16.84 + 5.04)/298.2 = 73.5$$

These values may be compared with the observed values:[10]

n-pentane	$\Delta H_f = -35.00$	$H^0 - H_0^0 =$	5.68
	$F^0 - H_0^0 = -18.56$	$S^0 = 83.2$	
neopentane	$\Delta H_f = -39.67$	$H^0 - H_0^0 =$	5.04
	$F^0 - H_0^0 = -16.80$	$S^0 = 73.2$	

The results are particularly good in this case, for the two compounds were important in establishing the values of the group contributions. In general, with unstrained compounds the thermodynamic functions will not be in error by more than 1 to 2 kcal/mole, although in some cases larger deviations will be found.

The method has been extended to nonhydrocarbon groups (Table 2-3), but here the values must be considered only as approximate because of the relatively small number of data on which to base the group contributions.

If one examines the data on the heats of formation of isomeric hydrocarbons (Table 2-4), one finds that the more branched hydrocarbon has the lower heat of formation (i.e., is the more stable). An interesting question is the origin of the greater stability of the more branched isomers.

There are several reasons for the difference in energy. The contribution which is most simply evaluated is the difference in zero-point energy

---

[9] The symmetry number for *n*-paraffins is defined as 2 in this treatment.

[10] American Petroleum Institute, Project 44, Carnegie Institute of Technology, "Selected Values of Properties of Hydrocarbons."

Table 2-2 Group Contributions for Hydrocarbon Groups[a]

Group	$H^0 - H_0^0$				ΔH_f^0			
	0°K	298°K	400°K	500°K	0°K	298°K	400°K	500°K
CH_3	0	1.43	2.15	3.00	−8.26	−10.12	−10.71	−11.22
CH_2	0	1.023	1.684	2.46	−3.673	−4.926	−5.223	−5.465
CH	0	−0.014	0.51	1.25	0.18	−1.09	−1.17	−1.12
C	0	−0.68	−0.16	0.55	1.74	0.80	1.07	1.45
$H_2C{=}$	0	1.26	1.86	2.56	7.26	6.25	5.88	5.77
$\mathrm{H\text{-}C{=}CH_2}$	0	1.81	2.84	4.08	16.73	15.00	14.47	14.01
$\mathrm{C{=}C}$ (H, H trans)	0	1.33	2.28	3.42	19.03	17.83	17.57	17.37
$\mathrm{C{=}C}$ (H, H cis)	0	1.12	1.84	2.84	20.31	18.88	18.42	18.07
$\mathrm{C{=}CH_2}$	0	1.22	2.20	3.41	18.20	16.89	16.68	16.53

Structure								
C=C (with H)	0	0.59	1.37	2.35	21.10	20.19	20.10	20.08
C=C	0	−0.02	0.61	1.45	25.08	24.57	24.74	24.88
=C	0	0.50	0.90	1.35	33.0	33.42	33.59	33.71
HC≡	0	1.20	1.77	2.40	27.16	27.10	27.07	27.02
≡C	0	0.47	0.81	1.18	27.12	27.34	27.42	27.48
C—H[b]	0	0.56	0.96	1.46	4.00	3.30	3.09	2.92
C[b]	0	0.08	0.32	0.67	5.76	5.57	5.59	5.63
C↔[b]	0	−0.74	−0.51	−0.20	5.29	4.28	4.33	4.28
↔CH₂[b]	0	1.26	1.96	2.79	11.3	10.08	9.81	9.64
↔C H[b]	0	0.75	1.41	2.14	12.65	12.04	12.11	12.16

Table 2-2 (continued)

Group	$H^0 - H_0^0$				ΔH_f^0			
	0°K	298°K	400°K	500°K	0°K	298°K	400°K	500°K
Cyclo C_6 ring	0	-1.55	-2.23	-2.77	1.10	-0.45	-1.13	-1.67
Cyclo C_5 ring	0	-1.04	-1.78	-2.44	6.72	5.68	4.94	4.28
Cyclo C_4 ring	0	-0.4	-0.8	-1.2	18.8	18.4	18.0	17.6
Cyclo C_3 ring	0	-0.26	-0.47	-0.89	24.4	24.22	23.87	23.58
Correction Factors for Paraffin Chains								
Ethyl side chain	0	-0.7	-0.7	-0.7	1.5	0.8	0.8	0.8
3 Adjacent CH groups	0	0.7	0.7	0.7	1.6	2.3	2.3	2.3
Adjacent C and CH groups	0	0	0	0	2.5	2.5	2.5	2.5
Adjacent quaternary C's	0	0.4	0.4	0.4	5.0	5.4	5.4	5.4
Quaternary C not adjacent to terminal methyl	0	-0.4	-0.4	-0.4	2.1	1.7	1.7	1.7
Correction Factors for Substituents on Aromatic Nucleus								
1,2-Dimethyl or 1,3-methylethyl	0	0.5	0.5	0.5	0.1	0.6	0.6	0.6
1,2-Methylethyl or 1,2,3-trimethyl	0	0.5	0.5	0.5	0.9	1.4	1.4	1.4

[a] J. L. Franklin, *Ind. Eng. Chem.*, **41**, 1070 (1949).
[b] The symbol ↔ refers to bonding in a conjugated system.

Group	$F^0 - F_0^0$					ΔF_f^0	
CH₃	0	−6.96	−9.92	−13.04	−8.26	−4.14	−2.00	0.24
CH₂	0	−1.714	−2.747	−3.944	−3.673	2.048	4.479	6.931
CH	0	3.51	4.52	5.55	0.18	7.46	10.39	13.26
C	0	9.53	12.88	16.15	1.74	11.44	15.00	18.45
$H_2C=$	0	−6.62	−9.43	−12.36	7.26	7.94	8.57	9.97
$\text{H}-\text{C}=\text{CH}_2$	0	−8.82	−12.64	−16.62	16.73	19.13	20.61	22.21
$\text{H}-\text{C}=\text{C}-\text{H}$	0	−3.42	−5.23	−7.21	19.03	23.19	25.03	26.93
$\text{H}-\text{C}=\text{C}-\text{H}$	0	−3.98	−5.86	−7.87	20.32	23.92	25.68	27.56
$\text{C}=\text{CH}_2$	0	−3.25	−5.07	−7.00	18.20	22.45	24.36	26.31
$\text{C}=\text{C}-\text{H}$	0	1.66	1.84	1.87	21.10	26.69	28.88	31.10

Table 2-2 (continued)

Group	$F^0 - F_0^0$				ΔF_f^0			
	0°K	298°K	400°K	500°K	0°K	298°K	400°K	500°K
C=C (four bonds)	0	1.89	9.06	11.13	25.08	32.26	34.80	37.36
=C=	0	−1.25	−1.90	−2.67	33.0	32.09	31.61	31.08
HC≡	0	−6.17	−8.78	−11.47	27.16	24.8	24.01	23.26
—C≡	0	−1.44	−2.14	−2.95	27.12	25.65	26.28	24.72
CH	0	−2.87	−4.11	−5.43	4.00	4.84	5.50	6.13
C	0	2.42	3.24	3.90	5.76	8.76	9.34	10.23
C	0	−0.33	0.17	0.63	5.29	5.43	5.80	6.49
CH₂	0	−5.46	−7.85	−10.39	11.3	13.17	14.17	15.26
C—H	0	−0.05	−0.45	−1.46	12.65	16.36	17.70	19.15

Group	$F^0 - F_0^0$				ΔF_f^0			
	0°K	298°K	400°K	500°K	0°K	298°K	400°K	500°K
Cyclo C_6 ring	0	−7.45	−9.08	−10.71	1.10	−6.35	−7.98	−9.61
Cyclo C_5 ring	0	−9.38	−12.30	−14.78	6.72	−2.66	−5.58	−8.06
Cyclo C_4 ring	0	−10.8	−14.8	−18.8	18.8	8.0	4.0	0.0
Cyclo C_3 ring	0	−9.89	−13.07	−16.28	24.4	14.51	11.33	8.12
Correction Factors for Paraffin Chains								
Ethyl side chain	0	−0.8	−0.8	−0.8	1.5	0.7	0.7	0.7
3 Adjacent CH groups	0	0.5	0.5	0.5	1.6	2.1	2.1	2.1
Adjacent C and CH groups	0	1.1	1.1	1.1	2.5	3.6	3.6	3.6
Adjacent quaternary C's	0	0.8	0.9	1.1	5.0	5.8	5.9	6.1
Quaternary C not adjacent to terminal methyl	0	−1.1	−1.1	−1.1	2.1	1.0	1.0	1.0
Correction Factors for Substituents on Aromatic Nucleus								
1,2 Substitution	0	0.5	0.5	0.5		0.5	0.5	0.5
1,3 Substitution	0	0.8	0.8	0.8		−0.7	−0.7	−0.7
1,2,3 Substitution	0	0.1	0.1	0.1		1.0	1.0	1.0
Correction for symmetry	0	←——— $RT \ln \sigma$ ——→			0.9			

Table 2-3   Group Equivalents for Nonhydrocarbon Groups, Radicals and Ions[a]

Group	ΔH_f			ΔF_f		
	0°K	298°K	600°K	0°K	298°K	600°K
—OH (primary)	−40.1	−41.9	−42.2	−40.1	−36.6	−31.1
—OH (sec)	−43.1	−44.9	−44.6	−43.1	−42.1	−37.4
—OH (tert)	−46.9	−49.2	−48.9	−46.9	−44.7	−37.1
—OH (phenol)	−44.0	−46.9	−45.6	−44.0	−39.9	−31.1
$\mathrm{C{=}O}$ (with H)	−32.7	−33.9	−34.0	−32.7	−27.9	−21.7
$\mathrm{C{=}O}$ (with O)	−30.6	−31.6	−31.2	−30.6	−28.6	−25.9
$\mathrm{-C({=}O)OH}$	−93.1	−94.6	−93.0	−93.1	−87.1	−79.6
$\mathrm{-C({=}O)O-}$ (ester)		−79.8			−71.6	
—O— (ether)		−27.2			−23.8	
$\mathrm{-C({=}O)O-C({=}O)}$		−102.6			−93.9	
—NH₂		2.8				
—NH—		12.0				
$\mathrm{-N<}$		−19.2				
↔NH₂		−0.8			−6.4	
—NO₂		−8.5				

Table 2-3 (continued)

Group	ΔH_f			ΔF_f		
	0°K	298°K	600°K	0°K	298°K	600°K
—ONO		−10.9				
—ONO$_2$		−18.4				
—C≡N		29.5				
—N=C		44.4				
—SH		5.7			3.1	
—S—		11.6			10.8	
↔S↔		11.3			7.8	
—CH$_2$·		34				
—CH·		34				
—C·		33				
—O·		7.5				
—O—O·		7.5				
—S·		43				
—CH$_2^+$		212				
—CH$^+$		209				
—C$^+$		195				
—C$\overset{+}{=}$CH$_2$		240				
—CH=CH$^+$		245				
—S$^+$		232				

[a] J. L. Franklin, *Ind. Eng. Chem.*, **41**, 1070 (1949); *J. Chem. Phys.*, **21**, 2029 (1953).

Table 2-4   Heats of Formation of Isomeric Hydrocarbons[a]

Compound	ΔH_f^0 (0°K)	ΔH_f^0 (298°K)
n-Butane	−23.67	−30.15
Isobutane	−25.30	−32.15
n-Pentane	−27.23	−35.00
Isopentane	−28.81	−36.92
Neopentane	−31.30	−39.67
n-Hexane	−30.91	−39.96
Isohexane	−32.08	−41.66
3-Methylpentane	−31.97	−41.02
2,3-Dimethylbutane	−32.73	−42.49

[a] American Petroleum Institute, Project 44, Carnegie Institute of Technology, "Selected Values of Properties of Hydrocarbons."

(i.e., the sum of $\frac{1}{2}h\nu$ for each vibrational mode). The necessary vibrational frequencies are known for a number of the smaller hydrocarbons, and it is found that neopentane has 1.0 kcal/mole lower zero-point energy than *n*-pentane, and isobutane has 0.24 kcal/mole lower zero-point energy than *n*-butane. These differences account for about 20% of the observed difference.[11]

Another factor is the dispersion or London force between nonbonded atoms. Because the "covalent radius" of hydrogen (i.e., the distance at which the van der Waals force becomes repulsive) is very small, the nonbonded interactions in compounds such as neopentane will be

Table 2-5 Isomerization Energies, 0°K

Reaction	ΔE_L	$\Delta E_{vib.}$	$\Delta E_{calc.}$	$\Delta E_{exp.}$
Isobutane $\rightleftharpoons$ *n*-Butane	1.28	0.24	1.52	1.63
Neopentane $\rightleftharpoons$ *n*-Pentane	3.8	1.0	4.8	4.1

attractive. Pitzer and Catalano have estimated the magnitude of the effect and have concluded that it should be given by

$$E_L = -[22.6\sum R_{C-C}^{-6} + 8.68\sum R_{C-H}^{-6} + 3.42\sum R_{H-H}^{-6}] \times 10^{-60} \text{ ergs.}$$

The results are summarized in Table 2-5. They are, in general, quite good, showing that a major factor stabilizing branched hydrocarbons is placing atoms in closer proximity to each other.

The increase in stability with increasing chain branching does not continue indefinitely. If one were to replace all the hydrogens in neopentane with methyl groups, the latter would be at sufficiently short distances to each other to cause a repulsive interaction. The magnitude of this interaction may, in principle, be calculated by a method to be described subsequently (Section 3-6), but relatively little work has been done in this direction. However, there have been a number of experimental demonstrations of such interactions.[12]

The reaction of trimethylboron with amines has received considerable study. The dissociation constants for a number of these adducts are given in Table 2-6. At first methyl substitution on the amine leads to more stable complexes, presumably due to the inductive effect of the alkyl group. However, with trimethylamine the complex becomes less stable

[11] K. S. Pitzer and E. Catalano, *J. Am. Chem. Soc.*, **78**, 4844 (1956); K. S. Pitzer, *Advances in Chemical Physics*, Interscience Publishers, New York, 1959, vol. II, p. 59.
[12] The entire subject of steric interactions has been reviewed in *Steric Effects in Organic Chemistry*, M. Newman (ed.), John Wiley and Sons, New York, 1956.

because of the repulsive interaction of the methyl groups. The same changes are amplified in the case of ethyl substitution. Similarly, methyl substitution in pyridine ring leads to a more stable complex, except when substituted in the 2-position. In this case, no complex could be isolated.

The same effects may be seen in the S_N1 solvolysis of tertiary halides, where the more branched isomer is the more reactive because of relief of

Table 2-6   **Dissociation Constants of Trimethylboron-Amine Compounds**[a]

Base	$K_{100°}^{\text{diss.}}$	$\Delta H°$ (kcal/mole)	$\Delta S°$ (eu)
NH_3	4.6	13.8	40
CH_3NH_2	0.035	17.6	41
$(CH_3)_2NH$	0.0214	19.3	44
$(CH_3)_3N$	0.477	17.6	46
$C_2H_5NH_2$	0.0705	18.0	43
$(C_2H_5)_2NH$	1.22	16.3	44
$(C_2H_5)_3N$		no compound	
$t\text{-}C_4H_9NH_2$	9.46	13.0	39
Quinuclidine	0.0196	19.9	46
Pyridine	0.301	17.0	43
2-Picoline		no compound	
3-Picoline	0.138	17.8	44
4-Picoline	0.105	19.4	48

[a] H. C. Brown and M. D. Taylor, *J. Am. Chem. Soc.*, **69**, 1332 (1947); H. C. Brown and G. K. Barbaras, *J. Am. Chem. Soc.*, **69**, 1137 (1947), **75**, 6 (1953); H. C. Brown and S. Sujishi, *J. Am. Chem. Soc.*, **70**, 2878 (1948).

strain in going from the tetrahedral reactant to the trigonal activated complex;[13] in the ultraviolet spectra of ortho-substituted anilines, nitrobenzenes, acetophenones, and related compounds where the ortho substituents prevent coplanarity of the ring and the substituent and reduce the resonance interaction;[14] and in the optical activity of di-ortho-substituted diphenyls.[15]

[13] See E. L. Eliel in M. Newman (ed.), *Steric Effects in Organic Chemistry*, John Wiley and Sons, New York, 1956, ch. 2.
[14] See L. L. Ingraham, *ibid.*, ch. 11.
[15] See F. H. Westheimer, *ibid.*, ch. 12.

Table 2-7 Bond Dissociation Energies (D) and Bond Energy Terms (E)[a,b]

Bond	D 0°K	E 25°C	Bond	D 0°K	E 25°C
H—H	103.24	104.18	H_3Si—H		76
CH_3—H	101	99.3	H_2P—H		~77
CH≡C—H	<121		HS—H	90?	
H_2C:CH—H	<121?		H—Cl	102.2	103.1
H_3CCH_2—H	96		H—Br	86.5	87.4
n-C_3H_7—H	100		H—I	70.5	71.4
i-C_3H_7—H	94		∖C—C∕ (ave)		82.6
n-C_4H_9—H	101		∖C=C∕ (ave)		145.8
t-C_4H_9—H	89		—C≡C— (ave)		199.6
neo-C_5H_{11}—H	95		HC≡CH	230	194.3
C_6H_5—H	102		$H_2C=CH_2$	125?	142.9
$C_6H_5CH_2$—H	77.5?		H_3C—CH_3	83	
$C_6H_5CH(CH_3)$—H	75		CH_2:$CHCH_2$—CH_3	61.5	
$C_6H_5C(CH_3)_2$—H	74		C_6H_5—CH_3	87?	
H—CN	114		$C_6H_5CH_2$—CH_3	63	
H—CHO	76		$C_6H_5CH_2$—$CH_2C_6H_5$	47	
CF_3—H	103		CH_3—CN	103	
CCl_3—H	90		CH_2=CO	~80	
CH_2Br—H	99		CH_3—CHO	~75	
NH_2—H	102	93.4	CH_3—$COCH_3$	72	
HO—H	117.5	110.6	∖C—N∕ (ave)		72.8
HOO—H	90		∖C=N— (ave)		147
H—F	134	135	—C≡N (ave)		212.6
HC≡N		207	CH_2:$CHCH_2$—Cl	60	
CH_3—NH_2	80	68.1	$C_6H_5CH_2$—Cl	68?	
CH_3N:N—CH_3	46		C_6H_5CO—Cl	73	
$C_6H_5CH_2$—NH_2	59		CF_3—Cl	83	
CH_3—NO_2	54?		CBr_3—Br	<50	
OC=O	127	192	—C—Br (ave)	65	68
∖C—O— (ave)		85.5	CH_3—Br	67	
∖C=O (ald)		176	CH_2:$CHCH_2$—Br	46	
∖C=O (ket)		179	C_6H_5—Br	71	
$H_2C=O$		166	$C_6H_5CH_2$—Br	51	
HCO—OH	~90		C_6H_5CO—Br	57	

Table 2-7 (continued)

Bond	D 0°K	E 25°C	Bond	D 0°K	E 25°C
CH_3—OH	~90	80.2	CF_3—Br	65	
CH_3CO—OH	~90		CCl_3—Br	49	
C_2H_5—OH	~90	83.8	CH_3—I	53	51
CH_3—F	107		C_2H_5—I	51	52
SC=S		128	CH_2:$CHCH_2$—I	46	
$\diagdown$ $\!$—C—S— (ave) $\diagup$		65	C_6H_5—I	57	
CH_3—SH	70?		$C_6H_5CH_2$—I	39	
C_2H_5—SH	69?		CH_3O—NO	36?	
t-C_4H_9—SH	65?		CH_3O—NO$_2$	40?	
$C_6H_5CH_2$—SH	53		HO—OH	51	35
CH_3—SCH$_3$	73?	65	CH_3O—OCH$_3$	37	
$C_6H_5CH_2$—SCH$_3$	51		CH_3COO—OCOCH$_3$	30	
OC=S		128	F_2	36	37
Cl_3C—Cl	68	78.2	Cl_2	57.07	57.87
CH_3—Cl	~80	78.2	Br_2	45.46	46.08
C_2H_5—Cl	83		I_2	35.55	36.06

ᵃ The data were taken from T. L. Cottrell, *The Strengths of Chemical Bonds*, 2nd ed., Butterworths Scientific Publications, London, 1958.
ᵇ The bond energy term is defined so that the sum of all terms for a molecule will equal its heat of atomization. Thus for methane it is one-fourth of the ΔH value for the reaction $CH_4 \rightarrow C + 4H$.

Steric effects such as those described above arise mainly from two factors—the van der Waals repulsion of nonbonded atoms and the distortion of the molecule resulting from an attempt to minimize the repulsive force. The calculation of steric factors such as these will be postponed to Section 3-6 where they may be applied to a specific, well-defined example.

In the preceding discussion we were concerned with the energy of a compound. In some cases the change in energy for a reaction may be considered in terms of the energies of individual bonds in the reactant and product molecules. For example, if we knew the bond dissociation energy for methane

$$CH_4 \rightarrow CH_3 \cdot + H \cdot \qquad \Delta E = 101 \text{ kcal/mole}$$

and for hydrogen iodide

$$HI \rightarrow H \cdot + I \cdot \qquad \Delta E = 70.5 \text{ kcal/mole}$$

the enthalpy change for the following reaction would be obtained by subtraction:

$$CH_4 + I \cdot \rightarrow CH_3 \cdot + HI \qquad \Delta H = \Delta E = 31 \text{ kcal/mole}$$

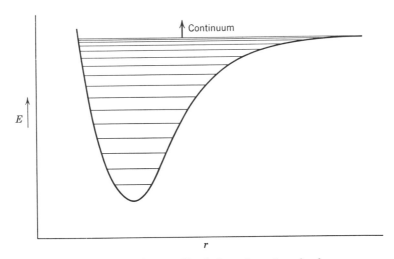

Fig. 2-3. Vibrational levels for a diatomic molecule.

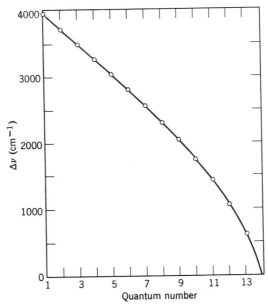

*Fig. 2-4. Birge-Spooner extrapolation for the vibrational energy levels of the hydrogen molecule (H. Beutler, Z. physik. Chem., **B27**, 287 (1934)).*

The bond dissociation energies are available from a number of sources.[16] For diatomic molecules, such as hydrogen chloride and bromide, they may be obtained from an analysis of the vibrational spectrum. If one can obtain the excitation energies for the transition from the ground vibrational level to a number of vibrationally excited states (i.e., the fundamental frequency and many of the overtones), one can construct the potential energy curve which on extrapolation will give the dissociation energy. In practice this is done by using the Birge-Sponer extrapolation.[17]

The vibrational levels of a molecule (Fig. 2-3) become more closely spaced as the quantum number increases until, finally, at the dissociation energy, the energy states become continuous. If one plots the difference in energy between states against the quantum number (Fig. 2-4), extrapolation to zero difference will give the quantum number at which the continuum begins. A summation of the energies up to this point will give the dissociation energy.

This method is not applicable to polyatomic molecules. Mass spectrometric methods are sometimes useful in determining dissociation energies of polyatomic molecules. However, the most generally useful method involves the study of the kinetics of gas phase reactions.

As an example, let us consider the photochemical bromination of methane, which involves the steps[18]

$$Br_2 \xrightarrow{h\nu} 2\ Br\cdot$$

$$CH_4 + Br\cdot \xrightarrow{k_1} CH_3\cdot + HBr$$

$$CH_3\cdot + Br_2 \xrightarrow{k_2} CH_3Br + Br\cdot$$

$$CH_3\cdot + HBr \xrightarrow{k_3} CH_4 + Br\cdot$$

$$Br\cdot + Br\cdot \xrightarrow{k_4} Br_2$$

The first step in this reaction will have no activation energy, for the production of bromine atoms will be governed only by the intensity of the light used. Knowing that reactions such as 2 and 4 have negligibly small activation energies, it can be shown that the observed activation

[16] A discussion of the methods of measurement and a complete list of values are available in T. L. Cottrell, *The Strengths of Chemical Bonds*, 2nd ed., Butterworths Scientific Publications, London, 1958.

[17] This method is discussed in detail in A. C. Gaydon, *Dissociation Energies*, 2nd ed. Chapman and Hall, London, 1953, particularly ch. V.

[18] G. B. Kistiakowsky and E. R. Van Artsdalen, *J. Chem. Phys.*, **12**, 469 (1944); B. H. Eckstein, H. A. Scheraga, and E. R. Van Artsdalen, *J. Chem. Phys.*, **22**, 28 (1954).

energy will be given by[19]

$$E_{obs.} = E_1 - E_3$$

Other data indicate that E_3 should be on the order of 1.5 kcal/mole. The observed activation energy is 17.8 kcal/mole, making $E_2 \sim 16.3$ kcal/mole.

The bond dissociation energy of hydrogen bromide (determined by the spectroscopic method) is 86.5 kcal/mole. The sum of this and E_2 is 102.8 kcal/mole (with an uncertainty of about 2 kcal/mole) and should correspond to the bond dissociation energy of methane.

In other cases the bond dissociation energy for a reaction may be obtained directly from the activation energy. All such determinations are based on the assumption that the activation energy for the reaction

$$R_1\cdot + R_2\cdot \rightarrow R_1R_2$$

will have essentially no activation energy. There is considerable evidence for such a view.[16]

As an example, consider the decomposition of an alkyl iodide

$$RI \xrightarrow{k_1} R\cdot + I\cdot$$

$$R\cdot + RI \xrightarrow{k_2} RH + R'$$

$$R' \xrightarrow{k_3} \text{olefin} + I\cdot$$

$$I\cdot + I\cdot \xrightarrow{k_4} I_2$$

The first step is the decomposition of the alkyl iodide to give alkyl radicals and iodine atoms. These disappear by reactions leading ultimately to

---

[19] The treatment of reactions of this type will be given in Section 3-2. Briefly, if one considers the potential energy surface for the reactions characterized by k_1 and k_3:

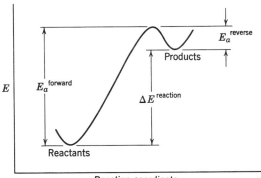

Reaction coordinate

it can be seen that the difference in energy between reactants and products will be given by the difference between the activation energies for the forward and backward reactions. If the reverse reaction has zero activation energy, then the energy change in the forward reaction is equal to the activation energy.

alkene and iodine. If there were no side reactions, and if the recombination of an alkyl radical with an iodine atom had zero activation energy, the observed activation energy would be equal to the bond dissociation energy.

A better and more generally applicable method is one introduced by Szwarc.[20] Here the compound is pyrolyzed in the presence of toluene. If an alkyl radical is formed, it will react with toluene, preventing any back reaction or most side reactions. Thus with ethylbenzene

$$C_6H_5CH_2CH_3 \rightarrow C_6H_5CH_2\cdot + CH_3\cdot \text{ (slow)}$$

$$CH_3\cdot + C_6H_5CH_3 \rightarrow C_6H_5CH_2\cdot + CH_4 \text{ (fast)}$$

$$2\,C_6H_5CH_2\cdot \rightarrow C_6H_5CH_2CH_2C_6H_5$$

one may follow the reaction by determining the rate of appearance of methane. Assuming the recombination of benzyl and methyl radicals to have zero activation energy, the observed activation energy may be equated with the bond dissociation energy in ethylbenzene.

It will be apparent that thermodynamic data for organic compounds, other than simple hydrocarbons, are not too available and often are not too precise. These data are important in determining whether a reaction is thermodynamically or kinetically controlled; in the study of steric and other effects operating in the ground states of molecules; and in the study of the conformations of molecules. This appears to be a fertile field for further experimental work.

References

Thermodynamic Data:
    American Petroleum Institute, Project 44, Carnegie Institute of Technology, "Selected Values of Properties of Hydrocarbons."
    J. Timmermans, *Physico-Chemical Constants of Pure Organic Compound*, Elsevier, New York, 1950.
Calculation of Thermochemical Properties:
    G. J. Janz, *Estimation of Thermodynamic Properties of Organic Compounds*, Academic Press, New York, 1958.
    K. S. Pitzer, *Advances in Chemical Physics*, Interscience Publishers, New York, 1959, vol. II, p. 59.
Steric Effects:
    M. Newman (ed.), *Steric Effects in Organic Chemistry*, John Wiley and Sons, New York, 1956.
Calorimetry:
    Experimental Thermochemistry, Interscience Publishers, New York, 1956, 1962, vols. I and II.

[20] M. Szwarc, *Proc. Roy. Soc.*, **A207**, 5 (1951).

Bond Dissociation Energies:

T. L. Cottrell, *The Strengths of Chemical Bonds*, 2nd ed. Butterworths Scientific Publications, London, 1958.

A. C. Gaydon, *Dissociation Energies*, 2nd ed., Chapman and Hall, London, 1953.

Problems

1. (a) The heat of combustion of cyclopropene is 485.4 kcal per mole (*J. Am. Chem. Soc.*, **84**, 3980 (1962)) and the moments of inertia are $I_A = 2.792 \times 10^{-39}$, $I_B = 3.846 \times 10^{-39}$ and $I_C = 6.085 \times 10^{-39}$ g. cm² (*J. Chem. Phys.*, **30**, 512 (1959)). The vibrational frequencies are 2906, 3159, 1650, 1390, 907, 580, ~700, ~650, 3115, 1011, 769, ~600, 2998, 1046, and 573 cm⁻¹. Calculate ΔH_f^0, $(H^0 - H_0^0)$, $(F^0 - H_0^0)$ and S^0 for cyclopropene at 25°.

(b) The heat of formation of methylacetylene is 44.3 kcal per mole at 25° (American Petroleum Institute Project 44, *Selected Values of Properties of Hydrocarbons*), and the entropy is 59.30 at 25°. Calculate the equilibrium constant for the reaction

$$\triangle \quad \rightleftharpoons \quad CH_3C{\equiv}CH$$

2. (a) Having the vibrational frequencies for cyclobutene (problem 3, Section 1-17), and assuming a reasonable geometry, calculate $(H^0 - H_0^0)$, $(F^0 - H_0^0)$ and S^0 for the compound at 25°.

(b) Assuming Franklin's group equivalents to be correct, calculate ΔH_f for cyclobutene at 25°.

(c) Using the available data for butadiene (American Petroleum Institute Project 44 tables), and the above data, calculate the approximate equilibrium constant for the reaction

$$\square \quad \rightleftharpoons \quad CH_2{=}CH{-}CH{=}CH_2$$

2-5 *Internal Rotation*

Ethane has 8 atoms and $3n$ or 24 degrees of freedom. There are 3 translational degrees of freedom, 3 rotational degrees of freedom, and 17 vibrational modes. This leaves one degree of freedom, the internal rotation of one methyl group with respect to the other.

The partition function for internal rotation may be obtained in a manner analogous to that for ordinary rotation and is

$$Q = \frac{(8\pi^3 I_r kT)^{1/2}}{mnh}$$

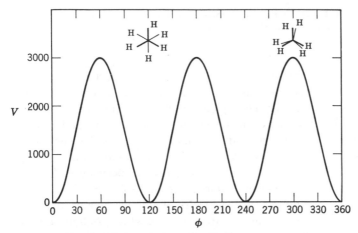

Fig. 2-5. Potential energy barrier for rotation in ethane.

where I_r is the "reduced" moment of inertia and n is the symmetry number for the internal rotation ($n = 3$ for ethane). For two coaxial symmetrical rotors, the reduced moment of inertia is given by

$$I_r = \frac{I_A + I_B}{I_A I_B}$$

where I_A and I_B are the moments of inertia of the two internal rotors. For more complex systems, the reduced moment of inertia must be evaluated in a different fashion.[21]

When the entropy term for ethane was calculated using the proper partition functions for all the degrees of freedom, it was found to be $S^0_{184°} = 51.2 \pm 0.2$ eu as compared to the observed value, $S^0 = 49.6$ eu.[22] The difference between the two values is much greater than the experimental error or the uncertainty in the calculation.

This observation led Pitzer[22] to propose that the internal rotation was hindered by a potential energy barrier. Assuming a barrier of the simple cosine type (Fig. 2-5)

$$V = \tfrac{1}{2}V_0(1 - \cos n\phi)$$

where n is the number of equivalent minima and V_0 is the barrier height, the change in entropy with increasing barrier height could be calculated.

[21] G. J. Janz, *Estimation of Thermodynamic Properties of Organic Compounds*, Academic Press, New York, 1958, pp. 26–27.
[22] J. D. Kemp and K. S. Pitzer, *J. Am. Chem. Soc.*, **59**, 276 (1937); *J. Chem. Phys.*, **4**, 749 (1936).

Assuming a barrier of 3 kcal/mole, the calculated entropy was brought into good agreement with the observed value.

Although of great importance historically, the "thermodynamic" method of determining barrier heights is limited in its applicability because both the heat capacity data from 0° to 298°K and the structure and vibrational frequencies must be known with considerable precision in order to use it. Further, a complete vibrational assignment must be made in order to know which of the observed frequencies are fundamentals and which are only overtones, and in order to know the degeneracy of each of the vibrational modes. A more generally useful and more precise method involves the analysis of the microwave spectrum.[23] Some of the data obtained in this way are summarized in Table 2-8.

An analysis of the microwave spectra of suitable deuterium substituted compounds will also permit one to determine which configuration has the lowest energy. Thus with ethyl chloride, methyl silane, and methyl germane, the equilibrium configuration is the one in which the atoms in each of the two halves are staggered. However, with acetaldehyde, acetyl fluoride, and propylene, the stable configuration is that in which one of the methyl hydrogens lies directly over the double bond.

Several things should be noted from the table. First, the change in barrier height on going from ethane to ethyl fluoride, chloride, and bromide is remarkably little, although the sizes of the groups change considerably. Only when a large group is on each atom does the barrier height increase. Second, we may note the relatively small decrease in barrier on going from ethane to methyl silane and methyl germane, although the H-H nonbonded distance is increased considerably.

The simplest explanation for the barrier would involve the postulation of H-H repulsion. The above data show that this cannot be correct, for larger changes would be expected. The H-H distance is actually in the attractive portion of the van der Waals curve, and on this basis we might expect the stable configuration to be the one in which the hydrogens are eclipsed. Further, we must remember that in propylene and related compounds, the preferred configuration is not the one in which the groups are staggered.

Wilson[23] has shown that essentially all the current explanations of the barrier are incorrect and has concluded by saying, "Though far from being proven, and certainly not now useful for prediction, the idea that the ethane barrier arises from the repulsion of C-H bond orbitals on the

---

[23] A review of the principles of the method and of its application has been presented by E. B. Wilson Jr. in *Advances in Chemical Physics*, Interscience Publishers, 1959, vol. II. This also contains a careful analysis of the possible explanations for the origin of the barrier.

Table 2-8 **Barriers to Internal Rotation**[a]

Molecule	V (μwave) kcal/mole	V (thermo.) kcal/mole
CH_3CH_3		2.7–3.0
CH_3CH_2F	3.30	
CH_3CHF_2	3.18	
CH_3CH_2Cl	3.56	2.7, 4.7
CH_3CH_2Br	3.57	
CH_3OH	1.07	1.6
CH_3SH	1.26	1.5
CH_3NH_2	1.94	1.9
CH_3CHO	1.15	1.0
CH_3CFO	1.08	
CH_3CClO	1.35	
CH_3COCN	1.27	
$CH_3CO_2CH_3$	1.17	
$CH_3CH{=}CH_2$	1.98	1.95
$CH_3CH{=}CHF$(trans)	2.20	
$CH_3CF{=}CH_2$	2.62	
$CH_3CH{=}C{=}CH_2$	1.59	1.65
CH_3COOH	0.48	2.5 ± 0.7
CH_3SiH_3	1.70	
CH_3SiHF_2	1.56	
CH_3CHOCH_2	2.56	
CH_3ONO_2	2.32	
CH_3GeH_3	1.2	
CH_3NO_2	0.006 (sixfold)	<0.025
CH_3BF_3	0.014 (sixfold)	

[a] E. B. Wilson, Jr. in *Advances in Chemical Physics*, Interscience Publishers, New York, 1959, vol. II p. 370.

carbons, due to their being more concentrated than *sp* hybrids, seems the most plausible picture available." Thus the barrier does not result from interaction between atoms but, rather, probably arises from an interaction of the orbitals at the two carbons involved.

With larger groups van der Waals interaction between the atoms of the two rotors becomes possible. For example, with hexachloroethane, the barrier is 10.8 kcal/mole. However, when the central bond distance is increased, as in hexachlorodisilane ($Cl_3SiSiCl_3$), the barrier drops to 1 kcal/mole, and the van der Waals interaction again becomes negligible.

Why should there be so much interest in the origin of these barriers? One reason is that an understanding of the origin might permit one to predict the magnitude of the barrier, and this would be useful in predicting thermodynamic functions. Another is the purely intellectual one of discovering something about the nature of bonding forces. But, for the organic chemist the most important reason is connected with the geometry of cyclohexane and related compounds.

Cyclohexane may exist in either of two forms, the chair or boat configurations:

Chair   Boat

The former is the more stable by approximately 6 kcal/mole. When it was believed that H-H repulsion accounted for the rotational barrier in ethane, the explanation for the chair form was obvious. The latter involves no eclipsed conformations about pairs of carbons, whereas in the boat form there are two eclipsed conformations.

It is clear that the preference for the chair form results from the same factors that contribute to the barrier in ethane and make the staggered conformation the more stable one. However, since we do not have a good understanding of the cause of the effect in ethane, we do not understand the difference in energy between the isomers of cyclohexane. Nevertheless, it is possible to make semiquantitative estimates of the difference in energy, assuming the barrier height found in ethane and related compounds and a cosine relationship in a semiempirical fashion.[24]

Problems

1. Assuming that the only factor involved in determining the difference in energy between the boat and chair forms of cyclohexane is the barrier to internal rotation, and that this barrier has a value of 3 kcal per mole, calculate the difference in energy between the two forms.

2. Calculate the energy term due to the barrier to internal rotation for cyclobutane and for cyclobutene. Then, assuming the normal bending force constants to be appropriate (Section 1-17), calculate the energy term for each which is due to bond bending. Should the heat of hydrogenation of cyclobutene be significantly different than that for *cis*-2-butene?

[24] The conformations of cyclohexane derivatives has been reviewed by W. G. Dauben and K. S. Pitzer, in M. Newman (ed.), *Steric Effects in Organic Chemistry*, John Wiley and Sons, New York, 1956, pp. 1–60.

2-6 Effect of Solvent on Equilibria; Energy of Ions in solution; The Debye-Hückle Relationship

Up until now the discussion has been concerned with the energy of compounds in the gas phase and with equilibria in the gas phase. We must now consider the effect of a solvent on an equilibrium reaction. In doing this we may often concentrate on the effect of solvent on each individual component of the system, for the equilibrium constant may always be evaluated if one knows the thermodynamic functions for each of the components.

The effect of a solvent on a nonpolar compound may often be quite small. Thus equilibrium constants for reactions such as the Diels-Alder reaction are often relatively unchanged on going from the gas phase to solution. Since the magnitude of the effects is small, they are relatively difficult to treat quantitatively.

One case for which considerable data are available is the equilibrium between a compound and its solution in a given solvent. The energy of the solid phase will be independent of the solvent, and thus differences in solubility on going from one solvent to another will give a measure of the effect of the solvent on the free energy of the dissolved compound. It should be apparent that the free energy of the compound in solution will be equal to that of the solid phase when the system is at equilibrium.

The solubility for the case in which an ideal solution is formed may be calculated as follows. The effect of temperature on the vapor pressure of a solid is given by

$$\frac{d \ln p_s}{dT} = \frac{\Delta H_s}{RT^2}$$

where ΔH_s is the heat of sublimation. Similarly, the vapor pressure of the liquid form of the compound will be

$$\frac{d \ln p_l}{dT} = \frac{\Delta H_v}{RT^2}$$

where ΔH_v is the heat of vaporization. Subtracting one from the other, we obtain

$$\frac{d \ln (p_s/p_l)}{dT} = \frac{\Delta H_f}{RT^2}$$

where ΔH_f is the heat of fusion.

Consider a solution which is cooled until crystals of the solute begin to form. The vapor pressure of these crystals, p_s, must equal the vapor pressure of the solute, p_1. Therefore at the temperature at which crystals begin to form,

$$\frac{d \ln (p_1/p_l)}{dT} = \frac{\Delta H_f}{RT^2}$$

Table 2-9   Solubility of Naphthalene in Different Solvents[a]

Solvent	Solubility at 25°	Mole Fraction Solute
Chloroform	54.0	0.340
Chlorobenzene	52.	0.314
Dibromoethylene	30.2	0.307
Nitrobenzene	45.	0.302
Toluene	58.	0.294
Benzene	67.5	0.291
Acetone	65	0.228
Carbon tetrachloride	23.0	0.221
Dichloroethylene	31.8	0.199
Carbon disulfide	41.0	0.195
Aniline	28.	0.169
Hexane	23.	0.077
Butyl alcohol	11.8	0.064
Acetic acid	14.0	0.061
Ethanol	11.6	0.040
Methanol	10.0	0.024

[a] Data from A. Seidel, *Solubilities of Organic Compounds*, D. Van Nostrand Co., Princeton, New Jersey, 1941, pp. 650–656.

If this expression is integrated—remembering that according to Raoult's law p_1/p_l is equal to the mole fraction of the solute, x—one obtains

$$\ln x = -\frac{\Delta H_f}{R}\left(\frac{1}{T} - \frac{1}{T_0}\right)$$

Here x is the solubility (expressed as the mole fraction) at the temperature T, and T_0 is the melting point of the pure solid.

If we take naphthalene as an example, we obtain the data given in Table 2-9. The heat of fusion of naphthalene is 4400 cal/mole, and the melting point is 353°K. At 298°K, the solubility given by the above expression is 0.311. It can be seen that the solvents which might be expected to give relatively ideal behavior give the expected solubility and

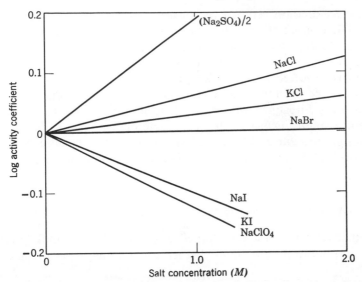

Fig. 2-6. Effect of salt concentration on the activity coefficient of β-propiolactone (F. A. Long, W. F. McDevit, and F. B. Dunkle, J. Phys. Colloid Chem., 55, 813 (1951).

that those which are either more polar (such as the alcohols) or less polar (hexane) than naphthalene give markedly lower solubility.

The same type of data may be obtained from the measurement of the partial pressure of a solute. According to Raoult's law, the ratio of the partial pressure of the solute to its normal vapor pressure should equal the mole fraction of the solute. Deviations from the expected partial pressure may then be interpreted in terms of the change in free energy of the solute caused by the solvent.[25]

The changes in free energy are often expressed in terms of the activity or activity coefficient of the solute. The activity (a) may be considered as the apparent concentration of the species as determined from vapor pressure or similar measurements. The activity coefficient (γ) is the ratio of the activity to the actual concentration. Thus an activity coefficient of unity implies an ideal solution.

A related problem is the effect of salts on the activity coefficients for nonpolar compounds in aqueous solution.[26] As an example, we may consider the data for β-propiolactone (Fig. 2-6). It can be seen that there

[25] For examples of measurements using this and related methods see R. A. Clement and M. R. Rice, *J. Am. Chem. Soc.*, **81**, 326 (1959); R. W. Taft, Jr., E. L. Purlee, and P. Riesz, *J. Am. Chem. Soc.*, **77**, 899 (1955); E. Grunwald and S. Winstein, *J. Am. Chem. Soc.*, **70**, 846 (1948); A. R. Olson and R. S. Halford, *J. Am. Chem. Soc.*, **59**, 2644 (1937).
[26] The data and theories concerning this subject have been reviewed by F. A. Long and W. F. McDevit, *Chem. Revs.*, **51**, 119 (1952).

is a linear relationship between the logarithm of the activity coefficient and the salt concentration. However, some salts increase the activity coefficient ("salting out") and others decrease the activity coefficient ("salting in"). The more common case is one in which the activity coefficient is increased by most, if not all, of the salts. However, the magnitude of the effect will vary considerably from salt to salt.

The theoretical treatment of this phenomenon is not too well developed and is not useful in predicting the magnitude of the effect to be expected with a given solute and salt. All one can do is to recognize that the effect exists and experimentally determine its magnitude when the need arises.

EFFECT OF SOLVENT ON IONS

Now that we have considered the effect of solvent on neutral species, we may turn to the effect on ions. Let us first consider the charging of a condenser.

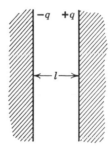

The capacity of the condenser C is given by the ratio of the charge on one plate q to the potential V required to produce the charge. If the area of the plates is large compared to the distance between them, the capacity is also given by

$$\frac{q}{V} = C = \frac{A}{4\pi l}$$

where A is the area of one plate.

We shall now define a new quantity, X, the field strength, as

$$X = \frac{V}{l}$$

The work required to charge a condenser to the potential V is

$$W = \tfrac{1}{2}qV$$

or in terms of the capacity of the condenser and the field strength

$$W = \tfrac{1}{2}CV^2 = \tfrac{1}{2}(Xl)^2 \frac{A}{4\pi l} = \left(\frac{X^2}{8\pi}\right)Al$$

Since Al is the volume of the condenser, the work per unit volume is given by $(X^2/8\pi)$. In this case the work done is equal to the change in free energy, and therefore, in general,

$$\Delta F = \int \frac{X^2}{8\pi}\, dv$$

Suppose a slab of a dielectric were inserted between the plates of the condenser. The dielectric would be attracted and would move up between the plates. Thus work is done on the dielectric and the free energy of the condenser is decreased. The dielectric constant ϵ of the material inserted between the plates is defined as the ratio of the potential on the plates in a vacuum to that with the dielectric in place, the total charge remaining the same:

$$\epsilon = \frac{V_0}{V} \text{ at constant } q$$

If the charge is constant, the product of the capacity of the condenser and the potential must be the same before and after the insertion of the dielectric.

$$C_0 V_0 = CV$$

and therefore

$$C = C_0\epsilon$$

The free energy of charging the condenser is now

$$\Delta F = \tfrac{1}{2}qV = \tfrac{1}{2}CV^2 = \tfrac{1}{2}C_0\epsilon\left(\frac{V_0}{\epsilon}\right)^2 = \frac{1}{2}\frac{C_0 V_0^2}{\epsilon}$$

Thus the free energy of charging the condenser to a charge q will be $1/\epsilon$ as great in the presence of a dielectric as in its absence. Similarly, the potential produced by the charge q will be $1/\epsilon$ as great as before, or, in other words, the capacity of the condenser is ϵ times as great as in the absence of the dielectric.

Let us now consider the entropy change. This is defined as

$$-\Delta S = \left(\frac{\partial \Delta F}{\partial T}\right)_p$$

and therefore

$$\Delta S = -\left(\frac{X^2}{8\pi}\right)\frac{d}{dT}\frac{1}{\epsilon}$$

per unit volume. For most compounds the temperature coefficient of ϵ is negative, and therefore $\dfrac{d}{dT}\left(\dfrac{1}{\epsilon}\right)$ is positive. Thus entropy is lost when a dielectric is subjected to an electrical field, and the change in entropy is a function of the temperature dependence of ϵ; the larger it is, the larger the change in S.

A physical interpretation of these conclusions is as follows. Compounds with high dielectric constants are those which are polar, that is, have large dipole moments. When placed between the plates of a condenser, the local dipoles of the compound are to a small extent oriented by the electrical field. This causes a decrease in entropy and requires a larger charge to be put on the condenser in order to produce a given potential, giving a larger capacity.

Let us now consider a sphere in a vacuum. Here

$$\Delta F = \int_{r_1}^{\infty} \left(\frac{X^2}{8\pi}\right) dv$$

where the integration is to be taken over all space outside the sphere. The volume of a spherical shell of thickness dr is

$$dv = 4\pi r^2 \, dr$$

and $X = q/r^2$, where r is the distance from the center of the sphere. Thus

$$\Delta F = \frac{q^2}{8} \int_{r_1}^{\infty} \frac{4r^2}{r^4} \, dr = \frac{q^2}{2r}$$

Let us see if this is reasonable. Consider the ionization of an atom, and calculate the work required to remove an electron.

$$q = 4.8 \times 10^{-10} \text{ esu}$$

$$r \sim 1 \text{ Å (depending on the size of the atom)}$$

$$\Delta F = \frac{(4.8 \times 10^{-10})^2}{2 \times 1 \times 10^{-8}} = 11.5 \times 10^{-12} \text{ ergs} = 7.2 \text{ ev} = 166 \text{ kcal/mole}$$

We may now compare the result with the ionization potential of lithium (5.4 ev) and beryllium (9 ev), and thus it has the correct magnitude.

Now, if the ion were formed in a solvent of dielectric constant ϵ, the work would have to be only $1/\epsilon$ as great. In water ($\epsilon = 80$), the work would have been only 2 kcal/mole, indicating the profound effect of a polar solvent on an ionic reaction.

Let us consider the charged sphere in a medium of dielectric constant ϵ. If r_1 is the radius of the sphere (Fig. 2-7), and $r_2 = 2r_1$, then since $\Delta F = q^2/2r$, ΔF outside r_2 is one half of ΔF outside r_1. Therefore one half of the net effect will be felt in the region between r_1 and r_2. For an ion in which r_1 is small, this imposes a very large field in a small volume element, and it is probably well outside of the range in which the polarization of the solvent will be proportional to the field intensity. This suggests that there are two types of solvation.[27] In the co-sphere between r_1 and r_2, the solvent molecules are strongly polarized, and there are probably fairly strong specific solvent effects. Outside the co-sphere the effects are much weaker, and the macroscopic dielectric constant would be expected to apply. It is obvious that the changes in energy of ions will not be affected solely by the bulk dielectric constant. However, it remains as the only conveniently measured quantity which can be used, and it should give a fair approximation to the desired quantity in many cases.

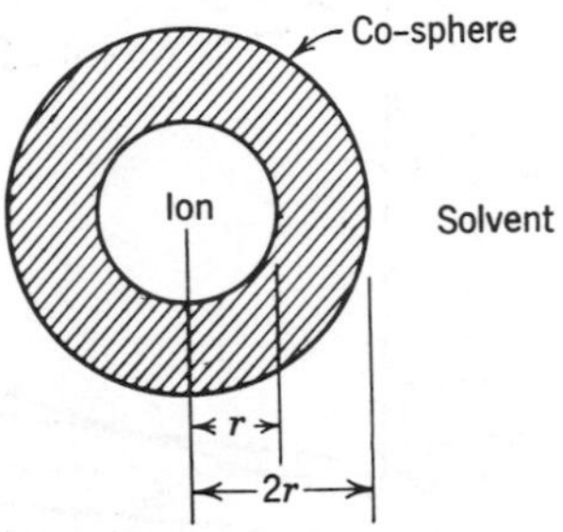

We may apply these ideas to the equilibrium

$$HA_1 + A_2^- \rightleftharpoons A_1^- + HA_2$$

Here the free energy change is given by

$$\Delta F = -RT \ln K = \Delta F_a + \frac{Ne^2}{2\epsilon}\left(\frac{1}{r_1} - \frac{1}{r_2}\right)$$

where ΔF_a is the nonelectrostatic contribution, r_1 is the radius of A_1^-, r_2 is the radius

Fig. 2-7. An ion and its co-sphere. One-half of the electrostatic work is done in the co-sphere, and the other half is done on the rest of the solvent.

of A_2^-, N is Avogadro's number, and e is the change on an electron. However, most organic ions are not spherical and cannot be treated in this simple fashion. Yet it is clear that the second term will be a function of $1/\epsilon$, and thus we may write

$$\Delta F = \Delta F_a + \frac{A}{\epsilon}$$

where A contains all the other terms. This also applies to cases in which there are dipole-dipole interactions. Properly, one should take into account the fact that part of the lines of force go through the molecule and part go through the medium and that the two dielectric constants are not the same. In the absence of better information, we will use the dielectric constant of the solvent. Therefore

$$\log K = -\frac{\Delta F}{2.3RT} = C - \frac{1}{\epsilon}\frac{A}{2.3RT}$$

[27] R. W. Gurney, *Ionic Processes in Solution*, McGraw-Hill Book Co., New York, 1953, chs. I and II.

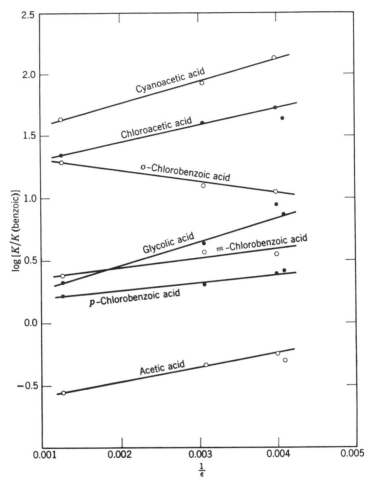

Fig. 2-8. Correlation of equilibrium constants with the reciprocal of the dielectric constant for ionization equilibria.

where C is a constant. A plot of log K against $1/\epsilon$ should give a straight line, and this is observed (Fig. 2-8)[28] for the range $\epsilon = 25$-80 in solvents of similar structure. With solvents of lower dielectric constant, there is probably some ionic association, and one finds that a change in solvent type often produces a large deviation.

This treatment applies only when compounds of the same type are compared; otherwise C would not be expected to be a constant. Thus

[28] L. J. Minnick and M. Kilpatrick, *J. Phys. Chem.*, **43**, 259 (1939); J. H. Elliot and M. Kilpatrick, *ibid*, **45**, 466 (1941).

when phenols and benzoic acids are used in the above treatment, a linear relationship is not obtained.

If ΔF_a is assumed to be temperature independent, then

$$\left(\frac{\partial \Delta F}{\partial T}\right)_p = -\Delta S = \frac{A}{\epsilon^2}\frac{d\epsilon}{dT} = \frac{A}{\epsilon}\frac{d\ln\epsilon}{dT}$$

Further, if ΔF_a is small with respect to A/ϵ, then

$$\Delta F^0 \sim \frac{A}{\epsilon}$$

$$\Delta S^0 \sim \frac{\Delta F^0 \, d\ln\epsilon}{dT}$$

For water, $d\ln\epsilon/dT = -0.005$. A test of this relationship is given in Table 2-10, and it can be seen that for many compounds there is a fairly good correlation between the two quantities.

Table 2-10   Correlation between ΔF^0 and ΔS^0 for the Ionization Equilibria of Carboxylic Acids[a]

Acid	K	ΔF^0	ΔH^0	ΔS^0	$-0.005\,\Delta F^0$
m-Nitrobenzoic	6.04	−1044	−94	3.2	5.2
m-Cyanobenzoic	3.57	−739	−449	1.3	3.7
m-Chlorobenzoic	2.48	−528	−400	0.5	2.5
m-Bromobenzoic	2.58	−551	−479	0.7	2.8
m-Iodobenzoic	2.30	−484	−230	0.9	2.4
m-Methylbenzoic	0.92	41	−350	−1.3	−0.2
p-Nitrobenzoic	6.11	−1050	−346	2.4	5.3
p-Cyanobenzoic	4.74	−904	−391	1.8	4.5
p-Chlorobenzoic	1.71	−310	−194	0.4	1.5
p-Bromobenzoic	1.64	−288	−313	0.0	1.4
p-Methylbenzoic	0.74	179	−120	−1.0	−0.9
Propionic	0.21	910	−650	−5.1	−4.6
Butyric	0.24	830	−1140	−6.5	−4.2
Acetic	0.27	750	−530	−4.2	−3.8

[a] Benzoic acid was used as HA_1 in each case (cf. L. P. Hammett, *J. Chem. Phys.*, **4**, 613 (1936)). Ortho-substituted benzoic acids were also compared with benzoic acid, but no correlation was found. The data in the table were taken from G. Briegleb and A. Bieber, *Z. Elektrochem.*, **55**, 250 (1951) and R. P. Bell, *The Proton in Chemistry*, Cornell University Press, Ithaca, New York, 1959, p. 64.

The ionization of carboxylic acids exhibits one peculiarity: K_a goes through a maximum at about room temperature.[29] This can be seen in the data of Table 2-11. The position of the maximum is different for different acids. This makes the use of ionization constants of acids as measures of inductive and field effects somewhat risky. If the maxima were significantly displaced, the ratio of ionization constants would be a function of temperature, and there might be a temperature at which the relative acidity passes through unity.

Table 2-11   Effect of Temperature on the Ionization of Carboxylic Acids[a]

$T°C.$

Compound	0	10	20	30	40	50	60
Formic	1.638	1.728	1.765	1.768	1.716	1.650	1.551×10^{-4}
Propionic	1.274	1.326	1.338	1.326	1.280	1.229	1.160×10^{-5}
Chloroacetic	1.528	1.488	1.379		1.230		$\times 10^{-3}$
Boric		4.17	5.26	6.34	7.38	8.32	$\times 10^{-10}$
Malonic(K_2)	2.14	2.15	2.08	1.948	1.768	1.575	1.362×10^{-6}

[a] The data are from R. W. Gurney, *Ionic Processes in Solution*, McGraw-Hill Book Co., New York, 1953, p. 121.

In each case the ionization constant data are found to fit the equation

$$\log K - \log K_{\max} = -p(T - \theta)^2$$

which is that for a parabola. Here θ is the temperature at which $K_{\max}$ is found, and $p = 5 \times 10^{-5}$ for all acids except boric ($p = 8 \times 10^{-5}$).

We have previously shown that the ionization constant may be expressed by

$$-RT \ln K = \Delta F_a + \frac{A}{\epsilon}$$

where ΔF_a is the nonelectrostatic part and A/ϵ is the electrostatic part (solvent dependent) of the total free energy change. For a number of common solvents (Table 2-12), the dielectric constant may be given by

$$\epsilon = \epsilon_0 e^{-T/\vartheta}$$

and therefore

$$-RT \ln K = \Delta F_a + \frac{A}{\epsilon_0} e^{T/\vartheta}$$

[29] R. W. Gurney, *Ionic Processes in Solution*, McGraw-Hill Book Co., New York, 1953, p. 121.

Let us first consider the cases in which $\Delta F_a = 0$. The maximum value of K is obtained by differentiation with respect to T and by setting the derivative equal to zero. Thus

$$0 = \frac{e^{T/\vartheta}}{T^2} - \frac{e^{T/\vartheta}}{\vartheta T}$$

and the ionization constant goes through a maximum at $T = \vartheta$. The addition of a ΔF_a term shifts the position of the maximum, and a positive value will shift it to higher temperatures (in the present case to about room temperature).

Table 2-12 **Effect of Temperature on the Dielectric Constants of Some Solvents**[a]

Solvent	ϵ_0	ϑ	f.p.
H_2O	305.7	219	273.1
D_2O	306.7	218	276.9
CH_3OH	157.1	185.4	175.3
C_2H_5OH	148.5	164.5	155.8
C_3H_7OH	150.4	148	146

[a] The values are the constants of the equation

$$\epsilon = \epsilon_0 e^{-T/\vartheta}$$

f.p. is the freezing point of the solvent, which is usually close to the temperature ϑ.

THE DEBYE-HÜCKEL EQUATION

In the previous discussion we were mainly concerned with the effect of solvents on reactions. Equally important is the effect of changing the concentration of ions in the solution. If we consider a given positively charged ion in a solution, there will, as a result of Coulombic forces, be a higher probability of finding a negatively charged ion near it than of finding a positively charged ion. An extreme example of this sort of order is found in a crystal, such as sodium chloride. In solution, of course, the degree of order is nowhere as great, but it is still appreciable. We shall now try to calculate the magnitude of this effect and the consequences thereof.

Let us first calculate the number of ions of each charge (dn_+ and dn_-) in a volume element dv at a distance r from the positively charged ion. The work required to bring a positively charged ion to this point from infinity is Z_+eV, where V is the average potential (*not* in this case the potential energy). Using the Boltzmann distribution, one obtains

$$dn_+ = n_+ e^{-(Z_+eV/kT)}\, dv$$
$$dn_- = n_- e^{-(-Z_+eV/kT)}\, dv$$

The charge per unit volume, ρ, is given by

$$\rho = \frac{e(Z_+ \, dn_+ - Z_- \, dn_-)}{dv}$$

$$= e(n_+ Z_+ e^{-(Z_+ eV/kT)} - n_- Z_- e^{-(-Z_+ eV/kT)})$$

However, in any solution of univalent ions, $n_+ = n_- = n$, and $Z_+ = Z_- = 1$. Thus

$$\rho = ne(e^{-eV/kT} - e^{+eV/kT})$$

The exponential may be expanded as a power series

$$e^{-x} = 1 - x + \frac{x^2}{2!} - \frac{x^3}{3!} + \cdots$$

and so

$$\rho = ne\left(1 + \frac{eV}{kT} + \frac{e^2V^2}{2k^2T^2} + \cdots - 1 + \frac{eV}{kT} - \frac{e^2V^2}{2k^2T^2} + \cdots\right)$$

For low concentrations of ions, the higher terms of the expansion are negligible, giving

$$\rho = \frac{2ne^2V}{kT}$$

There is another general relationship between the potential and the charge per unit volume, which is known as Poisson's equation:

$$\frac{1}{r^2}\frac{d}{dr}\left(r^2\frac{dV}{dr}\right) = -\frac{4\pi}{\epsilon}\rho$$

and thus

$$\frac{1}{r^2}\frac{d}{dr}\left(r^2\frac{dV}{dr}\right) = -\frac{4\pi}{\epsilon}\cdot\frac{2ne^2V}{kT}$$

If we define κ as

$$\kappa^2 = \frac{8\pi^2e^2n}{\epsilon kT}$$

then

$$\frac{1}{r^2}\frac{d}{dr}\left(r^2\frac{dV}{dr}\right) = -\kappa^2V$$

The solution of the differential equation is

$$V = \frac{e}{\epsilon r} - \frac{e}{\epsilon r}(1 - e^{-\kappa r})$$

If κ is small,

$$1 - e^{-\kappa r} \cong \kappa r$$

and so

$$V = \frac{e}{\epsilon r} - \frac{e\kappa}{\epsilon}$$

The first term is simply the potential due to the ion in the absence of surrounding ions, and the second is the potential due to the ionic atmosphere about the ion. For the general case where the ions may not be univalent, the expression for κ becomes

$$\kappa^2 = \frac{4\pi e^2}{\epsilon kT} \sum n_i Z_i^2 = \frac{8\pi e^2}{\epsilon kT} \mu$$

where μ is the ionic strength,

$$\mu = \frac{1}{2} \sum n_i Z_i^2$$

and the expression for the potential becomes

$$V = \frac{Z_i e}{\epsilon r} - \frac{Z_i e \kappa}{\epsilon}$$

We are more concerned with the free energy than with the potential. The free energy will be given as one-half the product of the charge $(Z_i e)$ and the potential

$$\Delta F = \frac{Z_i^2 e^2}{2\epsilon r} - \frac{Z_i^2 e^2 \kappa}{2\epsilon}$$

The first term is the work done at infinite dilution. The second term is responsible for the salt effect and may be equated with $kT \ln \gamma_i$, where γ is again the activity coefficient of the ion.

$$kT \ln \gamma_i = \Delta F' = -\frac{Z_i^2 e^2 \kappa}{2\epsilon}$$

or on a molar basis (1000 ml)

$$RT \ln \gamma_i = -\frac{N Z_i^2 e^2 \kappa}{2000\epsilon}$$

The value of κ may be substituted into the expression, giving

$$\log \gamma_i = -\frac{N^{3/2} e^3}{2.303 R^{3/2}} \left(\frac{2\pi}{1000}\right)^{1/2} \frac{Z_i^2}{(\epsilon T)^{3/2}} \sqrt{\mu}$$

$$= -1.823 \times 10^6 \frac{Z_i^2}{(\epsilon T)^{3/2}} \sqrt{\mu}$$

$$= -A Z_i^2 \sqrt{\mu} \tag{I}$$

For water at 25°, the constant A has the value 0.509.

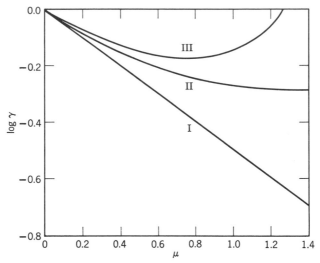

Fig. 2-9. A comparison of three Debye-Hückel expressions. They are numbered as shown in the text.

The Debye-Hückel equation is applicable only to dilute solutions (preferably $0.01 M$ or less, although the deviations are usually not too great up to $0.1 M$). If higher concentrations are used, corrections must be made. The first is a correction for the finite size of ions, leading to the expression

$$\log \gamma_i = - \frac{AZ_i^2 \sqrt{\mu}}{1 + \kappa a} = - \frac{AZ_i^2 \sqrt{\mu}}{1 + aB\sqrt{\mu}} \tag{II}$$

where a is the distance of closest approach of the ions, and B has the numerical value of 3.79×10^7. In practice, the value of a is not known and must be determined empirically for a given salt.

Finally, at higher salt concentrations, the ion in question is "salted out" by the other ions, and this requires the addition of a term similar to that for nonpolar electrolytes.

$$\log \gamma_i = - \frac{AZ_i^2 \sqrt{\mu}}{1 + aB\sqrt{\mu}} - C\mu \tag{III}$$

where C is an empirically determined parameter.

It must be recognized that the activity coefficients cannot be determined for individual ions, but, rather, one obtains the average activity coefficient for the cation and anion. The above expressions still apply, except that Z_i^2 is replaced by Z_+Z_-. The three Debye-Hückel expressions given above are compared in Fig. 2-9. The curves are very similar for low concentrations, but at higher concentrations only III will reasonably reproduce the experimental data for sodium chloride.

ION-PAIR ASSOCIATION

For solutions in solvents having a low dielectric constant, it is not sufficient to consider salt effects when dealing with ionic materials. This may be seen from the experimental observation that the specific conductance of a solution of ions in such a medium decreases sharply as the concentration is increased. The shape of the curve is similar to that found for the dissociation of a weak acid in water, and it is believed that an equilibrium of the type

$$A^+ + B^- \rightleftharpoons A^+B^-$$

obtains, where A^+B^- is an ion-pair, which because of its electrical neutrality contributes nothing to the conductance of the solution. We shall first consider the theoretical treatment of equilibria of this type, and then consider how the association constants are obtained.

The probability of finding an ion i at a distance r, from another ion j is given by the Boltzmann distribution in the form

$$P_i = \frac{Nc_i}{1000} e^{u/kT} 4\pi r^2 \, dr$$

where $Nc_i/1000$ is the number of i ions per milliliter. The $4\pi r^2 \, dr$ term relates to the volume of a spherical shell of thickness dr and radius r about the ion j. The quantity u is the potential energy required to move an ion from the separation r to infinity. At small distances it may be approximated by Coulomb's law

$$u = - \frac{Z_i Z_j e^2}{\epsilon r}$$

where the Z's are the charges on the ions, e is the charge on an electron, and ϵ is the dielectric constant. Therefore

$$P_i = \frac{Nc_i}{1000} (e^{-Z_i Z_j e^2/\epsilon r kT}) 4\pi r^2 \, dr$$

There is an increased probability of finding the ions near each other if they have opposite signs and a decreased probability if they have the same sign.[30]

A plot of this function against r is shown in Fig. 2-10 for oppositely charged ions except that it is terminated at a distance a corresponding to the nearest approach of two ions (the point at which the van der Waals repulsion between the two ions begins to be important). On the left-hand

[30] This formulation was first given by N. Bjerrum, *K. danske vidensk. Selsk.*, **7**, No. 9 (1926).

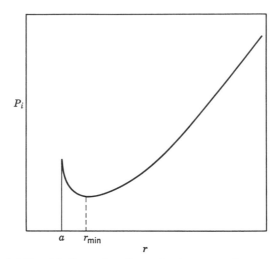

Fig. 2-10. Probability of finding an ion of opposite charge at a distance r from a given ion. This figure is drawn for a solvent of reasonably large dielectric constant, for which K_{ass} is small. As ϵ decreases, r_{min} increases.

side of the minimum probability, the curve rises because of the increasing Coulombic attraction, while on the right-hand side it also rises because the size of the volume element is increasing rapidly. Thus one factor favors a small value of r and the other favors large values.

To obtain r_{min} we differentiate the probability with respect to r and set the derivative equal to zero, giving

$$r_{min} = \frac{e^2 \, |Z_1 Z_2|}{2\epsilon kT}$$

Putting in numerical constants,

$$r_{min} = \frac{280 \, |Z_1 Z_2|}{\epsilon} \text{ (in Å at 25°)}$$

The movement of r_{min} to larger values as the dielectric constant decreases is a result of the increase in the Coulombic term. This formulation does not take specific solvation effects into account and only refers to the bulk dielectric constant. It does, however, work well for many systems, such as dioxane-water. The values of r_{min} for some common solvents is given in Table 2-13, and some typical data for ion-pair association are given in Table 2-14.

The significance of the value of r_{min} is that it is assumed that any pair of ions within this distance will behave as an electrically neutral unit, that is, an ion-pair. It can be seen that r_{min} is so large in a solvent such as dioxane that at any reasonable concentration all the ions will be in the form of ion-pairs or larger aggregates. If either of the ions forming the ion-pair has a multiple charge, the value of r_{min} for a given solvent will, of course, be increased. Thus for univalent ions, r_{min} in water (3.5 Å) corresponds

Table 2-13 Effect of Dielectric
Constant on r_{min}

Solvent	ϵ	r_{min}
Water	80	3.5 Å
Acetonitrile	38	7.5
Butyronitrile	20	14.0
Butyl bromide	7	40.0
Dioxane	2	140.

approximately to the distance of minimum approach, and there will be no ions at a smaller distance from each other, and consequently there will be no ion-pairs. For multiply charged ions, the distance becomes sufficiently large that ion-pairs may be formed even in aqueous solution.

Table 2-14 Ion-Pair Association Constants in Dioxane-Water Mixtures[a]

Salt: Tetraisoamylammonium nitrate

Wgt. % Water	ϵ	$\log K_{ass}$	$\epsilon \log K$[b]
0.60	2.38	15.7	37.4
1.24	2.56	14.0	35.8
2.35	2.90	12.0	34.8
4.01	3.48	9.6	33.4
6.37	4.42	7.53	33.3
9.50	5.82	5.78	33.6
14.95	8.50	4.00	34.0
20.2	11.9	3.08	36.7
53.0	38.0	0.60	(22.8)

[a] Data of R. M. Fuoss and C. A. Kraus, *J. Am. Chem. Soc.*, **55**, 1019 (1933).
[b] The theory predicts an approximately linear relationship between K_{ass} and $1/\epsilon$. Using the correct formulation, a deviation at higher dielectric constants is predicted and is observed.

The formation of ion-pairs is, of course, a dynamic process, and the equilibrium constant refers to the average concentration of species which may be described as ion-pairs. It is not implied that there is a continued association between a specific anion and cation.

Several procedures have been suggested for the evaluation of ion-pair association constants from experimental data. The following is the formulation given by Shedlovsky.[31] If we consider the formation of ion-pairs as an equilibrium process, we may write

$$A^+ + B^- \rightleftharpoons A^+B^-$$

$$K = \frac{[A^+B^-]}{[A^+][B^-]}$$

In terms of the specific conductance (Λ) and the total concentration (C_t), the equilibrium constant may be obtained as follows:

$$[A^+] = [B^-] = \frac{\Lambda}{\Lambda_0} C_t$$

$$[A^+B^-] = \left(1 - \frac{\Lambda}{\Lambda_0}\right) C_t$$

$$K = \frac{\left(1 - \dfrac{\Lambda}{\Lambda_0}\right) C_t}{\dfrac{\Lambda^2}{\Lambda_0^2} C_t^2} = \frac{\Lambda_0^2 - \Lambda}{\Lambda^2 C_t}$$

or

$$\frac{K C_t \Lambda}{\Lambda_0^2} = \frac{1}{\Lambda} - \frac{1}{\Lambda_0}$$

Thus a plot of $1/\Lambda$ against $C_t \Lambda$ should give a line of slope K/Λ_0^2 and an intercept of $1/\Lambda_0$. This equation has been applied to the ionization of weak acids, such as acetic acid, in aqueous solution, for here the concentration of ions is small and the activity coefficients close to unity. However, for partially aqueous solutions this is not true, and corrections must be made.

According to the Onsager limiting law for conductance[32]

$$\Lambda = \Lambda_0 - S_\Lambda \sqrt{C}$$

where Λ_0 is the specific conductance of infinite dilution, S_Λ is a constant which is characteristic of the solvent, and C is the concentration of ions. If the fraction of the electrolyte present as ions is α, then

$$\Lambda = \alpha(\Lambda_0 - S_\Lambda \sqrt{\alpha C})$$

where C is now the total concentration of salt.

[31] T. Shedlovsky, *J. Franklin Inst.*, **225**, 739 (1938).
[32] L. Onsager, *Physik. Z.*, **28**, 277 (1927).

The degree of dissociation is given by

$$\alpha = \frac{\Lambda}{\Lambda_0(1 - S_\Lambda\sqrt{\alpha C})}$$

If z is defined as

$$z = \sqrt{C\Lambda}\, \frac{S_\Lambda}{\Lambda_0^{3/2}}$$

and S_z as

$$S_z = 1 + z + \frac{z^2}{2} + \frac{z^3}{3} + \cdots$$

then

$$\alpha = \frac{\Lambda}{\Lambda_0}S_z$$

The value of S_Λ for a $1:1$ electrolyte is given by

$$S_\Lambda = \frac{8.18 \times 10^5}{(\epsilon T)^{3/2}}\Lambda_0 + \frac{82}{\eta(\epsilon T)^{1/2}}$$

and the activity coefficient for dilute solutions is given by the Debye-Hückel equation,

$$\log \gamma_\pm{}^2 = -2\beta\sqrt{\alpha C}$$

where η is the viscosity and the constant β is given by

$$\beta = \frac{1.814 \times 10^6}{(\epsilon T)^{3/2}}$$

The thermodynamic dissociation constant is given by

$$K = \frac{C\alpha^2\gamma_\pm{}^2}{1 - \alpha}$$

and combined with

$$\alpha = \frac{\Lambda}{\Lambda_0}S_z$$

this gives

$$\frac{1}{\Lambda S_z} = \frac{1}{\Lambda_0} + \frac{C\Lambda\gamma_\pm{}^2 S_z}{K(\Lambda_0)^2} \tag{I}$$

One then plots $1/\Lambda S_z$ against $C\Lambda\gamma_\pm{}^2 S_z$, giving $1/K\Lambda_0{}^2$ as the slope and $1/\Lambda_0$ as the intercept.

In order to apply these equations one must have a value of Λ_0 for the evaluation of S_Λ. However, a reasonable value may be obtained by extrapolating the experimental data to zero concentration. If the value of Λ_0 which results from the plot of equation I is significantly different from that used in calculating S_z, the calculation must be repeated using the new value.

In this fashion one can fairly readily obtain data on ion-pair formation from conductance data. In thinking about the results it is useful to consider both the value of the equilibrium constant and of α for the individual concentrations. The activity coefficients differ markedly from unity in solutions having low dielectric constants, and so the activity of the ions becomes quite different from the concentrations. The equilibrium constant as defined above refers to the activities of the ions, whereas α refers to the concentrations.

References

General:
  R. W. Gurney, *Ionic Processes in Solution*, McGraw-Hill Book, Co., New York, 1953.
  L. P. Hammett, *Physical Organic Chemistry*, McGraw-Hill Book Co., New York, 1940, ch. 3.
  R. A. Robinson and R. H. Stokes, *Electrolyte Solutions*, Butterworths Scientific Publications, London, 1955.
Acid-Base Equilibria:
  M. Kilpatrick, *Chem. Revs.*, 30, 159 (1942).
  J. Kirkwood and F. H. Westheimer, *J. Chem. Phys.*, 6, 506 (1938); F. H. Westheimer and J. Kirkwood, *ibid.*, 6, 513 (1938); F. H. Westheimer and M. W. Shookhoff, *J. Am. Chem. Soc.*, 61, 555 (1939).
  R. P. Bell, *The Proton in Chemistry*, Cornell University Press, Ithaca, New York, 1959.

Problems

1. Examine the available data on the effect of electrolytes on the activity coefficients of organic compounds (F. A. Long and W. F. McDevit, *Chem. Revs.*, 51, 119 (1952), and see if you are able to find any regularities. Is it possible to fit the data by an equation such as

$$\log (k/k_0) = ax + by$$

where x and y are constants characteristic of the cation and anion, respectively, and a and b are constants giving the relative sensitivity of a given compound to the cation and anion. If such an equation held, would it be useful? Why?

2. Suppose one were to compare lithium chloride with tetra-*n*-butyl ammonium chloride in acetone solution ($\epsilon = 20.7$). Would there be different ion-pair association constants, and if so, why? For each of these, approximately what dielectric constant of the solvent would be required in order to make ion-pair formation negligible?

2-7 *Isotope Effects on Equilibria*

In the study of organic reactions the use of isotopes has become an increasingly useful tool. Isotopic substitution may affect equilibrium constants and rate constants. These effects are often of importance and will be considered here and in Section 3-4.

Let us consider the following equilibrium:

$$CH_4 + DBr \rightleftharpoons CH_3D + HBr$$

If there were no effect of isotopic substitution on vibrational frequencies, the equilibrium constant at a low temperature would be four. This arises because there are four equivalent hydrogens which may be exchanged for deuterium in the reactant, whereas there is only one deuterium which may be exchanged for hydrogen in the product. The molecules have a zero-point energy, which will be the sum of $\frac{1}{2}h\nu$ for each vibrational frequency. Thus at a low temperature where the partition functions are unity,

$$K = \frac{e^{-\Sigma h\nu/2kT}(CH_3D) \cdot e^{-h\nu/2kT}(HBr)}{e^{-\Sigma h\nu/2kT}(CH_4) \cdot e^{-h\nu/2kT}(DBr)} \cdot 4$$

and if we designate $h\nu/kT$ as u,

$$K = \frac{\prod e^{-\frac{1}{2}u}(CH_3D) \cdot e^{-\frac{1}{2}u}(HBr)}{\prod e^{-\frac{1}{2}u}(CH_4) \cdot e^{-\frac{1}{2}u}(DBr)} \cdot 4$$

where the products are over all the vibrational frequencies of the molecules in question.

The vibrational frequencies for the four components of the equilibrium system are given in Table 2-15. The difference in zero-point energy between reactants and products is found to be 440 cal/mole. If this difference were the only factor involved, the equilibrium constant at room temperature would be

$$K = 4e^{(440 \times 1.43)/RT} = 4e^{1.06} = 11.6$$

This case was chosen as one which would give a large equilibrium constant (both bending and stretching modes are affected in the methane-*d*, whereas only a stretching mode is affected in the hydrogen bromide). Normally the equilibrium constant is smaller than this, and if isotopes other than those of hydrogen are used, the equilibrium constants will be very much smaller because the effect of isotopic substitution on the vibrational frequencies will be smaller (approximately proportional to the square root of the ratio of the masses of the two isotopes).

At a reasonable temperature, the partition functions will not be unity, and the zero-point energy is not the only term involved. For the equilibrium

$$A + B' \rightleftharpoons A' + B$$

Table 2-15 Vibrational Frequencies[a, b]

CH$_4$	CH$_3$D
2917 a	2200 a_1
1534 e	2945 a_1
3019 t	1310 a_1
1306 t	1471 e
	3021 e
	1155 e
HBr	DBr
2650	1880

[a] The values for methane-d_1 are from J. K. Wilmshurst and H. J. Bernstein, *Can. J. Chem.*, **35**, 226 (1957); for HBr, G. Herzberg, *Diatomic Molecules*, Prentice-Hall, New York, 1939, p. 487.

[b] The designations a, e, and t indicate the degeneracy of the vibrational levels: $a = 1$, $e = 2$, and $t = 3$.

where A and A' differ only by isotopic substitution, the equilibrium constant must be written[33]

$$K = \frac{Q_{A'} Q_B}{Q_A Q_{B'}} \cdot \prod^{3n-6} \frac{e^{-\frac{1}{2}u_{A'}}}{e^{-\frac{1}{2}u_A}} \cdot \prod^{3n-6} \frac{e^{-\frac{1}{2}u_B}}{e^{-\frac{1}{2}u_{B'}}}$$

[33] In this and the following expressions, any change in symmetry number between reactants and products must also be included. This may either be done by multiplying by the appropriate factor, as in the treatment of the methane-deuterium bromide equilibrium, or it may be included by retaining the symmetry numbers in the rotational partition functions. This would introduce a factor

$$\frac{\sigma_A \sigma_{B'}}{\sigma_{A'} \sigma_B}$$

into the expression. For the above reaction, the symmetry numbers are CH$_4$ = 12, DBr = 1, CH$_3$D = 3, HBr = 1, giving the proper factor of four.

The first term contains the partition functions and the second contains the zero-point energy terms. Here the products are over the $3n - 6$ vibrational frequencies of each molecule (or $3n - 5$ frequencies for linear molecules).

The partition function ratio may be expressed in terms of the translational, rotational, and vibrational components. A number of terms cancel, giving

$$K = \left(\frac{M_{A'}M_B}{M_A M_{B'}}\right)^{3/2} \cdot \frac{(I_A I_B I_C)_{A'}^{1/2}(I_A I_B I_C)_B^{1/2}}{(I_A I_B I_C)_A^{1/2}(I_A I_B I_C)_{B'}^{1/2}} \cdot \prod^{3n-6} \frac{1 - e^{-u(A)}}{1 - e^{-u(A')}}$$

$$\cdot \prod^{3n-6} \frac{1 - e^{-u(B')}}{1 - e^{-u(B)}} \cdot \prod^{3n-6} \frac{e^{-\frac{1}{2}u(A')}}{e^{-\frac{1}{2}u(A)}} \cdot \prod^{3n-6} \frac{e^{-\frac{1}{2}u(B)}}{e^{-\frac{1}{2}u(B')}}$$

Here the first term arises from the translational partition function (p. 220); the second arises from the rotational partition function (p. 223); the first two products come from the vibrational partition functions (p. 227), and the last two products are the zero-point energy terms. The expression may be simplified using the Teller-Redlich product rule for isotopically substituted compounds,[34]

$$\left(\frac{M_{A'}}{M_A}\right)^{3/2} \frac{(I_A I_B I_C)_{A'}^{1/2}}{(I_A I_B I_C)_A^{1/2}} = \prod_j^n \frac{m_j(A')}{m_j(A)} \prod_i^{3n-6} \frac{\nu_i(A')}{\nu_i(A)}$$

where the m's are the masses of the atoms in each molecule and the ν's are the vibrational frequencies. The equilibrium constant then becomes

$$K = \prod_j^n \frac{m_j(A')}{m_j(A)} \prod_j^n \frac{m_j(B)}{m_j(B')} \prod_i^{3n-6} \frac{u_i(A')}{u_i(A)} \cdot \frac{e^{-\frac{1}{2}u_i(A')}}{e^{-\frac{1}{2}u_i(A)}} \cdot \frac{1 - e^{-u_i(A)}}{1 - e^{-u_i(A')}}$$

$$\cdot \prod_i^{3n-6} \frac{u_i(B)}{u_i(B')} \cdot \frac{e^{-\frac{1}{2}u_i(B)}}{e^{-\frac{1}{2}u_i(B')}} \cdot \frac{1 - e^{-u_i(B')}}{1 - e^{-u_i(B)}}$$

Since the sum of all the atoms of each kind in A and B' is equal to that of A' and B, the product of the masses cancels, giving as the final expression

$$K = \prod_i^{3n-6} \frac{u_i(A')}{u_i(A)} \cdot \frac{e^{-\frac{1}{2}u_i(A')}}{e^{-\frac{1}{2}u_i(A)}} \cdot \frac{1 - e^{-u_i(A)}}{1 - e^{-u_i(A')}}$$

$$\cdot \prod_i^{3n-6} \frac{u_i(B)}{u_i(B')} \cdot \frac{e^{-\frac{1}{2}u_i(B)}}{e^{-\frac{1}{2}u_i(B')}} \cdot \frac{1 - e^{-u_i(B')}}{1 - e^{-u_i(B)}}$$

If one first obtains the values of u_i from the vibrational frequencies,[35] the several terms are easily evaluated, and the equilibrium constant may be

[34] The derivation of this expression for a simple case is given by K. S. Pitzer, *Quantum Chemistry*, Prentice-Hall, New York, 1953, p. 275.
[35] $h\nu/kT = 1.4387\nu/T$.

obtained. In the case of the methane-deuterium bromide equilibrium, the constant at 25°C is evaluated to be

$$K = 4e^{0.567} = 7.04$$

It can be seen that the translational and rotational partition functions reduce the effect of the zero-point energy difference. The vibrational partition function has essentially no effect in this case because the frequencies are reasonably large.

Table 2-16   Vibrational Frequencies for Water and Oxonium Ion[a, b]

H_2O	D_2O
3760 (1)	2786 (1)
3650 (1)	2667 (1)
1595 (1)	1178 (1)
H_3O^+	D_3O^+
2590 (1)	2000 (1)
1150 (1)	785 (1)
3235 (2)	2445 (2)
1700 (2)	1255 (2)

[a] C. C. Ferriso and D. F. Horning, *J. Chem. Phys.*, **23**, 1464 (1955); J. T. Mullhaupt and D. F. Horning, *ibid.*, **24**, 169 (1956).
[b] The first and third frequencies for H_3O^+ and D_3O^+ may be inverted.

A more important and generally interesting example is the effect of substituting deuterium oxide for water as the solvent for a reaction. Let us consider the two equilibria:

$$H_3O^+ + R_2C{=}O \rightleftharpoons R_2C{=}OH^+ + H_2O$$
$$D_3O^+ + R_2C{=}O \rightleftharpoons R_2C{=}OD^+ + D_2O$$

The equilibrium constants for each reaction could be calculated if the necessary vibrational frequencies were known and if the classical difference in energy (i.e., not including zero-point energies) were also known. The latter will be the same for both reactions, for the only change is an isotopic substitution, and thus the ratio of the two equilibrium constants may be obtained knowing only the vibrational frequencies. The available data are shown in Table 2-16. It must be remembered that the values are only approximate because of the effects of hydrogen bonding.

The vibrational frequencies for the two conjugate acids are not known but may be estimated as follows. The O—H stretching frequency should be higher than that for the oxonium ion, for the charge on the oxygen in the conjugate acid will be distributed in part to the carbon. Therefore it may be chosen as approximately equal to the higher of the two stretching frequencies of the oxonium ion. There will be two O—H bending frequencies. These should be on the order of the average of the two frequencies of the oxonium ion and may be taken as 1400 cm⁻¹ for $R_2C=OH^+$ and 1000 cm⁻¹ for $R_2C=OD^+$. The net zero-point energy change in H_2O solution is then 1425 cm⁻¹ and for D_2O solution, 891 cm⁻¹. The ratio of the two equilibrium constants will be[36]

$$\frac{K_{D_2O}}{K_{H_2O}} = e^{-(891-1425)\,\times\,1.43/RT} = 3.6$$

Thus the equilibrium constant should be about 3.6 times as great in D_2O solution as in H_2O solution. This has been observed in many cases,[37] and the ratio is usually found to be on the order of $K_{D_2O}/K_{H_2O} = 3$. This is particularly important in the consideration of the rates of acid-catalyzed reactions in these solvents, for here a prior equilibrium may result in a reduced or even apparently reversed isotope effect.

If one wishes to assign the effect to one of the species of the equilibrium, the hydronium (and deuteronium) ions must be chosen. The vibrational frequencies for water and deuterium oxide are normal. However, when a proton is placed on either, the vibrational frequencies drop markedly, reflecting a decreased force constant. The large drop makes the zero-point energy difference in the ions considerably less, per hydrogen, than in H_2O or D_2O, leading to the observed zero-point energy difference.

References

Isotope Effects on Equilibria:
   J. Bigeleisen and M. G. Mayer, *J. Chem. Phys.*, **15**, 261 (1947).
   R. P. Bell, *The Proton in Chemistry*, Cornell University Press, Ithaca, New York, 1959, p. 183 ff.
   E. L. Purlee, *J. Am. Chem. Soc.*, **81**, 263 (1959).
   C. G. Swain and R. F. W. Bader, *Tetrahedron*, **10**, 182 (1960); C. G. Swain, R. F. W. Bader and E. R. Thornton, *Tetrahedron* **10**, 200 (1960).

[36] This neglects the effect of the partition functions. Since the calculation is extremely crude, this further refinement seems unwarranted.
[37] R. P. Bell, *Acid-Base Catalysis*, Oxford University Press, Oxford, 1941, p. 143; K. B. Wiberg, *Chem. Revs.*, **55**, 713 (1955).

2-8 Linear Free Energy Relationships

It is well known that the introduction of a chlorine into an acid increases its acidity, whereas the introduction of a methyl group decreases the acidity. If the effect of the substituent is considered as a perturbation, and if the magnitude of the perturbation is not large, there should be a linear relationship between the change in electron density at the reaction site in going from the reactant to the activated complex, and the change during this transformation of the perturbation energy caused by the introduction of the substituent. Deviations from linearity should occur only if the perturbation becomes large.

There may be several terms comprising the perturbed part of the Hamiltonian operator, and the weighting factors for each term may vary from compound to compound. However, if one were to choose compounds in which the weighting factors would be in approximately the same ratio, then the perturbation energies caused by the introduction of substituents should be proportional for the two compounds. For example, one might expect that the effects would be similar in the ionization of benzoic acids and of phenylacetic acids. Figure 2-11 shows a plot of the logarithms of the relative ionization constants of the substituted acids of one series against those of the other. For most substituents the correlation is quite

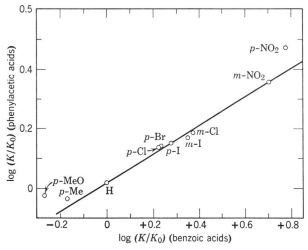

Fig. 2-11. Relation between the effects of substituents in the benzoic and phenylacetic acid series.

good, and the slope of the line is 0.49. The logarithms of the relative ionization constants are, of course, proportional to the perturbation energies, and thus when a substituent is introduced the perturbation energies in the phenylacetic acid series are about half as large as those for the benzoic acid series. This is expected, for the methylene group will attenuate the effect in the former case.

This type of relationship is known as a *linear free energy relationship* and has been formalized by Hammett[38] as follows. The equation of the line in Fig. 2-11 is

$$\log \left(\frac{K}{K_0} \right) = \rho \log \left(\frac{K'}{K'_0} \right)$$

where K is the ionization constant of a substituted phenylacetic acid, K_0 is the ionization constant of phenylacetic acid, and K' and K_0' are the corresponding terms for the substituted benzoic acids and benzoic acid. The constant ρ gives the ratio of the changes in the perturbation energies. Since this relationship has been found to apply to a number of reactions of aromatic compounds, it is convenient to use the ionization constants for one series of acids as the standard. More data are available for the ionization of benzoic acids than for any other compounds, and this was taken as the standard. Defining a new quality σ as

$$\sigma = \log \left(\frac{K'}{K_0'} \right)$$

where the K's refer to benzoic acids, the equation becomes

$$\log \left(\frac{K}{K_0} \right) = \sigma \rho$$

where σ is referred to as the substituent constant and ρ is referred to as the reaction constant. Values of σ for a number of groups are given in Table 2-17.

It must be emphasized that there may (and probably will be) several terms in the perturbed part of the total Hamiltonian operator. Further, the effect need not appear only in the enthalpy change—it may equally well appear in both the entropy and enthalpy terms. The latter will certainly be the case if changes in solvation energy occur during the reaction.

If one wishes to see what factors are important in determining the total perturbation energy, it is useful to compare acids of different structural

[38] L. P. Hammett, *Chem. Revs.*, **17**, 125 (1935); *Trans. Faraday Soc.*, **34**, 156 (1938); *Physical Organic Chemistry*, McGraw-Hill Book Co., New York, 1940, pp. 184–207. See G. N. Burkhardt, *Nature*, **136**, 687 (1935); G. N. Burkhardt, W. G. K. Ford, and E. Singleton, *J. Chem. Soc.*, **17** (1936).

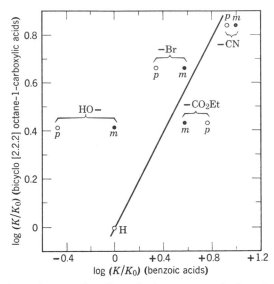

Fig. 2-12. Relation between the effect of substituents in the benzoic acid and bicyclo-[2.2.2]octane-1-carboxylic acid series.

types. Figure 2-12 shows a plot of the ionization constants of 4-substituted bicyclo[2.2.2]octane-1-carboxylic acids (A) against the ionization constants for both *m*- and *p*-substituted benzoic acids.[39]

$$COOH$$

(A)   X

We might first note that a *p*-hydroxy group decreases the acidity of benzoic acid, whereas it increases the acidity of the bicyclic acid (as well as other aliphatic acids). A *m*-hydroxy group has, however, no significant effect on the ionization constant of benzoic acid. From this alone it is evident that more than one effect is operative in the benzoic acid series.

The possible mechanisms by which an electrical effect may operate are

1. *The Inductive Effect.* This operates only through the bonds and corresponds to a displacement of electronic charge caused by the different

[39] J. D. Roberts and W. T. Moreland, Jr., *J. Am. Chem. Soc.*, **75**, 2167 (1953). The data for the bicyclic acids were determined in 50% ethanol; the ionization constants for benzoic acids in water have been approximately corrected for the change in going to 50% ethanol using the data of J. D. Roberts, E. A. McElhill, and R. Armstrong, *J. Am. Chem. Soc.*, **71**, 2923 (1949).

electron-withdrawing power of the two atoms forming a bond. Thus in chloroacetic acid the chlorine is electron withdrawing with respect to carbon, and consequently the electrons forming the C—Cl bond will be displaced toward the chlorine. The methylene carbon has now become electron deficient in comparison to the methyl carbon in acetic acid. This

Table 2-17 Substituent Constants for Some Common Groups[a]

Group	σ
p-NH$_2$	−0.660
p-OH	−0.357
p-OCH$_3$	−0.268
p-CH$_3$	−0.170
m-NH$_2$	−0.160
m-CH$_3$	−0.069
m-OH	−0.002
H	0.000
p-F	0.062
m-CH$_3$O	0.115
p-Cl	0.226
p-Br	0.232
p-I	0.276
m-F	0.337
m-I	0.352
m-Cl	0.373
m-Br	0.391
m-CO$_2$Et	0.398
p-CO$_2$Et	0.522 (0.68)[b]
p-CN	0.628 (1.00)[b]
m-CN	0.678
m-NO$_2$	0.710
p-NO$_2$	0.778 (1.27)[b]

[a] The data were taken from H. H. Jaffé, *Chem. Revs.*, **53**, 191 (1953).
[b] These values apply for the reactions of phenols, anilines, and thiphenols.

effect will have a relatively small consequence in the free acid. In the anion the greater electron-withdrawing power of the methylene carbon in chloroacetic acid will result in a greater dispersion of the negative charge on the carboxyl group than in the case of acetic acid. As a result, the energy of the anion of chloroacetic acid will be decreased as compared to the anion of acetic acid, and the former will be the stronger acid.

This effect will fall off rapidly with distance, for each atom involved will attenuate the electron displacement. An estimate of this attenuation has been made by Waters,[40] based on the polarizability of various groups. This gave a transmission factor of 0.022 per methylene of a saturated chain and 0.5 per carbon of an unsaturated chain. Although these numbers may be considerably in error, they do suggest that the effect will be negligible past two methylene groups.

2. *The Field Effect.* A dipole may interact with a charge directly through space. In the case of chloroacetate ion, the C—Cl dipole will have approximately the direction

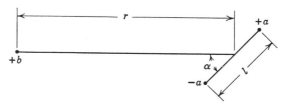

Since the negative part of the dipole is directed away from the negative charge, a net stabilization will occur. The magnitude of the effect may be calculated as follows.

Let us consider the interaction of a point charge $+b$ with the point charges $+a$ and $-a$ forming a dipole with the length l. It will be assumed that l is small compared to the distance between b and the dipole (r).

Defining the angle α as shown in the above diagram, the distance between $+a$ and $+b$ will be

$$r_+ = r + \frac{l}{2} \cos \alpha$$

and between $-a$ and $+b$,

$$r_- = r - \frac{l}{2} \cos \alpha$$

The potential energy of the interaction will be

$$V = \frac{ab}{r_+} - \frac{ab}{r_-} = \frac{ab}{r + (l/2) \cos \alpha} - \frac{ab}{r - (l/2) \cos \alpha}$$

[40] W. A. Waters, *J. Chem. Soc.*, 1551 (1933).

Multiplying this out, we find

$$V\left(r^2 + \frac{l^2}{4}\cos^2\alpha\right) = -ab(l\cos\alpha)$$

Since l is small compared to r, and since al is equal to the dipole moment (μ),

$$r^2 V = -b\mu\cos\alpha$$

$$V = -\frac{b\mu\cos\alpha}{r^2}$$

If the medium has a dielectric constant, ϵ, the potential energy will be reduced correspondingly, giving

$$V = -\frac{b\mu\cos\alpha}{\epsilon r^2}$$

Suppose we had two structurally similar acids which differed only in the magnitude of the dipole at some carbon (for example, chloroacetic acid with a C—Cl dipole and acetic acid with a C—H dipole). Then

$$V_2 - V_1 = \frac{b(\mu_1 - \mu_2)\cos\alpha}{\epsilon r^2}$$

However, since only potential energy is involved, the difference in energy will also be given by $RT\ln(K_1/K_2)$. Thus for the two acids,

$$-\Delta pK = \frac{b(\Delta\mu)\cos\alpha}{2.3RT\epsilon\, r^2}$$

Some of the interaction in a real molecular system will "feel" the dielectric constant of the solvent, whereas a large part will "feel" only the lower dielectric constant ($\sim$2) of the carbon chain in the molecule. This factor was first considered by Eucken,[41] who replaced the dielectric constant of the solvent by an effective dielectric constant, ϵ_E. The calculation of the latter quantity has been considered by Kirkwood and Westheimer[42] using two models, one in which the molecule was treated as a sphere and the other as confined in an ellipsoid of revolution with the dipole and the charge at the foci. The latter is the more generally useful model. If λ_0 is the ratio of the major axis of the elipse to the distance between the center of the dipole and the charge, it will be given by

$$\lambda_0^3 - \lambda_0 = \left(\frac{6}{\pi}\right)\left(\frac{V}{r^3}\right)$$

[41] A. Eucken, *Angew. Chem.*, **45**, 203 (1932).
[42] J. G. Kirkwood and F. H. Westheimer, *J. Chem. Phys.*, **6**, 506 (1938); F. H. Westheimer and J. G. Kirkwood, *ibid.*, **6**, 513 (1938).

where V is the partial molar volume estimated from Traube's rule[43] and r is the distance between the dipole and the charge. The values of ϵ_E obtained using this model are a function of the external dielectric constant and of λ_0 and are summarized in Table 2-18. The values which are appropriate to the interaction of two charges are also given. In each case the value was calculated assuming that the dielectric constant of the carbon framework was 2.

Table 2-18   Effective Dielectric Constants[a]

λ_0	ϵ_E (charge)	ϵ_E (dipole)
2.3	7.8	2.7
2.0	11.2	3.3
1.8	15.5	4.0
1.6	25.3	5.7
1.4	51	11.2
1.3	74	20.4
1.2	94	49
1.1	94	90
1.0	78	78

[a] The values of ϵ_E (charge) are used when the substituent introduced possesses a charge, and the values of ϵ_E (dipole) are used when the substituent leads to a dipole.

In the chloroacetate ion, the distance between the dipole and the charges will be a function of the angle between the O—C—O plane of the carboxyl group and the Cl—C—C plane. When the two planes are perpendicular, the distances r_1 and r_2 are equal and are 2.80 Å. When the two planes are parallel, $r_1 = 2.42$ and $r_2 = 3.41$ Å (using $r_{C—C} = 1.54$, $r_{C—Cl} = 1.78$, and $r_{C—O} = 1.30$ Å, a tetrahedral arrangement about the methylene carbon and

[43] Traube, *Saml. Chem. Chem.-Tech.*, Vortr., 4, 255 (1899).

Traube's rule states that the molar volume of an organic compound may be approximated by summing the following atomic contributions: 9.9 ml per carbon, 3.1 ml per hydrogen, 2.3 ml per hydroxy oxygen, 0.4 ml per 2nd hydroxy oxygen on the same or nearby carbon atom, 5.5 ml per carbonyl or ether oxygen, 5.9 ml per two oxygens of carboxyl group, 13.2 ml per chlorine in monohalogenated compound, 13.2 ml per cyano group, 17.7 ml per bromine, 21.4 ml per iodine, and 15.5 ml per thioether or thiocarbonyl sulfur. To this sum is added 12.4 ml as the co-volume of the molecule.

a trigonal arrangement about the carboxyl carbon). The value r in the above equations may be taken as the average of these values, or 2.80 Å,

and the negative charge of the carboxyl group may be formally considered as residing at that distance. The angle α is then 54°.

Traube's rule gives a partial molar volume of 60.6 ml/or 100.6 Å³, and these numbers give $\lambda_0 = 2.23$. From Table 2-18 the effective dielectric constant in an aqueous medium is 2.8. The difference between the C—Cl and C—H bond moments may be taken as that of an alkyl chloride, or 1.56 D.[42] The value of ΔpK may then be calculated to be 2.1. The observed value is 1.90, and thus the calculation is in good accord with theory. It can be seen that the field effect is able to account for the effect of substituents without the intervention of the inductive effect.[44]

When this procedure was applied to the calculation of the acidities of the bicyclic acids, the values obtained were about half the observed values. This is fairly good, for the internal dielectric constant of the bicyclic system may be significantly lower than the value appropriate for a straight chain of carbon atoms. In view of the approximations which must be made concerning the shape of the cavity in which the dipole and charge find themselves, and of the location of the electrical center of a dipole, it is not possible to say whether or not the field effect is the only important electrical effect which controls the relative acidity, or whether there is some contribution from the inductive effect. There can be no question, however, concerning the importance of the field effect in controlling relative acidity.

3. *The Resonance Effect.* This effect is defined as one which operates via the π-electrons in an unsaturated system and thus is present in the aromatic compounds but not in the bicyclic acids discussed above. It may be noted from Fig. 2-12 that *p*-carbethoxybenzoic acid is a stronger acid than *m*-carbethoxybenzoic acid, whereas if only the field or inductive effects were operative, the *m*-substituted compound would be the stronger acid because of the shorter distance between the substituent and the carboxyl group. A common explanation for this and related observations is as

---

[44] A number of additional examples have been given by F. H. Westheimer and N. W. Shookhoff, *J. Am. Chem. Soc.*, **61**, 555 (1939); Westheimer, *ibid.*, **61**, 1977 (1939).

follows. In benzoic acid, we may write the following resonance structures:

$$\text{HO}\diagdown\text{C}\diagup\!\!\diagup\text{O}\ (\text{C}_6\text{H}_5) \leftrightarrow \text{HO}\diagdown\overset{+}{\text{C}}\diagup\text{O}^- \leftrightarrow \text{HO}\diagdown\text{C}\diagup\text{O}^- \leftrightarrow \text{HO}\diagdown\text{C}\diagup\text{O}^- \leftrightarrow \text{HO}\diagdown\text{C}\diagup\text{O}^-$$

In the anion, however,

$$\text{O}\diagdown\text{C}\diagup\text{O}^- \leftrightarrow {}^-\text{O}\diagdown\text{C}\diagup\!\!\diagup\text{O}$$

structures of these sorts will be less important because they would involve placing two negative charges on the carboxylate group. If an electron-withdrawing substituent is introduced into the *p*-position, it will destabilize one of the resonance structures for the acid and raise the energy of the acid. The effect will be much smaller in the anion because of the smaller importance of resonance structures involving the ring, and consequently the introduction of an electron-withdrawing substituent in the *p*-position will result in a decrease in the free energy of ionization, leading to a stronger acid. This effect will not be important with *m*-substituted compounds because the positive charge is not distributed to the *m*-position in any of the resonance structures for the acid. Thus the *p*-substituted acid is a stronger acid than the *m*-substituted acid. The same argument will be used to explain the decrease in acidity when electron-releasing substituents are introduced, and the lower acidity of *p*-bromobenzoic acid as compared to *m*-bromobenzoic acid. (Here the bromine is electron releasing via the resonance effect, just as it is in electrophilic aromatic substitution.)

However, the plot shown as Fig. 2-11 indicates that this view is incorrect. It may be seen that the points for all substituents except *p*-methoxy and *p*-nitro fall on a good straight line. The resonance effect described above cannot operate in the phenylacetic acid series because of the methylene group introduced between the ring and the carboxyl group. Thus for most of the groups a different explanation must be found. This should not be surprising because the delocalization indicated by the resonance structures for benzoic acid cannot be too large, for the structures involve the relatively high energy of separating charges.

It is clear, however, that much of the effect in the aromatic series does involve the π-electrons. Any effect would be expected to be larger in the anion than in the acid, for in the former there is a full negative charge on which to operate. Thus, to a first approximation, let us assume that the resonance effect is negligible in the free acid (and this must be close to the case for phenylacetic acid). In going to the anion of the acid, the value of the Coulombic integral for the ring carbon nearest the carboxyl group will change as a result of the change in charge of the attached group. The effect will, of course, be greater in benzoic acid than in phenylacetic acid because of the attenuating effect of the methylene group. The change in Coulomb integral will cause a change in the π-electron distribution about the ring, and the change will be largest in the o- and p-positions and least at the m-position. The interaction of the o- or p-substituent with the change in electron density at the attached ring carbon will be reflected in the ionization constant of the acid.[45]

In some cases the resonance effect as described at first may contribute. It may be noted that in Fig. 2-11 the p-methoxy and p-nitro substituents fall off the line. Because of the relatively high basicity of the methoxy group, structures of the type shown at the top of next page presumably do contribute significantly to the stabilization of the acid. This is lost on going to the anion, resulting in a decrease in acidity which is greater than that expected on comparison with the phenylacetic acid case. Even here the effect is not large. The difference in pK between benzoic acid and

---

[45] As another related example, the difference in basicity of aniline and cyclohexylamine ($K = 3.8 \times 10^{-10}$ and 5×10^{-4}, respectively) may be considered. One explanation is that resonance structures of the type

contribute to the stabilization of aniline. No corresponding structures may be written for the anilinium ion, and the extra stabilization of the amine will result in a lower basicity. Although this effect may contribute, it should not be all important because of the energy involved in separating charges in the resonance structures shown. Possibly an equally important explanation is that the amino group in aniline is bonded to an sp^2 carbon orbital, whereas in cyclohexylamine it is bonded to an sp^3 carbon orbital. The change in hybridization will produce a change in basicity, for a carbon using an sp^3 orbital is more electron withdrawing than one using an sp^3 orbital. The same effect is observed in cyclopropylamine ($K = 4.6 \times 10^{-6}$ in 50% water-ethanol as compared with $K = 68 \times 10^{-6}$ for cyclohexylamine in the same solvent (J. D. Roberts and V. C. Chambers, *J. Am. Chem. Soc.*, **73**, 5030 (1951)), and it is known that the orbital used is between sp^2 and sp^3 (cf. Section 1-15).

anisic acid is only 0.27, corresponding to $\Delta\Delta F° = 0.4$ kcal/mole, and only a small amount must be added to this to correct for the field effect.

Effects of this type may become important, and in reactions of phenols the σ value for a nitro group derived from the benzoic acids turns out to be too small. Thus the p-nitrophenolate ion must be significantly stabilized by the structures involving the negative charge on the nitro group

This effect is also important in the free phenol, for the dipole moment of p-nitrophenol is about $0.4D$ smaller than would be expected on the basis of the dipole moments of phenol and of nitrobenzene. The dipole moments of the p-halophenols, for which the ordinary σ values apply, may be calculated as the sum of the two component dipoles.

Realizing that the difference between the field (and inductive) effect and the resonance effect may be seen by examining suitable groups of compounds, a number of investigators have attempted a semiquantitative separation of the σ values into the polar and resonance contributions. Roberts and Moreland obtained a set of substituent constants appropriate to the bicyclo[2.2.2]hexane derivatives (designated as σ'), and arguing that the polar effects should be the same for the bicyclic series and the aromatic series, used the difference between σ and σ' as a measure of the resonance component.

Relatively few groups could be compared in this fashion, for only a few 4-substituted bicyclo[2.2.2]octane-1-carboxylic acids have been prepared.

Taft has devised a kinetic method for obtaining "polar" substituent constants for aliphatic compounds[46] and has found that his values parallel σ'. If it is assumed that this relationship will hold for most groups, a larger set of σ' constants may be derived. These are compared with the Hammett values in Table 2-19.

It may be seen that the values of $(\sigma_m - \sigma')$ are relatively small except for the hydroxy group. Thus for most substituents the major effect at the *m*-position is the polar effect. The values of $(\sigma_p - \sigma')$ are generally negative, suggesting that most substituents will stabilize a positive charge

Table 2-19   A Comparison of σ with σ'

Substituent	σ_p	σ_m	σ'	$(\sigma_p - \sigma')$	$(\sigma_m - \sigma')$
OH	−0.36	0.00	+0.25	−0.61	−0.25
OCH_3	−0.27	+0.12	+0.23	−0.50	−0.11
Cl	+0.23	+0.37	+0.47	−0.24	−0.10
Br	+0.23	+0.39	+0.45	−0.22	−0.06
CH_3	−0.17	−0.07	−0.05	−0.13	−0.02
I	+0.28	+0.35	+0.38	−0.10	−0.03
CN	+0.66	+0.62	+0.59	−0.07	+0.03
NO_2	+0.78	+0.71	+0.63	+0.15	+0.08

via a resonance effect. Only with the strongly electron-withdrawing group NO_2 does the difference become small and, in fact, positive.

The free linear energy relationships may also give us information about the nature of reactions. As examples, the values of the Hammett ρ for several ionization equilibria are summarized in Table 2-20. Reactions having a negative ρ are those in which the carbon attached to the ring becomes relatively electron poor as a result of the reaction, and those having a positive ρ produce a relatively electron rich carbon as a result of the reaction. The magnitude of ρ gives information on the degree of electron density change.

It can be seen that the value of ρ usually increases as the dielectric constant of the solvent decreases. This is expected if the field effect is important, for the lower the effective dielectric constant, the larger will be the interaction. The decrease in ρ in going from the benzoic acids to the phenylacetic acids, and to the β-phenylpropionic acids is expected, for the field and resonance effects will drop off as the distance between the substituent and the reaction center increases.

---

[46] R. W. Taft, Jr., *J. Am. Chem. Soc.*, **74**, 3120 (1952); **75**, 4231 (1953);   Steric Effects in Organic Chemistry," M. S. Newman (ed.), John Wiley and Sons, New York, 1956, pp. 587 ff.

The transmission of electrical effects by various groups is indicated by the values in Table 2-21. The higher value for a vinyl group indicates that the field effect is not the only one which is operative and that the polarizability of the group transmitting the effect is important. A similar deduction must be made from the value for the phenyl group.

Table 2-20   Hammett ρ Values for Some Equilibrium Reactions[a]

Reaction	Temp.	Solvent	ρ
$C_6H_5CO_2H \rightleftharpoons C_6H_5CO_2^- + H^+$	25°	H_2O	(1.000)
	25	40% C_2H_5OH	1.668
	25	50% C_2H_5OH	1.601[b]
	25	50% C_2H_5OH	1.423[b]
	25	70% C_2H_5OH	1.738
	25	80% C_2H_5OH	1.791
	25	90% C_2H_5OH	1.896
	25	100% C_2H_5OH	1.957
	25	CH_3OH	1.537
$C_6H_5CH_2CO_2H \rightleftharpoons C_6H_5CO_2^- + H^+$	25	H_2O	0.489
$C_6H_5CH_2CH_2CO_2H \rightleftharpoons C_6H_5CH_2CH_2CO_2^- + H^+$	25	H_2O	0.212
$C_6H_5CH{=}CHCO_2H \rightleftharpoons C_6H_5CH{=}CHCO_2^- + H^+$	25	H_2O	0.466
$(C_6H_5)_2CH^+ + H_2O \rightleftharpoons (C_6H_5)_2CHOH + H^+$	25	H_2SO_4	6.67[c]
$(C_6H_5)_3C^+ + H_2O \rightleftharpoons (C_6H_5)_3COH + H^+$	25	H_2SO_4	3.55
$C_6H_5NH_3^+ \rightleftharpoons C_6H_5NH_2 + H^+$	25	H_2O	2.767
	25	CH_3OH	3.016
	25	30% C_2H_5OH	3.435
	25	100% C_2H_5OH	3.535`
	25	20% dioxane	3.256
	25	45% dioxane	3.558
	25	70% dioxane	3.567
$C_6H_5N(CH_3)_2H^+ \rightleftharpoons C_6H_5N(CH_3)_2 + H^+$	25	30% C_2H_5OH	3.426
	25	50% C_2H_5OH	4.191
$C_6H_5OH \rightleftharpoons C_6H_5O^- + H^+$	25	H_2O	2.113
	25	30% C_2H_5OH	3.197[d]
	~20	49% C_2H_5OH	2.545
	~20	95% C_2H_5OH	2.364

[a] The values were taken from H. H. Jaffé, *Chem. Revs.*, **53**, 191 (1953).
[b] The two values for 50% ethanol were obtained by different investigators and differ by much more than the experimental error.
[c] In this case the σ value for strongly electron-releasing groups (via the resonance effect) such as *p*-methoxy is too small.
[d] It is interesting to note that the value of ρ appears to go through a maximum at about 35% ethanol. However, the values were obtained by different investigators and may not be directly comparable.

It may also be noted that the ρ's for the ionization of anilinium ion and phenol are considerably greater than that of benzoic acid. In the former cases, the atom undergoing change in charge is directly attached to the aromatic ring, whereas in the latter it is one removed, which attenuates the effect.

The remarkable success of the Hammett treatment when dealing with aromatic compounds indicates that the three components of the σ constant discussed above are in roughly constant ratio for most reactions. The majority of the data concerning linear free energy relationships involves

Table 2-21   Transmission of Substituent Effects[a]

Group	ρ/ρ_0
—CH$_2$—	0.410
—CH$_2$CH$_2$—	0.206
—CH=CH—	0.508
(phenylene ring)	0.303
—CH=CH—C(=O)—	0.035

[a] H. H. Jaffé, *Chem. Revs.*, **53**, 191 (1953). The values given are average values, and the range is on the order of ±0.050.

kinetics rather than equilibria, and so a further discussion of this subject will be postponed until Part Three.

References

Field Effect and Inductive Effect:
N. Bjerrum, *Z. physik. Chem.*, **106**, 219 (1923) (original formulation of the field effect).
J. G. Kirkwood and F. H. Westheimer, *J. Chem. Phys.*, **6**, 506 (1938); F. H. Westheimer and J. G. Kirkwood, *ibid*, **6**, 513 (1938) (calculation of effective dielectric constant).
F. H. Westheimer, *J. Am. Chem. Soc.*, **61**, 1977 (1939); F. H. Westheimer and M. W. Schookhoff, *ibid*, **61**, 555 (1939); J. D. Roberts and W. T. Moreland, Jr., *ibid*, **75**, 2167 (1953) (application to equilibria).
F. H. Westheimer, N. A. Jones, and R. A. Ladd, *J. Chem. Phys.*, **10**, 478 (1942); S. Winstein, E. Grunwald, and L. L. Ingraham, *J. Am. Chem. Soc.*, **70**, 821 (1948) (application to kinetics).
W. A. Waters, *J. Chem. Soc.*, 1551 (1933) (early recognition of the importance of the field effect).
Linear Free Energy Relationships in Equilibria:
L. P. Hammett, *Chem. Revs.*, **17**, 125 (1935); *Physical Organic Chemistry*, McGraw-Hill Book Co., New York, 1940.
H. H. Jaffé, *Chem. Revs.*, **53**, 191 (1953).
R. P. Bell, *Acid-Base Catalysis*, Oxford University Press, London, 1949, ch. 5.

Problems

1. Using the Kirkwood-Westheimer equation, calculate the change in the dissociation constant in going from α-chloro to β- and γ-chlorobutyric acids.

2. Repeat the above calculations, using chloroacetic acid as the acid, and changing the dielectric constant of the medium. Make a plot of pK_a against the reciprocal of the dielectric constant of the solvent and see how large the deviations from linearity should be.

3. Calculate the values of ΔpK for the series of 4-substituted bicyclo[2.2.2]-octane-1-carboxylic acids (J. D. Roberts and W. T. Moreland, Jr., *J. Am. Chem. Soc.*, **75**, 2167 (1953)) using the same value of ϵ_E for each. How much of an effect is introduced by varying the value of ϵ_E as was done by Roberts and Moreland?

2-9 Acid-Base Equilibria; The Acidity Function

A particularly important aspect of acid-base equilibria is the protonation of a weak base, forming the conjugate acid.

$$B + H_3O^+ \rightleftharpoons BH^+ + H_2O$$

The evaluation of the equilibrium constant for the reaction is considerably simplified when the conjugate acid has a different absorption spectrum (particularly in the visible or ultraviolet region) than the base, for here the change in the spectrum with the concentration of the acid may be used to determine the constant. If a dilute acidic solution ($0.1M$ or less) will effect protonation, the equilibrium constant may be formulated as follows, where C_1 is the concentration of the base having ϵ_1 as its absorption coefficient, and C_2 is the concentration of the conjugate acid with the absorption coefficient ϵ_2. As is customary, the concentration of water will not be included in the constant. Thus

$$K' = K[H_3O^+] = \frac{C_2}{C_1} = \frac{C_2}{C_T - C_2}$$

Since the observed absorbance ($C_T\epsilon_T$) is the sum of that for the base ($C_1\epsilon_1$) and the conjugate acid ($C_2\epsilon_2$), and since $C_T = C_1 + C_2$, we have

$$C_T\epsilon_T = C_1\epsilon_1 + C_2\epsilon_2$$
$$\underline{C_T\epsilon_1 = C_1\epsilon_1 + C_2\epsilon_1}$$
$$C_T(\epsilon_T - \epsilon_1) = C_2(\epsilon_2 - \epsilon_1)$$

This may be used to eliminate C_2 from the above equation, giving

$$K' = \frac{(\epsilon_T - \epsilon_1)}{(\epsilon_2 - \epsilon_1) - (\epsilon_T - \epsilon_1)} = \frac{(\epsilon_T - \epsilon_1)}{(\epsilon_2 - \epsilon_T)}$$

Thus if one knows the absorption coefficients for the base and the conjugate acid (determined in neutral solution and in fairly strong acid, respectively), one may compute K' for each acid concentration from the observed absorption coefficient in that solution. The values of $K(=K'/[H_3O^+])$ thereby obtained may be extrapolated to zero-acid concentration to give the thermodynamic equilibrium constant corresponding to an ionic strength of zero.

Often a fairly strong acid is required to effect protonation. Then the activity of hydrogen ions (a_{H^+}) begins to deviate markedly from the concentration of hydrogen ions, and it is not possible to extrapolate to zero acid concentration. Thus a measure of a_{H^+} is required. Similarly, the activity coefficients for B and BH^+ will not be unity. If a measure of all three quantities could be obtained, then

$$K = \frac{[BH^+]}{[B]a_{H^+}} \cdot \frac{\gamma_{BH^+}}{\gamma_B}$$

Suppose we define a quantity, h_0, as[47]

$$h_0 = \frac{a_{H^+}\gamma_B}{\gamma_{BH^+}}$$

Then

$$K = \frac{[BH^+]}{[B]h_0}$$

and the question becomes, how may one determine h_0? The activity of hydrogen ions is potentially the simplest part, for this could, in principle, be determined potentiometrically. The glass electrode, for example, determines log a_{H^+}. The main problem here would be the determination of the liquid junction potentials in changing from one solvent to another. However, the activity coefficient ratio is not easily evaluated. The simplest thing would be to choose a standard and to relate everything to it.

This would be possible if γ_{BH^+}, for example, were independent of the nature of B and a function only of the environment. Hammett and Dyrup have investigated the behavior of a series of indicator bases in sulfuric acid-water mixtures. It was found that plots of log $[BH^+]/[B]$ against acid concentration were parallel, indicating that the ratio of the individual activity coefficients was close to unity.

$$\left(\frac{\gamma_{BH_1^+}}{\gamma_{B_1}}\right)\left(\frac{\gamma_{B_2}}{\gamma_{BH_2^+}}\right) \cong 1$$

[47] L. P. Hammett and A. J. Deyrup, *J. Am. Chem. Soc.*, **54**, 2721, 4239 (1932); *ibid.*, **55**, 1900 (1933).

This makes it practical to establish an indicator acidity scale based on the degree of protonation of suitable indicators.

For convenience, the negative logarithm of h_0 is usually used

$$H_0 = -\log h_0$$

and in dilute aqueous solution where γ_{BH^+} and γ_B are equal, H_0 is equal to pH. As the activity coefficients change, H_0 begins to deviate from pH, and, as we shall see later, this deviation between the two quantities is often useful in the study of mechanisms of reactions.

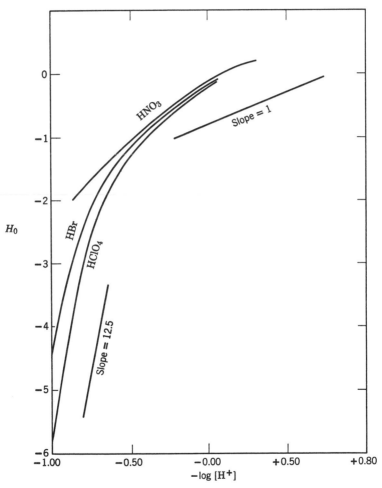

Fig. 2-13. Relationship between H_0 and $-\log [H^+]$ for three strong acids.

The H_0 scale is set up by determining the pK_a of an indicator base*
spectrophotometrically in dilute aqueous solution

$$pK_a = pH - \log \frac{[B]}{[BH^+]}$$

It is assumed that the pK_a thereby determined, being a thermodynamic
equilibrium constant (i.e., including the activity coefficients, since the
latter will be unity in dilute solutions) will be independent of the solvent
and may be used to determine the H_0 of more concentrated acidic solutions.

$$pK_a = H_0 - \log \frac{[B]}{[BH^+]}$$

An indicator is usually useful where the ratio of $[B]/[BH^+]$ is between 0.1
and 10.

A new indicator which is a weaker base may then be used to continue the
H_0 scale by relating its pK_a to that of the first indicator in a solution of
suitable acidity. The standard indicator is p-nitroaniline with a pK_a of 0.99.
A list of common indicators,[48] along with their pK_a values, is given in
Table 2-22. The values of H_0, which have been determined for several
common acids, are given in Table 2-23 and are plotted in Fig. 2-13.

Using h_0 as the measure of acidity, the equation previously used for the
determination of K becomes

$$K = \frac{(\epsilon_2 - \epsilon_T)}{(\epsilon_T - \epsilon_1)h_0}$$

and, again, the value of K may be determined if ϵ_1 and ϵ_2 may be obtained.
Occasionally, it is not possible to obtain a value of ϵ_2 either because
complete protonation requires a solution with an h_0 value greater than that
attainable with a given acid or because the conjugate acid slowly decomposes. It is still possible to measure K. The above equation may be
rearranged to

$$\frac{(\epsilon_T - \epsilon_1)}{h_0} K - \epsilon_T = \epsilon_2$$

and if ϵ_T is determined for several solutions having different values of h_0,
the value of K may be determined by solving sets of simultaneous
equations, for the unknown quantity, ϵ_2, will be the same for all the
equations.[49]

---

* The pK_a is the negative logarithm of the ionization constant of the conjugate acid
of the amine.
[48] M. A. Paul and F. A. Long, *Chem. Revs.*, **57**, 1 (1957).
[49] L. A. Flexer, L. P. Hammett, and A. Dingwell, *J. Am. Chem. Soc.*, **57**, 2103 (1935).
V. Gold and B. W. V. Hawkes, *J. Chem. Soc.*, 2102 (1951) have discussed the determination of K in detail.

Table 2-22 pK_a Values for Weak Bases[a]

Base	pK_a
p-Aminoazobenzene	2.77[b]
m-Nitroaniline	2.50[b]
2,4-Dichloroaniline	2.00[b]
Benzeneazodiphenylamine	1.42[b]
p-Nitroaniline	0.99[b]
Diphenylamine	0.78[b]
p-Naphtholbenzein	0.41
2,4-Dinitro-N,N-diethylaniline-	0.18
2,6-Dichloro-4-nitro-N,N-dimethylaniline	−0.23
o-Nitroaniline	−0.29
4-Chloro-2-nitroaniline	−1.03
5-Chloro-2-nitroaniline	−1.52
p-Nitrodiphenylamine	−2.48
2,4-Dichloro-6-nitroaniline	−3.32
p-Nitroazobenzene	−3.47
2,6-Dinitro-4-methylaniline	−4.44
2,4-Dinitroaniline	−4.53
N,N-Dimethyl-2,3,6-trinitroaniline	−4.81[c]
Benzalacetophenone	−5.73[c]
β-Benzoyldiphenyl	−6.37
6-Bromo-2,4-dinitroaniline	−6.71
Anthraquinone	−8.27
2,4,6-Trinitroaniline	−9.41
p-Nitrotoluene	−10.46
Nitrobenzene	−11.38
2,4-Dinitrotoluene	−12.78

[a] The data were taken from a compilation by M. A. Paul and F. A. Long, Chem. Revs., **57**, 1 (1957).

[b] Determined by direct extrapolation to zero acid concentration. All others were determined by comparison with ultimate reference to p-nitroaniline.

[c] These are probably not good indicators for H_0 determination, for their behavior does not parallel that of other indicators.

If one examines Fig. 2-13, it may be seen that the slope of the plot of H_0 against $-\log [H^+]$ approaches unity at low acid concentrations but becomes as high as 12 at higher concentrations. The deviation between the two quantities may be considered in terms of two factors—a change in a_{H^+} which is not proportional to $[H^+]$ and a change in the activity coefficient ratio. The change in the latter may be minimized if the ionic strength is maintained constant in all the solutions,[50] and thus one may obtain a crude measure of the changes in a_{H^+} caused by changes in the environment at a constant ionic strength. The required data are given in Table 2-24. There is considerable evidence that in aqueous solution a proton is extensively hydrated. It is found, for example, that when strong acids are

Table 2-23   Values for the Acidity Function H_0 for Aqueous Acid Solutions, 25°[a]

Acid Concentration	$-\log$ [H⁺]	HNO₃	HCl	HBr	HClO₄	H₂SO₄	H₃PO₄	HF
0.1	+1.00	+0.98	+0.98	+0.98		+0.83	+1.45	
0.25	+0.60	+0.55				+0.44	+1.15	
0.5	+0.30	+0.21	+0.20	+0.20		+0.13	+0.97	
0.75	+0.12	−0.02	−0.03		−0.04	−0.07	+0.78	
1.0	0.00	−0.18	−0.20	−0.20	−0.22	−0.26	+0.63	+1.20
1.5	−0.18	−0.45	−0.47		−0.53	−0.56	+0.41	+1.04
2.0	−0.30	−0.67	−0.69	−0.71	−0.78	−0.84	+0.24	+0.91
2.5	−0.40	−0.85	−0.87		−1.01	−1.12	+0.07	+0.74
3.0	−0.48	−1.02	−1.05	−1.11	−1.23	−1.38	−0.08	+0.60
3.5	−0.54	−1.17	−1.23		−1.47	−1.62	−0.22	+0.49
4.0	−0.60	−1.32	−1.40	−1.50	−1.72	−1.85	−0.37	+0.40
4.5	−0.65	−1.46	−1.58		−1.97	−2.06	−0.53	+0.34
5.0	−0.70	−1.57	−1.76	−1.93	−2.23	−2.28	−0.69	+0.28
5.5	−0.74	−1.69	−1.93		−2.52	−2.51	−0.84	+0.21
6.0	−0.78	−1.79	−2.12	−2.38	−2.84	−2.76	−1.04	+0.15
6.5	−0.81	−1.89			−3.22	−3.03	−1.24	+0.08
7.0	−0.85	−1.99	−2.50	−2.85	−3.61	−3.32	−1.45	+0.02
7.5	−0.88				−3.98	−3.60	−1.66	−0.04
8.0	−0.90		−2.86	−3.34	−4.33	−3.87	−1.85	−0.11
8.5	−0.93				−4.69	−4.14	−2.04	−0.17
9.0	−0.95		−3.22	−3.89	−5.05	−4.40	−2.22	−0.24
9.5	−0.98				−5.42	−4.65	−2.40	−0.30
10.0	−1.00		−3.59	−4.44	−5.79	−4.89	−2.59	−0.36

[a] This table was taken from M. A. Paul and F. A. Long, *Chem. Revs.* **57**, 1 (1957).

extracted from water by organic solvents, they frequently take with them four molecules of water per proton.[51] Considerable other similar data exist which suggest that approximately four molecules of water are associated with each proton; one being involved in covalent bond formation and three more hydrogen bonded to the hydrogens of H_3O^+.[52]

---

[50] M. A. Paul, *J. Am. Chem. Soc.*, **76**, 3236 (1954) found that the "salt effect" of hydrochloric acid on the indicator ratio is similar to that of sodium and potassium chloride.
[51] D. G. Tuck and R. M. Diamond, *Proc. Chem. Soc.*, 236 (1958).
[52] E. Wicke, M. Eigen, and T. Ackermann, *Z. physik. Chem.* (Frankfurt), **1**, 340 (1954); E. Glueckauf, *Trans. Faraday Soc.*, **51**, 1235 (1955); E. Glueckauf and G. P. Kitt, *Proc. Roy. Soc.*, **A228**, 322 (1955).

Since the proton appears to be associated with about four waters of hydration, the acid-base equilibrium may be written as

$$H^+ \cdot 4H_2O + B \rightleftharpoons BH^+ \cdot nH_2O + (4 - n)H_2O$$

and here the equilibrium constant will be

$$K = \frac{[BH^+ \cdot nH_2O][H_2O]^{4-n}}{[B][H^+ \cdot 4H_2O]} \cdot \frac{\gamma_{BH^+}\gamma_{H_2O}^{4-n}}{\gamma_B\gamma_{H^+ \cdot 4H_2O}}$$

Table 2-24   The Acidity Function, H_0, for Perchloric Acid Solutions

% HClO$_4$	M_{HClO_4}	d^{25a}	M_{H_2O}	$H_0{}^b$	H_0 ($\mu = 6M$)^{c,d}	Δ
3.01	0.30	1.0140	54.6	+0.48	−0.85	1.33
5.02	0.50	1.0258	54.1	+0.20	−1.11	1.31
10.05	1.00	1.0562	53.1	−0.22	−1.46	1.24
20.09	2.00	1.1235	51.2	−0.78	−1.84	1.06
30.14	3.00	1.2012	49.9	−1.23	−2.13	0.90
40.18	4.00	1.2926	49.4	−1.72	−2.47	0.75
50.23	5.00	1.4022	49.9	−2.23	−2.77	0.52
60.26	6.00	1.5309	51.5	−2.84	−3.05	0.21

[a] A. E. Markham, *J. Am. Chem. Soc.*, **63**, 874 (1941).
[b] M. A. Paul and F. A. Long, *Chem. Revs.*, **57**, 1, (1957).
[c] G. Harbottle, *J. Am. Chem. Soc.*, **73**, 4024 (1951).
[d] The relatively poor agreement between Harbottle's value for 6M HClO$_4$ and the "best" value of Paul and Long should be noted. The same indicator was used in both determinations.

The equilibrium constant is also given by

$$K = \frac{[BH^+]}{[B]a_{H^+}} \cdot \frac{\gamma_{BH^+}}{\gamma_B}$$

Remembering that [BH$^+$] and [BH$^+ \cdot nH_2O$] are experimentally equivalent quantities, it can be seen that the "activity" of hydrogen ions will be given by

$$a_{H^+} = \frac{[H^+]}{[H_2O]^{4-n}} \cdot \frac{\gamma_{H^+}}{\gamma_{H_2O}^{4-n}}$$

Returning to the definition of H_0

$$H_0 = -\log h_0 = -\log a_{H^+} + \log\frac{\gamma_{BH^+}}{\gamma_B}$$

we can introduce this value of a_{H^+}, getting

$$H_0 = -\log [H^+] + (4 - n) \log [H_2O] + \log\frac{\gamma_{H_2O}^{4-n}}{\gamma_B} + \log\frac{\gamma_{BH^+}}{\gamma_{H^+}}$$

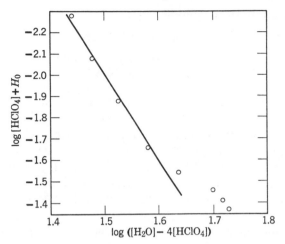

Fig. 2-14. Effect of water concentration on the acidity function, H_0, at a constant ionic strength.

At a constant ionic strength we might expect the last two terms to be roughly constant, and a plot of $H_0 + \log [H^+]$ against $\log [H_2O]$ would give $4 - n$ as the slope. When such a plot is made, correcting the concentration of water for that which is assumed to be associated with the proton, the slope is found to be 4 between 2-6M perchloric acid. (Fig. 2-14). This suggests that the conjugate acid has essentially no water of hydration associated with it. This is reasonable, for the conjugate acid is a relatively large molecule with a consequent much smaller electrostatic potential than the very small proton.

Although this treatment is very crude, it does indicate that an important factor contributing to the difference between H_0 and $-\log [H^+]$ is the difference in the degree of hydration of the proton and the conjugate acid. The curvature in Fig. 2-14 below 2M perchloric acid indicates either that the conjugate acid is hydrated in solutions having a higher concentration of free water, that the degree of hydration of a proton varies with water concentration, or that other factors are also important.

Bell has used the same treatment except that data for varying ionic strength were used (i.e., the H_0 values as ordinarily obtained.)[53] It is interesting to note that in this case the fit of the data to the equation was considerably better than when the ionic strength was maintained constant. It is apparent that we still have much to learn about concentrated solutions of electrolytes.

[53] R. P. Bell, "The Proton in Chemistry," Cornell University Press, Ithaca, 1959, pp. 81–83.

If we now return to the definition of H_0,

$$H_0 = -\log [\text{H}^+] - \log \gamma_{\text{H}^+} + \log \gamma_{\text{BH}^+} - \log \gamma_\text{B}$$

then the difference between the ordinary H_0 values and those obtained in solutions having $6M$ ionic strength will be given by

$$H_0 - H_0{}^{6M} = -\log \frac{\gamma_{\text{H}^+}}{\gamma_{\text{BH}^+}} + \log \left(\frac{\gamma_{\text{H}^+}}{\gamma_{\text{BH}^+}}\right)^{6M} - \log \frac{\gamma_\text{B}}{\gamma_\text{B}{}^{6M}}$$

Since salts, such as sodium perchlorate, appear to have a relatively small effect on the activity coefficients of neutral species; the last term would be expected to be relatively small[54] and may be neglected. As the concentration of acid approaches zero, the first term also vanishes, and at low acid concentrations the only important term will be $\log (\gamma_{\text{H}^+}/\gamma_{\text{BH}^+})^{6M}$. The limit of $H_0 - H_0{}^{6M}$ as $[\text{H}^+]$ approaches zero is between 1.2–1.4 (depending on how the discrepancy noted under Table 2-24 is taken into account). Thus

$$\log \left(\frac{\gamma_{\text{H}^+}}{\gamma_{\text{BH}^+}}\right)^{6M} \cong 1.2 - 1.4$$

or

$$\left(\frac{\gamma_{\text{H}^+}}{\gamma_{\text{BH}^+}}\right)^{6M} \cong 15 - 25$$

This is not unreasonable, for the effect of increasing ionic strength should be much more pronounced for a small ion than for a large one.

The acidity function may also be used in nonaqueous and in partially aqueous solution. Some care must be used in interpreting results so obtained; in solutions of low dielectric constant, ion-pair association becomes important, and the fundamental assumption

$$\left(\frac{\gamma_{\text{BH}_1^+}}{\gamma_{\text{B}_1}}\right)\left(\frac{\gamma_{\text{B}_2}}{\gamma_{\text{BH}_2^+}}\right) \cong 1$$

may no longer hold.[55] However, no more useful or generally applicable function has been devised, and since the acidity function will in all cases give a better measure of the protonating power of a given medium than the stoichiometric concentration of acid, the acidity function remains a valuable tool in studying acid-base equilibria in these solutions.

It will be useful to consider acetic acid-water solutions, for here data are available for low concentrations of acid in series of mixtures.[56] The data

[54] F. A. Long and W. F. McDevit, *Chem. Revs.*, **51**, 119 (1952).
[55] E. Grunwald and B. J. Berkowitz, *J. Am. Chem. Soc.*, **73**, 4939 (1951); B. Gutbezahl and E. Grunwald, *ibid.*, **75**, 559, 565 (1953); H. P. Marshall and E. Grunwald, *ibid.*, **76**, 2000 (1954).
[56] K. B. Wiberg and R. Evans, *J. Am. Chem. Soc.*, **80**, 3019 (1958).

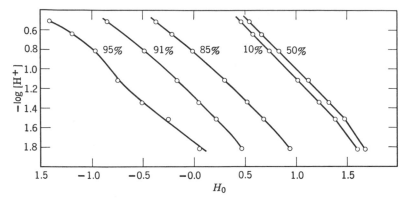

Fig. 2-15. A comparison of $-\log[H^+]$ *with* H_0 *for perchloric acid in acetic acid–water mixtures.*

are plotted in Fig. 2-15. It can be seen that for any given acid concentrations, the acidity increases as the water concentration decreases. This change may be considered in the same terms as the acidity function for aqueous solution. For solutions having a relatively small acid concentrations, and at a constant ionic strength, the ratio of $\gamma_{H^+}/\gamma_{BH^+}$ would ordinarily be expected to be relatively constant. As the water concentration in the solvent is decreased, the dielectric constant decreases, and this will cause the ratio of activity coefficients to decrease.

For the equilibrium

$$H_3O^+ \cdot aH_2O + B \rightleftharpoons BH^+ \cdot nH_2O + (a - n)H_2O$$

the following expression holds (cf. p. 298)

$$H_0 + \log[H^+] - \log\frac{\gamma_{BH^+}}{\gamma_{H^+}} = (a - n)\log[H_2O] + \log\frac{\gamma_{H_2O}^{a-n}}{\gamma_B}$$

Although the last term will be roughly constant with a change in solvent, the ratio $\gamma_{BH^+}/\gamma_{H^+}$ will increase with decreasing water concentration, for the small proton will be affected more than the larger conjugate acid. Thus the change in $-\log(\gamma_{BH^+}/\gamma_{H^+})$ will be negative with decreasing water concentration and will parallel that of H_0. As a result, a plot of $H_0 + \log[H^+]$ against $\log[H_2O]$ will give as its slope a number smaller than $a - n$.

The plot is shown in Fig. 2-16, and for solutions having less than 50% water the slope was found to be two. Remembering that this is a minimum value of $a - n$, it can be seen that this case is similar to that of perchloric acid in water. For *dilute* acid solutions in organic solvent-water mixtures, the above result will generally be true, and thus the change in solvent may be considered to have had only a small effect on acitivity coefficients, the

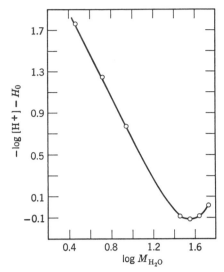

Fig. 2-16. Effect of water concentration on the difference between H_0 and $-\log [H^+]$ in acetic acid–water mixtures.

main change being in the proton level. When the organic component of the solvent mixture is relatively basic, such as ethanol and methanol, one must, of course, consider the formation of both the conjugate acid of water and the conjugate acid of the organic component. For more concentrated acid solutions or for pure organic solvents, such as acetic acid, the acidity function may have a more limited applicability.

Thus far we have only considered the H_0 acidity function which applies to the equilibrium

$$H^+ + B \rightleftharpoons BH^+$$

Several other equilibria are also important:

$$H^+ + B^- \rightleftharpoons BH$$

$$H^+ + BH^+ \rightleftharpoons BH_2^{+2}$$

$$H^+ + ROH \rightleftharpoons R^+ + H_2O$$

The acidity functions related to these equilibria are H_-, H_+, and H_R (or C_0). Relatively little work has been done using the first two indicator acidity functions in acidic solution. The main difficulty with the determination of H_- values has been the lack of suitable negatively charged indicators which would be protonated only in fairly strong acidic solution. This problem now appears to have been solved by the use of cyanocarbon acids as the indicators.[57]

[57] R. H. Boyd, *J. Am. Chem. Soc.*, **83**, 4288 (1961).

It is interesting to consider the difference between H_0 and H_-. The equilibria are

$$B + H^+ \cdot aH_2O \rightleftharpoons BH^+ \cdot nH_2O + (a - n)H_2O \qquad (H_0)$$

$$B^- + H^+ \cdot aH_2O \rightleftharpoons BH + aH_2O \qquad (H_-)$$

and thus

$$H_0 = -\log H^+ + (a - n) \log [H_2O] + \log \frac{\gamma_{BH^+}}{\gamma_{H^+}} + \log \frac{\gamma_{H_2O}^{a-n}}{\gamma_B}$$

$$H_- = -\log H^+ + a \log [H_2O] + \log \frac{\gamma_{B^-}}{\gamma_{H^+}} + \log \frac{\gamma_{H_2O}^a}{\gamma_{BH}}$$

The difference in the concentration of water term between the two expressions arises from the fact that in the H_0 function the product is still ionic and will be associated with some water of hydration (perhaps about one), whereas the product of the second reaction is neutral and will not be significantly solvated.

Subtracting the two functions, we obtain

$$H_- - H_0 = n \log [H_2O] + \log \frac{\gamma_{B^-}}{\gamma_{BH^+}} + n \log \gamma_{H_2O}$$

The last term would be negligible if an ideal solution were formed, and the other activity coefficient term might be expected to be relatively small. Thus a major difference between the two acidity functions should result from the difference in hydration of the products of the two reactions involved. Data have been obtained for dilute hydrochloric acid solutions[58] in ethanol-water mixtures for both of these acidity functions. It was found that from 0 to 80% ethanol, the difference between the acidity functions increased with decreasing water concentration, thus suggesting that the above relationship has some validity. Similar results were obtained with aqueous sulfuric acid solutions.[57] Kinetic data obtained in acetic-acid water mixtures also suggest that the difference between the two acidity scales is a function of the concentration of water in the medium.[59]

The H_R acidity function is quite different from the ones described above and is defined as [60]

$$H_R = -pK_{ROH} - \log \frac{[R^+]}{[ROH]}$$

Since water appears as one of the products of the reaction defining this acidity function, it is apparent that the H_R function should be more

[58] R. G. Bates and G. Schwarzenbach, *Helv. Chim. Acta*, **38**, 699 (1955).
[59] K. B. Wiberg and R. Evans, *Tetrahedron*, **8**, 313 (1960).
[60] F. H. Westheimer and M. S. Kharasch, *J. Am. Chem. Soc.*, **68**, 1871 (1946).

sensitive to the effective concentration of water in the medium than the H_0 function. A comparison of the two acidity functions is given in Table 2-25, and it can be seen that the excepted trend is realized.

Table 2-25   **Comparison of the H_0, H_-, and H_R Acidity Functions in Aqueous Sulfuric Acid Solutions**

H_2SO_4, %	H_0[a]	H_R[b]	H_-[c]	H_2SO_4, %	H_0	H_R	H_-[c]
10	−0.31	−0.72	−0.09	50	−3.38	−6.60	−3.91
15	−0.66	−1.32	−0.52	55	−3.91	−7.90	−4.39
20	−1.01	−1.92		60	−4.46	−8.92	−4.94
25	−1.37	−2.55	−1.46	70	−5.65	−11.52	
30	−1.72	−3.22	−1.96	80	−6.97	−14.12	
35	−2.06	−4.00	−2.47	90	−8.27	−16.72	
40	−2.41	−4.80	−2.93	95	−8.86	−18.08	
45	−2.85	−5.65		98	−9.36	−19.64	

[a] M. A. Paul and F. A. Long, *Chem. Revs.*, **57**, 15 (1957).
[b] N. C. Deno, J. J. Jaruzelski, and A. Schriesheim, *J. Am. Chem. Soc.*, **77**, 3044 (1955).
[c] R. H. Boyd, *J. Am. Chem. Soc.*, **83**, 4288 (1961).

References

Acidity Functions:
M. A. Paul and F. A. Long, *Chem. Revs.*, **57**, 1 (1957).
F. A. Long and M. A. Paul, *Chem. Revs.*, **57**, 935 (1957).
R. P. Bell, *The Proton in Chemistry*, Cornell University Press, Ithaca, New York, 1959.
N. C. Deno, J. J. Jaruzelski and Schriesheim, *J. Am. Chem. Soc.*, **77**, 3044 (1955).
R. H. Boyd, *J. Am. Chem. Soc.*, **83**, 4288 (1961).

Problem

1. In an investigation of the acidity function for perchloric acid in 95% acetic acid, the following data were obtained:

[HClO$_4$]	[dye][a]	Absorbance					
		410	408	406	404	402	400 mμ
0.300	5	0.344	0.348	0.353	0.353	0.356	0.355
0.225	5	0.504	0.505	0.514	0.512	0.515	0.513
0.150	3	0.463	0.466	0.472	0.472	0.474	0.472
0.075	2	0.528	0.532	0.537	0.537	0.537	0.534
0.045	2	0.676	0.680	0.687	0.687	0.688	0.685
0.030	1	0.390	0.395	0.396	0.399	0.396	0.394
[b]	1	0.559	0.562	0.566	0.567	0.566	0.565

[a] Relative concentrations of *o*-nitroaniline.
[b] This solution contained sodium acetate.
From these data, calculate the H_0 value for each solution.

PART THREE

Kinetics

3-1 Introduction

There are two main reasons for the importance of kinetics to organic chemists. First, the course and products of a very large number of organic reactions are controlled by the relative rates of several competing reactions, and it is only by understanding the dependence of the various rates on the reaction variables (concentration, temperature, solvent, etc.) that one can predict the conditions required for favoring the desired product. Second, as we have seen before, the study of equilibria does not give any information about the steps involved in the reaction, for it is only concerned with the energies of the reactants and of the products. A knowledge of the mechanism by which the reactants are converted to products has proved of value in a number of ways, as we shall see later, and a study of the kinetics of the reaction, coupled with other techniques, provides one of the more satisfactory ways of obtaining this information.

Some simple concepts and the methods of treating kinetic data in order to obtain rate constants and rate laws will first be reviewed. Then a consideration of the absolute rate theory and of kinetic isotope effects will lay the theoretical groundwork for the following discussion. Effects of solvents on reaction rates will be considered, and the general area of linear free energy relationships will also be examined.

3-2 Definitions: Treatment of Kinetic Data

The most important datum about any reaction which is to be studied kinetically is its stoichiometry. This is a statement of the number and kinds of molecules involved in the total reaction. The order of the reaction with respect to the concentration of a given reactant is the power to which its concentration must be raised in the general rate expression

$$-\frac{d[A]}{dt} = k[A]^n[B]^m[C]^o \cdots$$

where $-d[A]/dt$ is the rate of disappearance of A, and k is the rate constant. The order of a reaction is the sum of the orders with respect to each component. The rate law is the general rate expression containing the reacting species and their powers. The foregoing quantities are experimentally determined, and the definitions given may be said to be operational definitions. Another concept, the molecularity of a reaction, is derived from the mechanism of the reaction once this has been determined, and, as such, it may vary as our knowledge of the reaction increases. It is defined as the number of individual molecules which react in the slow step of the reaction. The concept is meaningless when applied to any other steps, for the ones preceding the slow step would be equilibria for which the mechanism would usually not be known, and we, of course, have no knowledge of what happens after the slow step—other than what products are ultimately formed—unless these subsequent reactions are studied separately.

As an example, we may consider the oxidation of isopropyl alcohol by chromic acid. The stoichiometry of the reaction is

$$3(CH_3)_2CHOH + 2\,HCrO_4^- + 8H^+ = 3(CH_3)_2CO + 2Cr^{+3} + 8H_2O$$

The rate of reaction is proportional to the concentrations of isopropyl alcohol and of the acid chromate ion and to the square of the acid concentration. Thus the rate law is

$$v = k[ROH][HCrO_4^-][H^+]^2$$

where v denotes the velocity of the reaction. It is therefore a fourth order reaction.

The above data do not indicate the molecularity of the reaction. However, extensive investigations[1] have indicated that the mechanism of

---

[1] See F. Holloway, M. Cohen, and F. H. Westheimer, *J. Am. Chem. Soc.*, **73**, 65 (1951).

the reaction may be expressed by

$$R_2CHOH + HCrO_4^- + 2H^+ \rightleftharpoons R_2C\underset{\underset{\displaystyle H}{|}}{-}OCrO_3H_2^+ + H_2O$$

$$R_2C\underset{\underset{\displaystyle H}{|}}{-}OCrO_3H_2^+ \rightarrow R_2C{=}O + H_3O^+ + H_2CrO_3$$

$$H_2O{:}$$

The rate determining step is therefore a bimolecular reaction, and it should be noted that one of the reactants is the solvent which, in general, does not appear in the rate expression for it is in constant concentration and in the present case could not appear because a molecule of water is generated in a previous step. It may be seen that the molecularity of a reaction may be equal to, less than, or more than the apparent order of the reaction.

If we are to study the kinetic behaviour of a reaction, we must first determine the order with respect to each component. This requires a knowledge of the extent of reaction as a function of time for different initial concentrations of reactants, and thus we must have some way in which to follow the extent of the reaction as a function of time. A great variety of methods are available, and convenient summaries of these methods have been published.[2]

It is extremely important to be sure that the analytical method properly measures the reaction in which one is interested. For this, one must know the stoichiometry of the reaction rather precisely so that one knows the relationship between the amounts of the various reagents being consumed. It is obvious, too, that one must know the products of the reaction, although this has not always been done in the past. If the results of the investigation are to be meaningful, it is usually desirable to have a reaction which goes almost quantitatively in the desired direction. Otherwise one may have to contend with varying stoichiometry as the concentrations of the reagents are varied, and one may have to determine the rates of disappearance of each of the reagents separately.

The precision which is required varies according to the use to be made of the data. If one is interested in determining the mechanism of a reaction, or wishes to use the data to determine quantitatively the effect of substituents on the rate of a type of reaction, one should strive for a reasonably high accuracy. This requires moderate care but rarely the recalibration of volumetric glassware and similar precautions. The precision of fairly good work is usually of the order of $\pm 3\%$. In many cases the purpose of

[2] R. Livingston in A. Weissberger *Technique of Organic Chemistry*, Interscience Publishers, New York, 1953, vol. VIII.

the investigation is to determine the best conditions for effecting a particular type of reaction. In this case great precision is not required, and if the rate constant can be determined to within 10 to 15%, this is usually sufficient. Of course, if a higher precision can easily be attained, it is desirable, for the data may then be of real use in some other connection. However, any data are often better than no data.

The data which have been obtained should now permit a determination of the order of the reaction with respect to each component. There are several ways in which to obtain this information. One of the simplest requires the estimation of the initial slope of a plot of concentration against time for a set of reactions in which the concentration of only one species has been varied. A line which is normal to the curve at zero time may be determined by placing a small mirror at the origin of the curve and adjusting it so that the reflection of the curve appears as a continuation of it. The plane of the mirror is then normal to the curve, and a line perpendicular to this gives the initial slope. This, of course, requires that the initial point be known with considerable accuracy and that there be no induction period.

We may consider the rate expression in the form

$$- \frac{d[A]}{dt} = k[A]^m[B]^n[C]^o \cdots$$

and taking logarithms of both sides, we obtain

$$\log \left(- \frac{d[A]}{dt} \right) = \log k + m \log [A] + n \log [B] + o \log [C] \cdots$$

Thus if, for example, the concentrations of B and C were maintained constant, a plot of the logarithm of the initial value of $(-d[A]/dt)$ against log [A] would give a line of slope m. The order with respect to B and C may be determined in a similar fashion.

The order may also be determined from the half-life of the reaction. The half-life is defined as the time required for half the reactant to be consumed. For a first order reaction:

$$- \frac{d[A]}{dt} = k[A]$$

$$- \frac{d[A]}{[A]} = k \, dt$$

$$\ln \left(\frac{[A]}{[A]_0} \right) = -kt$$

at the half-time $(t_{1/2})$

$$[A] = \frac{[A]_0}{2}$$

$$\ln 2 = + kt_{1/2}$$

$$t_{1/2} = \frac{0.69}{k}$$

It may be seen that for a first order reaction the half-life is independent of the concentration of the reactant.

In a similar fashion it may be shown that the half-life for a reaction which is not first order is

$$t_{1/2} = \frac{(2^{n-1} - 1)}{k(n-1)a^{n-1}}$$

where a is the initial concentration of the reactant. Lumping all the constants into a single value c, we have

$$t_{1/2} = \frac{c}{a^{n-1}}$$

and

$$\log t_{1/2} = \log c - (n-1) \log a$$

Thus the order may be determined from a plot of $\log t_{1/2}$ against $\log a$, the slope being $n - 1$. It may be noted that this last expression is applicable to all orders of reaction, although the expression from which it was derived did not apply to a first order reaction. If two or more reactants are involved, the method is applicable if they are present in the stoichiometric ratio.

A third method is the Ostwald isolation method. If we consider the general form of the rate expression again,

$$v = k[A]^m[B]^n[C]^o \cdots$$

it can be seen that if the concentrations of B and C are maintained high relative to that of A, the change in concentration of B and C will be negligible during the reaction. The rate expression then reduces to a relationship in A only:

$$-\frac{d[A]}{dt} = k'[A]^m$$

where $k' = k[B]^n[C]^o$.

The order with respect to A may then be determined as described before or by using the integrated form of the rate expression. The rate constants are obtained and the order with respect to B and C may be determined from the variation in the pseudo-first order rate constant with the change in the concentration of B and C, respectively.

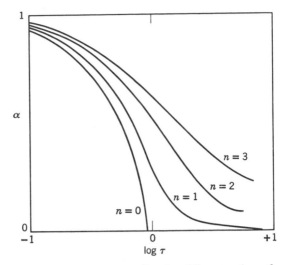

Fig. 3-1. Relative concentration-time profiles for different orders of reactions. From Frost and Pearson, Kinetics and Mechanism, Wiley, 1961.

A fourth method is one which was developed by Powell.[3] The concentrations of the reactants (which are normally at the stoichiometric concentrations for this procedure) are first converted to relative concentrations, and a new time parameter is used:

$$\alpha = \frac{C}{C_0} \quad \text{(relative concentration)}$$

$$\tau = kC_0^{n-1}t \quad \text{(time parameter)}$$

For a first order reaction, we obtain

$$\ln \alpha = -\tau$$

and for all other orders,

$$\alpha^{1-n} - 1 = (n - 1)\tau$$

When $\alpha = 0.5$ (corresponding to one half-life), these expressions become equivalent to those previously written for the half-lives in terms of concentrations and times.

It has been found that if α is plotted against $\log \tau$, a curve which is characteristic of the order of the reaction is obtained (Fig. 3-1). Since $\log \tau = \log t + \log kC_0^{n-1}$, where the last term is a constant, a plot of α against $\log t$ will give the same set of curves, with the axis shifted by an

[3] R. E. Powell, discussed in A. A. Frost and R. G. Pearson, *Kinetics and Mechanism*, John Wiley and Sons, New York, 1953, p. 14.

amount $\log k C_0^{n-1}$. A comparison of the curve for the reaction at hand with the set of standard curves will then give the order of the reaction.

The last method of determining the order of the reaction with respect to each component is to test the experimental data with the integrated forms of the rate expressions and then see which will give a constant value of the rate constant both within a given run and between runs having different initial concentrations of reactants. This method is commonly used when the rate law for an analogous reaction is known and there is reason to believe that the same rate law will apply.

One common complication in using the foregoing methods is found in those cases in which the rate expression has two terms. For example, a reaction may have one kinetic term not involving the acid concentration and one involving the first power of the acid concentration:

$$v = k_a[\text{A}][\text{B}] + k_b[\text{A}][\text{B}][\text{H}^+]$$

If, for example, we were to use the half-life method for obtaining the order with respect to the acid concentration, we would get a curve rather than a straight line. In such cases it is often better not to use a logarithmic relationship but simply to plot the initial rate against concentration. The above case would give a linear relationship with an intercept at a finite rate (k_a) at zero acid concentration.

The integrated forms of the rate expressions are usually required in order to obtain constants which are needed for the above determinations of the order of the reaction and also for the comparison of relative reactivities and related purposes. It will be convenient to consider each order of reaction separately.

First Order. The rate law for a first order reaction is

$$v = k_1[\text{A}] = \frac{-d[\text{A}]}{dt}$$

If the quantity of A which has reacted at time t is denoted as x, the equation becomes

$$\frac{-dx}{a - x} = k_1 \, dt$$

where a is the initial concentration of the species. Integration gives

$$\ln (a - x) - \ln a = -kt$$

Thus the slope of a plot of $\log (a - x)$ against t is equal to $-k_1/2.303$.

It should be noted that the logarithm is taken of a dimensionless quantity, for it is actually the ratio of the concentration of the reactant at time t divided by the initial concentration which is used, the latter being separated out and appearing as the intercept of the plot. Therefore any quantity which may be related to the concentration may equally well be used. For example, the volume of titrant for an aliquot of a given size, the optical rotation, the change in volume of the solution, etc., may be used in place of the concentration. Thus first order kinetics are particularly convenient.

As was mentioned previously, many reactions may be converted into pseudo-first order reactions by having all reagents except one in relatively high concentration. Then the concentrations of these compounds will not change significantly during the reaction, and the reaction will appear to be independent of their concentrations and will simply be first order in the reagent present in smallest concentration. Of course, the rate dependence on the other compounds will become apparent when the concentrations of these compounds are varied. The reaction will remain first order so long as their concentrations remain relatively high, but the first order rate constant will vary directly with the concentrations of these compounds.

When applicable, one of the most convenient methods of studying the rate of a reaction is to follow the change in absorbance of the solution. Here the value of absorbance may change from A_0 to A_∞, where A_∞ is often not zero because the products of the reaction have an absorption spectrum similar to that of the reactant. Let us obtain the form of the rate expression for this case. If we designate the reactant as R and the product as P and use subscripts indicating the time (0, t, ∞), then

$$[P]_t = [R]_0 - [R]_t$$
$$[R]_0 = [P]_\infty$$
$$[R]_\infty = [P]_0 = 0$$

In terms of absorbance,

$$A_0 = \epsilon_R[R]_0$$
$$A_t = \epsilon_R[R]_t + \epsilon_P[P]_t = \epsilon_R[R]_t + \epsilon_P[R]_0 - \epsilon_P[R]_t$$
$$A_\infty = \epsilon_P[P]_\infty = \epsilon_P[R]_0$$

Combining these equations,

$$A_t - A_\infty = \epsilon_R[R]_t - \epsilon_P[R]_t$$

and

$$[R]_t = \frac{A_t - A_\infty}{\epsilon_R - \epsilon_P}$$

Thus a plot of $\log (A_t - A_\infty)$ against time would be linear with a slope $-k/2.303$. This approach is general and applies to all other physical properties which might be measured, provided that they are linearly related to the concentrations of reactants and products. The difficulty with this approach is that the value of the physical property at "infinite time" must be known. A small drift in the apparatus used could easily cause a considerable error in the determination of this value. Guggenheim[4] has developed a method which permits the determination of the rate constant without knowing the infinity value.

Suppose readings are taken at times t_1, t_2, t_3, etc., and at times $t_1 + \Delta$, $t_2 + \Delta$, $t_3 + \Delta$, etc., where Δ is a constant increment of time. If we denote the value of the physical property being observed as λ, then λ_1 corresponds to t_1 and λ_1' corresponds to $t_1 + \Delta$. Using the exponential form of the first order rate expression

$$[R]_t = [R]_0 e^{-kt}$$

we have

$$(\lambda_1 - \lambda_\infty) = (\lambda_0 - \lambda_\infty)e^{-kt_1}$$

$$(\lambda_1' - \lambda_\infty) = (\lambda_0 - \lambda_\infty)e^{-k(t_1+\Delta)}$$

Subtracting

$$(\lambda_1 - \lambda_1') = (\lambda_0 - \lambda_\infty)e^{-kt_1}(1 - e^{-k\Delta})$$

and taking logarithms

$$\ln (\lambda_1 - \lambda_1') = -kt_1 + \ln [(\lambda - \lambda_\infty)(1 - e^{-k\Delta})]$$

gives the equation

$$\ln (\lambda_1 - \lambda_1') = -kt_1 + \text{constant}$$

A plot of log $(\lambda_1 - \lambda_1')$ against time will then give a straight line of slope $-k/2.303$. In order to obtain a precise value of k, it is desirable to use a fairly large time interval for Δ, usually in the order of 2 to 3 half-lives.

This method will sometimes give reasonable first order plots for reactions which are not first order, particularly if Δ is a relatively small increment of time. For example, data which give a good fit to second order kinetics (Fig. 3-2a) have been plotted using the Guggenheim method in Fig. 3-2b, with Δ equal to one half-life. Therefore one should test the result by calculating the value of λ_∞ required by the Guggenheim formulation and then considering if this value is reasonable for the reaction.

It would be preferable to have a method which used all the experimental points independently. Such a method may be developed as follows. The integrated form of the rate equation may be written as

$$\ln (\lambda_t - c) = -kt + b$$

where c is the value of λ at infinite time and b is the intercept. If each experimental point fits the data perfectly,

$$0 = \ln (\lambda_t - c) + kt - b$$

[4] E. A. Guggenheim, *Phil. Mag.*, **2**, 538 (1926).

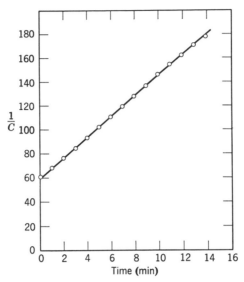

Fig. 3-2a. Data for a second order reaction plotted properly.

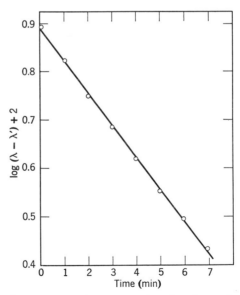

Fig. 3-2b. Data for a second order reaction plotted as first order using the Guggenheim method.

but since this is not the case, we shall designate the error as F and write

$$F_t = \ln (\lambda_t - c) + kt - b$$

If the derivative is taken, we obtain

$$dF_t = \frac{\partial F_t}{\partial c} dc + \frac{\partial F_t}{\partial k} dk + \frac{\partial F_t}{\partial b} db$$

$$= -\frac{dc}{\lambda_t - c} + t\,dk - db$$

In order to minimize the error, we shall try to obtain values of dF_t which will cancel the error F_t, and we will write

$$G_t = dF_t + F_t$$

We may now minimize $\Sigma\,|G_t|$ or, more conveniently, $\Sigma\,G_t^2$, which we shall designate as σ. This may be done by setting the derivative of σ with respect, to dc, dk, and db equal to zero.

$$\frac{\partial\sigma}{\partial(dc)} = 0 = \Sigma\,2G_t\frac{\partial G_t}{\partial(dc)} = 2\Sigma -\frac{G_t}{\lambda_t - c}$$

$$\frac{\partial\sigma}{\partial(dk)} = 0 = \Sigma\,2G_t\frac{\partial G_t}{\partial(dk)} = 2\Sigma\,G_t t$$

$$\frac{\partial\sigma}{\partial(db)} = 0 = \Sigma\,2G_t\frac{\partial G_t}{\partial(db)} = 2\Sigma -G_t$$

Substituting the value of G_t, we get

$$\frac{dc}{(\lambda_t - c)^2} - \frac{t\,dk}{\lambda_t - c} + \frac{db}{\lambda_t - c} - \frac{F_t}{\lambda_t - c} = 0$$

$$-\frac{t\,dc}{\lambda_t - c} + t^2\,dk - t\,db + tF_t = 0$$

$$\frac{dc}{\lambda_t - c} - t\,dk + db - F_t = 0$$

Starting with approximate values of c, k, and b, one may, by solving the above set of simultaneous equations, obtain values of the corrections, dc, dk, and db, which should be applied to the original values to obtain a better straight line. The procedure may be repeated until the results converge on the best values of c, k, and b. As a test of the results, the value of c must be in reasonable accord with that estimated from the kinetic data, and b must agree with the value expected for the initial concentrations of reactants. This type of calculation is ideally suited for use with high-speed digital computors (cf. Appendix 9).

One and One-Half Order. A one and one-half order reaction always arises from a series of reaction steps which give a net rate law of this type, for it is not possible for half a molecule to react. However, this type of result is met rather frequently, particularly with free radical reactions (cf. p. 325).

Let us consider the case in which the stoichiometry is

$$A + B \rightarrow products$$

Then if

$$\frac{dx}{dt} = k(a - x)(b - x)^{\frac{1}{2}}$$

$$\int_0^x \frac{dx}{(a - x)(b - x)^{\frac{1}{2}}} = k \int_0^t dt$$

and we let

$$(a - x) = u \qquad b - a = c$$

we find that

$$\int_{u=0}^{u=u} \frac{du}{u(u + c)^{\frac{1}{2}}} = k \int dt$$

For the case in which $c > 0$

$$\frac{2}{\sqrt{c}} \tanh^{-1} \sqrt{(u + c)/c} - \frac{2}{\sqrt{c}} \tanh^{-1} \sqrt{(a + c)/c} = kt$$

and a plot of $\tanh^{-1} \sqrt{(u + c)/c}$ against time will give a line of slope $\sqrt{ck}/2$. If $c < 0$, the form becomes

$$\frac{2}{\sqrt{-c}} \tan^{-1} \sqrt{u + c/-c} - \frac{2}{\sqrt{-c}} \tan^{-1} \sqrt{a + c/-c} = kt$$

The evaluation of rate constants is often greatly simplified if the reagents are present in their stoichiometric concentrations. Thus if the concentrations of A and B are equal, the expression becomes

$$\frac{dx}{dt} = k(a - x)^{\frac{3}{2}}$$

and

$$\frac{2}{(a - x)^{\frac{1}{2}}} - \frac{2}{a^{\frac{1}{2}}} = kt$$

and thus a plot of $(a - x)^{-\frac{1}{2}}$ against time will give a line of slope $k/2$.

Three-halves order reactions are commonly encountered in free radical chain reactions, where the order with respect to the substrate is first, and there is a half-order dependence on the initiator concentration (cf. p. 326).

Here there is no simple stoichiometric relationship between the substrate and initiator. Two cases may be considered. In the first the chain is long, and only a small fraction of the initiator is used for almost complete reaction of the substrate. Then the dependence on initiator concentration will not appear in a given run, the reaction being pseudo-first order. The order with respect to initiator will be obtained by determining the effect of initiator concentration on the first order rate constants.

In the second case the chain length is fairly short, and an appreciable amount of the initiator is used. The rate expression becomes

$$\frac{dx}{dt} = k_{3/2}(a - x)(b - y)^{1/2}$$

where B is the initiator, x is the amount of substrate which has reacted in the time t, and y is the amount of initiator which has reacted in this time. The rate of decomposition of B is usually independent of the chain reaction (except when induced decomposition occurs), and the rate of decomposition of the initiator may be determined separately. This may be done by using an inert solvent, for free radical reactions usually are not strongly affected by the nature of the medium, or it may be determined in the reaction mixture if a suitable initiator is used. A particularly good one is azo-bis-isobutyronitrile

$$CH_3-\overset{\overset{\displaystyle CH_3}{|}}{\underset{\underset{\displaystyle CN}{|}}{C}}-N=N-\overset{\overset{\displaystyle CH_3}{|}}{\underset{\underset{\displaystyle CN}{|}}{C}}-CH_3 \overset{\Delta}{\longrightarrow} N_2 + 2CH_3-\overset{\overset{\displaystyle CH_3}{|}}{\underset{\underset{\displaystyle CN}{|}}{C}} \cdot$$

since the rate of reaction may be determined by measuring the volume of nitrogen formed as a function of time. This is a first order reaction

$$\frac{dy}{dt} = k_1(b - y)$$

and knowing the rate constant

$$(b - y) = be^{-k_1 t}$$

this may be substituted into the preceding expression, giving

$$\frac{dx}{dt} = k_{3/2}(a - x)(b)^{1/2}e^{-k_1 t/2}$$

Integration gives

$$\ln(a - x) - \ln(a) = \frac{2k_{3/2}b^{1/2}}{k_1} e^{-k_1 t/2} + c$$

and a plot of $\ln(a - x)$ against $e^{-k_1 t/2}$ will give a line of slope $2k_{3/2}b^{1/2}/k_1$.

Second Order.   The rate law for a second order reaction is

$$- \frac{d[A]}{dt} = k_2[A][B]$$

and if there is a 1 : 1 stoichiometry

$$\frac{dx}{dt} = k_2(a - x)(b - x)$$

which on integration gives

$$\frac{1}{a - b} \ln \frac{b(a - x)}{a(b - x)} = k_2 t$$

If the stoichiometry is other than 1 : 1, this must be included in the differential equation [i.e., $(b - 2x)$ if the stoichiometry is 1 : 2], leading to the proper integrated form.

Again the expression is simplified by using stoichiometric concentrations (equal if the reaction has 1 : 1 stoichiometry), giving

$$\frac{dx}{dt} = k_2(a - x)^2$$

which on integration gives

$$\frac{1}{a - x} - \frac{1}{a} = k_2 t$$

A plot of $1/(a - x)$ against time will then give a line of slope k_2.

It is sometimes difficult to make the concentrations of A and B equal, and if they are only slightly different, it is inconvenient to use the first expression given, for ten-place logarithm tables will usually be required. The expression may be arranged into more convenient forms by putting it in terms of two new quantities defined as[5]

$$s = \frac{a - b}{2} \qquad a = d + s \qquad b = d - s$$

Then the equation becomes

$$\frac{1}{2s} \ln \frac{(d - s)(d + s - x)}{(d + s)(d - s - x)} = k_2 t$$

which may be rearranged to

$$\ln \left(1 - \frac{s}{d}\right) - \ln \left(1 + \frac{s}{d}\right) + \ln \left(1 + \frac{s}{d - x}\right) - \ln \left(1 - \frac{s}{d - x}\right) = 2skt$$

[5] S. Widequist, *Arkiv Kemi*, **26A**, 2 (1948).

Each term in this equation is of the form $\ln(1 - x)$, which may be expressed in term of its expansion

$$\ln(1 - x) = x - \frac{x^2}{2} + \frac{x^3}{3} \cdots$$

Using only the first three terms of the expansion, and putting all the above terms in this form, gives

$$-\frac{2s}{d} - \frac{2s^3}{3d^3} + \frac{2s}{d - x} + \frac{2s^3}{3(d - x)^3} = 2skt$$

This may also be expressed as

$$\frac{1}{d - x} - \frac{1}{d} + \frac{s^2}{3}\left(\frac{1}{(d - x)^3} - \frac{1}{d^3}\right) = kt$$

In the case in which the concentrations of A and B are very close (within a few per cent), then $s^2 \cong 0$ and

$$\frac{1}{d - x} - \frac{1}{d} = kt$$

Thus the expression reduces to one analogous to that for equal concentrations except that the mean concentration is used.

Higher order reactions are treated in exactly the same way and thus will not be considered in detail here. Many reactions are more complex than the simple cases we have considered. It seems appropriate to consider a number of the more common of these cases.

Competing First and Second Order Reactions. One of the more common types of these more complex reactions is one in which there is a competition between a first and second order reaction. A typical case would be in the reaction of some alkyl halides with base in which there is a competition between solvolysis (first order) and displacement (second order):

$$RCl(+ H_2O) \xrightarrow{k_1} ROH + H^+ + Cl^-$$

$$RCl + HO^- \xrightarrow{k_2} ROH + Cl^-$$

The stoichiometry is the same for both reactions, for base is required to neutralize the acid formed in the first reaction. If the halide is designed as a and the hydroxyl ion as b, and if the concentrations are equal (or, in general, stoichiometric), then the rate expression may be written as

$$\frac{dx}{dt} = k_1(a - x) + k_2(a - x)(b - x)$$

$$= k_1(a - x) + k_2(a - x)^2$$

which gives

$$\frac{dx}{(a - x)(a - x + k_1/k_2)} = k_2\,dt$$

and on integration, we obtain

$$\frac{k_2}{k_1} \ln \frac{(a - x + k_1/k_2)(a)}{(a - x)(a + k_1/k_2)} = k_2 t$$

Multiplying both sides by k_1/k_2 and raising to a power of e,

$$(a - x)\left(a + \frac{k_1}{k_2}\right)e^{k_1 t} = \left(a - x + \frac{k_1}{k_2}\right)a$$

which may be rearranged to

$$\frac{k_2}{k_1} = \frac{1}{(e^{k_1 t} - 1)}\left(\frac{1}{a - x} - \frac{e^{k_1 t}}{a}\right)$$

Suppose $k_2 \gg k_1$; then $e^{k_1 t} = 1 + k_1 t$, and $k_1 t \cong 0$. This gives

$$k_2 t = \frac{1}{a - x} - \frac{1}{a}$$

which is the expression previously obtained for a second order reaction.

It is convenient to multiply the equation by a and to define $x/a = r$, the fraction which has reacted. This gives

$$a\,\frac{k_2}{k_1} = \frac{1}{(e^{k_1 t} - 1)}\left(\frac{1}{1 - r_t} - e^{k_1 t}\right)$$

The value of k_1 may usually be determined separately, as in the present case by measuring the rate of reaction in the absence of base. If this is not possible, the reaction may be carried out with two different concentrations of the reactants (still in stoichiometric ratio), and since k_2/k_1 will be independent of concentrations, we have at any time t

$$\frac{1}{a_1}\left(\frac{1}{1 - r_t^1} - e^{k_1 t}\right) = \frac{1}{a_2}\left(\frac{1}{1 - r_t^2} - e^{k_1 t}\right)$$

$$e^{k_1 t}\left(\frac{1}{a_1} - \frac{1}{a_2}\right) = \frac{1}{a_1(1 - r_t^1)} - \frac{1}{a_2(1 - r_t^2)}$$

where the subscript 1 refers to the first set of concentrations and 2 refers to the second set. The only unknown is k_1, which may then be determined, and, knowing this, k_2 may be found.

Second Order Autocatalytic Reaction. An autocatalytic reaction is observed when one of the products of a reaction is a catalyst for the reaction. This type of behavior is found in the acid-catalyzed hydrolysis of esters under certain conditions and in other reactions, such as the bromination of acetone and the typsin-catalyzed hydrolysis of trypsinogen to trypsin. If the stoichiometry requires the formation of one molecule of catalyst for every molecule of substrate which has reacted, the rate expression may be written as

$$\frac{dx}{dt} = k(a - x)(b + x)$$

where a is the initial concentration of the substrate and b is the initial concentration of the catalyst. Integration gives

$$\frac{1}{a + b} \ln \frac{(b + x)(a)}{(a - x)(b)} = kt$$

This is very similar to the form of an ordinary second order reaction except that the sign of x is positive in the numerator. In order to see the form the experimental data will take, let us solve for $(b + x)$. This will correspond to the experimentally measured quantity. For convenience, the expression may be written as

$$\frac{1}{A_0 + B_0} \ln \frac{A_0 B}{B_0 A} = kt$$

where A_0 and B_0 are the initial concentrations (corresponding to a and b above) and A and B are the concentrations at time t. Raising the expression to the power of e, one obtains

$$\frac{A_0 B}{B_0 A} = e^{(A_0 + B_0)kt}$$

which may be solved for B, giving

$$B = \frac{A_0 + B_0}{1 + (A_0/B_0)e^{-(A_0 + B_0)kt}}$$

A plot of B against time (Fig. 3-3) will then give a sigmoid shaped curve. The rising portion is due to the $(b + x)$ term rising as the $(a - x)$ decreases, but toward the end of the reaction the quantity of A remaining becomes quite small, and although the catalyst concentration is high, the rate of the reaction must decrease.

Consecutive First Order Reactions.   Many reactions involve two successive first order (or pseudo-first order) steps. As an example, we may consider the reaction

$$BrCH_2CH_2Br + H_2O \xrightarrow{k_1} HOCH_2CH_2Br + H^+Br^-$$

$$HOCH_2CH_2Br + H_2O \xrightarrow{k_2} HOCH_2CH_2OH + H^+Br^-$$

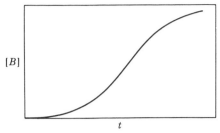

Fig. 3-3. Change of concentration with time for an autocatalytic reaction ([B]₀ = 0).

which will have pseudo-first order kinetic behavior when the concentration of water is large, and therefore constant. In general terms, this may be expressed as

$$A \xrightarrow{k_1} B$$

$$B \xrightarrow{k_2} C$$

The differential equations are

$$\frac{dA}{dt} = -k_1 A$$

$$\frac{dB}{dt} = k_1 A - k_2 B$$

$$\frac{dC}{dt} = k_2 B$$

The equation for A is the ordinary first order expression, which on integration gives

$$A = A_0 e^{-k_1 t}$$

This may be substituted into the expression for the rate of change of B, giving

$$\frac{dB}{dt} = k_1 A_0 e^{-k_1 t} - k_2 B$$

and if B_0 is 0, integration gives

$$B = \frac{A_0 k_1}{k_2 - k_1} (e^{-k_1 t} - e^{-k_2 t})$$

Since the sum of the concentrations must be equal to A_0,

$$C = A_0 - A - B$$

An interesting question is how the relative values of k_1 and k_2 affect the maximum concentration of the intermediate, B, and the time at which the concentration is at a maximum. The maximum in any curve is found by setting the derivative of the ordinate with respect to the abscissa equal to zero. Thus

$$0 = \frac{dB}{dt} = \frac{A_0 k_1}{k_2 - k_1} (-k_1 e^{-k_1 t} + k_2 e^{-k_2 t})$$

but since $A_0 k_1 / (k_2 - k_1)$ will normally not be zero,

$$0 = -k_1 e^{-k_1 t} + k_2 e^{-k_2 t}$$

$$-k_1 t = -k_2 t + \ln \frac{k_2}{k_1}$$

and

$$t_{max} = \frac{1}{k_2 - k_1} \ln \frac{k_2}{k_1}$$

Thus the time at which the maximum is reached decreases as k_2 increases with respect to k_1. If it is possible to determine the time at which the maximum is reached, a function of the two rate constants may be obtained from the above expression, and the value of k_1 may be estimated from the initial rate. However, the results obtained in this way are not very precise. The value of B at the maximum may be obtained by substituting t_{max} into the expression for B given above. The effect of the ratio of k_2/k_1 is shown graphically in Fig. 3-4, which gives the curves for $k_1 = 0.01$ sec^{-1} and the values of k_2 of 0.02, 0.01, and 0.005 sec^{-1}, respectively.

The range of k_2 with respect to k_1 which will lead to the observation of an intermediate is limited. If $k_2 = 10k_1$, for example, the maximum concentration of B occurs at about a third of a half-life for A, and at this time the concentration is only 0.08 A_0. Thus if $k_2 > 10k_1$, the intermediate has a negligible concentration, and after a brief induction period one observes the formation of C with a rate constant k_1. Similarly, if $k_1 = 10k_2$, the maximum concentration of B occurs at a time corresponding to about three half-lives for A, and the concentration of C is negligible. Thus if $k_1 > 10k_2$, one observes the conversion of A to B and of B to C as two separate reactions.

It should be noted that if pseudo-first order kinetics are observed, the rate constant k_1 contains the concentration of the compound in large excess. Thus by varying its concentration one may be able to go from $k_1 > k_2$ to $k_2 > k_1$.

The practical details of obtaining the rate constants from experimental data for this case, as well as other sets of consecutive reactions, will be considered in Appendix 7.

Steady State Approximation. In many reactions one or more intermediates may be involved but yet may not contribute appreciably to the total

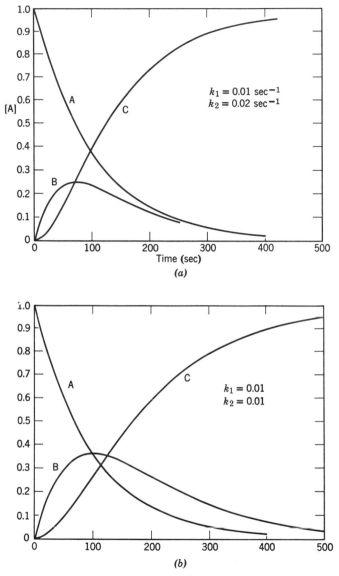

Fig. 3-4a and b Concentration-time relationships for consecutive first order reactions.

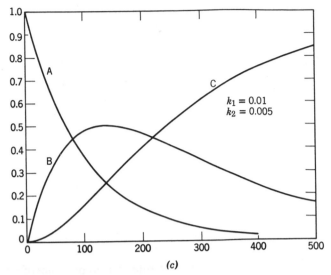

(c)

Fig. 3-4c. (continued).

concentration of reacting species. Consider the foregoing example of consecutive first order reactions for the case in which $k_2 \gg k_1$. Then the concentration of B will be small with respect to A at all times. If this is the case, after a short initial period the rate of change of B with time will be negligible compared to the rate of change of A, and we may set

$$\frac{d\text{B}}{dt} = k_1\text{A} - k_2\text{B} = 0$$

Thus

$$k_1\text{A} = k_2\text{B}$$

Substituting this into the expression for the rate of formation of C,

$$\frac{d\text{C}}{dt} = k_2\text{B}$$

we obtain

$$\frac{d\text{C}}{dt} = k_1\text{A} = -\frac{d\text{A}}{dt}$$

A more interesting example is a series of reactions such as

$$\text{A} \xrightarrow{k_1} 2\text{B}$$

$$\text{B} + \text{C} \xrightarrow{k_2} \text{D}$$

$$\text{D} + \text{C} \xrightarrow{k_3} \text{D}$$

$$2\text{D} \xrightarrow{k_4} \text{E}$$

which is typical of many free radical polymerization reactions. Here, for example, A might be the initiator which decomposes thermally to two free radicals (B), C would be the monomer, D would be the growing polymer chain, and the last reaction would be the termination step which destroys the radical at the end of a growing chain. Here the concentrations of B and D would normally be negligible. Thus

$$\frac{dA}{dt} = -k_1 A$$

$$0 = \frac{dB}{dt} = 2k_1 A - k_2 BC$$

$$\frac{dC}{dt} = -k_2 BC - k_3 CD$$

$$0 = \frac{dD}{dt} = k_2 BC - k_4 D^2$$

We wish to obtain the expression for the rate of disappearance of monomer. We may substitute the value of B from the second equation and D from the fourth equation into that for dC/dt, to give

$$\frac{dC}{dt} = -2k_1 A - k_3 C\sqrt{2(k_1/k_4)A}$$

If the chain is long, the first term corresponding to initiation will be small compared to the second, which corresponds to propagation. Thus

$$\frac{dC}{dt} = -k_3 \sqrt{(2k_1/k_4)} C A^{\frac{1}{2}}$$

illustrating the commonly observed half-order dependence on the initiator concentration.

First Order Reversible Reaction.   Many reactions proceed at a measurable rate to an equilibrium mixture of reactants and products. In order to evaluate the rate constant it is necessary to include the equilibrium constant in the rate expression. For the first order case

$$A \underset{k_{-1}}{\overset{k_1}{\rightleftharpoons}} B$$

the rate expression is

$$\frac{-d[A]}{dt} = k_1[A] - k_{-1}[B]$$

or

$$\frac{dx}{dt} = k_1(a - x) - k_{-1}(x)$$

$$= k_1 a - x(k_1 + k_{-1})$$

Integration gives

$$\ln \left[a - \left(1 + \frac{1}{K} \right) x \right] - \ln a = -k_1 t$$

where K is the equilibrium constant, or k_1/k_{-1}. It can be seen that if K is large, the expression reduces to that for an ordinary first order reaction.

The expressions for first and second order and for second order reversible reactions are obtained in the same way.

Reactions Involving Equilibria. Many reactions involve equilibria prior to the rate determining step as for the case

$$A + B \underset{k_{-1}}{\overset{k_1}{\rightleftharpoons}} C$$

$$C \xrightarrow{k_2} \text{products (P)}$$

$$\frac{-d[B]}{dt} = \frac{-d[A]}{dt} = k_1[A][B] - k_{-1}[C]$$

$$\frac{d[C]}{dt} = k_1[A][B] - k_{-1}[C] - k_2[C]$$

Consider first the case in which the concentration of the intermediate C is very small compared to the concentrations of the reactants. Then $d[C]/dt$ must be correspondingly smaller than $d[A]/dt$, and in comparison to the latter, the former may be considered to differ from zero by an inappreciable amount.

Setting the expression for $d[C]/dt$ equal to zero, we obtain

$$[C] = \frac{k_1[A][B]}{k_{-1} - k_2}$$

and

$$\frac{-d[A]}{dt} = k_2[C] = \frac{k_1 k_2[A][B]}{k_{-1} + k_2}$$

If k_{-1} were negligible compared to k_2, this would, of course, reduce to the rate expression for an ordinary second order reaction.

In other cases the concentration of the intermediate may be appreciable, and this approximation may not be valid. It will be convenient to consider two common examples, acid-base catalysis and a typical enzyme catalyzed reaction. As an example of acid-base catalysis, consider the example

$$A + H_3O^+ \underset{k_{-1}}{\overset{k_1}{\rightleftharpoons}} AH^+ + H_2O$$

$$AH^+ + B^- \xrightarrow{k_2} \text{products} + BH$$

which for convenience will be written as

$$A + C \underset{k_{-1}}{\overset{k_1}{\rightleftharpoons}} E$$

$$E + Y \overset{k_2}{\longrightarrow} \text{products} + Z$$

This actually involves two equilibria:

$$K_1 = \frac{[AH^+]}{[A][H_3O^+]} = \frac{E}{AC} \qquad K_2 = \frac{[BH]}{[B^-][H_3O^+]} = \frac{Z}{YC}$$

For a general treatment it is convenient to consider only the initial rate, at which time no product has been formed. Then

$$A = A_0 - E$$
$$C = C_0 - E$$

$$K_1 = \frac{E}{(A_0 - E)(C_0 - E)} \qquad K_2 = \frac{Z}{(C_0 - E)(Y)}$$

Equating $(C_0 - E)$ for the two equilibria,

$$\frac{K_1(A_0 - E)}{E} = \frac{K_2 Y}{Z}$$

and

$$E = \frac{K_1 Z A_0}{K_2 Y + K_1 Z}$$

But

$$-\left(\frac{dA}{dt}\right)_i = k_2 E Y$$

$$= k_2\left(\frac{K_1 Z Y A_0}{K_2 Y + K_1 Z}\right)$$

$$= k_2\left(\frac{K_1 [HB][A]_0[B^-]}{K_2[B^-] + K_1[HB]}\right)$$

If $K_2[B^-] \gg K_1[HB]$, the expression becomes

$$= k_2 \frac{K_1}{K_2} [A]_0 [HB]$$

giving general acid catalysis. If, on the other hand, $K_1[HA] \gg K_2[A]$

$$-\left(\frac{dA}{dt}\right)_i = k_2[A]_0[B^-]$$

This is observed at high acid concentration, where the substrate has been completely converted into the conjugate acid. The apparent order of the reaction for any set of conditions will be a function of the relative concentrations of the substrate and the catalyst.

In reactions involving an enzyme, the secondary equilibrium considered above is not operative, and the process is often described by

$$S + E \underset{k_{-1}}{\overset{k_1}{\rightleftharpoons}} ES$$

$$ES \xrightarrow{k_2} P + E$$

where S is the substrate and E is the enzyme. Since the order of the reaction changes as the ratio of substrate to enzyme is changed, we will again calculate initial rates. In the same fashion as above, we may set up the relationships

$$\frac{[ES]}{[E][S]} = K$$

$$[E] = [E]_0 - [ES] \qquad [S] = [S]_0 - [ES]$$

and

$$\frac{[ES]}{([E]_0 - [ES])([S]_0 - [ES])} = K$$

Suppose $[S]_0 \gg [E]_0$, as is usually the case; then

$$\frac{[ES]}{([E]_0 - [ES])([S]_0)} = K$$

$$[ES] = \frac{K[E]_0[S]_0}{K[S]_0 + 1}$$

and since

$$-\frac{d[S]}{dt} = k_2[ES]$$

$$-\left(\frac{d[S]}{dt}\right)_i = \frac{Kk_2[E]_0[S]_0}{K[S]_0 + 1}$$

This is commonly written as

$$-\left(\frac{d[S]}{dt}\right)_i = \frac{k_2[E_0][S]_0}{[S_0] + K_m}$$

where $K_m = 1/K$. This is the Michaelis-Menten equation. A plot of the initial rate against substrate concentration is shown in Fig. 3-5. When $[S]_0 \gg K_m$,

$$-\frac{d[S]}{dt} = k_2[E]_0 = k_2'$$

giving a pseudo-zero order reaction. At lower concentration of S, the reaction will become pseudo-first order (since [E] is a constant).

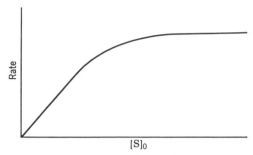

Fig. 3-5. Effect of substrate concentration on the initial rate for a typical enzyme catalyzed reaction.

If the concentration of the intermediate ES is small, the steady state approximation may be used to solve the equations.

$$0 = \frac{d[ES]}{dt} = k_1[E][S] - k_{-1}[ES] - k_2[ES]$$

$$[E] = [E]_0 - [ES]$$

$$[S] = [S]_0 - [ES] \cong [S]_0$$

Therefore

$$0 = \frac{d[ES]}{dt} = k_1[E]_0[S]_0 - k_1[ES][S]_0 - k_1[ES] - k_2[ES]$$

which gives

$$[ES] = \frac{k[E]_0[S]_0}{k_1[S]_0 + k_{-1} + k_2}$$

and

$$-\left(\frac{d[S]}{dt}\right)_i = k_2[ES] = \frac{k_1 k_2 [E]_0 [S]_0}{k_1[S]_0 + k_{-1} + k_2}$$

which is the same as the Michaelis-Menten equation if $K_m = (k_1 + k_2)/k_1$. In the case where $k_{-1} \gg k_2$ (i.e., where k_2 is rate determining and the equilibrium concentration of ES is present at all times) it is identical with the Michaelis-Menten equation.

References

Kinetic Data and Rate Constants:

A. A. Frost and R. G. Pearson, *Kinetics and Mechanism*, John Wiley and Sons, New York, 2nd ed., 1961, Chs. 2, 3 and 8.

S. W. Benson, *The Foundations of Chemical Kinetics*, McGraw-Hill Book Co. New York, 1960, Part I.
R. A. Livingston in A. Weissberger (Ed.), *Technique of Organic Chemistry*, Interscience Publishers, New York, 1953, vol. VIII.

Problems

1. Given the following data showing the decrease in absorbance of a solution due to the disappearance of compound A, calculate the first order rate constant. Note that the infinity absorbance is probably not zero.

Absorbance	Time (sec)
0.450	39
0.390	59
0.325	89
0.275	123
0.235	157
0.200	190
0.175	217
0.145	257
0.125	286
0.105	320
0.090	351

2. Given the following data showing the change in concentration of B with time, calculate the rate constants for the process

$$A \xrightarrow{k_1} B$$

$$B \xrightarrow{k_2} C$$

if $[A]_0 = 0.137M$

[B]	Time (sec)
0.000	0
0.024	25
0.052	75
0.060	100
0.065	125
0.068	150
0.069	175
0.066	225
0.060	275
0.054	325
0.047	375
0.039	440
0.032	500
0.021	625

3. Derive the rate law which would be expected for the following sequence of reactions.

$$R-N=N-R \xrightarrow{k_1} 2R\cdot + N_2$$

$$R\cdot + R'H \xrightarrow{k_2} R'\cdot + RH$$

4. Repeat problem 3, using as the termination step

$$2R'\cdot \xrightarrow{k_5'} R'R'$$

How does the nature of the termination step affect the overall kinetics?

3-3 Absolute Rate Theory

In considering the rates of chemical reactions it would be highly desirable to have available a method for calculating the rate of reaction, knowing only the physical properties (i.e., bond dissociation energy, vibrational frequency, and bond length) of the reacting molecules and the geometry of the assembly of atoms when they have reached the top of the potential energy barrier. Several approaches to this problem have been made. However, the one which appears best suited to the problems of interest to organic chemists is the absolute rate theory developed by Eyring,[6] and which is based on the work of Pelzer and Wigner.[7]

In the absolute rate theory, the species at the top of the potential energy barrier, known as the activated complex, is considered in most respects an ordinary chemical species which is in equilibrium with the reactants. This permits the problem to be divided into two parts—the calculation of the equilibrium constant for the reaction forming the activated complex and the calculation of the rate at which the activated complex decomposes to form the products of the reaction.

A simple bimolecular reaction will then be formulated as

$$A + B \underset{}{\overset{K^{\ddagger}}{\rightleftharpoons}} C^{\ddagger} \overset{k^{\ddagger}}{\longrightarrow} \text{products}$$

where $C^{\ddagger}$ is the activated complex. The velocity of the reaction will be given by

$$v = \kappa k^{\ddagger}[C^{\ddagger}]$$

where κ is the "transmission coefficient" or the fraction of activated complexes which give products; the rest return to reactants. The concentration of the activated complex may be given in terms of the concentrations of the reactants and the equilibrium constant

$$v = \kappa K^{\ddagger}k^{\ddagger}[A][B]$$

and thus it can be seen that the ordinary rate constant is given by

$$k_{\text{obs}} = \kappa K^{\ddagger}k^{\ddagger}$$

Rather than consider the further details of this theory in general terms, it seems preferable to take a specific example and to carry this through the entire process of calculating the rate of reaction. For this purpose the reaction between methane and a chlorine atom

$$CH_4 + Cl\cdot \rightarrow CH_3\cdot + HCl$$

is convenient, for the necessary experimental data are available for comparison with the calculated values.[8] The corresponding data for the reaction with bromine atoms and with iodine atoms are also available.[9,10] Further, since the reactions were carried out in the gas phase, the effects of solvent on the rate of reaction need not be considered. We shall first calculate the equilibrium constant for the reaction giving the activated complex, and then we shall consider the rate constant for its decomposition to products.

[6] H. Eyring, *Chem. Revs.*, **17**, 65 (1935).
[7] H. Pelzer and E. Wigner, *Z. physik. Chem.*, **B15**, 445 (1932).
[8] H. O. Pritchard, J. B. Pyke, and A. F. Trotman-Dickenson, *J. Am. Chem. Soc.*, **76**, 1201 (1954), *ibid*, **77**, 2629 (1955).
[9] G. B. Kistiakowsky and E. R. Van Artsdalen, *J. Chem. Phys.*, **12**, 469 (1944).
[10] R. R. Williams Jr. and R. A. Ogg Jr., *J. Chem. Phys.*, **15**, 696 (1947).

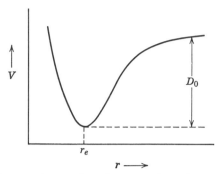

Fig. 3-6. Potential energy-internuclear distance relationship for a diatomic molecule.

In order to facilitate the calculation it will be assumed that methane may be considered as a diatomic molecule, CH_3—H, and thus it will be assumed (although it is certainly incorrect) that the energy of the non-reacting C—H bonds will not be changed as methane is converted to the methyl radical. The resultant error can be shown to be quite small, and, in fact, negligible compared to the other approximations we shall be forced to make.

Our previous consideration of the hydrogen molecule (Section 1-13) has indicated that the potential of a diatomic system as a function of inter-nuclear distance is given by a curve such as that in Fig. 3-6.

Here the standard state is that of the atoms separated to infinity, and this state is given the energy zero. Bonding is then represented by a negative energy.

The dissociation curve may be reproduced satisfactorily by the empirical Morse equation[11]

$$V = D_0[(1 - e^{-\alpha(r-r_e)})^2 - 1]$$

where D_0 is the observed dissociation energy plus the zero-point energy, r is the distance at which V is evaluated, and α is given by

$$\alpha = 1.218 \times 10^7 \omega_0 \sqrt{\mu/D_0}$$

where ω_0 is the equilibrium vibrational frequency of the bond, which may be approximated by the observed frequency, and μ is the reduced mass.

$$\mu = \frac{m_1 m_2}{m_1 + m_2}$$

The quantities ω_0 and D_0 are given in cm^{-1} (1 cal/mole = 0.350 cm^{-1}) and the unit of α which is obtained is cm^{-1}. The required values of the constants are given in Table 3-1.

[11] P. M. Morse, *Phys. Rev.*, **34**, 57 (1929).

As the chlorine atom approaches the methane molecule, an assembly is formed which may be considered to be composed of three particles, Cl· (X); H· (Y) and CH₃ (Z).

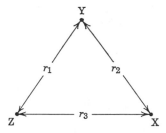

It is now necessary to calculate the energy of this assembly as a function of r_1, r_2, and r_3. The energy of a system of three particles of this type is given approximately by the London equation,[12]

$$E = A + B + C - \{\tfrac{1}{2}[(\alpha - \beta)^2 + (\alpha - \gamma)^2 + (\gamma - \beta)^2]\}^{\frac{1}{2}}$$

Table 3-1   Molecular Constants for the Methane-Halogen Atom Reaction

Compound	r_e	ν cm^{-1}	α	D_0 (kcal/mole)
Methane	1.090 Å	2970[a]	1.81	108.5
Hydrogen chloride	1.275	2990	1.85	106.5
Methyl chloride	1.780	732	1.72	81.0
Hydrogen bromide	1.414	2650	1.81	89.3
Methyl bromide	1.940	611	1.71	68.0
Hydrogen iodide	1.604	2310	1.75	73.8
Methyl iodide	2.140	533	1.71	54.0

[a] Average of symmetric and antisymmetric frequencies.

which is derived using the Valence Bond method. Here A, B, and C are the Coulombic parts of the energies of the molecules YZ, XY, and XZ, all evaluated at the appropriate internuclear distances, and α, β, and γ are the corresponding exchange terms. We can obtain the total energy of each of these molecules at the required distances using the Morse equation, and if there were some way in which to divide the total energy into Coulombic and exchange parts, the energy of the assembly of three particles could be calculated as a function of the three internuclear distances.

Eyring and Polanyi[13] have used the simple device of taking 10 to 20% of the total energy as the Coulombic part and the rest as the exchange part.

[12] F. London, *Z. Elektrochem.*, **35**, 552 (1929).
[13] H. Eyring and M. Polanyi, *Z. Physik. Chem.*, **B12**, 279 (1931).

This is a fair approximation at the larger internuclear distances but is not entirely satisfactory at the small internuclear distances at which activated complexes are often found.

A more satisfactory approximation is that of Sato,[14] which makes use of the results of the Heitler-London treatment of diatomic molecules (Section 1-13).

$$V_{\text{bonding}} = \frac{Q + L}{1 + s^2}$$

$$V_{\text{antibonding}} = \frac{Q - L}{1 - s^2}$$

where Q is the Coulombic part, L is the exchange part, and s is the overlap integral. The potential energy of the bonding state as a function of internuclear distance is given by the Morse equation, and the potential energy of the antibonding state has been shown by Sato to be given to a good approximation by

$$V_{\text{anti.}} = \frac{D_0}{2} [(1 + e^{-\alpha(r-r_e)})^2 - 1]$$

The Coulombic and exchange terms are then given by

$$Q = \frac{V_{\text{bond.}} + V_{\text{anti.}} + s^2[V_{\text{bond.}} - V_{\text{anti.}}]}{2}$$

$$L = \frac{V_{\text{bond.}} - V_{\text{anti.}} + s^2[V_{\text{bond.}} + V_{\text{anti.}}]}{2}$$

The value of s^2 which appears to be satisfactory in the region of the activated complex is 0.18.

As an example of the use of this method, Table 3-2 gives the values of the bonding and antibonding potentials for methane, hydrogen chloride, and methyl chloride for some values of the internuclear distance. From this may be obtained the associated values of the Coulombic and exchange terms. Having these values, we are now in a position to calculate the energy of the assembly of three particles as a function of the geometry. The London equation will be used for this purpose, but since the overlap integral was included in calculating the Coulombic and exchange terms, it must also be included in the London equation:

$$E = \frac{1}{1 + s^2} (A + B + C - \{\tfrac{1}{2}[(\alpha - \beta)^2 + (\alpha - \gamma)^2 + (\beta - \gamma)^2]\}^{1/2})$$

It should be noted that the energy thus calculated is at a minimum if one of the exchange terms is small compared to the others, indicating that

[14] S. Sato, *J. Chem. Phys.* **23**, 592, 2465 (1955).

in this approximation the activated complexes of lowest energy will be linear. If one makes this assumption for the arrangement of the activated complex, one of the internuclear distances (r_3) will be the sum of the other two, leading to only two independent variables (r_1 and r_2). The energies thus calculated are tabulated in Table 3-3.

These data should be represented by a three-dimensional surface with r_1, r_2, and E as the variables. However, for convenience they are usually plotted in a contour diagram which indicates points of equal energy as a

Table 3-2 Bonding and Antibonding Potentials for Methane, Hydrogen Chloride, and Methyl Chloride

	Methane			Hydrogen Chloride			Methyl Chloride	
r	$V_{bond.}$	$V_{anti.}$	r	$V_{bond.}$	$V_{anti.}$	r	$V_{bond.}$	$V_{anti.}$
1.00	−105.10	202.84	1.20	−104.14	192.62	2.20	−59.57	48.88
1.05	−107.89	179.35	1.25	−106.26	169.95	2.30	−52.69	39.89
1.10	−108.47	158.88	1.30	−106.28	150.23	2.40	−46.17	32.68
1.15	−107.35	140.99	1.35	−104.71	133.05	2.50	−40.15	26.88
1.20	−104.96	125.34	1.40	−101.96	118.04	2.60	−34.71	22.18
1.25	−101.64	111.62	1.45	−98.35	104.91	2.70	−29.87	18.35
1.30	−97.65	99.56	1.50	−94.15	93.40	2.80	−25.60	15.23
1.35	−93.21	88.94	1.55	−89.57	83.28	2.90	−21.88	12.66
1.40	−88.94	79.57	1.60	−84.75	74.37	3.00	−18.65	10.54
1.45	−83.63	71.29	1.65	−79.84	66.51	3.10	−15.87	8.80
1.50	−78.71	63.96	1.70	−74.93	59.57	3.20	−13.47	7.35
1.55	−73.85	57.45	1.75	−70.09	53.41	3.30	−11.43	6.15
1.60	−69.09	51.67	1.80	−65.38	47.96	3.40	−9.68	5.15

function of the two distances. A plot of the data for the methane-chlorine atom reaction is shown in Fig. 3-7. It might further be noted that these plots are often constructed using an acute angle between the two axes so that the cross terms (i.e., those involving $r_1 r_2$) in the internal kinetic energy expression will vanish.[15] Under this circumstance, the free frictionless motion, under the influence of gravity, of a particle sliding on the potential energy surface can be made to represent the motion of the reacting system.

The energy of methane (considered as a diatomic molecule) with a chlorine atom at infinity is −108.5 kcal/mole. The reaction could proceed by the dissociation of methane followed by the reaction of the chlorine atom with a hydrogen atom.

$$CH_3\text{—}H \rightarrow CH_3\cdot + H\cdot$$
$$H\cdot + Cl\cdot \rightarrow HCl$$

[15] See S. Glasstone, K. J. Laidler, and H. Eyring, *The Theory of Rate Processes*, McGraw-Hill Book Co., New York, 1941, pp. 100–107 for further details.

Table 3-3   Calculated Energies for the Methane-Chlorine Atom Activated Complex[a]

r_{H-Cl}	r_{CH_3-H}									
	1.05	1.10	1.15	1.20	1.25	1.30	1.35	1.40	1.45	1.50
1.20	−63.77	−71.13	−76.93	−81.53	−85.23	−88.24	−90.70	−92.74	−94.44	−95.87
1.25	−72.30	−78.88	−83.94	−87.87	−90.96	−93.42	−95.40	−97.03	−98.38	−99.51
1.30	−78.90	−84.73	−89.08	−92.33	−94.80	−96.70	−98.18	−99.37	−100.34	−101.15
1.35	−84.05	−89.19	−92.85	−95.44	−97.28	−98.61	−99.57	−100.31	−100.88	−101.34
1.40	−88.13	−92.61	−95.63	−97.59	−98.82	−99.57	−100.01	−100.26	−100.41	−100.50
1.45	−91.38	−95.28	−97.70	−99.07	−99.71	−99.90	−99.80	−99.57	−99.28	−98.98
1.50	−94.01	−97.40	−99.28	−100.10	−100.20	−99.84	−99.23	−98.50	−97.76	−97.05
1.55	−96.16	−99.10	−100.51	−100.84	−100.44	−99.57	−98.46	−97.25	−96.05	−94.93
1.60	−97.94	−100.49	−101.50	−101.39	−100.54	−99.21	−97.62	−95.95	−94.31	−92.77
1.65	−99.43	−101.65	−102.30	−101.82	−100.57	−98.82	−96.81	−94.71	−92.64	−90.69
1.70	−100.67	−102.61	−102.97	−102.17	−100.57	−98.47	−96.07	−93.58	−91.11	−88.76
1.75	−101.72	−103.43	−103.53	−102.46	−100.58	−98.15	−95.43	−92.58	−89.75	−87.03
1.80	−102.61	−104.12	−104.02	−102.72	−100.59	−97.90	−94.88	−91.73	−88.57	−85.52

[a] The energies are given in kcal mole.

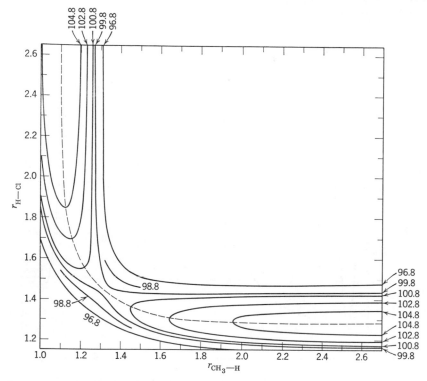

Fig. 3-7. Potential energy-distance profile for the methane–chlorine atom reaction.

The "classical" activation energy for this reaction (which neglects zero-point energies and the difference in partition functions for the ground state and activated complex) would be 108.5 kcal. An inspection of Fig. 3-7 makes it apparent that there is a much lower energy path for the reaction. The maximum energy contour over which the system must pass is −99.9 kcal. The classical activation energy would then be 108.5 − 99.9 or 8.6 kcal. This may perhaps be more easily seen in a plot of the reaction coordinate (the path of minimum potential energy) against the energy, as in Fig. 3-8. Here the lower parts of the dissociation energy curves for methane and hydrogen chloride are given to establish the starting and final points for the system, and the distance corresponding to 0.1 Å is also shown.

Similar calculations may be made for the reaction of methane with bromine and iodine atoms, and the results are summarized in Figs. 3-9 to 3-12. The values of the "classical" activation energies and interatomic distances which were obtained are summarized in Table 3-4, and the

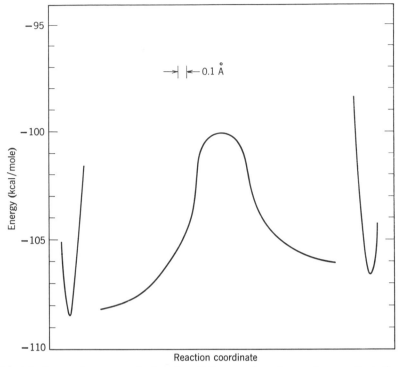

Fig. 3-8. Potential energy as the function of distance along the reaction coordinate for the methane–chlorine atom reaction.

observed values of the activation energy are also given. Considering that the calculated activation energies will be reduced when the zero-point energies are included, it can be seen that there is quite good agreement between the observed and calculated results.

Table 3-4   Classical Activation Energies and Intramolecular Distances for the Activated Complex in the Halogenation of Methane

Reaction	$\Delta E_{class.}$	$r^{\ddagger}_{CH_3-H}$	$r^{\ddagger}_{H-X}$	r_{CH_3-H}	r_{H-X}	$E_{a(obs.)}$
Chlorination	8.6	1.31	1.45	1.09	1.28	3.9
Bromination	20.5	1.69	1.45	1.09	1.41	18.0
Iodination	34.9	2.33	1.61	1.09	1.60	34.0

In order to obtain the equilibrium constant $K^{\ddagger}$, it is now necessary to consider the absolute rate theory in greater detail. In the activated complex there are $3n - 6$ vibrational degrees of freedom. However, one of these

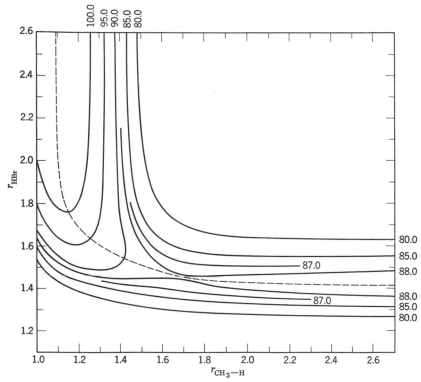

Fig. 3-9. Potential energy-distance profile for the methane–bromine atom reaction.

vibrations will correspond to motion along the reaction coordinate leading to products. For example, if we treat the methyl hydrogens as a pseudo-atom which is attached to the carbon by a relatively high stretching force constant,[16] vibrational modes for the activated complex will be

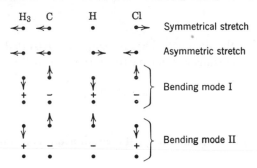

[16] H. L. Johnston, *Advances in Chemical Physics*, Interscience Publishers, New York. 1961, vol. 3, p. 131 ff.

It can be seen that in the asymmetric stretching mode, the hydrogen and chlorine move together, and this will lead to product formation. Thus this mode will be taken out from the rest of the vibrational frequencies and will be treated as a translation along the reaction coordinate.

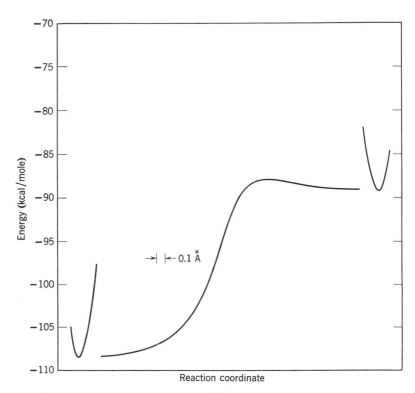

Fig. 3-10. Potential energy as a function of distance along the reaction coordinate for the methane–bromine atom reaction.

If we designate the distance characterizing the activated complex as δ (Fig. 3-13), then the translational partition function will be (p. 220)

$$Q = \frac{(2\pi m k T)^{\frac{1}{2}}}{h} \delta$$

In terms of the partition functions, the equilibrium constant will now be given by

$$K^{\ddagger} = \frac{(2\pi m k T)^{\frac{1}{2}}}{h} \delta \frac{Q^{\ddagger}}{Q_A Q_B} e^{-\Delta E_0/RT}$$

where A refers to methane, B refers to a chlorine atom, ΔE_0 is the difference in energy between the reactants and the activated complex at $0°K$ and $Q^{\ddagger}$ does not include the product forming mode discussed above.

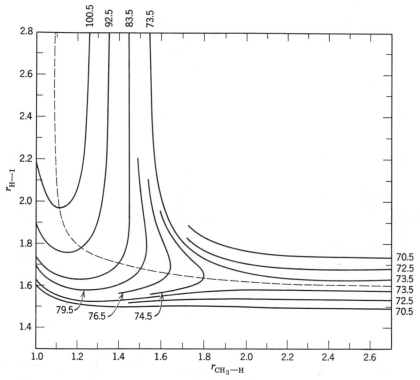

Fig. 3-11. Potential energy-distance profile for the methane–iodine atom reaction.

In order to have this in terms of the "classical" activation energy calculated above, the zero-point energy terms may be separated out from ΔE_0, giving

$$K^{\ddagger} = \frac{(2\pi mkT)^{\frac{1}{2}}}{h} \cdot \delta \cdot \frac{Q^{\ddagger}}{Q_A Q_B} \prod_i^{3n\ddagger-7} e^{-\frac{1}{2}u_i} \prod^{3n-6} e^{\frac{1}{2}u_i} \cdot e^{-\Delta E_{class.}/RT}$$

where the products are over the $3n - 7$ remaining vibrations in the activated complex and the $3n - 6$ vibrations for each of the reactants, and $u_i = h\nu_i/kT$.

Having an expression for $K^{\ddagger}$, the rate $(k^{\ddagger})$ at which the activated complex decomposes to products must now be obtained. Of all of the species which may be designated as activated complexes (i.e., those which

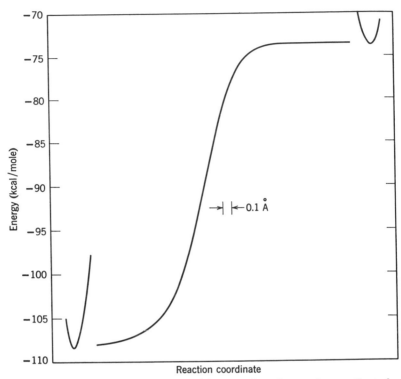

Fig. 3-12. Potential energy as a function of distance along the reaction coordinate for the methane–iodine atom reaction.

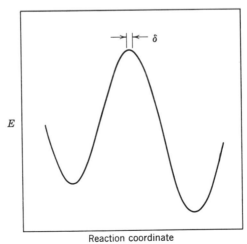

Fig. 3-13. Potential energy-reaction coordinate relationship for a hypothetical reaction. The distance δ characterizes the activated complex.

reside along the distance δ), one-half will be moving in the direction of forming products and the other half will be moving in the direction of the reactants. Using the Boltzman distribution law,

$$P_i = \frac{n_i}{n_0} = e^{-(\epsilon_i - \epsilon_0)/kT}$$

the probability of finding a molecule with a velocity between v and $v + dv$ is

$$P_{(v)} = e^{-\frac{1}{2}mv^2/kT}\, dv$$

since the energy will be $\frac{1}{2}mv^2$. The mean value of v in the forward direction will be obtained by integrating the product of the probability and the velocity for positive values of the latter and dividing by the total probability. Thus

$$\bar{v} = \frac{\displaystyle\int_0^\infty e^{-\frac{1}{2}mv^2/kT} v\, dv}{\displaystyle\int_{-\infty}^\infty e^{-\frac{1}{2}mv^2/kT}\, dv}$$

and

$$\bar{v} = \left(\frac{kT}{2\pi m}\right)^{\frac{1}{2}}$$

The rate at which molecules pass through the potential energy barrier will then be the average velocity divided by the length of the barrier

$$k^{\ddagger} = \frac{\bar{v}}{\delta} = \frac{(kT/2\pi m)^{\frac{1}{2}}}{\delta}$$

Substituting the above results into the expression for the observed rate constant,

$$k_{\text{obs.}} = \kappa k^{\ddagger} K^{\ddagger}$$

$$= \kappa\left(\frac{kT}{h}\right) \frac{Q^{\ddagger}}{Q_A Q_B} \prod_i^{3n^{\ddagger}-7} e^{-\frac{1}{2}u_i} \prod_i^{3n-6} e^{\frac{1}{2}u_i} \cdot e^{-\Delta E_{\text{class.}}/RT}$$

In terms of the familiar thermodynamic quantities this may also be written

$$k_{\text{obs.}} = \kappa\left(\frac{kT}{h}\right) e^{-\Delta H^{\ddagger}/RT}\, e^{\Delta S^{\ddagger}/R}$$

The problem has then been reduced to obtaining the thermodynamic functions using the procedure outlined in the discussion of the *n*-pentane-neopentane isomerization (p. 224). The masses, moments of inertia, and vibrational frequencies of the reactants are known; the mass of the activated complex is known; the moments of inertia may be obtained from the calculated dimensions; and if a set of vibrational frequencies for the activated complex may be deduced, the thermodynamic activation parameters may be obtained and the rate of reaction calculated.

The force constants for the nonreacting bonds may, to a reasonable approximation, be assumed to remain constant. It is then necessary to obtain the force constants for the reacting bonds. If we call the force constant for the reacting C—H bond k_{11}, that for the H—Cl bond k_{22}, and the interaction constant between the carbon and the chlorine k_{12} (cf. p. 148), the change in potential energy from the equilibrium position will be given by

$$V' = \tfrac{1}{2}k_{11}(r_1 - r_1^\ddagger)^2 + \tfrac{1}{2}k_{22}(r_2 - r_2^\ddagger)^2 + \tfrac{1}{2}k_{12}(r_1 - r_1^\ddagger)(r_2 - r_2^\ddagger)$$

where r_1 and r_2 are the CH_3—H and H—Cl distances corresponding to V', and $r_1^\ddagger$ and $r_2^\ddagger$ are the bond distances in the activated complex.

By drawing a line (Fig. 3-14) through the activated complex at a value of $r_2 = r_2^\ddagger$, a set of values of V' are obtained for which only terms in k_{11} are nonvanishing in the above expression. The value of k_{11} may then be

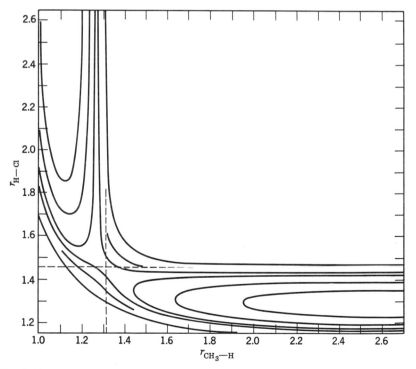

Fig. 3-14. Determination of the force constants for stretching the C—H and H—X bonds in the activated complex.

obtained. Similarly, taking the values of V' along a line having $r_1 = r_1{}^{\ddagger}$, the value of k_{22} may be obtained. The interaction constant, k_{12}, may then be obtained from the value of V' at a point off the two lines by substituting the appropriate values into the above expression. A more satisfactory procedure is to take a large number of points in the vicinity of the activated complex and then determine the values of k_{11}, k_{22}, and k_{12} which give the "best" fit using a statistical procedure, such as the method of least squares. The values thus obtained are

$$k_{11} = 0.711 \times 10^5 \text{ dynes/cm}$$
$$k_{22} = 1.050 \times 10^5 \text{ dynes/cm}$$
$$k_{12} = 1.470 \times 10^5 \text{ dynes/cm}$$

The interaction constant is large because of the shape of the potential energy surface at the saddle point. In one direction the potential energy increases with increasing distance as in a normal vibrational problem. In the other, along the reaction coordinate, the potential energy decreases with increasing distance, leading to an imaginary vibrational frequency. Thus there is a strong interaction between the motion of the carbon and the chlorine.

The force constant for the bending of the C—H—Cl bond in the activated complex may be obtained by calculating the energies of bent activated complexes in which the C—H and H—Cl distances are the same

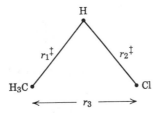

as for the linear complex. The change in energy with the change in angle leads to the force constant

$$V'' = \tfrac{1}{2}k_\phi \phi^2$$

where V'' is the change in energy and ϕ is the change in angle from 180°. The force constant was thereby calculated to be 0.113×10^{-11} ergs/rad.^{2} The value for the H—C—H bonds in methane is 0.52×10^{-11} ergs/rad.^{2} There is no way in which to get the force constant (k_θ) for the bending of the H_3—C—H bond. Since the activation energy is small, and the extent of bond cleavage is small, it presumably will not have changed markedly from that in the reactant. A reasonable value appeared to be one-half that found in methane, or 0.26×10^{-11} ergs/rad.^{2} The only remaining force constant is the C—H stretching constant, which for methane is 5.0×10^5 dynes/cm.

The vibrational frequencies may be calculated using two models. One is the four-atom model discussed above in which the methyl hydrogens are considered as a pseudo-atom, and the methyl C—H stretching vibrations are assumed not to interact with the vibrations of the reacting center. Using this model, the two stretching vibrational frequencies are given by

$$\lambda_1 + \lambda_2 = \left(\frac{1}{m_1} + \frac{1}{m_2}\right)k_{11} + \left(\frac{1}{m_2} + \frac{1}{m_3}\right)k_{22} - \frac{2k_{12}}{m_2}$$

$$\lambda_1\lambda_2 = \left(\frac{1}{m_1 m_2} + \frac{1}{m_1 m_3} + \frac{1}{m_2 m_3}\right)(k_{11}k_{22} - k_{12}{}^2)$$

$$\lambda = 4\pi^2 \nu^2 \quad \text{or} \quad \nu = 1303\lambda^{1/2}.$$

(cf. p. 148). Here m_1 is the mass of the methyl group, m_2 is the hydrogen or deuterium, and m_3 is the chlorine. The two bending frequencies may be obtained by finding the roots of the determinant

$$\begin{vmatrix} k_\theta\left[\left(\frac{1}{r_2}\right)^2 \frac{1}{m_C} + \left(\frac{1}{r_1}\right)^2 \frac{1}{m_A} \right. & -\dfrac{k_\theta}{r_2}\left[\dfrac{1}{m_B}\left(\dfrac{1}{r_1} + \dfrac{1}{r_2}\right)\right. \\ \left. + \left(\frac{1}{r_1} + \frac{1}{r_2}\right)^2 \frac{1}{m_B}\right] - \lambda & \left. + \dfrac{1}{m_C}\left(\dfrac{1}{r_2} + \dfrac{1}{r_3}\right)\right] \\ \dfrac{-k_\phi}{r_2}\left[\dfrac{1}{m_B}\left(\dfrac{1}{r_1} + \dfrac{1}{r_2}\right)\right. & k_\phi\left[\left(\dfrac{1}{r_2}\right)^2 \dfrac{1}{m_B} + \left(\dfrac{1}{r_3}\right)^2 \dfrac{1}{m_D}\right. \\ \left. + \dfrac{1}{m_C}\left(\dfrac{1}{r_2} + \dfrac{1}{r_3}\right)\right] & \left. + \left(\dfrac{1}{r_2} + \dfrac{1}{r_3}\right)^2 \dfrac{1}{m_C}\right] - \lambda \end{vmatrix} = 0$$

$$\text{A}\overset{k\theta}{\underset{r_1}{—}}\text{B}\overset{k\phi}{\underset{r_2}{—}}\text{C}\underset{r_3}{—}\text{D}$$

The vibrational frequencies thus obtained are summarized in Table 3-5.

The other model is the full model in which all the vibrational frequencies are obtained. This requires an additional parameter, α, the angle formed by a methyl hydrogen, the carbon, and the reacting hydrogen. Since the C—H bond is not stretched much, the angle should be close to tetrahedral and was taken as 107°. The results are given in Table 3-5. It can be seen that the four-particle model gives a fairly satisfactory representation of the situation (the difference in zero-point energy calculated from the two sets of frequencies differs by only 5%.) Thus this model is a convenient one for the rapid estimation of the effects of changes in force constants.

Table 3-5 Vibrational Frequencies for the Activated Complex Formed in the Chlorination of Methane

Mode	Frequency[a,b]	Frequency in Methane[c]
Four-Particle Model		
Symmetrical C—H—X stretching	380	3067(3019)
Asymmetric C—H—X stretching	1423i	——
Bending mode I	904 (2)	1328(1306)
Bending mode II	312 (2)	——
Full Model		
Symmetrical CH stretching	2934 (1)	2902(2917)
Asymmetric CH stretching	3070 (2)	3067(3019)
Symmetrical CH_3 bending	1104 (1)	1328(1306)
Asymmetric CH_3 bending	1445 (2)	1487(1534)
Bending mode I	1034 (2)	1328(1306)
Bending mode II	387 (2)	——
Symmetrical C—H—X stretching	432 (1)	3067(3019)
Asymmetric C—H—X stretching	1433i (1)	——

[a] The numbers in parentheses indicate the number of modes having the same frequency.
[b] $k_{11} = 0.711 \times 10^5$ dynes/cm, $k_{22} = 1.050 \times 10^5$, $k_{12} = 1.470 \times 10^5$; $k_\theta = 0.26 \times 10^{-11}$ ergs/rad^2, $k_\phi = 0.119 \times 10^{-11}$, $\alpha = 107°$.
[c] The numbers given first are those calculated using the same force constants as for the methyl part of the activated complex. Those given in parentheses are the observed frequencies. The difference is due to the neglect of interaction terms in the frequency calculation.

Table 3-6 Vibrational Frequencies for the Activated Complexes Formed in the Bromination and Iodination of Methane

Full Model Mode	Frequencies H_3C—H—Br[a]	H_3C—H—I[b]
Symmetric CH stretching	2913	2913
Asymmetric CH stretching	3080	3080
Symmetric CH_3 bending	690	629
Asymmetric CH_3 bending	1514	1514
Bending Mode I	568	317
Bending Mode II	261	98
Symmetrical C—H—X stretching	1897	2230
Asymmetric C—H—X stretching	192i	38i

[a] $k_{11} = -0.091 \times 10^5$ dynes/cm, $k_{22} = 3.12 \times 10^5$, $k_{12} = 0.486 \times 10^5$; $k_\theta = 0.10 \times 10^{-11}$ ergs/rad^2, $k_\phi = 0.054 \times 10^{-11}$, $\alpha = 100°$.
[b] $k_{11} = -0.0109 \times 10^5$, $k_{22} = 3.00 \times 10^5$, $k_{12} = 0.0306 \times 10^5$; $k_\theta = 0.05 \times 10^{-11}$, $k_\phi = 0.007 \times 10^{-11}$, $\alpha = 100°$.

One may ask how rapidly will the frequencies change with changes in the force constants. It is found that the frequencies for the stretching modes of the reaction site are not strongly affected by small changes in k_{11} or k_{22} (when they are about equal as are here). Changing the angle, α, to 100° instead of 107° changes the bending frequencies from 1445, 1104, 1034, and 388 cm^{-1} to 1515, 1034, 890, and 392 cm^{-1}. Similarly, changing

Table 3-7   Comparison of the Calculated and Observed Activation Parameters for the Chlorination, Bromination, and Iodination of Methane

Parameter		Chlorination	Bromination	Iodination
$\Delta E_{\text{class.}}$ (kcal/mole)		8.6	20.5	34.9
Reactants	ΔH_{tr}	2.96	2.96	2.96
	S_{tr}	70.86	73.32	74.70
	ΔH_{r}	1.78	1.78	1.78
	S_{r}	12.65	12.65	12.65
	ΔH_{v}	0.03	0.03	0.03
	S_{v}	0.11	0.11	0.11
	Zero-point energy for reactants	27.25	27.25	27.25
	Zero-point energy for activated complex	23.37	23.23	22.58
Activated Complex	ΔH_{tr}	1.48	1.48	1.48
	S_{tr}	37.61	39.60	40.79
	ΔH_{r}	0.89	0.89	0.89
	S_{r}	21.76	22.69	23.62
	ΔH_{v}	0.64	0.97	1.61
	S_{v}	3.10	4.98	10.42
$\Delta H_{\text{calcd.}}^{\ddagger}$		2.8	15.0	29.9
$\Delta S_{\text{calcd.}}^{\ddagger}$		-21.2	-18.8	-12.6
$\Delta H_{\text{obs.}}^{\ddagger}$		2.7	17.	34.
$\Delta S_{\text{obs.}}^{\ddagger}$		-17.8		

the force constant k_θ from 0.26 to 0.18 changes these frequencies to 1443, 1036, 920, and 363 cm^{-1}. Although these changes are significant, it can be seen that they will have little effect on the final result.

The enthalpy and entropy effects due to translation, rotation, and vibration may be calculated as before, and the zero-point energies may be obtained by summing the frequencies for the activated complex and for the reactants and converting to kcal/mole. The results are summarized in Table 3-7. It can be seen that the calculated values are in very good agreement with the observed values.

The results for a similar calculation for the bromination and iodination of methane are also given in Table 3-7. The frequencies used are those given in Table 3-6. Here again the results are quite satisfactory.

It can be seen that by the use of an empirical parameter (the overlap integral) which has been assigned a reasonable value, the activation parameters for simple systems of this type may be obtained. However, one cannot be sure that the potential energy surface thus calculated is a good approximation to the true surface, for the results are not too sensitive to the force constants which are derived from the surface. Thus a better test for the shape of the surface is needed, and this will be discussed in the next section.

References

Theoretical Treatment of Reaction Rates:
> S. Glasstone, K. J. Laidler and H. Eyring, *The Theory of Rate Processes*, McGraw-Hill Book Co., New York, 1941.
> S. W. Benson, *The Foundations of Chemical Kinetics*, McGraw-Hill Book Co., New York 1960.
> A. A. Frost and R. G. Pearson, *Kinetics and Mechanism*, John Wiley and Sons, New York, 2nd ed., 1961.

Problems

1. H. S. Johnston, *Advances in Chemical Physics*, **3**, 131 (1961), has suggested an empirical method for obtaining the force constants for the activated complex. Using the four-atom model, apply his method to the chlorination of methane, and see how large a change in vibrational frequencies result. How large an effect do the changes have on the calculated activation parameters? (Do not neglect the change in the moment of inertia.)

2. Use the alternate sets of frequencies given in the text (p. 350) for the chlorination of methane, and calculate the activation parameters. Do they differ significantly from those given in Table 3–7?

3. Knowing approximately the position of the activated complex, see how large a change in classical activation energy results from a change of s^2 from 0.18 to 0.22 ($s = 0.42$ and 0.47).

3-4 Kinetic Isotope Effects

It is not readily possible to test the absolute rate theory by a comparison of observed and calculated activation parameters, for the potential energy surface cannot be obtained with accuracy in any case, except possibly the reaction of hydrogen with hydrogen atoms.[17] The approximate methods

---

[17] I. Shavitt, *J. Chem. Phys.*, **31**, 1359 (1959).

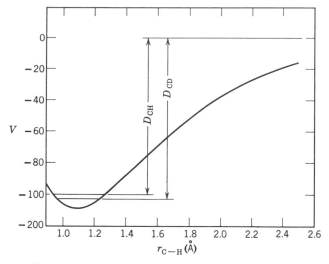

Fig. 3-15. Carbon–hydrogen bond dissociation curve for methane.

for obtaining the potential energy surface always involve an empirically determined parameter, and the agreement between observation and theory is a function of the choice of this parameter.

The kinetic isotope effect is more directly associated with the shape of the potential energy surface, and therefore a comparison of observed and calculated isotope effects provides a more definitive test of the theory. The reaction of chlorine atoms with methane is ideally suited to this purpose, and the use of this reaction permits the utilization of the data discussed in the preceding section.

It is first necessary to consider the origin of the isotope effect[18] and to differentiate between the several types of isotope effects. The C—H bond dissociation curve for methane is approximately as shown in Fig. 3-15. If we consider one of the C—H bonds, there will be a stretching vibration with a frequency near 3000 cm^{-1} and a degenerate bending vibration with a frequency near 1400 cm^{-1}. The total zero-point energy for this bond will then be one-half the sum of the three frequencies, and this may be converted to calories/mole by multiplying by 2.86. Thus the zero-point energy associated with this bond will be 8.3 kcal/mole.

The corresponding bond to deuterium will have a stretching frequency of about 2200 cm^{-1} and a degenerate bending vibration having a frequency of about 1000 cm^{-1}. The difference in frequency arises from the fact that

[18] J. Bigeleisen, *J. Chem. Phys.*, **17**, 675 (1949).

the force constant for the vibration does not change with deuterium substitution, whereas the reduced mass does. Thus Hooke's law

$$\nu = 1303\sqrt{k/\mu}$$

predicts that the frequencies for vibrations involving hydrogen and deuterium will have a ratio of approximately the square root of two. The zero-point energy for the C—D bond will then be about 6.0 kcal/mole. As a result, the observed bond dissociation energy for the C—D bond will be about 2.3 kcal/mole greater than that for the C—H bond.

Suppose we had an extreme case in which the C—H bond had been completely broken in the activated complex and a new bond to hydrogen had not been formed to an appreciable extent (i.e., the frequencies for the symmetrical stretching vibration and the four bending vibrations characteristic of the activated complexes (p. 341) had gone to zero). Then there would be no zero-point energy contribution arising from that hydrogen or deuterium in the activated complex. In this case there would be a difference of 2.3 kcal/mole between the activation energies for reaction at hydrogen and deuterium. Neglecting some smaller factors, the rate ratio for the two reactions at 25° would be approximately

$$\frac{k_H}{k_D} = e^{2300/1.99 \times 298} = 48$$

This case is illustrated in Fig. 3-16.

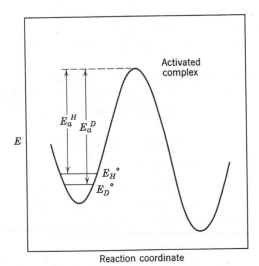

Reaction coordinate

Fig. 3-16. Origin of the kinetic isotope effect.

Of course, no ordinary reaction will have an activated complex of this type. Reactions have reasonable values of activation energy because bond making occurs simultaneously with bond breaking. As a result, the symmetrical stretching vibration and the four bending vibrations have reasonable frequencies which contribute a zero-point energy in the activated complex. This cancels part of the difference found in the reactants and leads to a reduced isotope effect. At 25° kinetic hydrogen isotope effects commonly lie in the range $k_H/k_D = 5$ to 8.[19]

The isotope effect discussed above refers to an intermolecular isotope effect and corresponds to the reactions

$$CH_4 + Cl\cdot \xrightarrow{k_H} CH_3\cdot + HCl$$
$$CH_3D + Cl\cdot \xrightarrow{k_D} CH_3\cdot + DCl$$

However, it is also possible to measure the relative rates of hydrogen and deuterium abstraction from the same molecule:

$$CH_2D_2 \xrightarrow{k_H} CHD_2\cdot + HCl$$
$$CH_2D_2 \xrightarrow{k_D} CH_2D\cdot + DCl$$

This is commonly referred to as the intramolecular isotope effect. Here there is no zero-point energy difference in the reactants, but, rather, the difference comes in the activated complexes. One contains two normal bonds to hydrogen and one to deuterium, and the other has two normal bonds to deuterium and one to hydrogen, leading to the zero-point energy difference between a bond to hydrogen and one to deuterium. This, in turn, will be modified by the residual zero-point energy associated with the hydrogen or deuterium in the bond being broken. This case is illustrated in Fig. 3-17.

The isotope effects described above are termed primary isotope effects, for they arise from the hydrogen or deuterium involved in the reaction. There is also a secondary isotope effect, which is indicated by the reactions:

$$CH_4 + Cl\cdot \xrightarrow{k_1} CH_3\cdot + HCl$$
$$CH_3D + Cl\cdot \xrightarrow{k_2} CH_2D\cdot + HCl$$

The difference between k_1 and k_2 arises from the change in the vibrational frequencies for the nonreacting bonds. This type of isotope effect has also been frequently observed[20] and commonly has a value between 1 to 2.

[19] K. B. Wiberg, *Chem. Revs.*, **55**, 713 (1955).
[20] L. Melander, *Isotope Effects on Reaction Rates*, Ronald Press, New York, 1960, ch. 5.

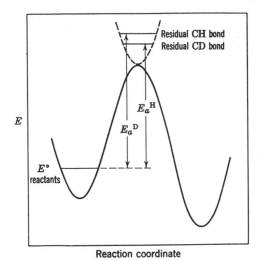

Fig. 3-17. *Origin of the intramolecular isotope effect.*

We shall now calculate the magnitude for each of the three types of isotope effects. Since the available experimental data refer to the intramolecular case, this will be considered first.[21] In the previous section, it was found that the rate constant for a reaction of a C—H bond was given by

$$k_H = \kappa_H \left(\frac{kT}{h}\right) \frac{Q_H^{\ddagger}}{Q_{A(H)}Q_{B(H)}} \cdot \prod_i^{3n\ddagger-7} e^{-\frac{1}{2}u_{i(H)}\ddagger} \cdot \prod_i^{3n-6} e^{\frac{1}{2}u_{i(H)}} \cdot e^{-\Delta E_{class.}/RT}$$

A corresponding equation may be written for the reaction of a C—D bond:

$$k_D = \kappa_D \left(\frac{kT}{h}\right) \frac{Q_D^{\ddagger}}{Q_{A(D)}Q_{B(D)}} \cdot \prod_i^{3n\ddagger-7} e^{-\frac{1}{2}u_{i(D)}\ddagger} \cdot \prod_i^{3n-6} e^{\frac{1}{2}u_{i(D)}} \cdot e^{-\Delta E_{class.}/RT}$$

When considering the intramolecular isotope effect, Q_A and Q_B are the same in both cases, the zero-point energy term for the reactants will be the same, and the transmission coefficient, κ, is usually assumed to be independent of isotopic composition. The potential energy surface should also be independent of isotopic substitution, and therefore $\Delta E_{class.}$ will be the same for k_H and k_D. The isotope effect will be given by

$$\frac{k_H}{k_D} = \frac{Q_H^{\ddagger}}{Q_D^{\ddagger}} \prod_i^{3n\ddagger-7} \frac{e^{-\frac{1}{2}u_{i(H)}}}{e^{-\frac{1}{2}u_{i(D)}}}$$

The ratio of the partition functions may be expressed in terms of the translational, rotational, and vibrational components. The first will give the ratio of total masses to the three-halves power, all other terms canceling.

[21] K. B. Wiberg and E. L. Motell, *Tetrahedron*, in press.

Similarly, the second will give the ratio of the products of the three principal moments of inertia raised to the one-half power, and the third will give the ratio of the products of the terms $(1 - e^{-u/kT})$ for each of the $3n - 7$ vibrations of the activated complex.

$$\frac{Q_H^\ddagger}{Q_D^\ddagger} = \frac{(Q_{tr}^\ddagger Q_r^\ddagger Q_v^\ddagger)_H}{(Q_{tr}^\ddagger Q_r^\ddagger Q_v)_D} = \left(\frac{M_H^\ddagger}{M_D^\ddagger}\right)^{3/2} \cdot \frac{(I_A^\ddagger I_B^\ddagger I_C^\ddagger)_H^{1/2}}{(I_A^\ddagger I_B^\ddagger I_C^\ddagger)_D^{1/2}} \cdot \prod_i^{3n\ddagger-7} \frac{1 - e^{-u_{i(D)}}}{1 - e^{-u_{i(H)}}}$$

Here M is the mass of the activated complex, and I_A, I_B, and I_C are the moments of inertia. However, the masses of the two activated complexes will be the same and will cancel. The isotope effect may then be written

$$\frac{k_H}{k_D} = \frac{(I_A^\ddagger I_B^\ddagger I_C^\ddagger)_H^{1/2}}{(I_A^\ddagger I_B^\ddagger I_C^\ddagger)_D^{1/2}} \cdot \prod_i^{3n\ddagger-7} \cdot \frac{e^{-\frac{1}{2}u_i(H)}}{e^{-\frac{1}{2}u_i(D)}} \times \frac{1 - e^{-u_i(D)}}{1 - e^{-u_i(H)}}$$

The major part of the temperature independent factor is simply the ratio of the products of the moments of inertia for the two activated complexes, A and B. By using the dimensions obtained for the methane-chlorine

$$\begin{array}{cc} D_2HC--H--Cl & H_2DC---D--Cl \\ A & B \end{array}$$

atom activated complex (Table 3-4), the ratio of the square root of the products of the moments of inertia was calculated to be 1.18.

The procedure for calculating vibrational frequencies for the activated complexes which was given in the previous section may be applied here. The results, using the full 12-atom model, are given in Table 3-8. Substitution of these values into the equation for the isotope effect gives the calculated values shown in Table 3-9. The observed isotope effect was given by

$$\frac{k_H}{k_D} = 1.09e^{1300/RT}$$

whereas the calculated isotope effect is given by

$$\frac{k_H}{k_D} = 1.15e^{1080/RT}$$

Although there is, of course, an experimental error associated with the observed isotope effect, it can be seen that the calculated value is about 200 cal/mole too low. Nothing more may be gained from the stretching frequencies at the reaction site, since the frequencies for the symmetrical mode are the same in the two activated complexes. The bending force constant, k_θ, may have been assigned too high a value. However, decreasing it to 0.18×10^{-11} ergs/rad^2 would give essentially no change in the exponential factor because the frequency shifts are almost identical for the two activated complexes. A decrease in k_ϕ would improve the agreement between the calculated and observed exponential factors.

Table 3-8   **Vibrational Frequencies for the Activated Complexes Formed in the Chlorination of Methane-d_2[a]**

Class	Type	CH$_2$D‑ ‑D‑ ‑Cl[b]	CD$_2$H‑ ‑H‑ ‑Cl[b]
A_1	Methyl CH stretching	2987	3031
A_1	Methyl CD stretching	2222	2158
A_1	H—C—H bending	1419	
A_1	H—C—D bending	1039	1120
A_1	D—C—D bending		1012
A_1	Bending Mode I	764	917
A_1	Bending Mode II	296	340
A_1	Symmetrical stretching	422	419
A_1	Asymmetrical stretching	1028i	1433i
A_2	Methyl C—H stretching	3069	
A_2	Methyl C—D stretching		2291
A_2	Bending Mode I	834	975
A_2	Bending Mode II	340	302
A_2	H—C—D bending	1229	1295

[a] The H—C—H angle, in which the second hydrogen is the one involved in the activated complex, was taken as 107°.
[b] Based on Cl^{35}.

Another factor must, however, be considered. The proton is a small particle and must be treated quantum mechanically rather than classically. Thus we must consider the possibility of the proton tunneling through the potential energy barrier. This would be more important for protons than for deuterons because of the lower mass of the proton. As a result, the observed exponential factor would be larger than the value calculated based on the potential energy surface. At the same time there would be a decrease in the temperature independent factor from that calculated above.

If one uses the tunneling correction given by Johnston,[16] and the imaginary frequencies for the asymmetrical stretching mode of the

Table 3-9   **Intramolecular Isotope Effect in the Chlorination of Methane**

Temp. (°C)	k_H/k_D (obs.)	k_H/k_D (calc.)	Ratio
−23	14.4	10.4	1.4
0	12.1	8.6	1.4
25	(9.9)	7.2	1.4
52	8.2	6.2	1.3
71	7.1	5.6	1.3

activated complex which were calculated above, one finds that the calculated isotope effect is overcorrected by a large amount, and the pre-exponential factor becomes much too low. It is clear that the frequencies obtained above are too large, and this appears to be a characteristic of Sato's method of constructing the potential energy surface; the calculated curvature along the reaction coordinate is too large.[22] It may be concluded that tunneling is of relatively minor importance in this reaction. However, this is not always the case.[23]

For the intermolecular isotope effect, we wish to determine the relative rates of hydrogen abstraction from methane and deuterium abstraction from methane-d_1. Thus we must be concerned with the activated complexes C and D. The rates of hydrogen and deuterium abstraction are again

$$\text{H}_3\text{C}--\text{H}--\text{Cl} \qquad\qquad \text{H}_3\text{C}--\text{D}--\text{Cl}$$
$$\text{C} \qquad\qquad\qquad\qquad \text{D}$$

given by the expressions obtained previously (p. 355), and the ratio of the rates will be

$$\frac{k_\text{H}}{k_\text{D}} = \frac{Q_\text{H}^{\ddagger}}{Q_\text{D}^{\ddagger}} \frac{Q_{\text{A(D)}}}{Q_{\text{A(H)}}} \prod_i^{3n\ddagger-7} \frac{e^{-\frac{1}{2}u_i(\text{H})\ddagger}}{e^{-\frac{1}{2}u_i(\text{D})\ddagger}} \prod_i^{3n-6} \frac{e^{-\frac{1}{2}u_i(\text{D})}}{e^{-\frac{1}{2}u_i(\text{H})}}$$

Here we must introduce the appropriate expressions for the partition functions for the two activated complexes and also for the two reactants (CH_4 and CH_3D). The rate ratio would then be given by

$$\frac{k_\text{H}}{k_\text{D}} = \left(\frac{M_\text{H}^{\ddagger}}{M_\text{D}^{\ddagger}}\right)^{3/2} \left(\frac{M_\text{D}}{M_\text{H}}\right)^{3/2} \times \frac{(I_\text{A}^{\ddagger} I_\text{B}^{\ddagger} I_\text{C}^{\ddagger})_\text{H}^{1/2}}{(I_\text{A}^{\ddagger} I_\text{B}^{\ddagger} I_\text{C}^{\ddagger})_\text{D}^{1/2}} \times \frac{(I_\text{A} I_\text{B} I_\text{C})_\text{D}^{1/2}}{(I_\text{A} I_\text{B} I_\text{C})_\text{H}^{1/2}}$$
$$\times \prod_i^{3n\ddagger-7} \frac{e^{-\frac{1}{2}u_i(\text{H})\ddagger}}{e^{-\frac{1}{2}u_i(\text{D})\ddagger}} \times \frac{1 - e^{-u_i(\text{D})\ddagger}}{1 - e^{-u_i(\text{H})\ddagger}} \times \prod_i^{3n-6} \frac{e^{-\frac{1}{2}u_i(\text{D})}}{e^{-\frac{1}{2}u_i(\text{H})}} \times \frac{1 - e^{-u_i(\text{H})}}{1 - e^{-u_i(\text{D})}}$$

Using the Teller-Redlich product rule, which relates the products of the frequencies in a molecule to those in an isotopically substituted molecule, we find for the ground state:[24]

$$\left(\frac{M_\text{H}}{M_\text{D}}\right)^{3/2} \cdot \frac{(I_\text{A} I_\text{B} I_\text{C})_\text{H}^{1/2}}{(I_\text{A} I_\text{B} I_\text{C})_\text{D}^{1/2}} = \prod_j^{n} \left(\frac{m_{j(\text{H})}}{m_{j(\text{D})}}\right)^{3/2} \prod_i^{3n-6} \frac{\nu_{i(\text{H})}}{\nu_{i(\text{D})}}$$

and for the activated complex

$$\left(\frac{M_\text{H}^{\ddagger}}{M_\text{D}^{\ddagger}}\right)^{3/2} \cdot \frac{(I_\text{A}^{\ddagger} I_\text{B}^{\ddagger} I_\text{C}^{\ddagger})_\text{H}^{1/2}}{(I_\text{A}^{\ddagger} I_\text{B}^{\ddagger} I_\text{C}^{\ddagger})_\text{D}^{1/2}} = \frac{\nu_{\text{L}(\text{H})}^{\ddagger}}{\nu_{\text{L}(\text{D})}^{\ddagger}} \cdot \prod_j^{n\ddagger} \left(\frac{m_{j(\text{H})}^{\ddagger}}{m_{j(\text{D})}^{\ddagger}}\right)^{3/2} \prod_i^{3n\ddagger-7} \frac{\nu_{i(\text{H})}^{\ddagger}}{\nu_{i(\text{D})}^{\ddagger}}$$

[22] J. Bigeleisen and M. Wolfsberg, *J. Chem. Phys.*, **23**, 1535 (1955).
[23] R. P. Bell, J. A. Fendley, and J. R. Hulett, *Proc. Roy. Soc. (London)*, **235A**, 453 (1956); V. J. Shiner, Jr. and M. L. Smith, *J. Am. Chem. Soc.*, **83**, 593 (1961).
[24] The derivation of this expression for a simple case is given by K. S. Pitzer, *Quantum Chemistry* Prentice-Hall, New York, 1953, p. 275.

where the m's are the masses of the atoms in each species, and the ν's are the vibrational frequencies. For the activated complex, we again take out from the product the vibration which corresponds to motion along the reaction coordinate (ν_L). Making these substitutions,

$$\frac{k_H}{k_D} = \frac{\nu_{L(H)}^{\ddagger}}{\nu_{L(D)}^{\ddagger}} \prod_j^{n\ddagger} \left(\frac{m_{j(H)}^{\ddagger}}{m_{j(D)}^{\ddagger}}\right)^{3/2} \prod_i^{3n\ddagger-7} \frac{u_{i(H)}^{\ddagger}}{u_{i(D)}^{\ddagger}} \times \frac{e^{-\frac{1}{2}u_i(H)\ddagger}}{e^{-\frac{1}{2}u_i(D)\ddagger}} \times \frac{1 - e^{-u_i(D)\ddagger}}{1 - e^{-u_i(H)\ddagger}}$$

$$\times \prod_j^{n} \left(\frac{m_{j(D)}}{m_{j(H)}}\right)^{3/2} \prod_i^{3n-6} \frac{u_{i(D)}}{u_{i(H)}} \times \frac{e^{-\frac{1}{2}u_i(D)}}{e^{-\frac{1}{2}u_i(H)}} \times \frac{1 - e^{-u_i(H)}}{1 - e^{-u_i(D)}}$$

Table 3-10 **Vibrational Frequencies of the Activated Complex in the Chlorination of Methane and Methane-d**

	Mode	H_3C--H--Cl	H_3C--D--Cl
A_1	Methyl C—H stretching	2934	2934
A_1	Methyl C—H bending	1102	1103
A_1	Symmetrical stretching‡	432	430
A_1	Asymmetric stretching‡	1433i	1028i
E	Methyl C—H stretching	3070	3070
E	Methyl C—H bending	1444	1444
E	Bending mode I‡	1034	838
E	Bending mode II‡	388	343

The atomic masses will cancel, for the sum of the atoms in the activated complex for k_H and the reactants for k_D will equal the sums of the atoms of the activated complex for k_D and the reactants for k_H. This leaves

$$\frac{k_H}{k_D} = \frac{\nu_{L(H)}^{\ddagger}}{\nu_{L(D)}^{\ddagger}} \prod_i^{3n\ddagger-7} \frac{u_{i(H)}^{\ddagger}}{u_{i(D)}^{\ddagger}} \times \frac{e^{-\frac{1}{2}u_i(H)\ddagger}}{e^{-\frac{1}{2}u_i(D)\ddagger}} \times \frac{1 - e^{-u_i(D)}}{1 - e^{-u_i(H)}}$$

$$\times \prod_i^{3n-6} \frac{u_{i(D)}}{u_{i(H)}} \times \frac{e^{-\frac{1}{2}u_i(D)}}{e^{-\frac{1}{2}u_i(H)}} \times \frac{1 - e^{u_i(H)}}{1 - e^{u_i(D)}}$$

The temperature independent factor is now primarily the ratio of the imaginary frequencies for the product forming mode in the activated complex.

The vibrational frequencies calculated for the two activated complexes are given in Table 3-10. Again we shall use the calculated frequencies for methane and methane-d_1 in order to minimize the error introduced by neglecting interaction constants. At 25° the isotope effect is calculated to be $k_H/k_D = 7.70$. This is only slightly higher than the calculated intramolecular isotope effect.

Finally, we may estimate the magnitude of the secondary isotope effect for the reactions

$$CH_4 + Cl\cdot \xrightarrow{k_1} CH_3\cdot + HCl$$
$$CH_3D + Cl\cdot \xrightarrow{k_2} CH_2D\cdot + HCl$$

The vibrational frequencies for methane and the activated complex formed from it were given in Table 3-5. The frequencies for methane-d_1 and the activated complex formed from it are 3067(2), 2952, 2222, 1437(2), 1313 and 1165(2) cm^{-1} for the former and 3070, 2987, 2222, 1420, 1232, 1061, 1028, 959, 431, 384 and 318 cm^{-1} for the latter. The zero-point energy change in the reaction of methane is 1360 cm^{-1}, whereas that for methane-d_1 is 1357 cm^{-1}. The difference between these values, 3 cm^{-1}, is negligible and would result in an isotope effect of about 1%. This is generally the case when the force constants for the nonreacting bonds are assumed to be unchanged during the reaction.

A larger secondary isotope effect would be expected if the carbon involved in the reaction were to acquire a positive change and/or change its hybridization. This would result in a significant change in force constants for the nonreacting bonds and a change in the corresponding vibrational frequencies.[25]

At this point it seems appropriate to consider the general question of the magnitude of kinetic isotope effects. The largest problem rests with the correction for quantum mechanical tunneling by the proton. There are temperature dependence data on so few reactions that it is not possible to say in which cases tunneling is important or whether it is a common phenomenon.[26]

For most purposes, however, this is not as big a problem as it might seem. The effect of tunneling is to raise the apparent activation energy difference between the reaction at hydrogen and at deuterium and to decrease the pre-exponential factor, usually to a value less than unity. To the first approximation, at room temperature, the two effects cancel.[23] Thus the observed isotope effect still gives a good approximation to the zero-point energy change, in the absence of tunneling.

It can be seen from the preceding treatment that the symmetrical stretching frequency for the activated complex has the major effect on the

[25] A. Streitwieser, Jr., R. H. Jagow, R. C. Fahey, and S. Suzaki, *J. Am. Chem. Soc.*, **80**, 2326 (1958).
[26] Besides examining the ratio of activation parameters for the hydrogen and the deuterium abstraction (for which tunneling leads to a low ratio of pre-exponential factors—usually less than unity—and a high activation energy difference), one could also look at the isotope effect for abstraction of a tritium as compared to deuterium. The tunneling correction will be much smaller for this pair than for hydrogen-deuterium because of the greater masses.

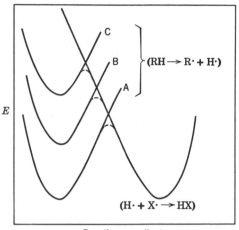

E

C

B $\left.\begin{array}{c}\\\\\\\end{array}\right\}$ (RH $\rightarrow$ R· + H·)

A

(H· + X· $\rightarrow$ HX)

Reaction coordinate

Fig. 3-18. Change in the potential energy-reaction coordinate curves with structure in the bromination of hydrocarbons. The compounds are A, toluene, B, ethylbenzene, and C, cumene.

magnitude of the isotope effect. The sum of the four bending frequencies in the activated complex is about equal to the sum of the two bending frequencies in the reactant, leading to only a small contribution to the isotope effect. If the symmetrical stretching frequency is the same for activated complexes involving H as for those involving D (as when $k_1 \sim k_2$), one finds a maximum isotope effect. If, on the other hand, $k_1 > k_2$, or $k_2 > k_1$, the two frequencies will be different, leading to a difference in zero-point energy in the activated complex and a reduced isotope effect.

If one looks at the available data,[19,21] it can be seen that the hydrogen atom, hydride ion, and proton abstraction reactions give a range of values of k_H/k_D with the maximum being on the order of 8. In any series of related reactions, the activated complex which is most "symmetrical" (i.e., has $k_1 \sim k_2$) leads to the largest iostope effect and the effect decreases with decreasing symmetry. As an example, one may consider the bromination of toluene, ethylbenzene, and cumene with N-bromosuccinimide,[27] which at 77° gives k_H/k_D = 4.9, 2.7, and 1.8, respectively. The activated complex for the reaction with toluene would be expected to be reasonably "symmetrical," whereas with the other compounds k_1 becomes larger than k_2, leading to a decreased isotope effect. This is illustrated in Fig. 3-18, which gives the C—H bond dissociation curves for the three hydrocarbons and the reverse of the dissociation curve for hydrogen bromide. The

[27] K. B. Wiberg and L. H. Slaugh, *J. Am. Chem. Soc.*, **80**, 3033 (1958).

intersections of the two curves are set at energies corresponding to the observed activation energies, and the dotted lines are drawn to represent the effect of electron delocalization on the energy of the activated complex.

The case in which one would expect a relatively small value as the

Table 3-11   Isotope Effects for Reactions Having Nonlinear Activated Complexes

Reaction	k_H/k_D
$\phi_2C-CH\phi + H^+ \rightarrow \phi_2CHC\phi$ (with OH, OH; product C=O)	3.3[a]
$(CH_3)_2C-CHCH_3 + H^+ \rightarrow (CH_3)_2CHCCH_3$ (with HO, OH; product C=O)	1.8[b]
$(CH_3)_2CH-CH-CH_3 \xrightarrow{HOAc} (CH_3)_2CCH_2CH_3$ (with OTs; product OAc)	2.3[c]

[a] C. J. Collins, W. T. Rainey, W. B. Smith, and I. A. Kaye, *J. Am. Chem. Soc.*, **81**, 460 (1959).

[b] W. B. Smith, R. E. Bowman and T. J. Kmet, *J. Am. Chem. Soc.*, **81**, 997 (1959).

[c] S. Winstein and J. Takahashi, *Tetrahedron*, **2**, 316 (1956).

maximum isotope effect is that of a nonlinear activated complex, such as that for hydrogen migration in a pinacol rearrangement. For such an

activated complex, it is difficult to represent the normal modes of vibration pictorially, for they depend on the three bond distances and force constants. Further, it is probable that the translation of the hydrogen does not correspond to any one normal vibrational mode. However, a semi-quantitative argument may be made by considering the motion to be largely carbon-hydrogen bending[28] and then basing the expected maximum value on the loss of one bending mode in going to the activated complex. This leads to $k_H/k_D \cong 3.6$, which is in good agreement with the available data (Table 3-11).

[28] M. F. Hawthorne and E. S. Lewis, *J. Am. Chem. Soc.*, **80**, 4296 (1958).

Kinetic Isotope Effects   363

It should be evident from this discussion that the kinetic isotope effect is a useful tool in determining whether or not a bond to hydrogen is broken in the slow step of a reaction. If a bond to hydrogen is broken in this step, and if k_1 is not very much larger than k_2 (or vice versa), a kinetic isotope effect should be observed. If the bond is broken prior to the rate controlling step, it would presumably occur in an equilibrium step, and this would usually result in hydrogen-deuterium exchange for the labeled compound. If it occurred after the rate controlling step, it would have no kinetic consequences. This fact has proven to be a useful tool in examining a wide variety of reactions.[19,20]

References

General:
L. Melander, *Isotope Effects on Reaction Rates*, Ronald Press, New York, 1960.
J. Bigeleisen and M. Wolfsberg in *Advances in Chemical Physics*, I. Prigogine (ed.), Interscience Publishers, New York, 1958, vol. I, p. 15.
K. B. Wiberg, *Chem. Revs.*, **55**, 713 (1955).
F. H. Westheimer, *Chem. Revs.*, **61**, 265 (1961).
Tunneling Through Potential Energy Barriers:
R. P. Bell, *Trans. Faraday Soc.*, **55**, 1 (1959).
H. S. Johnston, in *Advances in Chemical Physics*, Interscience Publishers, New York, 1961, vol. III, p. 131.
Secondary Isotope Effects:
A Streitwieser, Jr., R. H. Jagow, R. C. Fahey, and S. Suzuki, *J. Am. Chem. Soc.*, **80**, 2326 (1958).

Problems

1. For the reactions
$$CH_4 + Cl\cdot \longrightarrow CH_3\cdot + HCl$$
$$CH_3D + Cl\cdot \longrightarrow CH_3\cdot + DCl$$
approximately how large a secondary isotope effect would be expected if in the activated complex
(a) the CH_3 stretching force constants decreased in value by 10%?
(b) the CH_3 bending force constants decreased in value by 10%?
2. Knowing the value of k_H/k_D for the chlorination of methane at 0°C, and assuming that there is no contribution from quantum mechanical tunneling through the potential energy barrier, what will be the value of k_D/k_T for this reaction?
3. How would substituents in the aromatic ring effect the magnitude of the isotope effect in
(a) the bromination of toluene?
(b) the acid-catalyzed bromination of acetophenone?
(c) the base-catalyzed bromination of acetophenone?

4. The neutralization of an anion such as that derived from acetone has a large kinetic isotope effect, whereas the neutralization of a carbanion donor such as the Grignard reagent gives a small isotope effect. Explain.

3-5 Calculation of Reaction Rates Using Steric Parameters

If we wished to calculate the rate constant for a reaction occurring in solution, we would first have to develop a method for approximating the potential energy surface, including solvent effects. For a reaction of

Table 3-12   Rates of Racemization of Sterically Hindered Biphenyls

W	X	Y	Z	$T(°C)$	$k_1(sec^{-1}) \times 10^4$	Other Groups
NO_2	Br	CO_2H	H	118	0.036	5′ CH_3
NO_2	CH_3	CO_2H	H	118	0.64	
NO_2	Cl	CO_2H	H	118	0.75	5′ CH_3
NO_2	NO_2	CO_2H	H	118	0.92	
NO_2	CO_2H	CO_2H	H	118	1.26	
NO_2	OCH_3	CO_2H	H	25	12.2	
NO_2	F	CO_2H	H	25	too fast to measure	5′ CH_3
NO_2	OCH_3	CO_2H	H	25	10.6	5′ OCH_3
NO_2	OCH_3	CO_2H	H	25	10.0	5′ CH_3
NO_2	OCH_3	CO_2H	H	25	3.7	5′ Cl
NO_2	OCH_3	CO_2H	H	25	3.6	5′ Br
NO_2	OCH_3	CO_2H	H	25	3.2	5′ NO_2

moderate complexity, it is essentially impractical to calculate a detailed potential energy surface, and it is even more difficult to include the effect of the solvent on the reactants and the activated complex.

There are, however, some cases of interest in which electronic effects are relatively unimportant or are constant throughout a series, and where the main rate controlling factor is steric. Two reactions of this type are the racemization of ortho-substituted optically active biphenyls, and the

S_N2 displacement reaction on primary halides. Quantitative calculations have been made for each of these cases, and the method of calculation and the results will be presented here.

It has been known for many years that biphenyls having bulky groups in the *o*- and *o'*-positions may be resolved, and that they are racemized in solution with a rate inversely proportional to the size of the *o*-substituent. As examples, the rates of racemization of several compounds of this type are given in Table 3-12.[29] Since no bonds are made or broken in the reaction, this is a good case in which to consider only the steric effects. The following discussion is based on the formulation given by Westheimer and Mayer.[30]

If one examines a scale model of 2,2'-dibromo-4,4'-dicarboxydiphenyl, it is seen that the two bromines cannot pass each other and that racemization must occur by having the bromines pass by the *o*-hydrogens. In the planar conformation which should correspond to the activated complex we must be concerned with the repulsion of the two hydrogen-bromine pairs at the distance *d* and with the energy terms due to the stretching and

bending of the C-H and C-Br bonds and of the biphenyl framework. If no bond distortion occurred, the activation energy would be extremely large because the van der Waals repulsion is large at short distances. The distortion of the molecule occurs in order to decrease the hydrogen-bromine repulsion. At the same time work must be done in order to effect the distortion.

The problem is best considered in terms of the internal coordinates of motion, $q_1, q_2, q_3, \ldots, q_n$. These represent displacements from the normal bond distances and angles for each of the possible modes of motion of the bonds. For example, q_1 might refer to the stretching of the C-Br bond, and q_2 might refer to the bending of the C-Br bond in the plane of the ring. With each of these internal coordinates is associated a force constant, and appropriate values for these constants (obtained from an analysis of vibrational spectra and some reasonable assumptions about bond stiffening due to resonance effects) are given in Table 3-13.

[29] R. Adams and H. C. Yuan, *Chem. Revs.*, **12**, 261 (1933).
[30] F. H. Westheimer and J. E. Mayer, *J. Chem. Phys.*, **14**, 733 (1946); T. L. Hill, *ibid.*, **14**, 465 (1946); F. H. Westheimer, *ibid.*, **15**, 252 (1947); M. Rieger and F. H. Westheimer, *J. Am. Chem. Soc.*, **72**, 19 (1950).

The total change in energy due to the displacements of atoms is then given by

$$E = \sum_i \tfrac{1}{2} k_i q_i^2$$

To this must be added the van der Waals potential for the bromine-hydrogen interactions, giving as the total energy due to steric effects

$$E = \sum_i \tfrac{1}{2} k_i q_i^2 + 2V(d)$$

Table 3-13   **Internal Coordinates and Force Constants for the Activated Complex in the Racemization of Optically Active Biphenyls**[a]

Internal Coordinate		Force Constant
q_1	Stretching C-Br bond	$5.0 \times 10^{+5}$ dynes/cm
q_2	Bending C-C-Br bond	1.07×10^{-11} ergs/rad²
q_3	Stretching C-H bond	$5.0 \times 10^{+5}$ dynes/cm
q_4	Bending C-C-H bond	0.86×10^{-11} ergs/rad²
q_5	Stretching interannular bond	$5.5 \times 10^{+5}$ dynes/cm
q_6	Bending interannular bond	1.13×10^{-11} ergs/rad²

[a] Besides these internal coordinates, there is a set associated with the aromatic rings. For these, see the original paper, ref. 30.

Although, as we have seen previously, the van der Waals potential may be attractive, at the short distances involved here one finds a repulsive interaction. The repulsive interaction may be approximated by an exponential function

$$V(d) = Ae^{-d/\rho}$$

It is difficult to know what values of A and ρ should be used, for there is no direct way in which one may measure the interaction between a pair of covalently bonded bromines and hydrogens.

The potential function at short distances may be determined with reasonable accuracy for rare gases by allowing a beam of atoms having a high velocity penetrate another sample of the same gas. The scattering of the beam may be correlated with the van der Waals function; the greater the interaction, the larger will be the scattering. The potential function for two neon atoms determined by the above procedure is[31]

$$V(d) = 5.00 \times 10^{-10}/d^{9.99} \text{ ergs/molecule} \quad 1.96 \text{ Å} < d < 2.2 \text{ Å}$$

[31] I. Amdur, C. F. Glick, and H. Pearlman, *Proc. Am. Acad. Arts Sci.*, **76**, 101 (1948); I. Amdur and A. L. Harkness, *J. Chem. Phys.*, **22**, 664 (1954); I. Amdur and E. A. Mason, *ibid.*, **22**, 670 (1954).

The potential function at larger distances may be evaluated from the compressibility of rare gases at high pressure.[32] By using the two known parts of the curve, and fitting it by using the exponential relationship, one may obtain an expression for the van der Waals repulsion. The constants used by Westheimer were $A = 2.45 \times 10^7$ and $\rho = 0.165 \times 10^{-8}$.

The sum of the covalent radii for two neon atoms (3.15 Å) is the same as that for a bromine atom (1.95 Å) and a hydrogen atom (1.2 Å), suggesting that this might be a suitable function for the hydrogen-bromine interaction.

Finally, we must have a relationship between the distance d and the internal coordinates. For small displacements the value is given by

$$d = d_0 + \sum_i b_i q_i$$

where d_0 is the value of d in the planar, undistorted molecule, and the b's are constants which may be evaluated from the geometry of the molecule. For example, b for the stretching of the bond between the two rings is 0.91, because when the distance between the rings is increased by 0.01 Å, the distance between the hydrogen and bromine is increased by 0.0091 Å. Combining the above equations, we obtain[33]

$$E = \sum_i \tfrac{1}{2} k_i q_i^2 + 2A e^{-d_0/\rho} e^{-\sum_i b_i q_i/\rho}$$

The reaction will occur via a molecular configuration which leads to the smallest value of E. Thus we wish to minimize E, and this requires that we solve the set of equations which result when we set the partial derivative of E with respect to each of the internal coordinates equal to zero. Thus for q_j,

$$\frac{\partial E}{\partial q_j} = 0 = k_j q_j - \frac{2b_j}{\rho} A e^{-d_0/\rho} e^{-\sum_i b_i q_i/\rho}$$

This set of equations must now be solved for the values of the q's, and, having these, the energy E may be evaluated.

In order to obtain a solution, the set of simultaneous equations should be reduced to a linear form (i.e., not involving exponential functions). In the present case this may be done if one remembers that the term

$$e^{-\sum_i b_i q_i/\rho}$$

is a constant, for the activated complex must have a fixed geometry. Thus there is a unique set of q's which characterize the activated complex. Let us define a new constant, Z, so that

$$A e^{-d_0/\rho} e^{-\sum_i b_i q_i/\rho} = Z$$

[32] O. K. Rice, *J. Am. Chem. Soc.*, **63**, 3 (1941).
[33] An explicit example of the evaluation of one of the b's is given by F. H. Westheimer in *Steric Effects in Organic Chemistry*, M. Newman (Ed.), John Wiley and Sons, New York, 1956, pp. 545-546. The values of b_i are given in ref. 30.

The quantity Z is simply the van der Waals repulsion due to one hydrogen-bromine pair at the distance found in the activated complex. The equations then take the simpler linear form

$$k_j q_j - \frac{2b_j}{\rho} Z = 0$$

Here only the q's and Z are unknown. From the set of equations (one for each q_j) one may obtain values for $q_1, q_2, q_3, \ldots, q_j$ in terms of Z. These values are substituted back into the equation which defined Z and in which Z remains as the only unknown. Having a numerical value of Z, one can obtain the values of the q_i's, and from these one obtains the energy E. The results derived using the constants given in Table 3-13 are

Table 3-14   Displacements and Energies in the Activated Complex

Internal Coordinate		Displacement	Energy (kcal/mole)
q_1	Stretching C-Br bond	+0.004 Å	0.00
q_2	Bending C-C-Br bond	+12.3°	7.22
q_3	Stretching C-H bond	−0.020 Å	0.30
q_4	Bending C-C-H bond	+5.0°	0.96
q_5	Stretching interannular bond	+0.040 Å	0.65
q_6	Bending interannular bond	−3.9°	0.78
	All benzene ring deformations		2.46
	Total energy for bending and stretching		12.37
	van der Waals repulsion		5.8
	Calculated activation energy		18.2

summarized in Table 3-14. The activation energy thus calculated is 18.2 kcal/mole. The value of d was found to be 2.31 Å as compared to $d_0 = 1.61$ Å.

Before proceeding, it must be emphasized that the calculation is a relatively crude one, for it neglects such factors as the resonance stabilization of the biphenyl system in the planar activated complex, the change in force constants for large displacements and dipole-dipole interactions, and it uses only an approximate van der Waals potential function which may be considerably in error. The error caused by the latter could easily be on the order of 3 to 5 kcal/mole. However, the result is in good agreement with the observed enthalpy of activation, 17.3 kcal/mole, indicating that the method of calculation is fundamentally sound. For comparison, the activation energy for a model in which no bending or stretching was permitted is about 200 kcal/mole, and for one in which bending and stretching were permitted, but no penetration of the van der Waals radii was permitted, it is about 70 kcal/mole.

It is interesting to note that the major effect in going to the activated complex is the bending of the C-Br bond. It would be expected that the bending deformations would be more important than stretching, for the force constants for bending are smaller than those for stretching. Of the total energy change, about two-thirds arise from deformation of bonds, and only one-third arises from the van der Waals interaction.

The importance of bond bending in cases such as this may be experimentally demonstrated by comparing the rates of racemization of 2,2'-diiodo-5,5'-dicarboxydiphenyl (I) and 2,2',3,3'-tetraiodo-5,5'-dicarboxy-diphenyl (II).[30] The relative rates for the racemization of I and II are

30,000:1, and the activation enthalpies are 21 and 27 kcal/mole. Thus the introduction of iodines *ortho-* to the iodines in I leads to a marked decrease in rate of reaction and an increase in the enthalpy of activation. This can only arise from a "buttressing" effect of the second iodine, which raises the energy for pushing the first out of the way. This "buttressing" effect will operate on the bending motion of the C-I bond, and the result is therefore a striking confirmation of the results of the above calculation.

The energy calculated above corresponds to the "classical" activation energy, and this must be corrected for the change in the energy level distribution between ground state molecules and the activated complex. Translational and rotational contributions to the partition functions may be neglected, for the mass remains constant and the products of the moments of inertia will remain roughly constant. Thus one may concentrate on the vibrational terms. A relatively large number of vibrational modes are affected by the passage to the activated complex. The carbon-bromine stretching and bending vibrations, the carbon-hydrogen stretching and bending vibrations, the stretching and bending of the bond between the two rings, and the vibration corresponding to the hindered rotation of one aromatic ring with respect to the other are the principal contributors. The force constant for each of these will change, and some will probably become markedly anharmonic. Although it would be extremely difficult to do a complete calculation, it is clear that the vibrational frequencies will increase in going to the activated complex, and this will result in a decrease in entropy. The entropy of activation was found to be about $\Delta S^{\ddagger} = -8$ eu.[30]

The racemization of the biphenyls is an ideal reaction to study using steric parameters, for the activated complex is relatively well defined, and no bonds are being made or broken. The S_N2 displacement reaction is quite a different case, but an effort has been made by Ingold and his group[34] to calculate the difference in steric effects of various alkyl groups. This requires the assumption that a change in alkyl group will not affect the electronic contribution to the activation energy.

It would be difficult to consider all the interactions between atoms in the reactants and in the activated complexes, and thus they were led to use a "plastic" model in which every form of deformation was allowed for the atoms undergoing reaction but in which the remaining alkyl groups were allowed only conformational rotation and neither bond stretching nor bond bending. The latter may, of course, be rather important, but it is interesting to see what results may be obtained without resorting to a full treatment.

In order to simplify the problem further, the calculations were performed for the symmetrical exchange reactions, such as

$$CH_3Br + \overset{*}{Br^-} \rightarrow CH_3\overset{*}{Br} + Br^-$$

This leads to a symmetrical activated complex with regard to the entering and leaving groups. The model for the activated complex is shown in Fig. 3-19. The three atoms attached to the reacting carbon are assumed to lie in the xy plane, with one of the groups aligned along the x direction. The entering and leaving atoms are designed as X_1 and X_2. They will lie at equal distances on the two sides of the xy plane. The groups attached to C_α may move the halogen out of the xz plane. If this is the case, a new x_0z_0 plane will be drawn which will contain the halogen, and the angle between the xz and x_0z_0 planes will be designated as ϕ.

The angle ϕ must first be evaluated, and this may be done by considering the van der Waals interaction between the halogen and the three groups attached to C_α. By using the potential function mentioned below, the angles were found to be $11°$ for an ethyl or n-propyl group and $21°$ for a neopentyl group, where the $C_\alpha C_\beta$ bond is the reference for the x direction. The angle for the other groups is zero because of the symmetrical location of the carbons in the β position.

Having established, in general, the geometry of the activated complex, we may consider the energy. This will be a sum of at least eight terms.

[34] P. B. D. de la Mare, L. Fowden, E. D. Hughes, C. K. Ingold, and J. D. H. Mackie, *J. Chem. Soc.*, 3200 (1955); I. Dostrovsky, E. D. Hughes, and C. K. Ingold, *J. Chem. Soc.*, 173 (1946); C. K. Ingold, *Quart. Revs.*, **11**, 1, 1957.

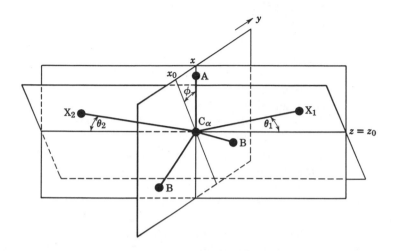

Fig. 3-19. *Arrangement of the groups in the activated complex for the* S_N2 *displacement reaction. The halogen atoms,* X *and* X_2*, are in the* x_0z_0 *plane. The angle* ϕ *is the angle by which the halogens are out of the original plane containing* A *and* C_α*.*

1. The energy required to bend the C-Br bond of the initial molecule from the z direction through an angle θ, which is assumed to be small. This bending relieves part of the van der Waals interaction between the halogen and the β-carbon atoms.

2. The energy required to bend the other bonds to C_α into the xy plane. This corresponds to going from the tetrahedral arrangement in the reactant to the trigonal arrangement (as far as the nonreacting bonds are concerned) in the activated complex.

3. The energy required to remove part of the solvating solvent from the entering halogen. It was symmetrically solvated as the free ion and can only be partially solvated in the activated complex.

4. The energy required to force the entering halide ion against the α-carbon at the angle θ and the separation r, characteristic of the activated complex.

5. The energy required to stretch the original carbon-halogen bond to the length r.

6. The energy involved in dividing the ionic charge between the two halogen atoms.

7. The energy involved in releasing any nonbonding pressures in the initial state. If, for example, the alkyl groups are crowded in the reactant, some of this may be relieved in going to the activated complex because of the larger bond angles between the groups.

8. The energy required to do the necessary work against the van der Waals repulsion exerted on the halogen atom by all the other atoms in the system except the α-carbon.

Of these energy terms, 6 and 7 tend to stabilize the activated complex, whereas all of the others contribute to the potential energy barrier. Other energy terms are ignored. They include the resonance interaction between the two bromines and the α-carbon in the activated complex and the deformations in the alkyl groups attached to the α-carbon.

The energy term 1 is readily calculated if one assumes that a simple harmonic potential is valid over the angle involved (0.8°). The energy terms 2 and 3 may be treated as independent of r and θ, and energy 6 may also be treated as independent of these parameters for configurations near that of the activated complex, about which these terms must pass through a stationary value. The energy terms 4 and 5 may be treated as dependent on r and independent of θ for the small angles involved, but energies 7 and 8 must be computed as functions of both r and θ.

Several of the energy terms need not be calculated explicitly, for they will always cancel in the energy differences with which we shall be concerned. For example, energy 6 must be the same for all the activated complexes; energy 3 may be approximately the same for all activated complexes; and energy 2 will be approximately the same for all, since the C-C-C and H-C-C bending force constants are about the same. This leaves terms 1, 4, 5, 7, and 8.

The energy terms were evaluated as follows.[35] The term, 1, was obtained from the bending force constant and the angular displacement; 5 was obtained from the Morse potential curve for the methyl halides and the change in carbon-halogen bond distance; 8 was obtained from the van der Waals potential functions which they thought appropriate for halogen-carbon and halogen-hydrogen interactions (including both the attractive and repulsive terms); and 4 was calculated in a fashion similar to that for 8. The quantity, 7, was estimated to be small in all cases and was neglected.

Each term was evaluated for many values of r and θ, and the results were plotted, giving the energy contours shown in Fig. 3-20. The force constants for the bonds involved in the activated complex were obtained as described previously for the chlorination of methane (p. 346), and this allowed an evaluation of the vibrational partition function. The rotational and translational partition functions were obtained in the usual fashion, giving the data summarized in Table 3-15. It can be seen that the results

[35] The details are not given here, for better approximations can be made than were possible at the time the work was done. The discussion should serve to indicate the type of approach which may be used.

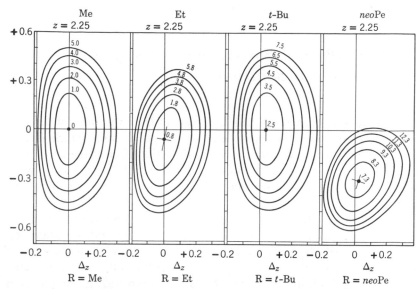

Fig. 3-20. Potential energy contours for the S_N2 *displacement reaction. The values against the contours are energies (kcal/mole) with respect to the lowest point of the methyl surface. The dark circle gives the calculated position of the halogen atom in the activated complex.* (P. B. D. de la Mare, L. Fowden, E. D. Hughes, C. K. Ingold and J. D. H. Mackie, *J. Chem. Soc.*, 3200 (1955).

for the relative activation parameters and relative rates were remarkably good, especially considering the number of approximations which were made. However, more recent data (see Table 3-15) indicate that the results are not nearly as good as originally believed.

Table 3-15 Calculated and Observed Rate Parameters for S_N2 Displacement Reactions

	Observed			*Calculated*		
Group	$k_{rel.}$	$\Delta\Delta H^{\ddagger}$	$\Delta\Delta S^{\ddagger}$	$k_{rel.}$	$\Delta\Delta H^{\ddagger}$	$\Delta\Delta S^{\ddagger}$
Methyl	1.00	0.0	0.0	1.00	0.0	0.0
Ethyl	0.013	1.7	−2.1	0.017	1.8	−2.7
i-Propyl	0.00014	3.9	−4.6	0.00035	3.6	−3.8
t-Butyl[a]	0.000039	6.0	0.0	0.000053	5.5	−1.1
n-Propyl	0.0085	1.7	−4.1	0.0090	3.3	−3.3
i-Butyl	0.00044	3.1	−5.0	0.00035	3.3	−4.7
Neopentyl	0.00000020	6.2	−9.6	0.000000037	8.3	−6.3

[a] These data have recently been shown to be incorrect for *t*-butyl (S. Winstein, S. Smith, and D. Darwish, *Tetrahedron Letters*, No. 16, 24 (1959)) and the rate of the S_N2 displacement on this halide must be much lower than the value given.

3-6 The Effect of Solvent on Rates of Reaction in Solution

So far we have considered the application of theory to rates of reaction which proceed in the gas phase and some special cases which largely involve steric effects. We must now consider the effect of the solvent on the rate of reaction. In order to do so we must first distinguish between two types of reactions which occur in solution—diffusion controlled and kinetically controlled.

Some reactions, such as the combination of iodine atoms[36] and the combination of organic free radicals,[37] have very large rate constants on the order of 10^8–10^9 liters mole^{-1} sec^{-1}. This is similar to the rate of collision between molecules in solution. It is assumed that reaction occurs at nearly every collision and that the rate is controlled by the diffusion of molecules toward each other in the solvent.

The rate at which reactant molecules collide in solution is about 100 times smaller than in the gas phase as a result of the interference by the solvent molecules. At the same time the solvent also causes the two reactant molecules to stay in contact with each other for a longer time than in the gas phase. Thus once they have collided, they have an enhanced possibility of reacting as compared to the gas phase.

This leads to an important phenomenon usually referred to as the "cage effect."[38] When a free radical initiator, such as azo-bis-isobutyronitrile, is allowed to decompose in a polymerizable monomer as the solvent, only about 60% of the initiator leads to chain propagation, and 40% is found as a dimerization product of the initially formed free radicals.[39] It is assumed that the latter arises from the combination of free radicals before they have diffused away from each other.

Most organic reactions have much smaller rate constants (usually under 1 liter mole^{-1} sec^{-1} for a second order reaction). Thus it is usually safe to assume that they are not diffusion controlled. It is still possible that one

[36] S. Aditya and J. E. Willard, *J. Am. Chem. Soc.*, **79**, 2680 (1957).

[37] H. W. Melville et al., *Discussions Faraday Soc.*, **14**, 150 (1953); G. M. Burnett, *Trans. Faraday Soc.*, **46**, 772 (1950); M. S. Matheson et. al., *J. Am Chem. Soc.*, **71**, 497 (1949); **73**, 1700 (1951).

[38] J. Frank and E. Rabinowitch, *Trans. Faraday Soc.*, **30**, 120 (1934).

[39] G. S. Hammond, J. N. Sen, and C. E. Boozer, *J. Am. Chem. Soc.*, **77**, 3244 (1955); C. Walling, *Free Radicals in Solution*, John Wiley and Sons, New York, 1957, ch. 3.

of the steps of a multistep process may be diffusion controlled, and this is often the case with free radical chain reactions where the termination step may be diffusion controlled.

In considering kinetically controlled reactions in solution, it is no longer practical to consider partition functions for the reactants and the activated complex. The partition function for translation (diffusion) in solution is not well defined as it is in the gas phase, and one has little information on the effect of solvent on internal rotation. One may still, of course, make corrections for the changes in vibrational frequencies both in the zero-point energy and in the heat capacity terms, and in some cases one may relate the energies of the reactants in solution to those in the gas phase.

Returning to the absolute rate theory, we shall write the equilibrium constant between activated complex and reactants in terms of activities rather than concentrations, as is done in most thermodynamic problems involving solutions,

$$A + B \rightleftharpoons X^{\ddagger} \rightarrow products$$

$$K^{\ddagger} = \frac{a_{X^{\ddagger}}}{a_A a_B} = \frac{[X^{\ddagger}]}{[A][B]} \cdot \frac{\gamma_{\ddagger}}{\gamma_A \gamma_B}$$

and we shall assume that the rate of conversion of the activated complex to products is proportional to the concentration of the activated complex and not to its activity.

$$k = k^{\ddagger}[X^{\ddagger}]$$

Thus

$$k = \kappa \left(\frac{kT}{h}\right) K^{\ddagger} \frac{\gamma_A \gamma_B}{\gamma_{\ddagger}} = \kappa \left(\frac{kT}{h}\right) e^{-\Delta F^{\ddagger}/RT} \frac{\gamma_A \gamma_B}{\gamma_{\ddagger}}$$

as compared to

$$k = \kappa \left(\frac{kT}{h}\right) e^{-\Delta F^{\ddagger}/RT}$$

for the gas phase. The problem is then to determine the appropriate activity coefficients, and it is this problem which we shall now consider.

In discussing the effect of solvent on reaction rates, it is convenient to distinguish between four types of reactions:

1. Reactions between neutral, nonpolar molecules giving nonpolar activated complexes.
2. Reactions of neutral molecules giving dipolar activated complexes.
3. Reactions between neutral molecules and ions.
4. Reactions between ions.

Each of these cases will be considered in turn.

REACTIONS BETWEEN NEUTRAL NONPOLAR COMPOUNDS

Relatively few examples of this type of reaction have been studied in a wide range of solvents. One of these examples is the dimerization of cyclopentadiene, the data for which are shown in Table 3-16. It can be seen that the activation parameters vary only slightly in going from the gas phase to solution and in going from one solvent to another. The

Table 3 Effect of Solvent on the Rate of Dimerization of Cyclopentadiene[a]

Medium	$\Delta H^{\ddagger}$ (kcal/mole)	$\Delta S^{\ddagger}$ (eu)	$-log\ k$ (50°)
Gas	15.5 ± 0.6	−34 ± 2	5.2
Ethanol	15.8 ± 0.8	−31 ± 4	4.7
Acetic acid	14.1 ± 1.0	−38 ± 4	5.0
Nitrobenzene	14.5 ± 0.4	−35 ± 2	4.7
Carbon disulfide	16.3 ± 0.5	−32 ± 2	5.2
Benzene	15.8 ± 0.6	−32 ± 2	5.0
Carbon tetrachloride	16.5 ± 0.4	−30 ± 2	4.9
Paraffin	16.8 ± 0.3	−28 ± 1	4.7
Pure liquid	15.6 ± 0.8	−34 ± 3	5.2

[a] A. Wasserman, *Monatsh.*, **83**, 543 (1952).

small observed changes in $\Delta H^{\ddagger}$ are balanced by changes in $\Delta S^{\ddagger}$, leading to an even smaller variation in the rate constant.

The magnitude of the entropy of activation is also of interest. The value -30 e.u. corresponds closely to $\Delta S°$ for the equilibrium between cyclopentadiene and its dimer. Thus it is reasonable to assume that the activated complex has a geometry resembling that of the dimer. In this way the changes in translational and rotational entropy will be about the same for both the activated complex and the product of the reaction. Conversely, the reverse reaction has $\Delta H^{\ddagger} = 34$ kcal/mole and $\Delta S = 0$ eu, both essentially independent of solvent. The very small entropy change for the reverse reaction again shows that the activated complex has a geometry similar to that for the dimer.

Another reaction which has been studied in a number of solvents is the decomposition of azo-bis-isobutyronitrile into nitrogen and cyanoisopropyl radicals. The data are shown in Table 3-17. The average rate constant is 3.00 ± 0.26, giving a 9% average deviation. Thus these rate constants are for all practical purposes the same, although they include a wide variation in solvent type.

There appears to be a significant variation in the enthalpy and entropy of activation, and if one were to plot one against the other, a good linear relationship would be found. Such relationships between the changes in activation parameters have been noted and discussed.[40] The validity of

Table 3-17 Effect of Solvent on the Rate of Decomposition of Azo-Bis-Isobutyronitrile[a]

$$
\begin{array}{ccc}
CH_3 & CH_3 & CH_3 \\
| & | & | \\
CH_3\!-\!C\!-\!N\!=\!N\!-\!C\!-\!CH_3 \rightarrow 2CH_3\!-\!C\cdot & + N_2 \\
| & | & | \\
CN & CN & CN
\end{array}
$$

Solvent	$k \times 10^5$ (67°)	$\Delta H^\ddagger$	$\Delta S^\ddagger$
Dibutyl carbitol	2.44		
Butyl carbitol	2.72		
Propylene carbonate	2.74	31.8	13.7
Diphenylmethane	2.89	31.2	12.3
N-Methylpropionamide	2.94	31.9	14.2
1,2-Bis-(benzyloxy)-ethane	3.10		
N-Methyl-N-benzylaniline	3.28		
N,N-Diethylaniline	3.38		
N,N-Dimethylaniline	3.39	30.1	9.2

[a] R. C. Petersen, J. H. Markgraf, and S. D. Ross, *J. Am. Chem. Soc.*, **83**, 3819 (1961).

these relationships has been considered by Petersen, Markgraf, and Ross[41] in the following way. According to the absolute rate theory, the rate of reaction is given by

$$
k = \kappa\left(\frac{kT}{h}\right)e^{-\Delta H^\ddagger/RT}e^{\Delta S^\ddagger/R}
$$

and thus to obtain $\Delta H^\ddagger$ one plots log (k/T) against $1/T$ and equates the slope to $-2.303\,\Delta H^\ddagger/R$. Regardless of how the slope is evaluated, it is largely determined by the first and last point. If three temperatures are used, the slope is exactly determined by the first and third point, and the middle point controls only the value of the intercept. Even when four

[40] J. E. Leffler, *J. Org. Chem.*, **20**, 1202 (1955).
[41] R. C. Petersen, J. H. Markgraf, and S. D. Ross, *J. Am. Chem. Soc.*, **83**, 3819 (1961).

temperatures are used, the slope is almost entirely controlled by the first and fourth point. Thus the value of $\Delta H^{\ddagger}$ is given by

$$\Delta H^{\ddagger} = R \frac{T'T}{T' - T} \ln \frac{k_1'T}{k_1 T'}$$

where T and T' are the extreme temperatures and k and k' are the corresponding rate constants.

If one wishes to test a relationship between $\Delta H^{\ddagger}$ and $\Delta S^{\ddagger}$, the burden of proof is on the investigator, and so one must consider the maximum error

Table 3-18   Effect of Errors in Rate Constants on the Error in the Enthalpy of Activation[a]

α	$T = 0°C.$			$T = 100°$			$T = 200°$		
	$\Delta T = 10°$	20°	30°	$\Delta T = 10°$	20°	30°	$\Delta T = 10°$	20°	30°
0.01	0.3	0.2	0.1	0.6	0.3	0.2	1.0	0.5	0.3
0.03	0.9	0.5	0.3	1.7	0.9	0.6	3.0	1.5	1.0
0.05	1.5	0.8	0.5	2.8	1.4	0.9	5.0	2.5	1.7
0.10	3.0	1.5	1.0	5.6	2.8	1.9	10.0	5.0	3.3
0.20	6.0	3.0	2.0	11.2	5.6	3.7	20.0	10.0	6.7

[a] The entries in the table are the errors in kcal/mole. The constant α is the fractional error in the rate constants.

and not the usually much smaller "probable error." Let α be the maximum fractional error in the rate constants, and δ be the error in $\Delta H^{\ddagger}$. Then

$$\Delta H^{\ddagger} + \delta = R \frac{T'T}{T' - T} \ln \frac{(1 + \alpha)k_1'T}{(1 - \alpha)k_1 T'}$$

or

$$\delta = R \frac{T'T}{T' - T} \ln \frac{1 + \alpha}{1 - \alpha}$$

When $\alpha \ll 1$, as is usually the case, the logarithmic part may be expanded as a series and only the first term taken. Then

$$\delta = 2R \frac{T'T}{T' - T} \alpha$$

The magnitude of the error which results from this treatment is shown in Table 3-18. In order for the differences in enthalpy of activation in a series to be significant, they should be twice these errors, since both values may be in error by this amount. In the work on the decomposition of azo-bis-isobutyronitrile, the rate constants were obtained with unusually high precision, 0.8%. This leads to a value of 2δ of 1.4 kcal/mole, as compared to the observed range of $\Delta H^{\ddagger}$, 1.8 kcal/mole. Since the calculated error does not include the possibility of nonrandom errors, it can be seen that the entire range of values of $\Delta H^{\ddagger}$ may be explained as due to experimental error. Similar calculations have been made for a number of other reactions[41] and in all cases 2δ was as large or larger than the range of $\Delta H^{\ddagger}$.

If σ is the error in $\Delta S^{\ddagger}$, we may write

$$\Delta S^{\ddagger} + \sigma = (\Delta H^{\ddagger} + \delta)\left(\frac{1}{T}\right) + R \ln (1 + \alpha)\left(\frac{hk'}{kT}\right)$$

and

$$\sigma = \delta\left(\frac{1}{T}\right) + R \ln (1 + \alpha)$$

For the case in which $\alpha \ll 1$, this becomes

$$\sigma = \delta\left(\frac{1}{T}\right) + \alpha R = \delta\left[\frac{1}{T} + \frac{T' - T}{2T'T}\right]$$

Thus the error in $\Delta S^{\ddagger}$ is linearly related to the error in $\Delta H^{\ddagger}$, and the often-found correlation must in many cases be attributed to the above relationship.

The above examples, and the few others available, all indicate that this type of reaction has remarkably little solvent dependence. Even when a small change in dipole moment might be expected in going from reactants to products, as in the Diels-Alder reaction between cyclopentadiene and benzoquinone, only a small solvent effect is noted.[42]

REACTIONS FORMING DIPOLAR ACTIVATED COMPLEXES

Common examples of reactions between relatively nonpolar reactants giving dipolar activated complexes are the Menschutkin reaction (the reaction of an amine with an alkyl halide) and the solvolysis of tertiary alkyl halides. Some typical data on the Menschutkin reaction are given in Table 3-19.

In this reaction the activated complex may be formulated as

$$R_3N: + RCH_2X \rightarrow \left[R_3N \overset{\delta+}{\underset{}{\cdots}} C \overset{\delta-}{\underset{R}{\cdots}} X \right] \rightarrow R_3\overset{+}{N}-CH_2R + X^-$$

[42] A. Wasserman, *Trans. Faraday Soc.*, **34**, 128 (1938).

Table 3-19   Solvent Effects on the Menschutkin Reaction

A. $(C_2H_5)_3N + C_2H_5I \rightarrow (C_2H_5)_4N^+I^-$[a]

Solvent	$k \times 10^5$ (100°)	ϵ_{25}	$\Delta H^{\ddagger}$	$\Delta S^{\ddagger}$
Hexane	0.5	1.89[c]	15.3	−42
Dioxane	89.2	2.20	12.0	−41[b]
Benzene	39.8	2.27	10.7	−47
Benzene	40.8	2.27	12.0	−42[b]
Diphenyl ether	116.	2.53 (75°)	11.0	−44
Toluene	25.3	2.37	12.3	−43
Diphenylmethane	96.3	2.57	11.1	−44
Iodobenzene	265.	4.60	11.2	−41
Bromobenzene	160.	5.40	11.8	−40
Fluorobenzene	91.	5.42	11.0	−44
Chlorobenzene	138.	5.62	11.2	−43
Acetone	422.	20.7	11.5	−39[b]
Benzonitrile	1120.	25.2	11.2	−38
Nitrobenzene	1380.	34.8	10.9	−39

[a] II. G. Grimm, H. Ruf, and H. Wolff, *Z. physik. Chem.*, **B13**, 301 (1931).
[b] E. Tommila and P. Kauranen, *Acta Chem. Scand.*, **8**, 1152 (1954).
[c] A. A. Maryott and E. R. Smith, *Table of Dielectric Constants of Pure Liquids*, National Bureau of Standards Circular 514, August 10, 1951.

B. $C_5H_5N + CH_3I \rightarrow C_5H_5N^+CH_3 + I^-$[d]

Solvent	$k \times 10^5$ (100°)	ϵ_{25}	$\Delta H^{\ddagger}$	$\Delta S^{\ddagger}$
Toluene	108.	2.37	13.8	−34
Benzene	141.	2.27	13.4	−34
Chloroform	335.	4.8	12.5	−35
Chlorobenzene	398.	5.62	13.2	−33
Dioxane	407.	2.20	12.9	−34
Bromobenzene	501.	5.40	13.0	−33
Anisole	676.	4.33	12.5	−34
Iodobenzene	1150.	4.60	13.1	−31
Benzonitrile	3160.	25.2	13.0	−29
Nitrobenzene	3720.	24.8	13.0	−29

[d] N. J. T. Pickles and C. N. Hinshelwood, *J. Chem. Soc.*, 1353 (1936).

Table 3-19 (continued)

C. $C_6H_5NH_2 + C_6H_5COCH_2Br \rightarrow C_6H_5\overset{+}{N}H_2CH_2COC_6H_5 + Br^{-e}$

Solvent	$k \times 10^5$ (28°)	$\Delta H^{\ddagger}$	$\Delta S^{\ddagger}$	$T(\Delta S^{\ddagger} + 20)$	$\Delta H^{\ddagger}$ (corr.)
Benzene	1.07	7.5	−61	12.3	19.8
Chloroform	1.62	10.2	−51	9.3	19.5
Acetone	23.2	10.5	−45	7.5	18.0
Ethanol	48.4	13.3	−34	4.2	17.5
Methanol	64.8	11.8	−39	5.7	17.5
Nitrobenzene	10.3	12.9	−39	5.7	18.6

[e] H. E. Cox, *J. Chem. Soc.*, **119**, 142 (1921).

D . $(C_2H_5)_3N + CH_3I \rightarrow (C_2H_5)_3N^+CH_3 + I^{-f}$

Solvent	$k \times 10^3$ (25°)	$\Delta H^{\ddagger}$	$\Delta S^{\ddagger}$
Benzene	1.40	9.1	−41
25% Nitrobenzene	7.75	8.9	−38
50% Nitrobenzene	14.8	9.2	−36
75% Nitrobenzene	24.4	9.4	−34
90% Nitrobenzene	32.1	9.2	−34
100% Nitrobenzene	33.5	9.1	−35

[f] H. C. Raine and C. N. Hinshelwood, *J. Chem. Soc.*, 1378 (1939).

and it can be seen that a dipole is developed as the reaction proceeds. In the simplest terms, we would expect the dipolar activated complex to be stabilized by an increase in the dielectric constant of the solvent, whereas the reactants would be affected relatively little. Thus an increase in the dielectric constant should lead to an increase in rate, and it can be seen from the above data that this expectation is approximately realized.

Kirkwood[43] has calculated the free energy change resulting from a transfer of a dipole from a medium of dielectric constant unity to one having a dielectric constant ϵ, making the assumption that only electrostatic interactions are involved. As long as this is the major factor, we may write

$$\Delta F_{el} = kT \ln \gamma = -\frac{\mu^2}{r^3}\left(\frac{\epsilon - 1}{2\epsilon + 1}\right)$$

where μ is the dipole moment and r is the molecular radius (assuming the molecule to be spherical).

The accuracy of this equation has been tested by some equilibrium measurements, and for different compositions of mixed solvents the

[43] J. G. Kirkwood, *J. Chem. Phys.*, **2**, 351 (1934).

agreement is fairly good.[44] It might be noted that the corresponding change in free energy of an ion is

$$\Delta F_{el} = \frac{Z^2 e^2}{2\epsilon r} - \frac{Z^2 e^2}{2r} = -\frac{Z^2 e^2}{r}\left(\frac{\epsilon - 1}{2\epsilon}\right)$$

where the first term corresponds to the energy in a vacuum and the second to the energy in a solvent of dielectric constant ϵ. The dipole moment is given by

$$\mu = Zer$$

and it can be seen that the two equations are formally equivalent with

$$\left(\frac{\epsilon - 1}{2\epsilon}\right) \quad \text{replacing} \quad \left(\frac{\epsilon - 1}{2\epsilon + 1}\right)$$

The use of $(\epsilon - 1)/2\epsilon$ is equivalent to using $1/2\epsilon$, the difference being in the choice of standard state (a vacuum on one hand, and a solvent with an infinite dielectric constant on the other). Data for reactions of this sort are often correlated with the reciprocal of the dielectric constant. For solvents having a dielectric constant greater than 7, this is proportional to the Kirkwood function (Fig. 3-21), and the two are related by

$$\frac{1}{2\epsilon} = 0.359 - 0.72\left(\frac{\epsilon - 1}{2\epsilon + 1}\right)$$

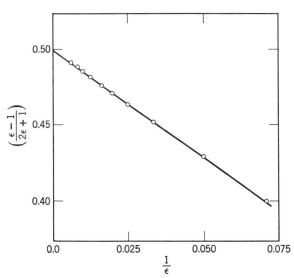

Fig. 3-21. A comparison of the functions $(\epsilon - 1/2\epsilon + 1)$ and $1/\epsilon$.

[44] A. R. Martin, *Trans. Faraday Soc.*, **33**, 191 (1937).

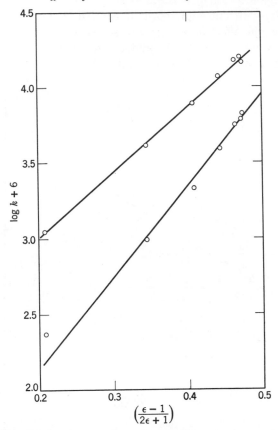

Fig. 3-22. Effect of dielectric constant on the rate of reaction between triethylamine and benzyl bromide (upper line), and pyridine and benzyl bromide (lower line) in benzene-alcohol mixtures.

Let us apply this formulation to the Menschutkin reaction. If we wish to give the correlation a maximum chance for success, we should use various mixtures of two solvents as the reaction medium, for in this way specific effects of the solvent will in part be canceled out. The results for the reaction of benzyl bromide with pyridine or triethylamine in benzene-alcohol and benzene-nitrobenzene mixtures are shown in Fig. 3-22.[45] It can be seen that correlation with the Kirkwood function is quite good with the benzene-alcohol mixtures but only fair with the nitrobenzene-benzene mixtures. Actually the latter is atypical, and fairly good results are usually obtained.

[45] G. Muchin, R. Ginsberg, and C. Moissejewa, *Ukraine Chem. J.*, **2**, 136 (1926) (*Chem. Zentr.* **II**, 2376 (1926)); cf. S. Glasstone, K. J. Laidler, and H. Eyring, "*The Theory of Rate Processes*, McGraw-Hill Book Co., New York, 1941, p. 420.

The difficulty with this approach is illustrated by Figs. 3-23 and 3-24. The first shows the effect of a variety of solvents on the rate of reaction between triethylamine and ethyl iodide.[46] Although there is a general trend, there is a marked scatter of points. Note in particular the high

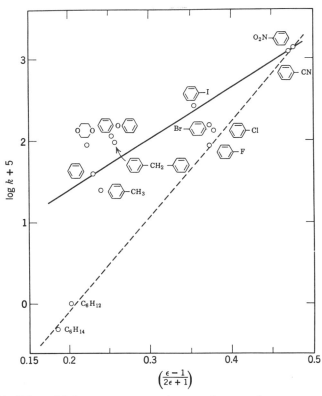

Fig. 3-23. *Effect of dielectric constant on the rate of reaction between triethylamine ana ethyl iodide.*

rate of reaction in dioxane and the low rate of reaction in hexane. In the second is plotted the effect of several solvent mixtures on the rate of the same reaction.[47] A good linear relationship is obtained for all three solvent mixtures, but the slopes are markedly different. One might, however, expect them to be the same if the Kirkwood equation were applicable, unless the solvents had some specific effect on the μ^2/r^3 term.

[46] H. G. Grimm, H. Ruf, and H. Wolff, *Z. physik. Chem.*, **B13**, 301 (1931); E. Tommila and P. Kauranen, *Acta Chem. Scand.*, **8**, 1152 (1954).

[47] E. Tommila, *Acta Chem. Scand.*, **13**, 622 (1959).

It is evident that the dielectric constant is not a useful value for describing the effect of the solvent on a dipolar species (or an ion) except in certain special cases, such as the use of a mixture of two solvents. It may be noted (Fig. 3-23) that although the three halobenzenes have similar dielectric constants, they lead to different rates of reaction when used as

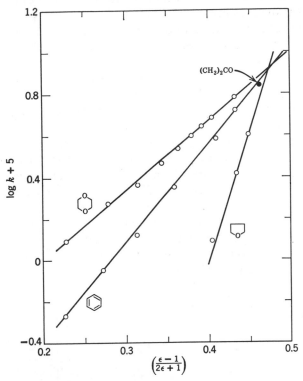

Fig. 3-24. Effect of dielectric constant on the rate of reaction between triethylamine and ethyl iodide. E. Tommila, *Acta Chem. Scand.*, **13**, 622 (1959).

the solvent. Iodobenzene, with the lowest dielectric constant, gives the largest rate. This strongly suggests that the polarizability of the solvent is important in stabilizing the dipolar activated complex.

The polarizability of hexane is about as low as one will find for an organic molecule, and one might expect that polarizability would become relatively less important with the solvent having a large dielectric constant. Thus an approximation to the normal effect of dielectric constant alone is shown by the dotted line in Fig. 3-23. All the solvents lie on or above this line. The deviation from the line might be taken as a very rough measure of the other effects contributing to the change in rate.

It might also be noted that dioxane and tetrahydrofuran, when used as the solvent, lead to the same value of the rate constant, whereas they have quite different values of the dielectric constant. The latter difference arises because dioxane has two opposing dipoles, which give it a low dipole moment. When dioxane is in the co-sphere of an ion (p. 259), it might be expected to behave in a fashion similar to that of tetrahydrofuran, only one of the oxygens being involved.

These observations make it appear that the solvents might best be characterized using a linear free energy relationship. This approach is discussed in Section 3-7.

A possibly advantageous way in which to look at the rate effects in mixed solvents is to assume that the two solvents act independently and that the rate constant should be correlated with the mole fraction of one component of the solvent. A plot of the rate constant against the mole fraction of benzene for the pyridine-benzyl bromide reaction is shown in Fig. 3-25, and it can be seen that this correlation is better than that with $(\epsilon - 1/2\epsilon + 1)$. The curvature which is sometimes noted might well be attributed to preferential solvation of the activated complex by the component having the higher dielectric constant. In any event it is apparent that we have much to learn about the properties of solutions.

If our understanding of the effect of solvent properties on rate constants is poor, that with respect to the activation parameters is abysmal. Let us again consider the data in Table 3-19. The entropy of activation usually

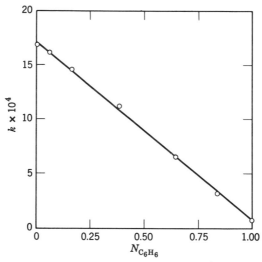

Fig. 3-25. Rate constant for the reaction of benzyl bromide with pyridine as a function of the mole fraction of benzene in benzene-ethanol mixtures.

either remains constant or becomes less negative as the dielectric constant increases.[48] If the free energy of activation changes could properly be correlated with the reciprocal of the dielectric constant, the entropy change would be given by

$$\Delta S_{el}^{\ddagger} = - \left(\frac{\partial \Delta F_{el}^{\ddagger}}{\partial T} \right)_p = \text{constant} \cdot \frac{1}{\epsilon} \left(\frac{d \ln \epsilon}{dT} \right)$$

The term $d \ln \epsilon / dT$ is on the order of -0.8×10^{-3} for the solvents which have no dipole moment and is about $-5. \times 10^{-3}$ for the other solvents. It can be seen that a smooth change in $\Delta S^{\ddagger}$ ($= \Delta S_{el}^{\ddagger} + \Delta S_a^{\ddagger}$, the latter presumably being a constant) should not be expected on going from one type of solvent to another and that the value of $\Delta S^{\ddagger}$ should be less negative for benzene, toluene, and hexane than for other solvents, such as chloroform, chlorobenzene, and ethyl bromide. The experimental data are not in agreement with these expectations.

If we consider the physical process involved in the stabilization of the activated complex by the solvent, we can see that the motion of some of the solvent molecules will be restricted in the process. The solvents having a permanent dipole moment will have some structure corresponding to dipoles being preferentially oriented for an attractive interaction rather than repulsion. The ones which do not have a dipole moment will be relatively unoriented and consequently have a higher entropy. These latter solvents will have more of a loss in entropy as a result of the solvation process, and as a consequence the reactions in these solvents should have a large negative entropy of activation.

It can also be seen that the enthalpies of activation often either remain constant or increase with increasing dielectric constant, whereas the opposite would be expected based on a simple model. Suppose we assume that solvation is an important factor. The entropy change for a bimolecular reaction should be on the order of -20 eu because of the loss of translational and rotational degrees of freedom. If we assume that the excess over this value is $\Delta S_{el}^{\ddagger}$, we may estimate $\Delta H_{el}^{\ddagger}$ from $T \Delta S_{el}^{\ddagger}$, for the free energy change in "freezing" the solvent will be small.[49] This correction

---

[48] One cannot take the recorded values of the activation parameters too seriously. The reaction forms an ionic species, and thus the ionic strength of the solutions will increase with time. This will, in turn, affect the rate constants. If the effect is not proportional at all temperatures, the activation parameters will also be affected. Further, the accuracy of some of the kinetic data might be questioned. As an example, the activation energy for the reaction of triethylamine with ethyl iodide has been determined in benzene solution by two groups of investigators, giving values of 12.7 and 11.4 kcal/mole.[46] It is likely that many of the activation enthalpies have an error of ± 1 kcal or more.

is made to the data of Table 3-19C, and it can be seen that the values of $\Delta H^{\ddagger}$ are closer to being constant and that they change in the expected direction. This treatment is, however, not unique, for, as shown in the preceding section, the errors in $\Delta S^{\ddagger}$ are related to those in $\Delta H^{\ddagger}$ by the factor of the temperature. The changes in $\Delta S^{\ddagger}$ may simply reflect the experimental error in measuring $\Delta H^{\ddagger}$, and the neglect of the salt effect might lead to low values of $\Delta H^{\ddagger}$ in solvents of low dielectric constant.

The status of solvent effects on S_N1 solvolytic reactions of halides and alcohol derivatives is in about the same position as for the Menschutkin reaction. For mixed solvents containing water as one component, the rate of reaction is better correlated with the water content of the solvent than with the dielectric constant.[50] The entire problem of solvent effects on dipole forming reactions needs to be reviewed, particularly with the view of obtaining very precise data on a large number of systems so that some sense may be made of the entropy-enthalpy relationships.

THE REACTION OF MOLECULES WITH IONS

A typical case of the reaction of an ion with a molecule is the S_N2 displacement reaction

$$\text{Y}^- + \overset{\diagdown}{\underset{\diagup}{}}\text{C—X} \rightarrow \left[\overset{\delta-}{\text{Y}} \cdots \overset{\diagup}{\underset{|}{\text{C}}} \cdots \overset{\delta-}{\text{X}} \right]^- \rightarrow \text{Y—}\overset{\diagup}{\underset{\diagdown}{\text{C}}} + \text{X}^-$$

The effect of solvent on this type of reaction is most easily seen by considering the electrostatic energy associated with converting a neutral species to an ion. This is given by

$$\Delta F_{el} = \frac{Z^2 e^2}{2\epsilon r}$$

where Z is the charge on the ion, ϵ is the dielectric constant of the solvent, and r is the radius of the ion.

For the difference between reactants and the activated complex,

$$\Delta F_{el}^{\ddagger} = \frac{Z^2 e^2}{2\epsilon} \left(\frac{1}{r} - \frac{1}{r_{\ddagger}} \right)$$

Thus the effect on the rate of reaction becomes

$$\ln k = \ln k_0 + \frac{N Z^2 e^2}{2\epsilon R T} \left(\frac{1}{r} - \frac{1}{r_{\ddagger}} \right)$$

[49] The idea of "freezing" solvent molecules during the solvation process was used by J. L. Magee, T. Ri, and H. Eyring, *J. Chem. Phys.*, **9**, 419 (1941) for aqueous solutions.
[50] D. A. Brown and R. F. Hudson, *J. Chem. Soc.*, 3352 (1953); R. F. Hudson and B. Saville, *J. Chem. Soc.* 4114 (1955).

In the above case, $r_{\ddagger} > r$, and thus the correction term will be positive. The rate constant will increase as the dielectric constant decreases. The effect is usually not very large, but it is in the expected direction. For example, for the reaction of methyl bromide with iodide ion,[51] the rate constant in water is 6.84×10^{-4} l. mole^{-1} sec^{-1}, that in methanol is 9.42×10^{-4}, in ethylene glycol, 32.6×10^{-4}, and in acetone, 3550×10^{-4}.[52]

The displacement reaction is often carried out in solvents of low dielectric constant in which ionic species are present in the form of ion-pairs. In ethanol, it has been observed that the rate constant is given by

$$k_{\text{obs.}} = k_0 \alpha$$

where α is the degree of dissociation of the ion-pairs (determined conductometrically). Apparently the ion-pairs are not reactive in this displacement reaction.[53] This often leads to unusual effects as the solvent composition is changed. For example, in the reaction of *p*-nitrobenzyl bromide with lithium chloride in aqueous dioxane, the rate constant increases on going from 90 to 70% dioxane, and then decreases on going to 50% dioxane. The first change is probably due to a change in the ion-pair association constants, leading to a higher concentration of chloride ions, and the second change is probably due to the change in dielectric constant.[54]

In solvents having a higher dielectric constant, ion-pair association is not important, but one must still consider the effect of ion concentration on the rate of reaction. This is done by considering the effect of the salt concentration on the ion and on the activated complex. Since both species have a single charge, at low salt concentrations there will be parallel changes in activity coefficients. At higher concentrations there will be a small salt effect due to the difference in *a* (the closest approach of ions) in the Debye-Hückel equation between the reactant ion and the activated complex. However, this is generally a small factor. The general subject of salt effects on rates of reaction is discussed in the next section.

[51] J. S. McKinley-McKee and E. A. Moelwyn-Hughes, *J. Chem. Soc.*, 838 (1952). Note the unusually large effect of acetone as the solvent. This is a general phenomenon on going from a hydroxylic to a nonhydroxylic solvent (cf. S. Winstein, L. G. Savedoff, S. Smith, I. D. R. Stevens and J. S. Gall, *Tetrahedron Letters*, No. 9, 24, (1960)).

[52] Other examples may be found in: E. Bergmann, M. Polanyi, and A. Szábo, *Z. physik. Chem.*, **B20**, 161 (1933); E. D. Hughes and C. K. Ingold, *J. Chem. Soc.*, 1571 (1933); E. D. Hughes, C. K. Ingold, and U. G. Shapiro, *J. Chem. Soc.*, 225 (1936); L. J. LeRoux and S. Sugden, *J. Chem. Soc.*, 1279 (1939); R. D. Heyding and C. A. Winkler, *Can. J. Chem.*, **29**, 790 (1951).

[53] S. S. Woolf. *J. Chem. Soc.*, 1172 (1937); J. A. Mitchell, *J. Chem. Soc.*, 1792 (1937).

[54] J. W. Hackett and H. C. Thomas, *J. Am. Chem. Soc.*, **72**, 4962 (1950).

REACTIONS BETWEEN IONS. PRIMARY SALT EFFECTS

The effect of solvent on the reaction between two ions may be considered in the same terms as the reaction between ions and molecules. Suppose two positively charged ions were to react with each other. The activated complex would have a double positive charge, and the free energy of forming the ion would be a function of the square of the charge. An increase in the dielectric constant of the solvent would stabilize the activated complex more than it would the reactants, and the rate of reaction would increase.

Conversely, if a negatively charged ion were to react with a positively charged ion, the activated complex would have no charge (although it would presumably still be dipolar). An increase in dielectric constant of the reaction medium would then stabilize the reactants more than the activated complex, leading to a decrease in the rate of reaction.

Table 3-20 Effect of Dielectric Constant on the Rate of Reaction Between Two Ions

A. Azodicarboxylate Ion and Hydrogen Ion in Aqueous Dioxane[a]

Vol % Dioxane	ϵ	$\log k$ ($\mu = 0$)	$\Delta S^{\ddagger}$	$\Delta H^{\ddagger}$
0	78.5	10.34	12.9	10.2
10	71.2	10.60	14.1	10.2
20	62.2	10.89	14.9	10.1
30	53.5	11.22	15.3	9.8
40	44.3	11.64	15.7	9.3
50	35.6	12.20	20.2	9.9
60	27.0	12.95	25.3	10.4

B. Bromphenol Blue and Hydroxyl Ion in Aqueous Ethanol[b]

Wgt % Ethanol	ϵ	k ($\mu = 0$)	$\log k$
0.0	78.5	25.2	1.401
10.2	72.5	9.71	0.987
15.4	69.5	5.46	0.737
20.6	66.5	3.01	0.479
31.5	60.0	1.03	0.013

[a] C. V. King and J. J. Josephs, *J. Am. Chem. Soc.*, **66**, 767 (1944).
[b] E. S. Amis and V. K. LaMer, *J. Am. Chem. Soc.*, **61**, 905 (1939).

This may be considered in semiquantitative terms as follows. The change in free energy of converting a neutral species to an ion was

$$\Delta F_{el} = \frac{Z^2 e^2}{2\epsilon r}$$

In the present case we are, in effect, discharging two ions and forming a new one having the sum of the original charges. Thus we may write

$$\Delta F_{el}^{\ddagger} = -\frac{Z_A^2 e^2}{2\epsilon r_A} - \frac{Z_B^2 e^2}{2\epsilon r_B} + \frac{Z_{\ddagger}^2 e^2}{2\epsilon r_{\ddagger}}$$

To a fair approximation, $r_{\ddagger} \approx r_A \approx r_B$, and, of necessity, $Z_{\ddagger} = Z_A + Z_B$, where A and B are the two reactant ions. Making these substitutions, one obtains

$$\Delta F_{el}^{\ddagger} = \frac{Z_A Z_B e^2}{\epsilon r_{\ddagger}}$$

or

$$\ln k = \ln k_0 - \frac{N Z_A Z_B e^2}{\epsilon R T r_{\ddagger}}$$

where k_0 is the rate constant in a medium of infinite dielectric constant. It can be seen that a plot of log k against $1/\epsilon$ should give a straight line, and this may be tested using the data in Table 3-20. The results are shown graphically in Fig. 3-26, and it can be seen that a reasonably good fit is obtained.

The reaction of the azodicarboxylate ion with hydrogen ion

$$N_2(CO_2)_2^{-2} + H_3O^+ \rightarrow [H_2O\text{----}H\text{----}N_2(CO_2)_2]^- \rightarrow \text{products}$$

involves the reaction of oppositely charged species, and, as expected, the plot has a positive slope. In the reaction of bromphenol blue with hydroxyl ions

blue   colorless

two similarly charged species react with each other, and the slope of the plot is negative. The relative slopes are about what one might expect

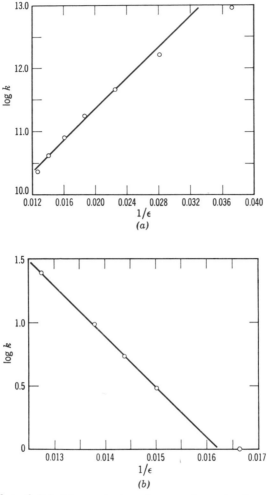

Fig. 3-26. *Effect of dielectric constant on the rate of reaction between two ions.* (a) *Azodicarboxylate ion plus* H^+. (b) *Bromphenol blue plus* HO^-.

based on the difference in charges between the two reactions. It must be noted that the good correlation in the plots of $\log k$ against $1/\epsilon$ results from the use of different mixtures of the same solvent pair. If different solvents had been used, a much poorer correlation would have been found.

The entropy change which results from this type of reaction may also be obtained. Again the entropy change is given by

$$-\Delta S = \left(\frac{\partial \, \Delta F}{\partial T}\right)_p$$

and so

$$\Delta S_{el}^{\ddagger} = \frac{Z_A Z_B e^2}{r_{\ddagger}} \frac{d}{dT}\left(\frac{1}{\epsilon}\right)$$

For water, $\epsilon \sim 80$, $d \ln \epsilon/dT = -0.005$, and $r \sim 2$Å. Making these substitutions, one finds

$$\Delta S_{el}^{\ddagger} \sim -10 Z_A Z_B$$

Table 3-21 Entropy Changes in Reactions Between Ions[a]

Reaction	$\Delta S^{\ddagger}$
$S_2O_4^= + S_2O_4^= \rightarrow S_2O_5^= + S_2O_3^=$	-41 eu
$S_2O_3^= + SO_3^= \rightarrow SO_3^= + S_2O_3^=$	-31
$BrCH_2CO_2^- + S_2O_3^= \rightarrow {}^-O_3S_2CH_2CO_2^- + Br^-$	-28
$ClO^- + ClO^- \rightarrow ClO_2^- + Cl^-$	-20
$ClO^- + ClO_2^- \rightarrow ClO_3^- + Cl^-$	-20
$Co(NH_3)_5Br^{+2} + HO^- \rightarrow Cr(NH_3)_4Br(OH)^+ + NH_3$	$+20$

[a] These data were taken from a summary given by A. A. Frost and R. G. Pearson, *Kinetics and Mechanism*, John Wiley and Sons, New York, 1961, 2nd ed., p. 144.

Some typical data are summarized in Table 3-21, and it can be seen that there is general agreement with this equation. However, it must be remembered that other factors contribute to the entropy change and that these bimolecular reactions would be expected to have $\Delta S^{\ddagger} = -10$ or so in the absence of electrical interactions.

Table 3-22 Effect of Entropy of Activation Changes on Rate Constants at a Constant Enthalpy of Activation

$\Delta(\Delta S^{\ddagger})$	k/k_0
1	1.64
2	2.72
5	12.2
10	148.
20	21900.
30	3,240,000.

In this connection it is interesting to note the effect of an entropy change on the rate of reactions. This is shown in Table 3-22. Although at first the entropy changes have a relatively small effect on the rate constant, the effect is exponential and becomes very large with larger entropy changes.

An interesting aspect of this type of reaction is the effect of ionic concentration on the rate of reaction (salt effect). If we wish to consider the effect of salt concentration on the rate of a reaction, we may apply the Debye-Hückel equation to the evaluation of the several activity coefficients. The rate constant will be given by

$$k = k_0 \frac{\gamma_A \gamma_B}{\gamma_\ddagger}$$

and

$$-\ln \gamma_i = \frac{Z_i^2 \alpha \sqrt{\mu}}{1 + \beta a_i \sqrt{\mu}}$$

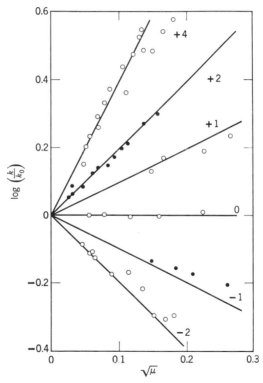

Fig. 3-27. *Effect of ionic strength on the rates of reaction between two ions. The slopes and reactions are:* $+4$, $Co(NH_3)_5Br^{++} + Hg^{++}$ (Brönsted and Livingston, *J. Am. Chem. Soc.*, **49**, 435 (1927); $+2$, $S_2O_8^= + I^-$ (King and Jacobs, *ibid.*, **53**, 1704 (1931); $+1$, $[NO_2=N-CO_2C_2H_5]^- + HO^-$ [Brönsted and Delbanco, *Z. Anorg. Chem.*, **144**, 248 (1925)); 0, $CH_3CO_2C_2H_5 + HO^-$ (Arrhenius, *Z. Physik Chem.* **1**, 111 (1887); -1, $H_2O_2 + H^+ + Br^-$ (Livingston, *J. Am. Chem. Soc.*, **48**, 53 (1926); -2, $Co(NH_3)_5Br^{++} + HO^-$ (Brönsted and Livingston, *ibid.*, **49**, 435 (1927)). (From V. K. LaMer, *Chem. Revs.*, **10**, 179 (1932).

where α and β are constants depending only on the solvent and the temperature, a is the closest approach of ions, and μ is the ionic strength ($\mu = \frac{1}{2}\Sigma c_i Z_i^2$). For water at 25°, $\alpha = 1.172$ (or 0.509 using common logarithms) and $\beta = 0.329 \times 10^8$.

Making the above substitution for the activity coefficients, the rate constant becomes

$$\ln k = \ln k_0 + \ln \gamma_A + \ln \gamma_B - \ln \gamma_\ddagger$$

$$= \ln k_0 - \frac{Z_A^2 \alpha \sqrt{\mu}}{1 - \beta a_A \sqrt{\mu}} - \frac{Z_B^2 \alpha \sqrt{\mu}}{1 - \beta a_B \sqrt{\mu}} + \frac{Z_\ddagger^2 \alpha \sqrt{\mu}}{1 - \beta a_\ddagger \sqrt{\mu}}$$

If we now assume that $a_A \sim a_B \sim a_\ddagger$, and remember that $Z_\ddagger = Z_A + Z_B$, the equation may be rewritten as

$$\ln k = \ln k_0 + \frac{2Z_A Z_B \alpha \sqrt{\mu}}{1 - \beta a \sqrt{\mu}}$$

It can be seen that if $Z_A = Z_B$, an increase in the ionic strength will cause an increase in rate. Similarly, if $Z_A = -Z_B$, an increase in ionic strength will cause a decrease in rate. Some typical results are shown in Fig. 3-27. It can be seen that for low concentrations of ions, linear relationships are obtained, and that the slopes give the charges on the ions which react to form the activated complex. This interpretation must, however, be made with care because of the secondary salt effect, which is discussed in the next section.

SECONDARY SALT EFFECTS

The ionic strength affects not only the rate determining step but also all equilibria preceding it. For example, if a specific hydronium ion catalyzed reaction were catalyzed by acetic acid in water solution, the rate would be a function of the degree of ionization of acetic acid, and this would in turn depend on the ionic strength.

The equilibrium constant would be given by

$$HOAc \underset{}{\overset{K_a}{\rightleftharpoons}} H^+ + OAc^-$$

$$K_a = \frac{[H^+][OAc^-]}{[HOAc]} \cdot \frac{\gamma_H^+ \gamma_{OAc}^-}{\gamma_{HOAc}}$$

and the hydrogen ion concentration would be

$$[H^+] = \frac{K_a[HOAc]}{[OAc^-]} \cdot \frac{\gamma_{HOAc}}{\gamma_H^+ \gamma_{OAc}^-}$$

This may be placed in a form for which the Debye-Hückel equation may be applied:

$$\log [\mathrm{H}^+] = \log K_a + \log \frac{[\mathrm{HOAc}]}{[\mathrm{OAc}^-]} + \log \frac{\gamma_{\mathrm{HOAc}}}{\gamma_{\mathrm{H}} + \gamma_{\mathrm{OAc}^-}}$$

We may assume that the activity coefficient of the acid will be only slightly affected by a change in salt concentration. Thus the effect of ionic strength on the concentration of hydronium ions will be given by

$$\log [\mathrm{H}^+] = \log K_a + \log \frac{[\mathrm{HOAc}]}{[\mathrm{OAc}^-]} + \frac{2\alpha\sqrt{\mu}}{1 + \beta a\sqrt{\mu}}$$

As the ionic strength increases, the concentration of hydrogen ions will increase, and the rate of reaction will increase.

When one examines a reaction for general acid catalysis by noting the changes in rate constant with changes in the buffer concentration (Section 3-7), the ionic strength must be kept constant; otherwise the ionic strength will increase with increasing buffer concentration, leading to an increase in rate due to the secondary salt effect. This could be mistaken for general acid catalysis.

Also if a reaction involves one or more equilibria prior to the rate determining step, it may not be possible to use the primary salt effect to determine the charge types involved in the rate determining step. The secondary salt effect may lead to the same changes in rate with ionic strength as the primary salt effect.

References

Effect of Solvent on Rates of Reaction in Solution:
A. A. Frost and R. G. Pearson, *Kinetics and Mechanism*, 2nd ed., John Wiley and Sons, New York, 1961, ch. 7.
E. A. Moelwyn-Hughes, *Physical Chemistry*, Pergamon Press, London, 1957, ch. 24.
S. W. Benson, *The Foundations of Chemical Kinetics*, McGraw-Hill Book Co., 1960, Part IV.
E. Tommila et al., *Suomen Kemistilehti*, **33B**, 187 (1960) and previous papers.
S. Winstein, E. Grunwald and H. W. Jones, *J. Am. Chem. Soc.*, **73**, 2700 (1951).

3-7 Linear Free Energy Relationships

Many linear free energy relationships have been developed in order to correlate kinetic data. It is the purpose of this section to explore several that deal with the effect of catalysts, the effect of substituents, the effect of steric hindrance, and the effect of solvent on the rate of reaction.

BRØNSTED CATALYSIS LAW

Acid catalysis is a common feature of organic reactions. The acid catalysis may take one of several forms. Consider the case which has the following steps.

Type I

$$S + H^+ \rightleftharpoons SH^+$$

$$SH^+ (+Y) \xrightarrow{\text{slow}} \text{products}$$

as, for example, in the hydrolysis of acetals:[55]

$$\underset{\underset{H}{|}}{\overset{\overset{OCH_3}{|}}{R-C-OCH_3}} + H^+ \rightleftharpoons \underset{\underset{H}{|}}{\overset{\overset{\overset{+}{H}OCH_3}{|}}{R-C-OCH_3}}$$

$$\underset{\underset{H}{|}}{\overset{\overset{\overset{+}{H}OCH_3}{|}}{R-C-OCH_3}} \underset{\text{fast}}{\overset{\text{slow}}{\rightleftharpoons}} \underset{\underset{H}{|}}{\overset{\overset{+}{R}-\overset{+}{C}-OCH_3}{}}$$

$$\underset{\underset{H}{|}}{\overset{+}{R}-\overset{+}{C}-OCH_3} + H_2O \rightleftharpoons \underset{\underset{H}{|}}{\overset{\overset{\overset{+}{H}OH}{|}}{R-C-OCH_3}} \rightleftharpoons \text{aldehyde}$$

Here

$$v = k[SH^+]$$

but

$$K = \frac{[SH^+]}{[S][H^+]}$$

and

$$v = kK[S][H^+]$$

This is an example of specific hydrogen ion catalysis.

[55] A. J. Deyrup, *J. Am. Chem. Soc.*, **56**, 60 (1934); R. P. Bell and A. D. Norris, *J. Chem. Soc.*, 118 (1941).

A somewhat different case is represented by the following equations,

Type II

$$HS + H^+ \rightleftharpoons \overset{+}{H}SH$$

$$\overset{+}{H}SH + A^- \xrightarrow{\text{slow}} HA + SH$$

which apply to the enolization of acetone.[56]

$$\underset{\substack{|| \\ O}}{CH_3-C-CH_3} + H^+ \rightleftharpoons \underset{\substack{|| \\ ^+OH}}{CH_3-C-CH_3}$$

$$\underset{\substack{|| \\ ^+OH}}{CH_3-C-CH_2-H} + A^- \xrightarrow{\text{slow}} \underset{\substack{| \\ OH}}{CH_3-C=CH_2} + HA$$

In this case

$$v = k[HSH^+][A^-]$$

but

$$K = \frac{[HSH^+]}{[SH][H^+]}$$

and

$$v = kK[SH][H^+][A^-] = kKK'[SH][HA]$$

Here we have catalysis by a general acid, usually a component of the buffer, because both the hydrogen ion and an ion (or other basic species such as the solvent) are required for the reaction. The product of the concentration of acid and of an anion is, of course, simply an equilibrium constant times the concentration of undissociated acid.

One usually tests for the occurrence of general acid catalysis by determining the rate of reaction as a function of buffer concentration. As long as the ratio $[A^-]/[HA]$ is constant, the pH will remain constant except for salt effects, which may be minimized by operating at a constant ionic strength. Then one plots the rate of reaction against buffer concentration to give a curve such as shown in Fig. 3-28. The slope of the line gives the catalytic rate constant, and the intercept gives the rate for a case in which the solvent acts as the hydrogen abstracting reagent. In the case of specific hydrogen ion catalysis, the above slope would be zero.

A third case may be represented by

Type III

$$HS + HA \rightleftharpoons HS \cdot HA$$

$$HS \cdot HA \xrightarrow{\text{slow}} \text{products}$$

[56] A. Lapworth, *J. Chem. Soc.*, **85**, 30 (1904); R. P. Bell and P. Jones, *J. Chem. Soc.*, 88 (1953).

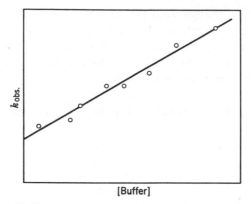

Fig. 3-28. *Effect of buffer concentration on the rate of a general acid catalyzed reaction. The slope gives the catalytic rate constant and the intercept gives the rate constant for* H_3O^+ *acting as the general acid.*

An example is the acid-catalyzed decomposition of some diazo compounds [57]

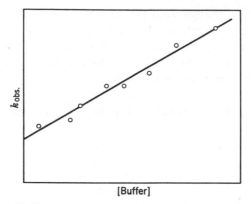

Here

$$v = k[\text{HS·HA}] = kK[\text{HS}][\text{HA}]$$

This is also a case of general acid catalysis, although of a fundamentally different type than the second case above. A differentiation between the two mechanisms for general acid catalysis may often be made by the use of deuterium oxide as the solvent. It may be remembered (Section 2-7) that D_3O^+ behaves as a stronger acid than H_3O^+; consequently, at a given acid concentration the concentration of conjugate acid will be about three times as great in D_2O as in H_2O. There should be no significant isotope effect on the slow step, and thus for reactions of Type II the rate ratio should be $k_{D_2O}/k_{H_2O} \sim 3$. Some typical examples are given in Table 3-23.

If the mechanism were of Type III, one might expect that the formation of the (presumably hydrogen bonded) complex HS·HA should not be

[57] J. D. Roberts and C. M. Regan, *J. Am. Chem. Soc.*, **74**, 3695 (1952).

largely affected by a change from HA to DA, for no bonds are broken or formed. However, the rate determining step involves the transfer of a proton from the acid to the substrate, and there will be a normal kinetic isotope effect for this reaction. As a consequence, k_{D_2O}/k_{H_2O} should be less than unity for this reaction (cf. Table 3-23).

Table 3-23 Solvent Kinetic Isotope Effects for ~~~ G~~~ ~~ral Acid-Catalyzed Reactions[a]

Reaction	Cataly~		k_{D_2O}/k_{H_2O}
Bromination of acetone	H_3O^+		2.1
	RCO_2H		2.
Decomposition of diphenyl-			
diazomethane (EtOH, EtOD solvent)	CH_3CO_2H	3.6	
	$C_6H_5CO_2H$	3.5	
Mutarotation of glucose	H_3O^+	1.37	
	CH_3CO_2H	2.6	

[a] Taken from a summary by K. B. Wiberg, *Chem. Revs.*, **55**, 713 (1955).

This criterion must be applied with care. As an example, we may consider the mutarotation of glucose in which α-D-glucose is converted in solution to an equilibrium mixture of α- and β-D-glucose. This reaction may involve the steps[58]

If this reaction were carried out in D_2O as the solvent, the concentration of the conjugate acid would be three times as great as in H_2O. However,

[58] See L. P. Hammett, *Physical Organic Chemistry*, McGraw-Hill Book Co., New York, 1940, p. 337; R. P. Bell and P. Jones, *J. Chem. Soc.*, 88 (1953).

the hydroxyl proton which is attacked in the next step will rapidly exchange with D_2O. Thus in D_2O the reaction will show a kinetic isotope effect which may have the usual magnitude, $k_H/k_D = 7$. Consequently, the observed isotope effect would be $k_{D_2O}/k_{H_2O} = 3 \times \frac{1}{7} = 1/2.3$, and it is observed to be 1/2.6. Thus the criterion applies only when the proton which is removed by the anion will not exchange with the solvent.

With reactions subject to general acid catalysis, it has been observed that the catalytic constant k_a is related to the strength of the acid, an increase in K_a giving an increase in k_a. Brønsted showed that there was a simple relationship between k_a and K_a[59]

$$k_a = G_a K_a{}^\alpha$$

where G_a and α are constants characteristic of the solvent, the reaction, and the temperature. The value of α commonly lies in the range 0.3 to 0.9. This is the earliest example of a linear free energy relationship for

$$RT \ln k_a = RT \ln G_a + \alpha RT \ln K_a$$

$$\Delta F^{\ddagger} - RT \ln \frac{kT}{h} = -RT \ln G_a + \alpha(\Delta F_a{}^\circ)$$

and in comparing two acids

$$(\Delta\Delta F^{\ddagger}) = \alpha(\Delta\Delta F_a{}^\circ)$$

Thus the Brønsted equation states that the free energy of activation changes linearly with the over-all change in free energy, and α is the proportionality constant. It might be mentioned that in applying this equation to acids having two or more equivalent acidic protons, the ionization constant must be taken as that of *one* of the protons. Thus the ionization constant for malonic acid must be divided by two and that for methanetriacetic acid by three.[60]

This equation has been applied to a large number of general acid-catalyzed (and also base-catalyzed) reactions with rather good results.[61] One of the more extensive investigations is that of Bell and Higginson on the dehydration of acetaldehyde hydrate in acetone solution using nearly fifty carboxylic acids and phenols as catalysts.[62] Part of the data are

[59] J. N. Brønsted and K. Pedersen, *J. physik. Chem.*, **108**, 185 (1924).
[60] The general subject of symmetry corrections has been discussed by S. W. Benson, *J. Am. Chem. Soc.*, **80**, 5151 (1958).
[61] See the summary in R. P. Bell, *Acid-Base Catalysis*, Oxford University Press, Oxford, 1941.
[62] R. P. Bell and W. C. E. Higginson, *Proc. Roy. Soc.*, **A197**, 141 (1949).

shown in Fig. 3-29, and it can be seen that there is a remarkably good fit to the equation even though they cover a range of 10^5 in the rate constant and 10^9 in acid dissociation constants. Catalysts of other types, such as β-diketones, nitroparaffins, and oximes, show marked deviations in both the positive and negative sense. Even with this relationship good correlations are obtained only when the compounds used in the comparison are of a similar structural type.

We must now consider the reason why general acid catalysis follows a linear free energy relationship. For the Type II acid catalysis, the rate law is

$$v = kKK_a[\text{S}][\text{HA}]$$

where K_a is the ionization constant for the acid HA. Thus the observed rate constants are given by

$$k_{\text{obs.}} = kKK_a$$

We are interested in k, the rate constant for the rate controlling step. This will be proportional to $k_{\text{obs.}}/K_a$, for K is a constant for a given substrate. The Brønsted equation is

$$k_{\text{obs.}} = G_a K_a{}^\alpha$$

and thus

$$k \approx \frac{K_a{}^\alpha}{K_a} = K_a{}^{(\alpha-1)}$$

It can be seen that if $\alpha = 1$, k will be constant for all acids, and if $\alpha < 1$, k will decrease as K_a increases.

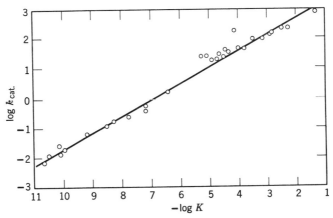

Fig. 3-29. Catalytic constants as a function of catalyst in general acid catalysis.

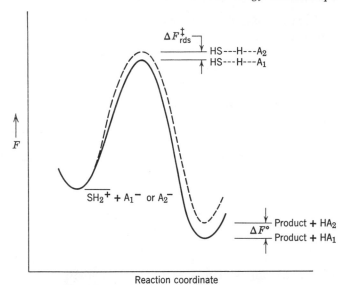

Fig. 3-30. Energy relationships in general acid catalysis.

Suppose the reaction of a given substrate with the acid HA_1 had the reaction coordinate plot shown in Fig. 3-30. If a stronger acid, HA_2, were used, the energy of the products would be increased with respect to the reactants. As we saw previously in the discussion of the halogenation of methane, an increase in the energy of the products will produce an increase in the energy of the activated complex. Thus the activation energy will increase, and the rate of reaction will decrease. The effect in the activated complex will generally be less than in the reactants, and the change in free energy of activation for the rate determining step (rds) will be

$$\Delta\Delta F_{rds}^{\ddagger} = (\alpha - 1)\Delta\Delta F_{ioniz.}^{\circ}$$

THE HAMMETT RELATIONSHIP

The derivation of the Hammett equation

$$\log\left(\frac{K}{K_0}\right) = \sigma\rho$$

was given previously (p. 279), and it was applied to equilibrium reactions. We shall now consider the application of this free energy relationship to kinetic phenomena. It will be used in the form

$$\log\left(\frac{k}{k_0}\right) = \sigma\rho$$

where k_0 is the rate constant for the reaction of an unsubstituted compound and k is the rate constant for the corresponding substituted compound. The constants σ and ρ have the same significance as before.

Let us first consider the variation in the reaction constant, ρ. Some

Table 3-24   Some Typical Reaction Constants[a]

Reaction	*Solvent*	*Temp.*	ρ
1. $Ar(C_6H_5)CHCl + C_2H_5OH \rightarrow$ $Ar(C_6H_5)CHOC_2H_5$	C_2H_5OH	25°	−5.09
2. $ArCHOHCH{=}CHCH_3 + H^+ \rightarrow$ $ArCH{=}CHCHOHCH_3$	40% dioxane	30	−4.67
3. $ArNH_2 + 2,4\text{-}(NO_2)_2C_6H_3Cl \rightarrow$ $2,4\text{-}(NO_2)_2C_6H_3NHAr$	C_2H_5OH	25	−3.98
4. $ArN(CH_3)_2 + CH_3I \rightarrow ArN(CH_3)_3{}^+I^-$	90% acetone	35	−3.30
5. $ArCH_2Cl + H_2O \rightarrow ArCH_2OH$	48% C_2H_5OH	30	−2.18
6. $ArOH + CH_3COBr \rightarrow ArOCOCH_3$	$CH_3CO_2C_2H_5$	0	−1.45
7. $ArO^- + C_2H_5I \rightarrow ArOC_2H_5$	C_2H_5OH	43	−0.99
8. $ArCH_3 + (CH_2CO)_2NBr \rightarrow ArCH_2Br$	CCl_4	80	−1.46
9. $ArCH_3 + Br_2 \rightarrow ArCH_2Br$	CCl_4	80	−1.37
10. $ArCH_3 + Cl_2 \rightarrow ArCH_2Cl$	CCl_4		−1.25
11. $ArCHO + C_6H_5CO_3\cdot \rightarrow ArCO\cdot$	Ac_2O	30	−0.50
12. $ArSH + R\cdot \rightarrow ArS\cdot$	$C_6H_5CH_3$		−0.4
13. $(ArCO_2)_2 \rightarrow ArCO_2\cdot$	$CH_3COC_6H_5$	80	−0.20
14. $ArOCOC_6H_5 + HO^- \rightarrow ArO^-$	60% acetone	0	0.98
15. $ArCN + HS^- \rightarrow ArC(SH){=}NH$	C_2H_5OH	61	2.15
16. $ArNHCOCH_3 + CH_3O^- \rightarrow ArNH_2$	CH_3OH		2.15
17. $ArCO_2CH_3 + HO^- \rightarrow ArCO_2{}^-$	60% acetone	25	2.23
18. $ArCHO + HCN \rightarrow ArCHOHCN$	95% C_2H_5OH	20	2.33
19. $ArCH_2ONO + OEt^- \rightarrow ArCHO$	C_2H_5OH	30	3.4

[a] The data were taken from H. H. Jaffé, *Chem. Revs.*, **53**, 191 (1953), G. A. Russell, *J. Org. Chem.*, **23**, 1407 (1958), E. Buncel and A. N. Bourns, *Can. J. Chem.*, **38**, 2457 (1960), R. E. Pearson and J. C. Martin, *J. Am. Chem. Soc.*, **85**, 354 (1963).

typical values are given in Table 3-24, which is divided into three sections. The reactions 1 to 7 refer to processes in which the electron density at the reaction center is decreased during the reaction; the reactions 8 to 13 lead to no formal change in charge; and the reactions 13 to 19 lead to an increase in electron density.

For the reactions in the first group, the value of ρ lies between -1 and -5. When the electron demand is large, as in the solvolysis of benzhydryl chlorides, ρ has a large negative value. At the same time, when the charge

$$\text{C}_6\text{H}_5\text{--CH(Cl)--C}_6\text{H}_5 \xrightarrow{\text{slow}} \text{C}_6\text{H}_5\text{--}\overset{+}{\text{C}}\text{H--C}_6\text{H}_5 \xrightarrow[\text{SOH}]{\text{fast}} \text{product}$$

is developed at a carbon adjacent to the aromatic ring, large deviations from the Hammett equation are noted with electron releasing p-substituents such as p-methoxy. This undoubtedly arises from the stabilization of the activated complex by the contribution of structures such as

$$\text{CH}_3\text{O--C}_6\text{H}_4\text{--}\overset{+}{\text{C}}\text{H--C}_6\text{H}_5 \, \text{Cl}^- \leftrightarrow \text{CH}_3\overset{+}{\text{O}}\text{=C}_6\text{H}_4\text{=CH--C}_6\text{H}_5 \, \text{Cl}^-$$

which is not possible with the carboxylate ion.

In order to have a more meaningful measure of the electron demand, we may use only the m-substituents, which would give only a small resonance effect of the type described above. If we do this, the ρ for the solvolysis of benzhydryl chlorides in ethanol is -4.1.

We have seen previously when considering equilibria (p. 290) that the value of ρ for the formation of benzhydryl cations from benzhydrols in sulfuric acid is -6.7 (again based on m-substituents). Recognizing that it is difficult to estimate the change in ρ in going from sulfuric acid as the medium to ethanol, it is still apparent that the change developed in the activated complex is large but not as great as in the cation itself.

The solvolysis of benzyl chlorides gives a ρ of only -2.2 in 48% ethanol, whereas we would expect the ρ for the formation of the benzyl cation to be even more negative than that for the benzhydryl cation. This is in accord with the generally accepted idea that the reaction is best described as an S_N2 displacement in which the charge on the carbon will be much less than in the S_N1 case because of the bonding to the entering solvent molecule.

The reaction of amines with organic halides (reactions 3 and 4) is similar to the protonation of the amines. The above reactions had values

$$\text{C}_6\text{H}_5\text{--N(CH}_3)_2: + \text{CH}_3\text{I} \rightarrow \left[\text{C}_6\text{H}_5\text{--}\overset{\delta+}{\text{N(CH}_3)_2}\overset{\text{H}_3\text{C} \quad \text{H}}{\text{------C------I}}\overset{\delta-}{} \right]^{\ddagger} \rightarrow \text{C}_6\text{H}_5\text{N(CH}_3)_3^+ + \text{I}^-$$

of $\rho = -4.0$ and -3.3, respectively, whereas the protonation of aniline and of dimethylaniline had $\rho = -3.5$ and ~ -4.2, respectively, for the same solvents. Thus in these reactions essentially a full positive charge is developed on the nitrogen in the activated complex.

In reaction 7 the process is similar to the protonation of phenoxide ions, for which $\rho = -2.5$. The lower value observed in the reaction (-1.0) is expected, for the activated complex may be represented as

$$\left[C_6H_5\!-\!\overset{\delta-}{O}\cdots\cdots\underset{\underset{CH_3}{|}}{\overset{\overset{\displaystyle H}{\diagdown}\;\;\overset{\displaystyle H}{\diagup}}{C}}\cdots\cdots\overset{\delta-}{I} \right]^{\ddagger}$$

and the charge on the oxygen might be approximately half that in the phenoxide ion.

In the second group of reactions (8 to 13), we might at first expect to find a very small or zero value of ρ because no formal charges are developed in the activated complex. This is indeed the case for the decomposition of the symmetrical dibenzoyl peroxide. However, in most hydrogen abstraction reactions, a negative value is observed. This has been attributed to the operation of polar effects,[63] which may be illustrated for the bromination of toluene.

$$C_6H_5CH_3 + Br\cdot \rightarrow \left[\begin{matrix} C_6H_5CH_2\text{--------}H\text{-------}Br \\ \updownarrow \\ C_6H_5CH_2^{+} \;\; H\cdot \;\; Br^{-} \end{matrix} \right]^{\ddagger} \rightarrow C_6H_5CH_2\cdot + HBr$$

The strong electron withdrawing tendency of the bromine will permit a small contribution of the dipolar cannonical structure in stabilizing the activated complex. The small positive charge developed on the benzylic carbon will then be stabilized by the electron releasing substituents. It can be seen that the value of ρ is generally quite small, which shows that the charge developed is also small. There is no reason why the polar factors could not operate in the opposite direction in a suitable case.

In the third group (14 to 19), in which a negative charge is developed in a position near the aromatic ring, a positive value of ρ is found. When the charge is relatively far away, such as in the hydrolysis of phenyl benzoates, the ρ is relatively small. In reactions such as ester hydrolysis where the charge is developed at an atom separated from the ring by one carbon, it is constant at about $\rho = 2.2$. Finally, when it is developed at the atom adjacent to the aromatic ring, as in reaction 19, it may increase further.

[63] F. R. Mayo and C. Walling, *Chem. Revs.*, **46**, 191 (1950); G. A. Russell, *J. Org. Chem.* **23**, 1407 (1958).

It can be seen that the value of ρ is a useful indicator of the charge which is developed in the activated complex. It must, however, be used with care in multistep processes, or where other prior equilibria are involved, for each step will have its characteristic value of ρ, and the observed value will be a composite of all of these effects. For example, the reaction of anilines with nitrous acid has a $\rho = 2.31$.[64] However, the reaction was carried out in aqueous acidic solution, and so the amine was present as the amine salt. The ρ for the protonation of aniline is -2.77, and this must be added to the observed value for the reaction to obtain the ρ for the reaction of the amine with nitrous acid (actually dinitrogen trioxide). Thus this reaction has $\rho = -0.5$.

Whenever the rate of a reaction may be characterized by a single rate constant (even if it is the product of a number of individual equilibrium constants and a rate constant), the over-all ρ is given as the sum of the ρ values for the individual steps. This can be seen if we write the rate constant for some reaction as

$$k_0' = K_0{}^a K_0{}^b K_0{}^c k_0$$

where K^a, K^b, and K^c are equilibrium constants for steps preceding the rate determining step, and k' is the observed rate constant. The rate for a substituted derivative would be

$$k' = K^a K^b K^c k$$

and the ratio of rates would be

$$\frac{k'}{k_0'} = \frac{K^a K^b K^c k}{K_0{}^a K_0{}^b K_0{}^c k_0}$$

Taking logarithms

$$\log\left(\frac{k'}{k_0'}\right) = \log\left(\frac{K^a}{K_0{}^a}\right) + \log\left(\frac{K^b}{K_0{}^b}\right) + \log\left(\frac{K^c}{K_0{}^c}\right) + \log\left(\frac{k}{k_0}\right)$$

or

$$\log\left(\frac{k'}{k_0'}\right) = \sigma(\rho^a + \rho^b + \rho^c + \rho) = \sigma\rho'$$

This is, however, not the case when the rate expression must be given in terms of the sum of two or more rate constants multiplied by the appropriate concentrations. Thus if a reaction proceeded by two different paths, and the rate constant could be given by

$$k_0 = k_0{}^a + k_0{}^b$$

for the unsubstituted compound, and

$$k = k^a + k^b$$

[64] S. Ueno and T. Suzuki, *J. Soc. Chem. Ind. (Japan)*, **36B**, 615 (1933).

for the substituted compound, the Hammett equation would take the form

$$\log \left(\frac{k}{k_0}\right) = \log \left(\frac{k^a + k^b}{k_0{}^a + k_0{}^b}\right)$$

This cannot be further simplified. If the two rate constants k^a and k^b are similarly affected by substituents, a normal Hammett plot will be obtained. However, if k^a were increased by electron withdrawing substituents, and if k^b were decreased by these groups, then the former would be the more important with a p-nitro substituted compound, and the latter would be the more important with the p-methoxy substituted compound. Thus the Hammett plot would give a curve which is concave downward (Fig. 3-31).

One may well ask, "Why is the Hammett equation useful?" Two reasons may be given. The most common (in textbooks) is that it permits the correlation of a vast body of data and enables one to predict rate constants for reactions of substituted compounds with reasonable accuracy if the ρ value for the reaction has been determined. To this writer that reason seems relatively unimportant, for almost no worker in the field uses the relationship for this purpose; it is normally used in order to obtain σ values for new substituent groups and ρ values for new reactions. These parameters are then useful in giving us information concerning the electrical characteristics of substituents and the electron demand of reactions.

If this latter point of view were accepted, then the deviations which are observed with electron releasing groups and reactions with high electron demand, and with electron withdrawing groups and reactions which lead to negative charges on atoms adjacent to the aromatic ring, would not be disturbing. The former would simply be attributed to a direct resonance effect of the type

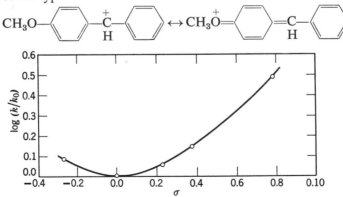

Fig. 3-31. Hammett plots for competitive reactions. $\rho_A = +1$; $\rho_B = -1$, *and the points are for* p-MeO⁻, H⁻, p-Cl, m-Cl, *and* p-NO₂.

which will give additional stabilization over the cases in which this resonance interaction is not found. In the latter case it would be attributed to a corresponding resonance effect.

One would look for these deviations as additional support for the mechanisms of certain reactions.

If, however, one took the first point of view, the deviations would be very disturbing, and new σ values would be sought. This was done quite early for the reactions of phenols and anilines, for which σ_p^- values were obtained.[65] Since resonance contributions from the m-position would be very small, $\sigma_m^- = \sigma_m$, and for electron releasing substituents which would not give the above resonance effect, $\sigma_p^- = \sigma_p$. For most groups which may stabilize a negative charge by a conjugative effect, $\sigma_p^- > \sigma_p$.

The same has been done for reactions with a high electron demand, such as solvolysis reactions. Here Brown and Okamoto[66] took the solvolysis of cumyl chloride as the standard and assumed that the σ_m values would still be applicable for most groups. The value of ρ based on these substituents was then determined, and this in turn permitted the assignment of new σ values (designated as σ^+) for the groups which gave a deviation from the ordinary σ values. These and other σ values are summarized in Table 3-25.

These σ^+ values presumably are the sum of the contribution from the field effect and from the direct resonance interaction. It would be surprising if the two effects were in constant proportion for a series of carbonium ion forming reactions having different values of ρ. Remarkably, this does appear to be the case (within the usual limits) for a large number of reactions.

SEPARATION OF POLAR AND STERIC EFFECTS

In some reactions, such as the hydrolysis of ortho-substituted benzoic acids and in the hydrolysis of aliphatic esters, steric effects play an important role in governing the rate of reaction. Following a suggestion by Ingold,[67] a separation of the total effect of a substituent into a steric term

---

[65] L. P. Hammett, *Physical Organic Chemistry*, McGraw-Hill Book Co., New York, 1940, p. 193.

[66] H. C. Brown and Y. Okamoto, *J. Am. Chem. Soc.*, **79**, 1913 (1957); Y. Okamoto and H. C. Brown, *J. Org. Chem.*, **22**, 485 (1957).

[67] C. K. Ingold, *J. Chem. Soc.*, 1032 (1932).

Table 3-25 A Comparison of Various σ Values

Group	$\sigma_p{}^a$	$\sigma_m{}^a$	$\sigma_p{}^{-a}$	$\sigma_p{}^{+b}$	$\sigma_m{}^{+b}$	σ'^c	σ^{*c}	$\sigma_0{}^c$
-O-	-1.00	-0.71	-1.00					
H₂N-	-0.660	-0.161	-0.660					
(CH₃)₂N-	-0.600	-0.211	-0.600					
HO-	-0.357	-0.002	-0.357			+0.25	+0.555	-0.39
CH₃O-	-0.268	+0.115	-0.268	-0.764	+0.047	+0.23	+0.52	
(CH₃)₃C-	-0.197	-0.120	-0.197	-0.250	-0.058	-0.07	-0.165	
CH₃-	-0.170	-0.069	-0.170	-0.306	-0.069	-0.05	-0.100	-0.17
C₂H₅-	-0.151	-0.043	-0.151	-0.291	-0.063			
(CH₃)₂CH-	-0.151	—	-0.151	-0.276	-0.059			
(CH₃)₃Si	-0.01	+0.08	-0.01			-0.12	-0.26	
CH₃S-	-0.047	+0.144	-0.047					
C₆H₅O-	-0.028	—	-0.028			+0.38	+0.850	
CH₃CONH-	-0.015	—	-0.015					
H	0.000	0.000	0.000	0.000	0.000	0.000	0.000	0.000
C₆H₅-	+0.009	+0.06	+0.009	+0.071		+0.10	+0.215	
F-	+0.062	+0.337	+0.062		+0.337	+0.50	+1.10	+0.24
-O₂C-	+0.132	+0.104	+0.132					
ClH₂C-	+0.184	—	+0.184			+0.17	+0.385	
Cl-	+0.226	+0.373	+0.226	+0.112	+0.373	+0.47	+1.050	+0.20
OHC-	+0.216	+0.355	+1.126					

Group								
Br—	+0.232	+0.391	+0.232	+0.148	+0.391	+0.45	+1.00	+0.21
HO₂C—	+0.265	+0.355	+0.728	+0.132	+0.352	+0.38	+0.85	
I—	+0.276	+0.352	+0.276					
(HO)₂B—	+0.454							
C₆H₅CO—	+0.459							
CH₃CO—	+0.516	+0.306	+0.874			+0.27	+0.60	
EtO₂C—	+0.522	+0.398	+0.678			+0.32	+0.071	
F₃C—	+0.551	+0.415	+0.74			+0.41	+0.92	
CH₃SO—	+0.567	+0.551						
CN—	+0.628	+0.678	+1.00			+0.59	+1.30	
CH₃SO₂—	+0.728	+0.647	+1.05			+0.59	+1.32	
O₂I—	+0.760	+0.700						
NO₂—	+0.778	+0.710	+1.27	+0.777	+0.662	+0.63	+1.40	+0.80 (+1.22)[d]
(CH₃)₃N⁺—	+0.86	+0.90				+0.86	+1.90	

[a] These values were taken from the review by H. H. Jaffé, *Chem. Revs.*, **53**, 191 (1953), with the exception of the $(CH_3)_3Si$-group (J. D. Roberts and C. M. Regan, *J. Am. Chem. Soc.*, **75**, 4102 (1953)) and the $m\text{-}C_6H_5$-group (N. N. Lichtin and H. P. Leftin, *J. Am. Chem. Soc.*, **74**, 4207 (1952)).

[b] These values were taken from Y. Okamoto and H. C. Brown, *J. Org. Chem.*, **22**, 485 (1957).

[c] These data were taken from R. W. Taft, Jr., in *Steric Effects in Organic Chemistry*, M. Newman, (ed.), John Wiley and Sons, New York, 1956, ch. 13. The σ_0 values are corrected for steric effects and may not be used in the original Hammett equation.

[d] Values used in reactions of phenols and amines, i.e., σ_0^-.

and a polar term has been effected by Taft.[68] The basis of the method is as follows. The acid-catalyzed hydrolysis of substituted benzoic acids has a ρ of -0.2 to $+0.5$, which is so small that it may be considered to be zero. The lack of effect of substituents arises because it is a multistep reaction, with the effect of substituents for some steps canceling those of others.

Electron releasing substituents will, for example, help step 1 and hinder step 2. There is a fortuitous balancing of effects leading to essentially no effects of substituent.

The base-catalyzed reaction has a fairly large value of ρ ($+2.2$ to $+2.8$), and hence substituent effects are easily measured in this reaction. The activated complexes for the two reactions have similar geometry and may roughly be represented by I for the acid-catalyzed reaction and II for the

base-catalyzed. Thus steric effects on this type of reaction may be determined from the rates of acid-catalyzed hydrolysis of esters (in which there

[68] R. W. Taft, Jr., *J. Am. Chem. Soc.*, **74**, 3120 (1952), **75**, 4231 (1953).

is essentially no polar factor), and the sum of the steric and polar effects may be obtained from the relative rates of the base-catalyzed reactions.

The values of the polar parameter (designated as σ^*) may be obtained from

$$\sigma^* = \frac{1}{2.48}\left[\log\left(\frac{k}{k_0}\right)_B - \log\left(\frac{k}{k_0}\right)_A\right]$$

where A and B refer to the acid- and base-catalyzed hydrolyses, k is the observed rate constant, k_0 is the rate constant for the standard compound (benzoate esters in the aromatic series and acetate esters in the aliphatic series), and the constant, $1/2.48$, is the reciprocal of the average ρ for several ester hydrolyses for which there are no steric effects. This makes changes in σ^* comparable to those in σ. The steric parameter, E_s, is obtained from the equation

$$\log(k/k_0) = \sigma^*\rho^* + \delta E_s$$

where $\delta = 1.0$ for the hydrolysis of esters. The values of σ_o ($\equiv \sigma^*$ for ortho-substituted aromatic compounds) are given in Table 3-25, whereas the other σ^* values and the E_s values are given in Tables 3-26 and 3-27.

The values of σ_o can be seen to be quite reasonable in comparison with the values of σ_p. The main difference between the two appears in the field effect term of the total effect of the substituent, and since the resonance effect is quite important, it is not surprising that the values are fairly similar. For comparison, the values of σ^* for aliphatic compounds (actually the values for XCH_2—) and the values of σ' which are appropriate for the 4-substituted bicyclo[2.2.2]octyl-1 derivatives are also given in Table 3-25. As noted previously (p. 280), the values are quite different from the other σ values. Thus the hydroxy group is electron withdrawing in the aliphatic series, whereas it is electron releasing (via the resonance effect) in the aromatic series.

The values of σ^* for the aliphatic series (Table 3-27) are in the order one would expect for the operation of a field effect. Thus the values increase in the series $H < -OH < -Cl = -Br = -I < -N(CH_3)^+$, and this is the order of increasing electron-withdrawing power which one finds from other data, such as dipole moments. The σ^* values provide one of our most useful sets of data on the electrical nature of substituents, relatively uncomplicated by resonance effects.

A reasonable amount of caution must, however, be exercised in using these values. For example, it may be noted that the σ^* values for CH_3, C_2H_5, $i\text{-}C_3H_7$, and $t\text{-}C_4H_9$ are 0.00, -0.100, -0.190, and -0.300, respectively. One may then be tempted to attribute this to hyperconjugation and to formalize it in terms of a correction constant multiplied by the

Table 3-26   Steric Substituent Constants, E_s[a]

A. *o*-Substituted Benzoates

Substituent	E_s	Substituent	E_s
—OCH₃	+0.99	—CH₃	0.00
—OC₂H₅	+0.90	—I	−0.20
—F	+0.49	—NO₂	−0.75
—Cl	+0.18	—C₆H₅	−0.90
—Br	+0.00		

B. Aliphatic Series, RCOOR′

Substituent	Acyl Component R E_s	Substituent	Acyl Component R E_s
H(C₆H₅)[b]	+1.24	*i*-C₄H₉	−0.93
CH₃	0.00	cyclo-C₆H₁₁CH₂	−0.98
C₂H₅	−0.07	(CH₃)(C₂H₅)CH	−1.13
cyclo-C₄H₇	−0.06	F₃C	−1.16
CH₃OCH₂	−0.19	cyclo-C₇H₁₃	−1.10
ClCH₂, FCH₂	−0.24	(CH₃)(C₆H₅)CH	−1.19
BrCH₂	−0.27	*t*-C₄H₉	−1.54
CH₃SCH₂	−0.34	(C₆H₅)(C₂H₅)CH	−1.50
ICH₂	−0.37	Cl₂CH	−1.54
n-C₃H₇	−0.36	*t*-C₄H₉CH₂	−1.74
n-C₄H₉	−0.39	(C₆H₅)₂CH	−1.76
n-C₅H₁₁	−0.40	(CH₃)(neopentyl)CH	−1.85
i-C₅H₁₁	−0.35	Br₂CH	−1.86
n-C₈H₁₇	−0.33	(C₂H₅)₂CH	−1.98
t-C₄H₉CH₂CH₂	−0.34	Cl₃C	−2.06
C₆H₅OCH₂	−0.33	(*n*-C₃H₇)₂CH	−2.11
C₆H₅CH₂	−0.38	(*i*-C₄H₉)₂CH	−2.47
C₆H₅CH₂CH₂	−0.38	Br₃C	−2.43
C₆H₅CH₂CH₂CH₂	−0.45	(CH₃)₂(neopentyl)C	−2.57
i-C₃H₇	−0.47	(neopentyl)₂CH	−3.18
Cyclo-C₅H₉	−0.51	(CH₃)(*t*-C₄H₉)CH	−3.33
F₂CH	−0.67	(CH₃)₂(*t*-C₄H₉)C	−3.9
cyclo-C₆H₁₁	−0.79	(C₂H₅)₃C	−3.8
CH₃OCH₂CH₂	−0.77	(CH₃)(*t*-C₄H₉)	
ClCH₂CH₂	−0.90	(neopentyl)C	−4.0

[a] R. W. Taft, Jr. in *Steric Effects in Organic Chemistry*, M. Newman, Ed., John Wiley and Sons, New York, 1956, p. 598.
[b] The value for phenyl is not a pure steric parameter. If the discussion is ref. a, p. 670.

Table 3-27　Polar Substituent Constants, $\sigma*$[a]

Substituent	σ	Substituent	σ
Cl_3C	+2.65	$Cl(CH_2)_2$	+0.385
F_2CH	+2.05	$CH_3CH{=}CH$	+0.360
CH_3O_2C	+2.00	$CF_3(CH_2)_2$	+0.32
Cl_2CH	+1.940	$C_6H_5CH_2$	+0.215
$(CH_3)_3N^+CH_2$	+1.90	$CH_3CH{=}CHCH_2$	+0.13
CH_3CO	+1.65	$CF_3(CH_2)_3$	+0.12
$C_6H_5C{\equiv}C$	+1.35	$C_6H_5(CH_3)CH$	+0.11
$CH_3SO_2CH_2$	+1.32	$C_6H_5(CH_2)_2$	+0.080
$CNCH_2$	+1.300	$C_6H_5(C_2H_5)CH$	+0.04
FCH_2	+1.10	$C_6H_5(CH_2)_3$	+0.02
HO_2CCH_2	+1.05	CH_3	0.00
$ClCH_2$	+1.050	cyclo-$C_6H_{11}CH_2$	−0.06
$BrCH_2$	+1.000	C_2H_5	−0.100
ICH_2	+0.85	n-C_3H_7	−0.115
CF_3CH_2	+0.92	i-C_4H_9	−0.125
$C_6H_5OCH_2$	+0.850	n-C_4H_9	−0.130
$C_6H_5(OH)CH$	+0.765	cyclo-C_6H_{11}	−0.15
CH_3COCH_2	+0.60	t-$C_4H_9CH_2$	−0.165
C_6H_5	+0.600	i-C_3H_7	−0.190
$HOCH_2$	+0.555	cyclo-C_5H_9	−0.20
CH_3OCH_2	+0.520	s-C_4H_9	−0.210
$NO_2(CH_2)_2$	+0.50	$(C_2H_5)_2CH$	−0.225
H	+0.490	$(CH_3)_3SiCH_2$	−0.26
$C_6H_5CH{=}CH$	+0.410	$(t$-$C_4H_9)(CH_3)CH$	−0.28
$(C_6H_5)_2CH$	+0.405	t-C_4H_9	−0.300

[a] R. W. Taft, Jr. in *Steric Effects in Organic Chemistry*, M. S. Newman (ed.), John Wiley and Sons, New York, 1956, p. 619. The values given to three figures after the decimal point are derived from several reactions and have an average deviation of about 0.05. The others were derived from one or two reactions and probably should be considered as ±0.1 or more.

number of α-hydrogens.[69] However, as discussed previously (p. 132), an effect such as hyperconjugation should not be important unless it involves the distribution of a charge present in the molecule (such as in the *t*-butyl cation). This is not the case in the present example. An equally reasonable (but not unique) explanation is that the activated complexes for acidic and basic hydrolysis are sufficiently different to permit a small discrimination in steric effects between the two activated complexes when the differences are as large as between methyl and *t*-butyl. This effect would also be

[69] M. M. Kreevoy and R. W. Taft, Jr., *J. Am. Chem. Soc.*, **77**, 5590 (1955).

proportional to the number of α-hydrogens. Here again, the fact that an experimental result may be correlated with one theoretical idea does not demonstrate that the theoretical idea applies, for there may be many other influences which will have the same dependence on the experimental variables.

The steric term E_s is also of considerable interest, for it provides one of the best sets of data on the effective size of substituent groups. Thus in the ortho-substituted benzoic acid series, the order of groups is $-OCH_3 <$ $-F < -Cl < -Br < -CH_3 < -I < -NO_2$. The order of the halogens is in accord with the change in size of the atom with the change in

Table 3-28 A Comparison of ρ and ρ^* for Corresponding Reactions[a]

Reaction	ρ^* for o-Substituted Benzene Derivatives	ρ for m- or p-Substituted Benzene Derivatives	ρ^* for Aliphatic Groups
Alkaline hydrolysis of esters	+2.5	+2.2 to +2.8	+2.5
Ionization of carboxylic acids	+1.79	+1.00	+1.72
Acid-catalyzed dehydration of acetaldehyde hydrate	+0.77	+0.57	+0.80
Ionization of amines	+2.90	+2.77	
Reaction of amines with benzoyl chloride	−2.66	−2.78	

[a] R. W. Taft, Jr., in *Steric Effects in Organic Chemistry*, M. Newman (ed.), John Wiley and Sons, New York, 1956, p. 649.

principal quantum number of the outer electrons. The difference between methyl and methoxy is in accord with the effect of these groups on the equilibrium between the axial and equatorial conformations for cyclohexane derivatives.[70]

The values of ρ^* which result from this treatment may be used as a measure of electron density changes at the reaction site during the reaction, just as with the ρ values. The two constants have been obtained for a few reactions and are compared in Table 3-28. It can be seen that the values are generally similar, as should be the case, except for the ionization of benzoic acids. Here the values are disturbingly different, indicating that the treatment still requires further consideration. However, on the

[70] S. Winstein and N. J. Holness, *J. Am. Chem. Soc.*, **77**, 5562 (1955).

favorable side, the values of ρ^* for ortho-substituted benzoic acid derivatives and for aliphatic compounds are the same for any given reaction.[71] For example, ρ^* for the ionization of aliphatic acids is $+1.72$ as compared to $+1.79$ for the ortho-substituted benzoic acids.

SOLVENT EFFECTS ON RATES

As discussed previously (p. 388), it has generally been noted that when the water concentration in a mixed solvent is increased, the rates of solvolysis of alkyl halides, tosylates, and other similar compounds are also increased. With some solvent mixtures, the change in rate may be correlated reasonably well with changes in dielectric constant. However, this correlation is poor with other solvent mixtures and is generally poor when different solvents are compared.

It has been observed that the changes in rate constant for one compound usually parallel those for other compounds. Grunwald and Winstein were therefore led to suggest the use of a linear free energy equation of the type[72]

$$\log \left(\frac{k}{k_0}\right) = m\mathbf{Y}$$

where k is the rate constant for the solvolysis of a compound in any solvent, k_0 is the rate constant for the solvolysis of the same compound in the standard solvent (80% ethanol), $\mathbf{Y}$ is a measure of the ionizing power of the solvent, and m gives the sensitivity of the substrate to changes in the medium. The application of the equation requires that the $\mathbf{Y}$ values be determined with respect to a standard compound, and this has been chosen as t-butyl chloride ($m = 1.00$). The standard solvent and the standard compound were chosen because a great deal of data are available on the rates of solvolysis in 80% ethanol and because the rate constants for the solvolysis of t-butyl chloride in a variety of solvents are available. In addition, t-butyl chloride reacts cleanly by an S_N1 process. Typical values of m and $\mathbf{Y}$ are given in Tables 3-29 and 3-30.

It is interesting to compare the $\mathbf{Y}$ values with the function $(\epsilon - 1/2\epsilon + 1)$ (Fig. 3-32). It can be seen that there is a general correlation between the two, but that there is also considerable scatter in the points. The data for the dioxane-water mixtures give a very marked deviation from the other solvents, and this peculiarity of dioxane has been noted previously (p. 386).

[71] R. W. Taft, Jr., in *Steric Effects in Organic Chemistry*, M. Newman (ed.), John Wiley and Sons, New York, 1956, pp. 607–609.
[72] E. Grunwald and S. Winstein, *J. Am. Chem. Soc.*, **70**, 846 (1948).

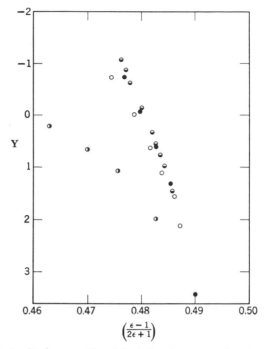

Fig. 3-32. *Relationship between Y and the dielectric constant function. The solvents are:* ○ = *Ethanol-Water;* ◐ = *Methanol-Water;* ◑ = *Dioxane-Water, and* ● = *Acetone-Water.* A. Streitwieser, Jr., *Chem. Revs.,* **56,** 620 (1956).

Table 3-29   **Grunwald-Winstein *m* Values[a]**

Compound	T	$\log k_0$	m
t-Butyl chloride	25	−5.034	(1.00)
t-Butyl bromide	25	−3.472	0.940
t-Amyl bromide	25	−3.21	0.90
α-Phenethyl chloride	50	−3.808	1.195
Neopentyldimethylcarbinyl chloride	25	−3.661	0.858
α-Methallyl chloride	25	−6.314	0.894
Dineopentylmethylcarbinyl chloride	25	−2.264	0.698
Benzhydryl chloride	25	−2.779	0.757

[a] E. Grunwald and S. Winstein, *J. Am. Chem. Soc.,* **70,** 846 (1948).

The values of m are generally close to unity for compounds which react by an S_N1 process (Table 3-29). However, when compounds which react by an S_N2 process are studied, it is found that the value of m is much

Table 3-30 Grunwald-Winstein Y Values[a]

Solvent[b]	N_{H_2O}	Y
100% Ethanol	0.00	−1.974
90 Ethanol	0.262	−0.727
80 Ethanol	0.448	(0.000)
70 Ethanol	0.582	0.644
60 Ethanol	0.684	1.139
50 Ethanol	0.765	1.604
40 Ethanol	0.829	2.151
100% Methanol	0.000	−1.052
96.8 Methanol	0.070	−0.722
91.4 Methanol	0.175	−0.329
88.3 Methanol	0.230	−0.112
85.1 Methanol	0.282	0.088
81.1 Methanol	0.346	0.361
74.7 Methanol	0.432	0.757
69.5 Methanol	0.497	1.023
Water		3.56
Formic acid		2.08
Acetic acid		−1.633
97.5% Acetic anhydride, 2.5% acetic acid		−3.287
50.6% Dioxane (water)		1.292

[a] E. Grunwald and S. Winstein, *J. Am. Chem. Soc.*, **70**, 846 (1948).
[b] Vol %.

smaller, usually in the range 0.25 to 0.35[73] (Table 3-31). This is expected, for the S_N1 process may be roughly described as

$$R_3C\text{—}Br \rightarrow [R_3\overset{\delta+}{C}\text{--------}\overset{\delta-}{Br}]^{\ddagger} \rightarrow R_3C^{+} + Br^{-}$$

whereas the S_N2 process would be described as

$$RCH_2Br + SOH \rightarrow \left[\begin{array}{ccc} S & H & H \\ & & \\ \overset{\delta+}{O}\text{--------}C\text{--------}\overset{\delta-}{Br} \\ H & R & \end{array}\right]^{\ddagger} \rightarrow RCH_2OS + H^{+} + Br^{-}$$

Although the charge separation might be expected to be about the same in both activated complexes, the radius of the second would be expected

[73] See H. D. Cowan, C. L. McCabe, and J. C. Warner, *J. Am. Chem. Soc.*, **72**, 1194 (1950).

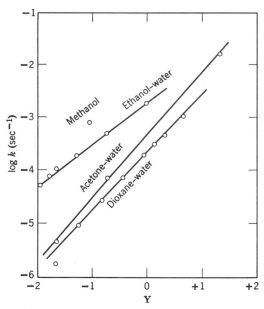

Fig. 3-33. Rates of solvolysis of benzyl chloride as a function of Y. A. Streitwieser, Jr., *Chem. Revs.*, **56**, 620 (1955).

to be greater than that for the first, leading to a smaller susceptibility toward the ionizing power of the solvent for the S_N2 process.

Although the treatment is useful both in the study of solvolytic reactions and in estimating the change in rate constant in going from one solvent to another, it has serious limitations. Even for such compounds as benzhydryl chloride, which would be expected to react via an S_N1 process, plots of log k against **Y** for different solvent mixtures give different lines, whereas there should be only a single line (Fig. 3-33). Thus there must be at least two properties of the solvent which are important, and different compounds lead to different rate contributions from these factors.

Besides the dielectric constant effect, the nucleophilicity of the solvent is of importance in determining the rates of solvolysis of at least some compounds. This can be seen from the fact that methyl bromide reacts 200 times as fast in 41% ethanol as in formic acid, whereas both solvents have the same **Y** value. The necessity of including this property of the solvent led Winstein, Grunwald, and Jones[74] to propose the relationship

$$d \ln k = \left(\frac{\partial \ln k}{\partial \mathbf{Y}}\right)_\mathbf{N} d\mathbf{Y} + \left(\frac{\partial \ln k}{\partial \mathbf{N}}\right)_\mathbf{Y} d\mathbf{N}$$

[74] S. Winstein, E. Grunwald, and H. W. Jones, *J. Am. Chem. Soc.*, **73**, 2700 (1951).

where **Y** is again a measure of the ionizing power of the solvent and **N** is a measure of the nucleophilicity of the solvent.

These functions are not directly accessible. However, water, ethanol, and methanol should be of comparable nucleophilicity, and the m values determined in these solvents should be a reasonable measure of $(\partial \ln k / \partial Y)_N$. An estimate of relative values for the last term, $(\partial \ln k / \partial N)_Y$,

Table 3-31 Effect of Solvent Nucleophilicity on Solvolysis Rates[a]

Compound	T	m (aq. alcohol)	$\dfrac{k \text{ (aq. alcohol)}}{k \text{ (RCOOH)}}$	
			CH$_3$CO$_2$H	HCO$_2$H
Methyl bromide	50°	0.26		200
Methyl tosylate	75	0.23	97	55
Ethyl bromide	55	0.34		80
Ethyl tosylate	50	0.26	80	18
n-Propyl chloride	102	0.39		~30
n-Propyl bromide	95	0.34		63
n-Butyl brosylate	60	0.32	30	20
i-Propyl bromide	50	0.54		20
i-Propyl brosylate	70	0.41	6	2
2-Pentyl tosylate	58	0.41	4	0.4
t-Butyl chloride	25	(1.00)	(1)	(1)
1-Bromobicyclo[2.2.2]-octane	100	0.88	0.7	0.5
Benzyl chloride	50	0.43	58	4
Benzyl tosylate	25	0.39	30	
α-Phenethyl chloride	50	0.81	2.5	
Allyl chloride	45	0.40		40

[a] The data were taken from S. Winstein, E. Grunwald, and H. W. Jones, *J. Am. Chem. Soc.*, **73**, 2700 (1951) and from A. Streitwieser, Jr., *Chem. Revs.*, **56**, 571 (1956).

may be obtained from the ratio of the rates of solvolysis of a compound in a solvent of high nucleophilicity (aqueous ethanol) and one of low nucleophilicity (acetic or formic acids) both having the same value of **Y**. The data are shown in Table 3-31.

It can be seen that the compounds which typically react by an S$_N$2 process have values of this ratio of 20—200, whereas the compounds which react by an S$_N$1 process have values near unity. Thus compounds which are characterized by a high value of m have a low sensitivity toward solvent nucleophilicity, and those having small values of m have a high sensitivity toward this factor.

Basically the same equation has been used by Swain, Mosely, and Brown in the form[76]

$$\log \left(\frac{k}{k_0} \right) = sn + s'e$$

where n is the nucleophilicity of the solvent, e is the ionizing power of the solvent, and s and s' are the relative sensitivities and are characteristic of

Table 3-32   Constants for the Swain-Mosely-Brown Equation[a]

Compound	c_1	c_2	c_1/c_2
Methyl bromide	0.80	0.27	(3.00)
Ethyl bromide	0.80	0.36	2.2
Ethyl tosylate	0.65	0.24	2.7
n-Butyl bromide	0.77	0.34	2.2
Benzyl chloride	0.74	0.44	1.7
i-Propyl bromide	0.90	0.58	1.5
i-Propyl brosylate	0.63	0.48	1.33
Benzhydryl chloride	1.24	1.25	0.99
t-Butyl chloride	1.00	1.00	(1.00)
Triphenylmethyl fluoride	0.37	1.12	(0.33)

Solvent	d_1	d_2	$d_1 - d_2$
100% Methanol	−0.05	−0.73	+0.7
100% Ethanol	−0.53	−1.03	+0.5
80% Ethanol	0.0	0.0	0.0
60% Ethanol	−0.22	+1.34	−1.6
50% Ethanol	+0.12	+1.33	−1.2
40% Ethanol	−0.26	+2.13	−2.4
90% Acetone	−0.53	−1.52	+1.0
80% Acetone	−0.45	−0.68	+0.2
70% Acetone	−0.9	−0.75	+0.7
50% Acetone	−0.25	+0.97	−1.2
Water	−0.44	+4.01	−4.5
100% Acetic acid	−4.82	+3.12	−7.9
100% Formic acid	−4.40	+6.53	−10.9

[a] C. G. Swain, R. B. Mosely, and D. E. Brown, *J. Am. Chem. Soc.*, **77**, 3731 (1955).

the substrate. Since there were no good standards on which to base values of n and e, they were led to determine a set of parameters which would give the best fit to the data for a large set of compounds. Recognizing that this

[75] C. G. Swain, R. B. Mosley, and D. E. Brown, *J. Am. Chem. Soc.*, **77**, 3731 (1955).

procedure would at best lead to a tenuous relationship between the calculated and desired quantities, they used the equation in the form

$$\log \left(\frac{k}{k_0}\right) = c_1 d_1 + c_2 d_2$$

but still retained, in essence, the original idea. The defining parameters were

$$c_1 = 3.00 c_2 \text{ for methyl bromide}$$
$$c_1 = c_2 = 1.00 \text{ for } t\text{-butyl chloride}$$
$$3.00 c_1 = c_2 \text{ for triphenylmethyl fluoride}$$
$$d_1 = d_2 = 0.00 \text{ for } 80\% \text{ ethanol}$$

The results are given in Table 3-32.

The difficulty with any such approach is that the rates of reaction are usually determined by a variety of factors besides the ones being considered. The numbers which lead to the best correlation with the experimental data must of necessity be a hybrid of the various factors. If the true functions are not linear but contain higher power terms, a four-parameter equation will not cleanly separate the various factors: all parameters will have partial contributions from the others. Thus it is not surprising to find that the d_1 value for water and ethanol is about the same, whereas that for 80% ethanol is higher, and that t-butyl chloride has a higher value of c_1 than methyl bromide.

In considering the difference in approach between Winstein-Grunwald-Jones and Swain-Mosely-Brown, we are again led to consider the reason for trying to discover linear free energy relationships. If we wish to predict new rate constants, then the latter approach is sound, although the values of the parameters must be adjusted periodically as new data appear. If, on the other hand, one wishes to learn something about the nature of the reaction, the former approach is more desirable.

EFFECT OF ENTERING SPECIES ON THE RATE OF $S_N 2$ DISPLACEMENT REACTIONS

Anions which are particularly reactive nucleophilic reagents in one displacement reaction are usually found to be quite reactive in other displacement reactions. The nucleophilicity of an anion might be expected to be an intrinsic property, and, again, a linear free energy relationship might be expected. If one plots the logarithms of the rates of reaction of a series of anions with one substrate against the corresponding quantities for another, a reasonably straight line is obtained, in agreement with the expectation.

Swain and Scott have suggested the use of the relationship[76]

$$\log \left(\frac{k}{k_0}\right) = sn$$

where k is the rate constant for the reaction with a given anion, k_0 is the rate constant for the reaction of the same substrate with water, n is the nucleophilicity constant, and s is the susceptibility factor. This is essentially the same as the Swain-Mosely-Brown equation discussed in the last section, except that $s'e$ will remain constant, for all comparisons are made

Table 3-33   Nucleophilicity Constants[a]

Ion	n	Ion	n
$HPSO_3^=$	6.6	$HPO_4^=$	3.8
$S_2O_3^=$	6.36	HCO_3^-	3.8
$SO_3^=$	5.1	$C_5H_5N:$	3.6
SH^-	5.1	Cl^-	3.04
CN^-	5.1	OAc^-	2.72
I^-	5.04	$SO_4^=$	2.5
SCN^-	4.77	F^-	2.0
$C_6H_5NH_2:$	4.49	Picrate	1.9
OH^-	4.20	NO_3^-	1.03
$(H_2N)_2CS$	4.1	$p\text{-}TsO^-$	<1.0
N_3^-	4.00	H_2O	0.00
Br^-	3.89	$\left.\begin{array}{l}ClO_3^- \\ ClO_4^- \\ BrO_3^- \\ IO_3\end{array}\right\}$	<0.00

[a] C. G. Swain and C. B. Scott, *J. Am. Chem. Soc.*, **75**, 141 (1953).

in the same solvent. The scale is defined by setting $s = 1.00$ for methyl bromide.

Values of n and s are given in Tables 3-33 and 3-34. Let us consider the n values first. The rate of an S_N2 displacement reaction should, like most reactions, be dependent on the over-all free energy change. It has been observed that in the reaction of chloroacetate ion with a series of oxygen bases, the changes in the log k values were nearly proportional to the changes in the logarithms of the basicity constants. Thus the differences between perchlorate, sulfate, acetate, phosphate, and hydroxyl ions are quite reasonable on this basis.

[76] C. G. Swain and C. B. Scott, *J. Am. Chem. Soc.*, **75**, 141 (1953).

On the other hand, it may be observed that both iodide and hydrosulfide ions, which are derived from stronger acids than water, are considerably more reactive (higher n values) than the hydroxyl ion. Thus at least two factors are of importance in determining the nucleophilicity of a given anion. The success of the Swain-Scott treatment indicates that the sensitivities of most compounds to the two or more contributing factors must be approximately in a constant ratio.

Table 3-34   Swain-Scott s Values[a]

Compound	s
C_6H_5COCl	1.43
$C_6H_5SO_2Cl$	1.25
CH_3Br	(1.00)
$\begin{matrix} CH_2 \\ \quad\diagdown \\ \qquad S{-}CH_2CH_2Cl \\ \quad\diagup \\ CH_2 \end{matrix}$	0.95
$\begin{matrix} CH_2{-}\!\!-CH_2{-}CH_2OH \\ \diagdown\ \ \diagup \\ O \end{matrix}$	1.00
$\begin{matrix} CH_2{-}C{=}O \\ \ \mid\qquad\mid \\ CH_2{-}O \end{matrix}$	0.77
$C_6H_5CH_2Cl$	0.87
C_2H_5OTs	0.66

[a] C. G. Swain and C. B. Scott, *J. Am. Chem. Soc.*, **75**, 141 (1953). These values coupled with the n values permit one to predict k/k_0 with an average deviation of 60%, when the whole range is many orders of magnitude.

In general, large ions are more reactive than small ones. This may arise from the operation of one or more of the following factors. The activation energy for a reaction of this type must necessarily involve a Coulombic term for the repulsion of the two negative charges in the activated complex

$$\left[\begin{matrix} \quad H\qquad H \\ \ \ \ \diagdown\ \ \diagup \\ \overset{\delta-}{X}{-}\!\!\text{-}\!\!\text{-}\!\!\text{-}\!\!\underset{\mid}{C}\text{-}\!\!\text{-}\!\!\text{-}\!\!\overset{\delta-}{Y} \\ \ \ \ H \end{matrix} \right]^{\ddagger}$$

If this could be reduced, the free energy of activation would also be reduced, leading to a larger rate. This is possible with ions which may distribute their charge over several atoms, such as the thiocyanate ion

$$\left[\overset{\delta-}{N}\!\!\equiv\!\!C\!\!=\!\!S\text{------}\overset{\overset{\displaystyle H \quad\quad H}{\diagdown\;\diagup}}{\underset{\underset{\displaystyle H}{|}}{C}}\text{------}\overset{\delta-}{Y} \right]^{\ddagger}$$

and with the highly polarizable ions, for which the center of electron density need not correspond to location of the nucleus

$$\left[\overset{\delta-}{\bigcirc}\;I\text{------}\overset{\overset{\displaystyle H \quad\quad H}{\diagdown\;\diagup}}{\underset{\underset{\displaystyle H}{|}}{C}}\text{------}\overset{\delta-}{Y} \right]^{\ddagger}$$

With the hydroxyl ion and the fluoride ion this is not possible, and these ions are found to be less reactive than would be expected on the basis of the change in free energy for the reaction.

Another possibility is that the rate effect may be a result of the difference in hydration of the reactant ions. The small chloride ion will be more solvated than the large iodide ion, and there will be a greater loss in solvation energy with the chloride ion in going to the activated complex, than there will be for the iodide ion.

The latter explanation has been shown to be correct in the case of the halide ions, for in acetone solution the order of reactivity is $Cl^- > Br^- > I^-$.[77] On changing to a hydroxylic solvent, the rates of reaction decrease markedly, the effect being largest with chloride ion and least with iodide ion. The observed order in a hydroxylic solvent, $I^- > Br^- > Cl^-$, is therefore a result of the greater stabilization of the chloride ion as compared with iodide ion in the hydroxylic solvents. The polarizability factor may still be important in some cases, since the sulfite ion reacts with alkyl halides exclusively at the sulfur, leading to the alkylsulfonate ion rather than the sulfite ester.

Although the Swain-Scott correlation works fairly well, leading to an average deviation from the observed rate constants of 60%, whereas the range of rates is several orders of magnitude, there are some conspicuous discrepancies. For example, hydroxyl ion reacts with the mustard cation

[77] S. Winstein, L. G. Savedoff, S. Smith, I. D. R. Stevens, and J. S. Gall, *Tetrahedron Letters*, No. 9, 24 (1960). The opposite order is observed with lithium salts, but this results from the larger extent of ion-pair formation with lithium chloride than for lithium iodide.

forty times faster than calculated. This led Edwards[78] to try to use a four parameter equation which would combine the factor used by Swain and Scott with the basicity of the anions, the latter being related to the over-all change in free energy for the reaction.

It had been noted that the electrode potential for reactions such as

$$2I^- \rightleftharpoons I_2 + 2e^-$$

paralleled the nucleophilicity of many anions.[79] Edwards found that the electrode potentials for the corresponding reactions of $SO_4^=$, Cl^-, Br^-, OH^-, I^-, and $S_2O_3^=$ were linearly related to the Swain-Scott n values and thus was led to use the equation

$$\log \left(\frac{k}{k_0}\right) = \alpha E_n + \beta H$$

where the rate constants have the same significance as before and α and β are the constants characteristic of the substrate. The other parameters are defined as follows:

$$E_n = E^0 + 2.60$$

where the electrode potential for the reaction

$$2H_2O \rightleftharpoons H_4O_2^{+2} + 2e^-$$

is estimated as $E^° = -2.60$ v, and E^0 is the electrode potential for the ion in question. Similarly,

$$H = pK_a + 1.74$$

where pK_a is the pK of the conjugate acid of the ion and 1.74 is the pK_a of H_3O^+.

The values of α and β are then chosen for a given substrate so as to give the best fit to the available data. The values of the parameters E_n and H are given in Table 3-35 and the values of α and β for some representative substrates are given in Table 3-36. The data are generally fit better than with the Swain-Scott equation, and this would be expected for a four-parameter equation. The interesting thing is that the parameters characteristic of the anion are obtained from thermodynamic measurements rather than from kinetic data. Unfortunately, sufficient data were not available for all anions, and some values of E_n and H were chosen to fit the data.

For the purpose of predicting rate constants, the Edwards relation is an improvement over the Swain-Scott equation, but for giving one an insight

---

[78] J. O. Edwards, *J. Am. Chem. Soc.* **76**, 1540 (1954).

[79] O. Foss, *Acta Chem. Scand.*, **1**, 8, 307 (1947); *ibid.*, **3**, 1385 (1949).

Table 3-35 Values of Parameters for Edwards' Equation

Anion or Molecule	E^0	E_n	H
NO_3^-		0.29	(0.40)
$SO_4^=$	−2.01	0.59	3.74
$ClCH_2CO_2^-$		0.79	4.54
$CH_3CO_2^-$		0.95	6.46
C_5H_5N		1.20	7.04
Cl^-	−1.360	1.24	(−3.00)
$C_6H_5O^-$		1.46	11.74
Br^-	−1.087	1.51	(−6.00)
N_3^-		1.58	6.46
OH^-	−0.95	1.65	17.48
NO_2^-	−0.87	1.73	5.09
$C_6H_5NH_2$		1.78	6.28
SCN^-	−0.77	1.83	(1.00)
NH_3	−0.76	1.84	11.22
$(CH_3O)_2POS^-$	−0.56	2.04	(4.00)
$C_2H_5SO_2S^-$	−0.54	2.06	(−5.00)
I^-	−0.536	2.06	(−9.00)
$(C_2H_5O)_2POS^-$	−0.53	2.07	(4.00)
$CH_3C_6H_4SO_2S^-$	−0.49	2.11	(−6.00)
$SC(NH_2)_2$	−0.42	2.18	0.80
$S_2O_3^=$	−0.08	2.52	3.60
$SO_3^=$	−0.03	2.57	9.00
CN^-	0.19	2.79	10.88
$S^=$	0.48	3.08	14.66

[a] J. O. Edwards, *J. Am. Chem. Soc.*, **76**, 1540 (1954). The values of H in parentheses are estimated values. The values of E_n for species which do not have E^0 values given were estimated from other kinetic or thermodynamic data.

Table 3-36 Edwards α and β Parameters[a]

Compound	α	β
Ethyl tosylate	1.68	0.014
Benzyl chloride	3.53	−0.128
β-Propiolactone	2.00	0.069
Epichlorhydrin	2.46	0.036
Glycidol	2.52	0.000
Mustard cation	2.45	0.074
Methyl bromide	2.50	0.006
Benzoyl chloride	3.56	0.008
Diazoacetone	2.37	0.191
Iodoacetate ion	2.59	−0.052

[a] J. Edwards, *J. Am. Chem. Soc.*, **76**, 1540 (1954).

into the nature of the reaction it contributes very little. The difficulty is that the equation has not separated the factors involved but, rather, uses the H term to correct the E_n term. This can be seen if one compares, for example, hydroxyl and sulfate ions. No special effect can be invoked to explain the greater nucleophilicity of hydroxyl ion; it must arise from the difference in over-all free energy. Thus the entire difference between the two should come in the H term. One might be able to improve the separation of nucleophilicity into its several components by first obtaining data for the reaction of a series of tetra-*n*-butyl-ammonium salts with several substrates in a nonhydroxylic solvent such as acetone. It might be possible to correlate these data with a four parameter equation, one parameter of which would be the over-all free energy change in the reaction. The special parameter characteristic of the ion used might then be a measure of the special effect of the anion due to polarizability, charge dispersal or other factors.

References

The Brønsted Catalysis Law:
R. P. Bell, *Acid-Base Catalysis*, Oxford University Press, London, 1949.
R. P. Bell, *The Proton in Chemistry*, Cornell University Press, Ithaca, New York, 1959.
The Hammett Equation:
L. P. Hammett, *Physical Organic Chemistry*, McGraw-Hill Book Co., 1940.
H. H. Jaffé, *Chem. Revs.*, **53**, 191 (1953).
J. D. Roberts and W. T. Moreland, Jr., *J. Am. Chem. Soc.*, **75**, 2167 (1953).
Y. Okamoto and H. C. Brown, *J. Org. Chem.*, **22**, 485 (1957).
P. R. Wells, *Chem. Revs.*, **63**, 171 (1963).
Separation of Polar, Steric and Resonance Effects:
J. D. Roberts and W. T. Moreland, Jr., *J. Am. Chem. Soc.*, **75**, 2167 (1953).
R. W. Taft, Jr., in *Steric Effects In Organic Chemistry*, M. Newman, Ed., John Wiley and Sons, New York, 1956.
Solvent Effect Correlations:
E. Grunwald and S. Winstein, *J. Am. Chem. Soc.*, **70**, 846 (1948).
S. Winstein, E. Grunwald and H. W. Jones, *J. Am. Chem. Soc.*, **73**, 2700 (1951).
C. G. Swain, R. B. Mosely and D. E. Brown, *J. Am. Chem. Soc.*, **77**, 3731 (1955).
E. M. Kosower, *J. Am. Chem. Soc.*, **80**, 3253 (1958).
S. G. Smith, A. H. Fainberg and S. Winstein, *J. Am. Chem. Soc.*, **83**, 618 (1961).
P. R. Wells, *Chem. Revs.*, **63**, 171 (1963).
Nucleophilicity Correlations:
C. G. Swain and C. B. Scott, *J. Am. Chem. Soc.*, **75**, 141 (1953).
J. O. Edwards, *J. Am. Chem. Soc.*, **76**, 1540 (1954).
S. Winstein, L. G. Savedoff, S. Smith, I. D. R. Stevens and J. S. Gall, *Tetrahedron Letters*, No. 9, 24 (1960).
J. O. Edwards and R. G. Pearson, *J. Am. Chem. Soc.*, **84**, 16 (1962).

Problems

1. Data on the rates of the S_N2 displacement on methyl chloride, bromide and iodide by chloride, bromide and iodide ions in acetone solution are given by P. B. D. de la Mare, *J. Chem. Soc.*, 3169, 3180, 3196 (1955); E. D. Hughes, C. K. Ingold and J. D. H. Mackie, *J. Chem. Soc.*, 3173, 3177 (1955) and L. Fowden, E. D. Hughes and C. K. Ingold, *J. Chem. Soc.*, 3187, 3193 (1955). Since lithium salts were used, the observed rate constants do not refer to the total halide concentration, but only to that part due to the free ions, the rest being in the form of ion-pairs. Reinterpret the above data using ion-pair association constants calculated from the data given by S. Winstein, L. G. Savedoff, S. Smith, I. D. R. Stevens and J. S. Gall, *Tetrahedron Letters*, No. 9, 24 (1960).

2. The visible spectrum of

varies markedly with the nature of the solvent (K. Dimroth, G. Arnoldy, S. von Eicken and G. Schiffler, *Ann.*, **604**, 221 (1957)). A similar observation using N-alkylpyridinium iodides has been used by E. Kowsower (*J. Am. Chem. Soc.*, **80**, 3253 (1958)) as the basis for a set of Z values which appear to be related to Y. Is there a correlation between the changes in transition energies with solvent for the two compounds given above? If so, which appears to be the most generally useful in establishing Z (or similar) values for a wide variety of solvents?

3-8 Acid Catalysis in Strongly Acidic Solutions

We have previously seen (Section 2-9) that the Hammett acidity function, H_0, was a useful measure of the protonating ability of a given acid containing medium. Many reactions are acid catalyzed, and thus one might anticipate that the acidity functions would be generally useful in developing an understanding of the nature of acid catalysis.

A number of acid-catalyzed reactions have been found to have a rate of reaction which increased linearly with h_0 rather than with the concentration of acid. Reactions of this type include the hydrolysis of sucrose,[80]

---

[80] L. P. Hammett and M. A. Paul, *J. Am. Chem. Soc.*, **56**, 830 (1934).

the hydrolysis of hindered esters such as methyl mesitoate,[81] the hydrolysis of alkoxymethyl esters of acetic and formic acids,[82] and the hydrolysis of β-propiolactone,[83] The commonly accepted mechanisms for these reactions are

A

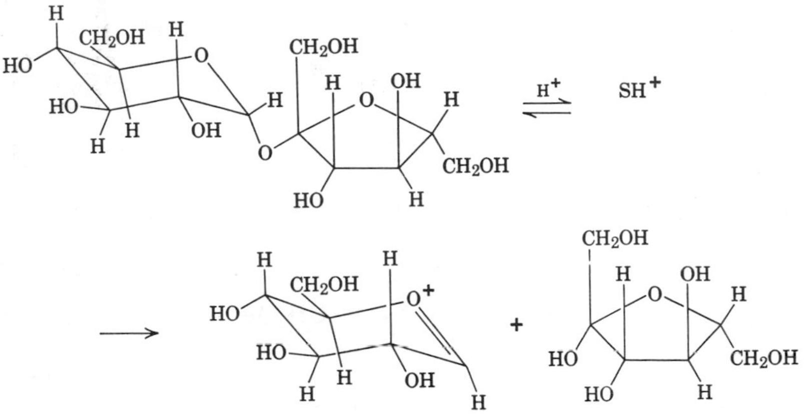

B

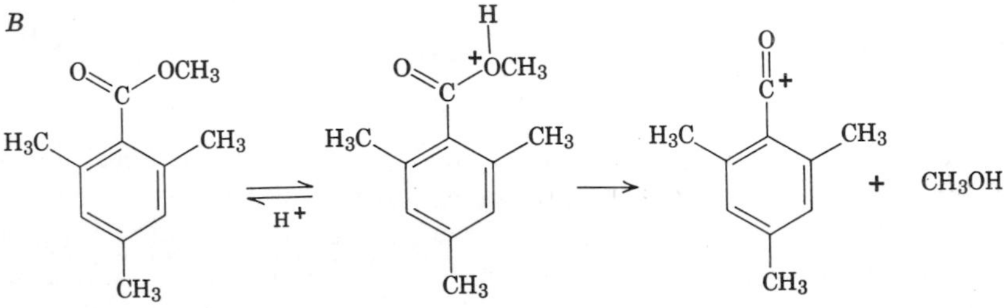

C

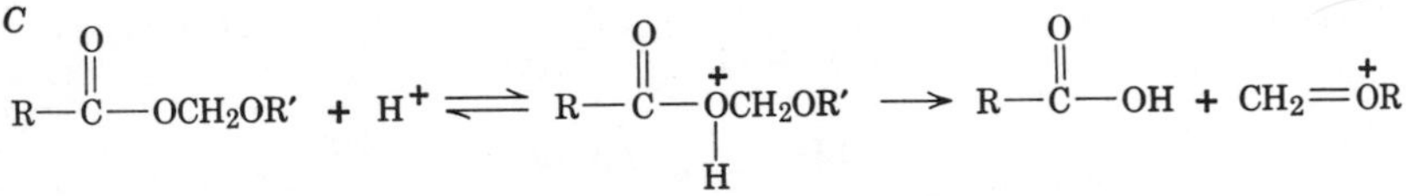

$$R-\overset{O}{\overset{\|}{C}}-OCH_2OR' + H^+ \rightleftharpoons R-\overset{O}{\overset{\|}{C}}-\overset{+}{\underset{H}{O}}CH_2OR' \longrightarrow R-\overset{O}{\overset{\|}{C}}-OH + CH_2=\overset{+}{O}R$$

D

$$\begin{matrix} CH_2-O \\ | \quad | \\ CH_2-C=O \end{matrix} + H^+ \rightleftharpoons \begin{matrix} CH_2-\overset{+}{O}H \\ | \\ CH_2-C=O \end{matrix} \longrightarrow \begin{matrix} CH_2-OH \\ | \\ CH_2-\underset{+}{C}=O \end{matrix}$$

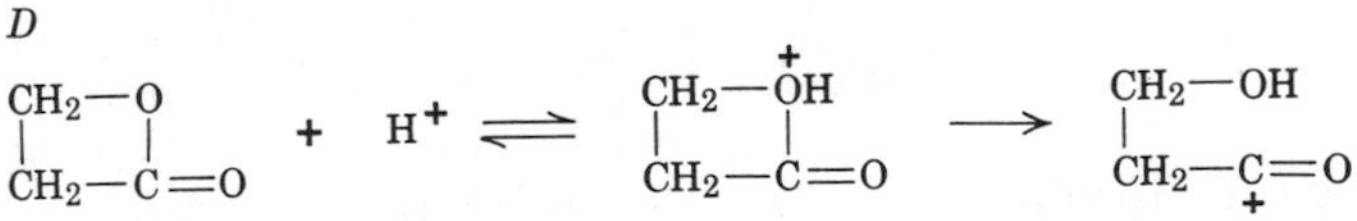

[81] C. T. Chmiel and F. A. Long, *J. Am. Chem. Soc.*, **78**, 3326 (1956); M. L. Bender, H. Ladenheim and M. C. Chen. *J. Am. Chem. Soc.*, **88**, 123 (1961).
[82] P. Salomaa, *Acta Chem. Scand.*, **11**, 132, 141, 235, 239 (1957).
[83] F. A. Long and M. Purchase, *J. Am. Chem. Soc.*, **72**, 3267 (1950).

On the other hand, there are a number of acid-catalyzed reactions whose rates are more closely dependent on the stoichiometric hydrogen ion concentration than on the acidity function. These include the enolization of acetophenone,[84] the hydrolysis of unhindered esters,[81] and the hydrolysis of γ-butyrolactone.[85] The commonly accepted mechanisms for these reactions are

A

$$\underset{\substack{\| \\ O}}{C_6H_5-C-CH_3} + H^+ \rightleftharpoons \underset{\substack{\| \\ +OH}}{C_6H_5-C-CH_3} \xrightarrow{H_2O} \underset{\substack{| \\ OH}}{C_6H_5-C=CH_2} + H_3O^+$$

B

$$\underset{\substack{\| \\ O}}{C_6H_5-C-OCH_3} + H^+ \rightleftharpoons \underset{\substack{\| \\ +OH}}{C_6H_5-C-OCH_3} \xrightarrow{H_2O} \underset{\substack{| \\ OH \\ | \\ {}^+OH_2}}{C_6H_5-C-OCH_3}$$

$$\rightarrow \rightarrow C_6H_5CO_2H + CH_3OH$$

C

$$\underset{\substack{| \\ CH_2}}{\overset{O}{CH_2}} \underset{\substack{| \\ CH_2}}{\overset{C=O}{}} + H^+ \rightleftharpoons \underset{\substack{| \\ CH_2}}{\overset{O}{CH_2}} \underset{\substack{| \\ CH_2}}{\overset{C=\overset{+}{O}H}{}} \xrightarrow{H_2O} \underset{\substack{| \\ CH_2}}{\overset{O}{CH_2}} \underset{\substack{| \\ CH_2}}{\overset{\overset{+}{O}H_2}{C}}_{OH}$$

$$\rightarrow \rightarrow HOCH_2CH_2CH_2CO_2H$$

Zucker and Hammett[84] noted that the difference between a number of reactions which followed h_0 and those which followed [H$^+$] was that the former did not involve a molecule of water before or during the rate determining step, whereas the latter did involve participation by a water molecule. The difference between the two may be formulated as follows. For the reactions which may be written as[86]

$$S + H^+ \underset{}{\overset{K}{\rightleftharpoons}} SH^+$$

$$SH^+ \xrightarrow{k} products$$

the rate expression will be

$$v = Kk[S][H^+]\frac{\gamma_S\gamma_{H^+}}{\gamma_\ddagger}$$

[84] L. Zucker and L. P. Hammett, *J. Am. Chem. Soc.* **61**, 2791 (1939).
[85] F. A. Long, W. F. McDevitt and F. B. Dunkle, *J. Phys. and Colloid Chem.*, **55**, 813 (1951); F. A. Long, F. B. Dunkle and W. F. McDevitt, ibid., **55**, 829 (1951).
[86] It is to be noted that throughout this section, the symbol H$^+$ refers to the proton in the state in which it is normally found in the medium used. In most cases it refers to the hydrated hydronium ion.

The acidity function was defined as

$$h_0 = a_{H^+} \frac{\gamma_B}{\gamma_{BH^+}} = [H^+] \frac{\gamma_B \gamma_{H^+}}{\gamma_{BH^+}}$$

Substitution of the acidity function equation into the rate expression gives

$$v = Kk[S]h_0 \frac{\gamma_S \gamma_{BH^+}}{\gamma_{\ddagger} \gamma_B}$$

If the activated complex should have an activity coefficient close to that of SH^+, and if

$$\frac{\gamma_S}{\gamma_{SH^+}} \simeq \frac{\gamma_B}{\gamma_{BH^+}}$$

The rate expression would become

$$v = Kk[S]h_0$$

This type of behavior would be expected for the above mechanism if S were structurally similar to B, the base used in determining the acidity function, and if the activated complex had a structure similar to SH^+ from which it was formed. Considering these requirements, it is not surprising to find that plots of $\log k$ against H_0 often give slopes which differ somewhat from unity (usually between 0.9 to 1.1). It is generally found that reactions of the above type give rate dependence on h_0, although this type of rate dependence does not necessarily indicate a mechanism in which SH^+ undergoes a unimolecular decomposition to products.

On the other hand, if we must write

$$S + H^+ \overset{K}{\rightleftharpoons} SH^+$$

$$SH^+ + H_2O \overset{k}{\longrightarrow} \text{products}$$

then

$$v = Kk[S][H^+][H_2O] \frac{\gamma_S \gamma_{H^+} \gamma_{H_2O}}{\gamma_{\ddagger}}$$

or

$$v = Kk[S][H^+]a_{H_2O} \frac{\gamma_S \gamma_{H^+}}{\gamma_{\ddagger}}$$

Substitution of the acidity function equation into the rate expression gives

$$v = Kk[S] \cdot h_0 \cdot a_{H_2O} \frac{\gamma_S \gamma_{BH^+}}{\gamma_{\ddagger} \gamma_B}$$

which differs from the rate expression for the previous mechanism in that it contains an extra term, a_{H_2O}. The value of a_{H_2O} changes relatively slowly with a change in acid concentration for the media commonly used.

For example, in going from 1 to 6 M perchloric acid, a_{H_2O} changes by a factor of two, whereas the ratio of $h_0/[H^+]$ changes by a factor of 70.

In this case, however, we would expect that

$$\frac{\gamma_S}{\gamma_{\ddagger}} \neq \frac{\gamma_B}{\gamma_{BH^+}}$$

because the structure of the activated complex would necessarily be different than that of SH^+ (the former contains an extra water molecule). If

$$\gamma_{\ddagger} \sim \gamma_S \gamma_{H^+}$$

the rate of reaction would be approximately proportional to $[H^+]$. Most, if not all, of the reactions which give rate dependence on $[H^+]$ do involve a water molecule in the rate determining step. On the other hand, there is no necessity for a reaction of this type to give rate dependence on $[H^+]$; an intermediate type of rate dependence, or even dependence on h_0 could be anticipated.[87] The Zucker-Hammett criterion of mechanism is a useful one, but it is not unique.

A more detailed treatment of acidity function dependence in aqueous solutions has been suggested by Bunnett.[88] He observed that plots of $(\log k_{\psi} + H_0)$ (where k_{ψ} is the observed psuedo-first order rate constant) against a_{H_2O} gave fairly linear plots with slopes, w, ranging from about -2 to $+7$. The empirical observation was that the reactions which clearly fell into the category of a unimolecular rate determining decomposition of the conjugate acid gave values of w between -2.5 to 0.0; those which involved a rate determining addition of water to SH^+ gave values of w between $+1.2$ to $+3.3$; and those which involved a rate determining proton abstraction from SH^+ by water gave values of w greater than about $+3.3$. A value $w = 0.0$ corresponds to a slope of unity in a plot of $\log k_{\psi}$ against H_0, negative values of w correspond to slopes greater than unity and positive values of w correspond to slopes smaller than unity. For 3 to 7 M aqueous solutions of sulfuric and perchloric acids, a linear relationship between $\log k_{\psi}$ and $[H^+]$ leads to a value of w of about 4.5.

Let us consider the relationship between w and a_{H_2O}.[88] If we write the reactions leading to the activated complex, including the hydration of each of the species,

$$S(H_2O)_s + H(H_2O)_n{}^+ \rightleftharpoons SH(H_2O)_p{}^+ + (s + n - p)H_2O$$

$$SH(H_2O)_p{}^+ + (t - p)H_2O \rightleftharpoons C^{\ddagger}(H_2O)_t{}^+ \rightarrow products$$

[87] E. Grunwald, A. Heller and F. S. Klein, *J. Chem. Soc.*, 2604 (1957); R. W. Taft, Jr., N. C. Deno and P. S. Skell, *Ann. Rev. Phys. Chem.*, **9**, 306 (1958); J. Koskikallio and E. Whalley, *Can. J. Chem.*, **37**, 788 (1959); H. Kwart and A. L. Goodman, *J. Am. Chem. Soc.*, **82**, 1947 (1960); L. Melander and P. C. Myhre, *Arkiv. Kemi*, **13**, 507 (1959).
[88] J. F. Bunnett, *J. Am. Chem. Soc.*, **83**, 4956, 4968, 4973, 4978 (1961).

and add, we obtain

$$S(H_2O)_s + H(H_2O)_n{}^+ + (t - s - n)H_2O \rightleftharpoons C^{\ddagger}(H_2O)_t{}^+ \rightarrow products.$$

The rate expression derived from the above is

$$v = Kk[S(H_2O)_s][H(H_2O)_n{}^+]a_{H_2O}^{(t-s-n)} \frac{\gamma_{S(H_2O)_s}\gamma_{H(H_2O)_n{}^+}}{\gamma_{C^{\ddagger}(H_2O)_t{}^+}}$$

or in more conventional terms

$$v = Kk[S][H^+]a_{H_2O}^{(t-s-n)} \frac{\gamma_S\gamma_{H^+}}{\gamma_{\ddagger}}$$

Writing the acidity function relationship in the same way,

$$B(H_2O)_b + H(H_2O)_n{}^+ \rightleftharpoons BH(H_2O)_a{}^+ + (b + n - a)H_2O$$

we obtained (Section 2-9)

$$h_0 = \frac{[H^+]}{a_{H_2O}^{(b+n-a)}} \frac{\gamma_B\gamma_{H^+}}{\gamma_{BH^+}}$$

If this expression is substituted into that for the rate of reaction, we obtain

$$v = Kk[S] \cdot h_0 \cdot a_{H_2O}^{(t-s+b-a)} \frac{\gamma_S\gamma_{BH^+}}{\gamma_{\ddagger}\gamma_B}$$

Bunnett now makes the assumption that the activity coefficients when corrected for effects of hydration depend *only* on the charge type and that the activity coefficient ratio in the above rate expression is unity. Then, since

$$v = k_{\psi}[S]$$

he concludes that

$$\log k_{\psi} + H_0 = (t - s + b - a) \log a_{H_2O} + constant$$

This is of the same form as used in evaluating w, and w is then identified as

$$w = t - s + b - a$$

The value of w, based on activity coefficient assumption, equals the hydration of the activated complex less that of the substrate on a scale set by the "water balance" in protonation of the indicator base.

The difficulties with this interpretation are as follows. The value of w results from a plot of the small difference between two quantities, both of which have an inherent experimental uncertainty, against a_{H_2O}. The values of w therefore have a considerable experimental uncertainty. More important, the assumption that the activity coefficients (after correction for changes in hydration) are dependent only on charge type can be only a rough approximation, and this may lead to rather different w values for reactions which are mechanistically similar. For example, over the same range of concentration of hydrogen chloride in water, the reaction of 4-(*p*-sulfophenylazo)-anisole gave $w = +2.85$, whereas the reaction of 4-(*p*-sulfophenylazo)-1-naphthyl methyl ether gave $w = +4.51$.[88] The change from a benzene to a naphthalene ring would not be expected to change the mechanism of the reaction but might be expected to effect the activity coefficient ratio. Similarly, the change from one acid catalyst to another often causes large changes in w and the direction of the change is not constant from one reaction to another.

It is clear that the use of the w plots is an improvement over the use of the Zucker-Hammett criterion. The w plots must still be interpreted with care, caution, and preferably a few auxiliary pieces of data.

The discussion given above applies only to media containing relatively large concentrations of water. We may now examine a case in which higher concentrations of acid were used, going up to pure sulfuric acid. One of the most extensively studied of these reactions is the decarbonyl-ation of mesitaldehyde and other sterically hindered aldehydes.[89] At

lower concentrations of acid, the rate of reaction is a linear function of h_0. As the acidity is increased and the equilibrium

is driven to the right, one would expect the rate of reaction to become independent of the acid concentration. The observed behavior is sum-marized in Fig. 3-34.[89]

The dashed line indicates the expected behavior for mesitaldehyde based on rate dependence on h_0, and it can be seen that a considerable deviation

---

[89] W. M. Schubert and R. E. Zahler, *J. Chem. Soc.*, **76**, 1 (1954); W. M. Schubert and H. Burkett, *J. Am. Chem. Soc.*, **78**, 64 (1956).

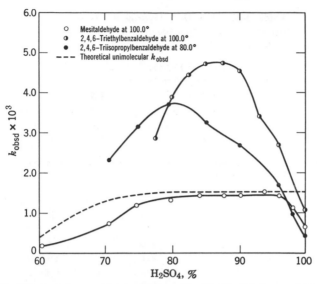

Fig. 3-34. Change in k_{obsd} with % sulfuric acid. W. M. Schubert and R. G. Zahler, J. Am. Chem. Soc., 76, 1 (1954).

was found, particularly near 100% sulfuric acid where the rate constant began to decrease. The trend was much more noticeable with 2,4,6-triethylbenzaldehyde and 2,4,6-trisopropylbenzaldehyde and it appears to be related to the degree of steric hindrance about the carbonyl group.

Further information was obtained by examining kinetic isotope effects, and the data are given in Tables 3-39 and 3-40.[89] It is clear that the cleavage of the aldehyde C—H bond occurs in the rate determining step, regardless of acid concentration. The solvent isotope effect is particularly informative. Below 80% sulfuric acid, the rate was higher in D_2SO_4 than in H_2SO_4 because of the higher concentration of conjugate acid in D_2SO_4 as compared with H_2SO_4. The difference in conjugate acid concentration could be determined spectrophotometrically, and the values given in the last column are corrected for this effect.

At higher acid concentrations, one might expect to find no solvent isotope effect, since mesitaldehyde is completely protonated under these conditions, and $[SH^+] = [SD^+]$. However, the reaction was now found to proceed more rapidly in H_2SO_4 than in D_2SO_4, suggesting that a rate determining proton transfer from sulfuric acid to mesitaldehyde occurs in the region in which the rate of reaction decreases with increasing sulfuric acid concentration.

Since the aldehyde is in the form of its conjugate acid in solutions containing 75% or more sulfuric acid, the data suggest that the ordinary

Table 3-37 Kinetic Hydrogen Isotope Effect in the Decarbonylation of Mesitaldehyde-d

Concentration of H_2SO_4	k_H/k_D
100.0%	1.8
96.3	2.8
85.2	2.8
59.9	1.8

Table 3-38 Solvent Hydrogen Isotope Effect in the Decarbonylation of Mesitaldehyde

Concentration of Acid	$k_{H_2SO_4}/k_{D_2SO_4}$ (obs.)	$k_{H_2SO_4}/k_{D_2SO_4}$ (corr.)
99.5	2.4	1.4
96.0	2.1	2.1
85.0	1.5	1.5
70.0	0.85	0.98
65.0	0.72	1.03
59.0	0.56	0.98

conjugate acid is not involved in the rate determining step. Rather, the reaction may be written as involving the steps

The experimental data may be correlated if one assumes that reaction 3 is rate determining if the sulfuric acid concentration is less than 80% and that reactions 2 and 3 are both partially rate controlling when the acid concentration is greater than 80%.

The change in rate determining step is reasonable if we remember that the relatively small molecule, water, is the base A^- in the less concentrated acid solutions and the larger bisulfate ion is the base in the more concentrated acid solutions. Both k_2 and k_{-2} will be decreased by a change from H_3O^+ as the acid HA to H_2SO_4 because of the steric effects associated with the ortho-methyl groups. The rate constant k_3 will be relatively little affected, since the proton which is removed is not subject to as much steric hindrance as one directly attached to the aromatic ring.

In the less concentrated acid solutions

$$\sum k_{-2}[A^-] \gg \sum k_3[A^-]$$

where the summation refers to all the basic species (H_2O and HSO_4^-). This leads to a small equilibrium concentration of the ring protonated conjugate acid, and step 3 becomes rate controlling. In the more concentrated acid solutions

$$\sum k_{-2}[A^-] \sim \sum k_3[A^-]$$

because of the change in the nature of the acid and base used. This leads to a case in which both k_2 and k_3 are partially rate controlling. It can be seen that one must carefully consider the nature of the acidic species present in strongly acidic solutions when discussing the mechanisms of reactions in such a medium.

The preceding discussion has been concerned with the H_0 acidity function because this is the one most commonly used. The other functions, particularly H_R, are also important and often may give important evidence concerning the mechanism of a reaction. The classical example is found in the study of nitration by Westheimer and Kharasch.[90] The nitration of benzene is catalyzed by sulfuric acid, suggesting that either one of two species may be the active nitrating agent:

$$HONO_2 + H_2SO_4 \rightleftharpoons H_2\overset{+}{O}NO_2 + HSO_4^-$$

$$H_2\overset{+}{O}NO_2 + H_2SO_4 \rightleftharpoons NO_2^+ + H_3O^+ + HSO_4^-$$

It was possible to distinguish between the two alternatives by the use of the acidity functions. On going from 80 to 90% sulfuric acid the rate of nitration is increased by a factor of about 3000. The H_0 acidity function

[90] F. H. Westheimer and M. S. Kharasch, *J. Am. Chem. Soc.*, **68**, 1871 (1946).

would predict a rate increase of only 20. Using tris-(p-nitrophenyl) methanol as the indicator, which reacts by

$$R_3COH + 2H_2SO_4 \rightleftharpoons R_3C^+ + H_3O^+ + 2HSO_4^-$$

(and is the basis for the H_R acidity function scale), it was found that the acidity scale thus obtained correlated well with the change in rate of nitration. It was then presumed that the ionization process for nitric acid would be similar to that for the triaryl carbinol, indicating that the NO_2^+ ion was the active nitrating agent.

References

Kinetic Applications of the Acidity Functions:
    F. A. Long and M. A. Paul, *Chem. Revs.*, **57**, 935 (1957).
    J. F. Bunnett, *J. Am. Chem. Soc.*, **83**, 4956, 4968, 4973, 4978 (1961).

Values of Physical Constants, and
Conversion Factors

Planck's constant	$h = 6.625 \times 10^{-27}$ erg-sec
Boltzmann's constant	$k = 1.380 \times 10^{-16}$ erg deg^{-1}
Velocity of light	$c = 2.998 \times 10^{10}$ cm sec^{-1}
Charge on an electron	$e = 4.803 \times 10^{-10}$ e.s.u.
Mass of an electron	$m = 9.108 \times 10^{-28}$ gm
Avogadro's number	$N = 6.023 \times 10^{23}$ mole^{-1}
Gas constant	$R = 8.314 \times 10^7$ erg deg^{-1} mole^{-1}
	$= 1.986$ cal deg^{-1} mole^{-1}
	$= 82.06$ liter atm. deg^{-1} mole^{-1}
	$k/h = 2.083 \times 10^{10}$ deg^{-1} sec^{-1}

$$1 \text{ electron-volt} = 3.829 \times 10^{-23} \text{ kcal/molecule}$$
$$= 23.07 \text{ kcal/mole}$$
$$1 \text{ erg/molecule} = 2.390 \times 10^{-11} \text{ kcal/molecule}$$
$$= 1.440 \times 10^{13} \text{ kcal/mole}$$
$$1 \text{ cm}^{-1}/\text{molecule} = 1.986 \times 10^{-16} \text{ ergs/molecule}$$
$$= 1.2398 \times 10^{-4} \text{ electron-volts}$$
$$= 4.747 \times 10^{-27} \text{ kcal/molecule}$$
$$= 2.860 \times 10^{-3} \text{ kcal/mole}$$
$$1 \text{ kcal/mole} = 6.945 \times 10^{-14} \text{ ergs/molecule}$$
$$= 4.335 \times 10^{-2} \text{ electron-volts}$$
$$= 3.496 \times 10^2 \text{ cm}^{-1}$$

Determinants and Matrices

In our study of molecular orbital theory, molecular vibrations, and nmr energy levels, we repeatedly encountered secular determinants. The following discussion is designed to show how the energy levels and wave functions may be obtained from the secular determinants and to consider other aspects of matrix algebra which are useful in solving other problems such as fitting experimental data by the method of least squares. We shall begin by considering the origin and properties of determinants.

Suppose we had two equations with two unknowns, x and y:

$$a_1 x + b_1 y = c_1$$
$$a_2 x + b_2 y = c_2$$

If we wished to obtain the values of x and y which satisfy both equations, we would eliminate the unknowns, one at a time, thus obtaining

$$(a_1 b_2 - a_2 b_1)x = c_1 b_2 - c_2 b_1$$
$$(a_1 b_2 - a_2 b_1)y = a_1 c_2 - a_2 c_1$$

For the case in which $a_1 b_2 - a_2 b_1$ is not zero, the values of x and y are given by

$$x = \frac{c_1 b_2 - c_2 b_1}{a_1 b_2 - a_2 b_1} \quad y = \frac{a_1 c_2 - a_2 c_1}{a_1 b_2 - a_2 b_1}$$

Combinations such as $a_1 b_2 - a_2 b_1$ are encountered frequently, are given a special notation

$$a_1 b_2 - a_2 b_1 = \begin{vmatrix} a_1 & b_1 \\ a_2 & b_2 \end{vmatrix}$$

and are referred to as determinants. The elements of a determinant may be referred to as constituting a row $(a_1 b_1)$ or a column $(a_1 a_2)$, and the order of a determinant is given by the number of elements in a given row or column. The determinant shown above is then of the second order.

In terms of determinants, the solutions for x and y may be written

$$x = \frac{\begin{vmatrix} c_1 & b_1 \\ c_2 & b_2 \end{vmatrix}}{\begin{vmatrix} a_1 & b_1 \\ a_2 & b_2 \end{vmatrix}}, \quad y = \frac{\begin{vmatrix} a_1 & c_1 \\ a_2 & c_2 \end{vmatrix}}{\begin{vmatrix} a_1 & b_1 \\ a_2 & b_2 \end{vmatrix}}$$

If we can expand this treatment to the general case of n simultaneous equations, we will be able to hand secular determinants. However, it will first be necessary to define determinants of the nth order and to obtain some of their properties.

Suppose we had an array of numbers arranged in a square of n rows and n columns. An array of this type is called a square matrix, and the individual numbers are called its elements. The order of such a matrix is n. As an example, a third order matrix would be

$$\begin{pmatrix} a_1 & b_1 & c_1 \\ a_2 & b_2 & c_2 \\ a_3 & b_3 & c_3 \end{pmatrix}$$

With each square matrix is associated a determinant of the same order which is defined as follows. We form all possible products of n elements chosen so that no two belong to the same row or column. The sign of each product is obtained by taking the elements involved, in the position they occupy in the matrix, and joining pairs by straight lines. If the number of lines which slope upward to the right is even or zero, the product has a $+$ sign, and if the number is odd, it has a $-$ sign. Each of the products and its associated sign is called a term, and the sum of all such terms is called the determinant of a matrix.

The determinant of the third order matrix given above is

$$\begin{vmatrix} a_1 & b_1 & c_1 \\ a_2 & b_2 & c_2 \\ a_3 & b_3 & c_3 \end{vmatrix}$$

(Note that determinants are designated by vertical bars, whereas matrices are enclosed in parentheses). Following the rules given above, the following products may be formed:

$$a_1b_2c_3 \quad b_1c_2a_3 \quad c_1a_2b_3$$

$$a_1c_2b_3 \quad b_1a_2c_3 \quad c_1b_2a_3$$

The first three will be associated with a $+$ sign, and the last three with a $-$ sign. Thus

$$\begin{vmatrix} a_1 & b_1 & c_1 \\ a_2 & b_2 & c_2 \\ a_3 & b_3 & c_3 \end{vmatrix} = a_1b_2c_3 + b_1c_2a_3 + c_1a_2b_3 - a_1c_2b_3 - b_1a_2c_3 - c_1b_2a_3$$

For a third order determinant, it is easy to remember that one operates on the diagonal, taking the following products with a positive sign

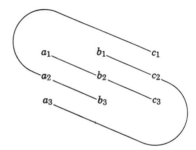

and the following with a negative sign

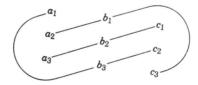

Certain general properties of determinants are a direct result of the definition given above, and these may be summarized as:

1. If all elements of a row or column are zero, the determinant is zero.

2. If all elements of a row or column are multiplied by a factor d, the determinant is multiplied by that factor:

$$\begin{vmatrix} da_1 & db_1 & dc_1 \\ a_2 & b_2 & c_2 \\ a_3 & b_3 & c_3 \end{vmatrix} = d \begin{vmatrix} a_1 & b_1 & c_1 \\ a_2 & b_2 & c_2 \\ a_3 & b_3 & c_3 \end{vmatrix}$$

3. If two rows or columns are interchanged, the determinant changes its algebraic sign:

$$
\begin{vmatrix} b_1 & a_1 & c_1 \\ b_2 & a_2 & c_2 \\ b_3 & a_3 & c_3 \end{vmatrix} = - \begin{vmatrix} a_1 & b_1 & c_1 \\ a_2 & b_2 & c_2 \\ a_3 & b_3 & c_3 \end{vmatrix}
$$

4. If the rows are changed into columns without changing the order, the value of the determinant is not changed:

$$
\begin{vmatrix} a_1 & b_1 & c_1 \\ a_2 & b_2 & c_2 \\ a_3 & b_3 & c_3 \end{vmatrix} = \begin{vmatrix} a_1 & a_2 & a_3 \\ b_1 & b_2 & b_3 \\ c_1 & c_2 & c_3 \end{vmatrix}
$$

5. If two rows or two columns are identical, the determinant is zero:

$$
\begin{vmatrix} a_1 & b_1 & c_1 \\ a_2 & b_2 & c_2 \\ a_1 & b_1 & c_1 \end{vmatrix} = 0
$$

6. If corresponding elements of two rows or two columns are proportional, the determinant is zero:

$$
\begin{vmatrix} a_1 & b_1 & 2a_1 \\ a_2 & b_2 & 2a_2 \\ a_3 & c_3 & 2a_3 \end{vmatrix} = 0
$$

7. The values of a determinant is not changed if each element of one row is increased by a constant times the corresponding elements of another row, or if each element of one column is increased by a constant times the corresponding elements of another column:

$$
\begin{vmatrix} a_1 + nb_1 & b_1 & c_1 \\ a_2 + nb_2 & b_2 & c_2 \\ a_2 + nb_3 & b_3 & c_3 \end{vmatrix} = \begin{vmatrix} a_1 & b_1 & c_1 \\ a_2 & b_2 & c_2 \\ a_3 & b_3 & c_3 \end{vmatrix}
$$

The application of these properties are best seen by an example:

$$\begin{vmatrix} 3 & 4 & 5 & 7 \\ 2 & 4 & 6 & -3 \\ -1 & 2 & 3 & 1 \\ 2 & -1 & 4 & -1 \end{vmatrix} = \begin{vmatrix} 2 & 6 & 8 & 8 \\ 2 & 4 & 6 & -3 \\ -1 & 2 & 3 & 1 \\ 2 & -1 & 4 & -1 \end{vmatrix}$$

$$= 2 \begin{vmatrix} 1 & 3 & 4 & 4 \\ 2 & 4 & 6 & -3 \\ -1 & 2 & 3 & 1 \\ 2 & -1 & 4 & -1 \end{vmatrix} = 2 \begin{vmatrix} 1 & 3 & 0 & 4 \\ 2 & 4 & 9 & -3 \\ -1 & 2 & 2 & 1 \\ 2 & -1 & 5 & -1 \end{vmatrix}$$

$$= 2 \begin{vmatrix} 1 & 0 & 0 & 4 \\ 2 & -2 & 9 & -3 \\ -1 & 5 & 2 & 1 \\ 2 & -7 & 5 & -1 \end{vmatrix}$$

$$= -4 \begin{vmatrix} 1 & 0 & 0 & 4 \\ 2 & 1 & 9 & -3 \\ -1 & -\frac{5}{2} & 2 & 1 \\ 2 & \frac{7}{2} & 5 & -1 \end{vmatrix} = -4 \begin{vmatrix} 1 & 0 & 0 & 4 \\ 2 & 1 & 9 & -3 \\ -\frac{1}{3} & -\frac{4}{3} & \frac{11}{3} & \frac{2}{3} \\ 2 & \frac{7}{2} & 5 & -1 \end{vmatrix}$$

As an exercise, it is valuable to demonstrate that each step is correct.

The operation of obtaining the value of a determinant of order greater than three using the rule given above is difficult, but the problem may be simplified if one reduces a large determinant to a series of smaller determinants. This operation will now be described.

Let us take a matrix and delete the row and column to which a given element k belongs. The determinant formed from the remaining elements without change of order is called the minor of k. Thus, for the determinant

$$\begin{vmatrix} a_1 & b_1 & c_1 \\ a_2 & b_2 & c_2 \\ a_3 & b_3 & c_3 \end{vmatrix}$$

the minor of a_1 is

$$\begin{vmatrix} b_2 & c_2 \\ b_3 & c_3 \end{vmatrix}$$

and the minor of a_2 is

$$\begin{vmatrix} b_1 & c_1 \\ b_3 & c_3 \end{vmatrix}$$

A related quantity, the cofactor, is related to the minor by

$$\text{cofactor} = (-1)^{r+s}(\text{minor})$$

where the element in question was in the rth row and sth column. For the example given above, the cofactor of a_1 is

$$\begin{vmatrix} b_2 & c_2 \\ b_3 & c_3 \end{vmatrix}$$

and the cofactor of a_2 is

$$-\begin{vmatrix} b_1 & c_1 \\ b_3 & c_3 \end{vmatrix}$$

These cofactors are of importance because the sum of the products of the elements in any row or column and their cofactors is equal to the determinant. Thus if $a_1, a_2, \ldots, a_n$ are the elements of a row or column, and $A_1, A_2, A_3, \ldots; A_n$ are the cofactors, then a_1A_1 is the sum of all the terms containing a_1, a_2A_2 is the sum of all the terms containing a_2, and so on. It can be seen that the sum of all terms of the determinant will be

$$a_1A_1 + a_2A_2 + a_3A_3 + \cdots + a_nA_n$$

In the case of the determinant given above, we find that

$$\begin{vmatrix} a_1 & b_1 & c_1 \\ a_2 & b_2 & c_2 \\ a_3 & b_3 & c_3 \end{vmatrix} = a_1 \begin{vmatrix} b_2 & c_2 \\ b_3 & c_3 \end{vmatrix} - a_2 \begin{vmatrix} b_1 & c_1 \\ b_3 & c_3 \end{vmatrix} + a_2 \begin{vmatrix} b_1 & c_1 \\ b_2 & c_2 \end{vmatrix}$$

When we considered the molecular orbital treatment of butadiene, we obtained the determinant

$$\begin{vmatrix} E' & q & 0 & 0 \\ q & E' & q & 0 \\ 0 & q & E' & q \\ 0 & 0 & 0 & E' \end{vmatrix}$$

and the values of E' were obtained by setting the value of the determinant equal to zero. Let us obtain the terms for this determinant by the use of cofactors (commonly known as the Laplace expansion):

$$\begin{vmatrix} E' & q & 0 & 0 \\ q & E' & q & 0 \\ 0 & q & E' & q \\ 0 & 0 & 0 & E' \end{vmatrix} = E' \begin{vmatrix} E' & q & 0 \\ q & E' & q \\ 0 & q & E' \end{vmatrix} - q \begin{vmatrix} q & q & 0 \\ 0 & E' & q \\ 0 & q & E' \end{vmatrix}$$

The 3×3 determinants are easily multiplied out, giving

$$0 = E'[(E')^3 - 2E'q^2] - q[q(E')^2 - q^3]$$
$$0 = (E')^4 - 3(E')^2 q^2 + q^4$$
$$= [(E')^2 + \sqrt{5}E'q + q^2][(E')^2 - \sqrt{5}E'q + q^2]$$
$$E' = 1.62, \, 0.62q, \, -0.62q, \, -1.62q$$

We must now consider the method of solving sets of simultaneous equations which was assumed in writing secular determinants. Suppose we had the three equations:

$$a_{11}x_1 + a_{12}x_2 + a_{13}x_3 = c_1$$
$$a_{21}x_1 + a_{22}x_2 + a_{23}x_3 = c_2$$
$$a_{31}x_1 + a_{32}x_2 + a_{33}x_3 = c_3$$

with the unknowns x_1, x_2, and x_3. The determinant of the coefficients of the unknowns is

$$\begin{vmatrix} a_{11} & a_{12} & a_{13} \\ a_{21} & a_{22} & a_{23} \\ a_{31} & a_{32} & a_{33} \end{vmatrix} = A$$

Let A_{ij} be the cofactor of a_{ij}, and let us multiply the first equation by A_{11}, the second by A_{21}, the third by A_{31}, and add. This gives

$$a_{11}A_{11}x_1 + a_{21}A_{21}x_1 + a_{31}A_{31}x_1 + a_{12}A_{11}x_2 + a_{22}A_{21}x_2 + a_{32}A_{31}x_2$$
$$+ a_{13}A_{11}x_3 + a_{23}A_{21}x_3 + a_{33}A_{31}x_3 = c_1A_{11} + c_2A_{21} + c_3A_{31}$$

If we write out the coefficient of x_2

$$a_{12}A_{11} + a_{22}A_{21} + a_{32}A_{31}$$

and evaluate it term by term, we obtain

$$a_{12}\begin{vmatrix} a_{22} & a_{23} \\ a_{32} & a_{33} \end{vmatrix} - a_{22}\begin{vmatrix} a_{12} & a_{13} \\ a_{32} & a_{33} \end{vmatrix} + a_{32}\begin{vmatrix} a_{12} & a_{13} \\ a_{22} & a_{23} \end{vmatrix}$$

or

$$a_{12}a_{22}a_{33} - a_{12}a_{23}a_{32} - a_{22}a_{12}a_{33} + a_{22}a_{13}a_{32} - a_{32}a_{12}a_{23} - a_{32}a_{13}a_{22}$$

and it can be seen that this sum is equal to zero. Thus the coefficient of x_2, and also of x_3, in the sum is zero. There remains

$$(a_{11}A_{11} + a_{21}A_{21} + a_{31}A_{31})x_1 = c_1A_{11} + c_2A_{21} + c_3A_{31}$$

or

$$\begin{vmatrix} a_{11} & a_{12} & a_{13} \\ a_{21} & a_{22} & a_{23} \\ a_{31} & a_{32} & a_{33} \end{vmatrix} x_1 = \begin{vmatrix} c_1 & a_{12} & a_{13} \\ c_2 & a_{22} & a_{23} \\ c_3 & a_{32} & a_{33} \end{vmatrix}$$

If A is not zero, we have

$$x_1 = \frac{\begin{vmatrix} c_1 & a_{12} & a_{13} \\ c_2 & a_{22} & a_{23} \\ c_3 & a_{32} & a_{33} \end{vmatrix}}{\begin{vmatrix} a_{11} & a_{12} & a_{13} \\ a_{21} & a_{22} & a_{23} \\ a_{31} & a_{32} & a_{33} \end{vmatrix}}$$

and similar expressions are obtained for x_2 and x_3. This is the basis for Cramer's rule, which states that if one has n equations in n unknowns:

$$a_{11}x_1 + a_{12}x_2 + a_{13}x_3 + \cdots + a_{1n}x_n = c_1$$
$$a_{21}x_1 + a_{22}x_2 + a_{23}x_3 + \cdots + a_{2n}x_n = c_2$$
$$\cdots\cdots\cdots\cdots\cdots\cdots\cdots\cdots\cdots\cdots\cdots$$
$$a_{n1}x_1 + a_{n2}x_2 + a_{n3}x_3 + \cdots + a_{nn}x_n = c_n$$

and if the determinant

$$A = \begin{vmatrix} a_{11} & a_{12} & a_{13} & \cdots & a_{1n} \\ a_{21} & a_{22} & a_{23} & \cdots & a_{2n} \\ \cdots & \cdots & \cdots & \cdots & \cdots \\ a_{n1} & a_{n2} & a_{n3} & \cdots & a_{nn} \end{vmatrix}$$

is not zero, each unknown is a fraction with A as the denominator, and a numerator obtained from A by replacing the coefficients of that unknown by the corresponding constant terms $c_1, c_2, c_3, \ldots, c_n$. The value of x_2 would then be given by

$$x_2 = \frac{\begin{vmatrix} a_{11} & c_1 & a_{13} & \cdots & a_{1n} \\ a_{21} & c_2 & a_{23} & \cdots & a_{2n} \\ \cdots & \cdots & \cdots & \cdots & \cdots \\ a_{n1} & c_n & a_{n3} & \cdots & a_{nn} \end{vmatrix}}{\begin{vmatrix} a_{11} & a_{12} & a_{13} & \cdots & a_{1n} \\ a_{21} & a_{22} & a_{23} & \cdots & a_{2n} \\ \cdots & \cdots & \cdots & \cdots & \cdots \\ a_{n1} & a_{n2} & a_{n3} & \cdots & a_{nn} \end{vmatrix}}$$

The case with which we were particularly interested was that in which the constant terms were zero. Thus, from the variation method treatment, we obtained equations such as

$$a_{11}x_1 + a_{12}x_2 + a_{13}x_3 = 0$$
$$a_{21}x_1 + a_{22}x_2 + a_{23}x_3 = 0$$
$$a_{31}x_1 + a_{32}x_2 + a_{33}x_3 = 0$$

These equations are commonly referred to as homogeneous. They have as one trivial solution, $x_1 = x_2 = x_3 = 0$, but this is not a solution having physical significance.

If we treat these equations in the same way as before, that is, by multiplying the first equation by A_{11}, the second by A_{21}, the third by A_{31}, and adding, we would obtain

$$(a_{11}A_{11} + a_{21}A_{21} + a_{31}A_{31})x_1 = 0$$

Similarly, using A_{12}, A_{22} and A_{32}, we get

$$(a_{13}A_{13} + a_{23}A_{23} + a_{33}A_{33})x_3 = 0$$

and in the same fashion, we could show that

$$(a_{13}A_{13} + a_{23}A_{23} + a_{33}A_{33})x_3 = 0$$

These three equations may be rewritten as

$$Ax_1 = 0$$
$$Ax_2 = 0$$
$$Ax_3 = 0$$

In order for x_1, x_2 and x_3 to have nonzero values, it can be seen that the determinant A must equal zero:

$$\begin{vmatrix} a_{11} & a_{12} & a_{13} \\ a_{21} & a_{22} & a_{23} \\ a_{31} & a_{32} & a_{33} \end{vmatrix} = 0$$

This is the necessary and sufficient condition for obtaining solutions for the three unknowns, and it is the method which we employed in Part I without proof.

The method for obtaining the energy levels from a secular determinant which was given above is inconvenient for large determinants. Much better methods for handling these problems are available, but in order to consider them we must first discuss the properties of matrices.

A matrix is simply an array of numbers, and if the matrix should have equal numbers of rows and columns, it is referred to as a square matrix. Arithmetic operations may be carried out using matrices, and we must consider the nature of this type of arithmetic. We will often need to refer to a given element of a matrix which will be designated as a_{ij} belonging to the ith row and the jth column. In all cases the rows are numbered from the top down, and the columns are numbered from left to right.

The addition of two matrices is defined as follows. If we add matrix A having the elements a_{ij} to a matrix B having the elements b_{ij}, the result is a matrix C, for which the elements are $c_{ij} = a_{ij} + b_{ij}$. Addition of two matrices is defined only if A and B have the same size (i.e., have the same number of rows and columns). It may further be noted that $A + B = B + A$, which is referred to as the commutative law of addition.

In defining multiplication of matrices, we must return to a set of equations which a matrix may represent. As an example, suppose we had the set of equations

$$x_1 = a_{11}y_1 + a_{12}y_2 + a_{13}y_3$$
$$x_2 = a_{21}y_1 + a_{22}y_2 + a_{23}y_3$$
$$x_3 = a_{31}y_1 + a_{32}y_2 + a_{33}y_3$$

and also had another set

$$y_1 = b_{11}z_1 + b_{12}z_2 + b_{13}z_3$$
$$y_2 = b_{21}z_1 + b_{22}z_2 + b_{23}z_3$$
$$y_3 = b_{31}z_1 + b_{32}z_2 + b_{33}z_3$$

If we wished to obtain equations giving the relationship between x and z, we would substitute the second set of equations into the first. This is tedious to write in the expanded form, and so we shall introduce an abbreviation and write for the first set of equations

$$x_i = \sum_{k=1}^{3} a_{ik}y_k \qquad i = 1, 2, 3$$

and for the second set

$$y_k = \sum_{j=1}^{3} b_{kj}z_j \qquad k = 1, 2, 3$$

Then, substituting the second into the first, we obtain

$$x_i = \sum_{k=1}^{3} a_{ik}y_k = \sum_{k=1}^{3} a_{ik}\left(\sum_{j=1}^{3} b_{kj}z_j\right)$$
$$= \sum_{j=1}^{3}\left(\sum_{k=1}^{3} a_{ik}b_{kj}\right)z_j \qquad i = 1, 2, 3$$

In general, we may write

$$x = Ay$$
$$y = Bz$$

where A and B are the matrices containing the coefficients of the y's and z's, respectively, and x, y, and z are column matrices containing the values of the quantities (i.e., x_1, x_2, x_3, . . . , x_n for x, etc.). Then, from the above,

$$x = ABz$$

The operation given above is the basis for matrix multiplication. We might write the relationship between x and z as

$$x = Cz$$

where the matrix C is defined as

$$C = AB$$

It can be seen from the above that the elements of C are given by

$$c_{ij} = \sum_{k=1}^{n} a_{ik} b_{kj}$$

for all pairs ij. It may be noted that the product is defined only if B has as many rows as A has columns.

As an example, consider the multiplication of the matrices:

$$\underset{A}{\begin{pmatrix} 2 & 1 & 2 \\ 0 & 3 & 1 \\ 1 & 1 & 0 \end{pmatrix}} \times \underset{B}{\begin{pmatrix} 1 & 1 & 0 \\ 1 & 0 & 1 \\ 0 & 1 & 1 \end{pmatrix}} = \underset{C}{\begin{pmatrix} 3 & 4 & 3 \\ 3 & 1 & 4 \\ 2 & 1 & 2 \end{pmatrix}}$$

The element of C, c_{11}, is given by $a_{11}b_{11} + a_{12}b_{21} + a_{13}b_{31}$, and any element of C is given by the sum of the products of the elements of its row in matrix A and its column in matrix B. With square matrices such as the above, two products are possible, AB and BA, and these will generally be different:

$$\underset{B}{\begin{pmatrix} 1 & 1 & 0 \\ 1 & 0 & 1 \\ 0 & 1 & 1 \end{pmatrix}} \times \underset{A}{\begin{pmatrix} 2 & 1 & 2 \\ 0 & 3 & 1 \\ 1 & 1 & 0 \end{pmatrix}} = \underset{D}{\begin{pmatrix} 2 & 4 & 3 \\ 3 & 2 & 2 \\ 1 & 4 & 1 \end{pmatrix}}$$

However, the following rules apply: $(AB)C = A(BC)$ (the associative law) and $(A + B)C = AC + BC$ (distributive law).

In dealing with matrices, the elements a_{11}, a_{22}, a_{33}, . . . , a_{nn} are referred to as the principal diagonal elements. If all other elements are zero, the matrix is known as a diagonal matrix, and if all the principal diagonal elements of a diagonal matrix are unity, it is known as the identity matrix (I). We will have occasion to use these terms in the following discussion.

Let us again consider the set of equations

$$x_1 = a_{11}y_1 + a_{12}y_2 + a_{13}y_3$$
$$x_2 = a_{21}y_1 + a_{22}y_2 + a_{23}y_3$$
$$x_3 = a_{31}y_1 + a_{32}y_2 + a_{33}y_3$$

It is also possible to write these equations in the form

$$x_1 = c_{11}y_1$$
$$x_2 = c_{22}y_2$$
$$x_3 = c_{33}y_3$$

where the coefficients c_{11}, c_{22}, and c_{33} are determined from the solution of the first set of equations. The matrix of the coefficients of y for the first set of equations is

$$\begin{pmatrix} a_{11} & a_{12} & a_{13} \\ a_{21} & a_{22} & a_{23} \\ a_{31} & a_{32} & a_{33} \end{pmatrix} = A$$

and that for the second set of equations is

$$\begin{pmatrix} c_{11} & 0 & 0 \\ 0 & c_{22} & 0 \\ 0 & 0 & c_{33} \end{pmatrix} = C$$

and the two matrices are equivalent. Thus, if it were possible to convert A into the diagonal form, C, the solutions for the set of equations could be easily found, The process for effecting this transformation is known as matrix diagonalization. A number of methods have been devised for this purpose; only one will be illustrated here. This method uses the properties of determinants deduced previously, which also apply to matrices. As an example, suppose we wished to obtain the matrix

$$\begin{pmatrix} 3 & 4 & 1 & 4 \\ 3 & 4 & 1 & 2 \\ 6 & 8 & 5 & 4 \\ 2 & 4 & 0 & 4 \end{pmatrix}$$

in diagonal form. One possible set of operations starts with subtracting column 4 from column 2, and then proceeds as shown below:

$$
\begin{pmatrix} 3 & 4 & 1 & 4 \\ 3 & 4 & 1 & 2 \\ 6 & 8 & 5 & 4 \\ 2 & 4 & 0 & 4 \end{pmatrix}
=
\begin{pmatrix} 3 & 0 & 1 & 4 \\ 3 & 2 & 1 & 2 \\ 6 & 4 & 5 & 4 \\ 2 & 0 & 0 & 4 \end{pmatrix}
=
\begin{pmatrix} 3 & 0 & 1 & 4 \\ 3 & 2 & 0 & 2 \\ 6 & 4 & 3 & 4 \\ 2 & 0 & 0 & 4 \end{pmatrix}
$$

$$
=
\begin{pmatrix} 3 & 0 & 1 & 4 \\ 3 & 2 & 0 & 2 \\ 0 & 0 & 3 & 0 \\ 2 & 0 & 0 & 4 \end{pmatrix}
=
\begin{pmatrix} 3 & 0 & 0 & 4 \\ 3 & 2 & 0 & 2 \\ 0 & 0 & 3 & 0 \\ 2 & 0 & 0 & 4 \end{pmatrix}
=
\begin{pmatrix} 1 & 0 & 0 & 4 \\ 2 & 2 & 0 & 2 \\ 0 & 0 & 3 & 0 \\ 0 & 0 & 0 & 4 \end{pmatrix}
$$

$$
=
\begin{pmatrix} 1 & 0 & 0 & 0 \\ 2 & 2 & 0 & 2 \\ 0 & 0 & 3 & 0 \\ 0 & 0 & 0 & 4 \end{pmatrix}
=
\begin{pmatrix} 1 & 0 & 0 & 0 \\ 0 & 2 & 0 & 0 \\ 0 & 0 & 3 & 0 \\ 0 & 0 & 0 & 4 \end{pmatrix}
$$

It is always possible to convert a matrix into diagonal form by a succession of operations like these, and of interchanging rows and columns. The difficulty remains of deciding which transformation should be used and in which order they should be taken. Efficient computor programs have been written for matrix diagonalization, and these are commonly used in the solution of practical problems. The use of these programs is discussed in Appendix 8.

Before proceeding further, we must define the inverse of a matrix.[1]

[1] Although not directly connected with the present discussion, it should be noted that matrix inversion is useful for the solution of sets of equations. If we have

$$a_{11}y_1 + a_{12}y_2 + a_{13}y_3 = c_1$$
$$a_{21}y_1 + a_{22}y_2 + a_{23}y_3 = c_2$$
$$a_{31}y_1 + a_{32}y_2 + a_{33}y_3 = c_3$$

and we write the matrix

$$
\begin{pmatrix} a_{11} & a_{12} & a_{13} & c_1 \\ a_{21} & a_{22} & a_{23} & c_2 \\ a_{31} & a_{32} & a_{33} & c_3 \end{pmatrix} = A
$$

Then, the inverse of A, A^{-1}, will have the values of y_1, y_2, and y_3 as its first column. A computor program for matrix inversion is given in Appendix 8.

This is a matrix which when multiplied by the original matrix gives the identity matrix. Thus

$$A^{-1}A = I$$

The inverse of a matrix may be obtained as follows:

$$\begin{pmatrix} a & b & c \\ d & e & f \\ g & h & i \end{pmatrix} \times \begin{pmatrix} 2 & 1 & 1 \\ 1 & 1 & 3 \\ 3 & 2 & 1 \end{pmatrix} = \begin{pmatrix} 1 & 0 & 0 \\ 0 & 1 & 0 \\ 0 & 0 & 1 \end{pmatrix}$$

$$\qquad A^{-1} \qquad\qquad A \qquad\qquad I$$

By matrix multiplication, we find

$$2a + b + 3c = 1$$
$$a + b + 2c = 0$$
$$a + 3b + c = 0$$

and therefore $a = 1\frac{2}{3}$, $b = -\frac{1}{3}$, and $c = -\frac{2}{3}$. Similarly, the other elements may be evaluated giving

$$A^{-1} = \begin{pmatrix} 1\frac{2}{3} & -\frac{1}{3} & -\frac{2}{3} \\ -2\frac{1}{3} & \frac{2}{3} & 1\frac{1}{3} \\ -\frac{1}{7} & \frac{2}{7} & -\frac{1}{7} \end{pmatrix}$$

Quantities of interest in connection with matrices are the eigenvalues. They are defined by the equation

$$|A - EI| = 0$$

where E is a column matrix whose elements are the eigenvalues of the matrix A and where I is the identity matrix. Thus the value of the determinant formed by subtracting the values of E from the principal diagonal elements of A is zero. The number of eigenvalues is equal to the order of the matrix A. The determinant given above should be recognized as being a secular determinant. It should be clear that if A were transformed into the diagonal form, the principal diagonal elements would be the eigenvalues. Thus matrix diagonalization is the operation used in solving eigenvalue problems.

The eigenvalues of a matrix are column matrices which have the property

$$A \begin{pmatrix} r_1 \\ r_2 \\ r_3 \\ \cdot \\ \cdot \\ \cdot \\ r_n \end{pmatrix} = c \begin{pmatrix} r_1 \\ r_2 \\ r_3 \\ \cdot \\ \cdot \\ \cdot \\ r_n \end{pmatrix}$$

where c, a constant, is an eigenvalue of A. Thus, when an eigenvector of a matrix is multiplied by the matrix, the result is a constant times the eigenvector. If the eigenvectors are formed into a matrix

$$R = \begin{pmatrix} r_{11} & r_{12} \cdots r_{1n} \\ r_{21} & r_{22} \cdots r_{2n} \\ r_{31} & r_{32} \cdots r_{3n} \\ \cdot & \cdot & \cdot \\ \cdot & \cdot & \cdot \\ \cdot & \cdot & \cdot \\ r_{n1} & r_{n2} & r_{nn} \end{pmatrix}$$

where $r_{11}, r_{21}, \ldots, r_{n1}$, is one vector, $r_{12}, r_{22}, \ldots, r_{n2}$ is the next, and so on, the resultant matrix has the property

$$AR = \Lambda R$$

where Λ is a diagonal matrix which is equivalent to A. Thus R transforms A into a diagonal form.

If, for example, we had the matrix

$$A = \begin{pmatrix} 0 & 1 & & & & 1 \\ 1 & 0 & 1 & & & \\ & 1 & 0 & 1 & & \\ & & 1 & 0 & 1 & \\ & & & 1 & 0 & 1 \\ 1 & & & & 1 & 0 \end{pmatrix}$$

where all the missing elements are zero, the eigenvalues would be found to be 2, 1, 1, -1, -1, -2. It may be recognized that A is related to the secular determinant we wrote when considering the π electronic energy of benzene and that the eigenvalues are the energy values which we obtained. Thus

$$\Lambda = \begin{pmatrix} -2 & & & & & \\ & -1 & & & & \\ & & -1 & & & \\ & & & 1 & & \\ & & & & 1 & \\ & & & & & 2 \end{pmatrix}$$

The corresponding R matrix may be found to be

$$R = \begin{pmatrix} 0.408 & 0.000 & -0.577 & 0.000 & -0.577 & 0.408 \\ 0.408 & 0.500 & -0.289 & 0.500 & 0.289 & -0.408 \\ 0.408 & 0.500 & 0.289 & -0.500 & 0.289 & 0.408 \\ 0.408 & 0.000 & 0.577 & 0.000 & -0.577 & -0.408 \\ 0.408 & -0.500 & 0.289 & 0.500 & 0.289 & 0.408 \\ 0.408 & -0.500 & -0.289 & -0.500 & 0.289 & -0.408 \end{pmatrix}$$

Each column may be recognized to correspond to the coefficients of the atomic orbitals for benzene for the corresponding eigenvalues in Λ. One method for obtaining the eigenvectors is the one described when considering the variation method: the substitution of the eigenvalues into the set of simultaneous equations which led to the matrix, and the evaluation of the unknowns. The eigenvectors are usually computed along with the eigenvalues by matrix diagonalization programs for computors.

Since $R^{-1}R = I$, and since Λ is a diagonal matrix, the following relationship also holds

$$R^{-1}AR = R^{-1}\Lambda R = \Lambda$$

Thus, if one knows the eigenvectors, the eigenvalues may be obtained.

If we write the secular determinant for benzene, including the overlap integrals, setting $\alpha = 0$, we see that the energy

$$\begin{vmatrix} -E & \gamma - sE & & & & \gamma - sE \\ \gamma - E & -E & \gamma - sE & & & \\ & \gamma - sE & -E & \gamma - sE & & \\ & & \gamma - sE & -E & \gamma - sE & \\ & & & \gamma - sE & -E & \gamma - sE \\ \gamma - sE & & & & \gamma - sE & -E \end{vmatrix} = 0$$

appears in the off-diagonal terms. Since this is not of the form

$$|A - EI| = 0$$

the eigenvalues are not easily obtained. If we call the matrix which contains the H components of the secular determinant, H, and the matrix which contains the Δ components, S, the equation may be written

$$|H - SE| = 0$$

$$H = \begin{pmatrix} 0 & 1 & & & & 1 \\ 1 & 0 & 1 & & & \\ & 1 & 0 & 1 & & \\ & & 1 & 0 & 1 & \\ & & & 1 & 0 & 1 \\ 1 & & & & 1 & 0 \end{pmatrix}$$

$$S = \begin{pmatrix} 1 & \tfrac{1}{4} & & & & \tfrac{1}{4} \\ \tfrac{1}{4} & 1 & \tfrac{1}{4} & & & \\ & \tfrac{1}{4} & 1 & \tfrac{1}{4} & & \\ & & \tfrac{1}{4} & 1 & \tfrac{1}{4} & \\ & & & \tfrac{1}{4} & 1 & \tfrac{1}{4} \\ \tfrac{1}{4} & & & & \tfrac{1}{4} & 1 \end{pmatrix}$$

where the elements of H are given in units of γ. Now, if we multiply both H and S by S^{-1}, we obtain

$$|S^{-1}H - S^{-1}SE| = |S^{-1}H - EI| = 0$$

The eigenvalues and eigenvectors of $S^{-1}H$ will then be the desired ones.

Group Character Tables

A. CHARACTER TABLE FOR THE CYCLIC GROUP $\mathscr{C}_2$

$\mathscr{C}_2$	E	C_2		
A	1	1	T_z; R_z	$IR, R(p)$
B	1	-1	T_x, T_y; R_x, R_y	$IR, R(dp)$

B. CHARACTER TABLES FOR THE DIHEDRAL GROUPS $\mathscr{D}_n$

($n = 2, 3, 4, 5, 6$)

$\mathscr{D}_2 = \mathscr{V}$	E	$C_2(z)$	$C_2(y)$	$C_2(x)$		
A	1	1	1	1		$R(p)$
B_1	1	1	-1	-1	T_z, R_z	$IR, R(dp)$
B_2	1	-1	1	-1	T_y, R_y	$IR, R(dp)$
B_3	1	-1	-1	1	T_x, R_x	$IR, R(dp)$

$\mathscr{D}_3$	E	$2C_3$	$3C_2$		
A_1	1	1	1		$R(p)$
A_2	1	1	-1	T_z; R_z	IR
E	2	-1	0	(T_x, T_y); (R_x, R_y)	$IR, R(dp)$

$\mathscr{D}_4$	E	$2C_4$	$C_4{}^2 = C_2$	$2C_2'$	$2C_2''$			
A_1	1	1	1	1	1			$R(p)$
A_2	1	1	1	-1	-1	$T_z,$	R_z	IR
B_1	1	-1	1	1	-1			$R(dp)$
B_2	1	-1	1	-1	1			$R(dp)$
E	2	0	-2	0	0	(T_x, T_y); (R_x, R_y)		$IR, R(dp)$

$\mathscr{D}_5$	E	$2C_5$	$2C_5{}^2$	$5C_2$			
A_1	1	1	1	1			$R(p)$
A_2	1	1	1	-1	T_z; R_z		IR
E_1	2	$2\cos 72°$	$2\cos 144°$	0	(T_x, T_y); (R_x, R_y)		$IR, R(dp)$
E_2	2	$2\cos 144°$	$2\cos 72°$	0			$R(dp)$

$\mathscr{D}_6$	E	$2C_6$	$2C_3$	C_2	$3C_2'$	$3C_2''$			
A_1	1	1	1	1	1	1			$R(p)$
A_2	1	1	1	1	-1	-1	T_z; R_z		IR
B_1	1	-1	1	-1	1	-1			
B_2	1	-1	1	-1	-1	1			
E_1	2	1	-1	-2	0	0	(T_x, T_y); (R_x, R_y)		$IR, R(dp)$
E_2	2	-1	-1	2	0	0			$R(dp)$

C. CHARACTER TABLES FOR THE GROUPS $\mathscr{C}_{nv}$

$$n = (2, 3, 4, 5, 6)$$

$\mathscr{C}_{2v}$	E	C_2	$\sigma_v(zx)$	$\sigma_v(yz)$	Ex: Water	
A_1	1	1	1	1	T_z	$IR, R(p)$
A_2	1	1	-1	-1	R_z	$R(dp)$
B_1	1	-1	1	-1	T_x; R_y	$IR, R(dp)$
B_2	1	-1	-1	1	T_y; R_x	$IR, R(dp)$

$\mathscr{C}_{3v}$	E	$2C_3$	$3\sigma_v$	Ex: Ammonia	
A_1	1	1	1	T_z	$IR, R(p)$
A_2	1	1	-1	R_z	
E	2	-1	0	$(T_x T_y)$; (R_x, R_y)	$IR, R(dp)$

$\mathscr{C}_{4v}$	E	$2C_4$	C_2	$2\sigma_v$	$2\sigma_d$	Ex: B_5H_9	
A_1	1	1	1	1	1	T_z	$IR, R(p)$
A_2	1	1	1	-1	-1	R_z	
B_1	1	-1	1	1	-1		$R(dp)$
B_2	1	-1	1	-1	1		$R(dp)$
E	2	0	-2	0	0	$(T_x, T_y); (R_x, R_y)$	$IR, R(dp)$

$\mathscr{C}_{5v}$	E	$2C_5$	$2C_5^2$	$5\sigma_v$		
A_1	1	1	1	1	T_z	$IR, R(p)$
A_2	1	1	1	-1	R_z	
E_1	2	$2\cos 72°$	$2\cos 144°$	0	$(T_x, T_y); (R_x, R_y)$	$IR, R(dp)$
E_2	2	$2\cos 144°$	$2\cos 72°$	0		$R(dp)$

$\mathscr{C}_{6v}$	E	$2C_6$	$2C_3$	C_2	$3\sigma_v$	$3\sigma_d$		
A_1	1	1	1	1	1	1	T_z	$IR, R(p)$
A_2	1	1	1	1	-1	-1	R_z	
B_1	1	-1	1	-1	1	-1		
B_2	1	-1	1	-1	-1	1		
E_1	2	1	-1	-2	0	0	$(T_x, T_y); (R_x, R_y)$	$IR, R(dp)$
E_2	2	-1	-1	2	0	0		$R(dp)$

D. CHARACTER TABLES FOR THE GROUPS $\mathscr{C}_{nh}$

$(n = 2, 3, 4)$

$\mathscr{C}_{2h}$	E	C_2	i	σ_h	Ex: Trans-Dichloroethylene	
A_g	1	1	1	1	R_z	$R(p)$
B_g	1	-1	1	-1	R_x, R_y	$R(dp)$
A_u	1	1	-1	-1	T_z	IR
B_u	1	-1	-1	1	T_x, T_y	IR

$\mathscr{C}_{3h}$	E	C_3	σ_h	S_3		
A'	1	1	1	1	R_z	$R(p)$
E'	2	-1	2	-1	(T_x, T_y)	$IR, R(dp)$
A''	1	1	-1	-1	T_z	IR
E''	2	-1	-2	1	(R_x, R_y)	$R(dp)$

$\mathscr{C}_{4h}$	E	C_4	C_2	i	σ_h	S_4		
A_g	1	1	1	1	1	1	R_z	$R(p)$
B_g	1	−1	1	1	1	−1		$R(dp)$
E_g	2	0	−2	2	−2	0	(R_x, R_y)	$R(dp)$
A_u	1	1	1	−1	−1	−1	T_z	IR
B_u	1	−1	1	−1	−1	1		
E_u	2	0	−2	−2	2	0	(T_x, T_y)	IR

E. CHARACTER TABLES FOR THE GROUPS $\mathscr{D}_{nh}$ ($n = 2, 3, 4, 5, 6$)

$\mathscr{D}_{2h} = \mathscr{V}_h$	E	$C_2(z)$	$C_2(y)$	$C_2(x)$	i	$\sigma(xy)$	$\sigma(zx)$	$\sigma(yz)$		Ex: Ethylene
A_g	1	1	1	1	1	1	1	1		$R(p)$
B_{1g}	1	1	−1	−1	1	1	−1	−1	R_z	$R(dp)$
B_{2g}	1	−1	1	−1	1	−1	1	−1	R_y	$R(dp)$
B_{3g}	1	−1	−1	1	1	−1	−1	1	R_x	$R(dp)$
A_u	1	1	1	1	−1	−1	−1	−1		
B_{1u}	1	1	−1	−1	−1	−1	1	1	T_z	IR
B_{2u}	1	−1	1	−1	−1	1	−1	1	T_y	IR
B_{3u}	1	−1	−1	1	−1	1	1	−1	T_x	IR

$\mathscr{D}_{3h}$	E	$2C_3$	$3C_2$	σ_h	$2S_3$	$3\sigma_v$		Ex: Cyclopropane
A_1'	1	1	1	1	1	1		$R(p)$
A_2'	1	1	−1	1	1	−1	R_z	
E'	2	−1	0	2	−1	0	(T_x, T_y)	IR, $R(dp)$
A_1''	1	1	1	−1	−1	−1		
A_2''	1	1	−1	−1	−1	1	T_z	IR
E''	2	−1	0	−2	1	0	(R_x, R_y)	$R(dp)$

$\mathscr{D}_{4h}$	E	$2C_4$	C_2	$2C_2'$	$2C_2''$	i	$2S_4$	σ_h	$2\sigma_v$	$2\sigma_d$		Ex: planar Cyclobutane
A_{1g}	1	1	1	1	1	1	1	1	1	1		$R(p)$
A_{2g}	1	1	1	−1	−1	1	1	1	−1	−1	R_z	
B_{1g}	1	−1	1	1	−1	1	−1	1	1	−1		$R(dp)$
B_{2g}	1	−1	1	−1	1	1	−1	1	−1	1		$R(dp)$
E_g	2	0	−2	0	0	2	0	−2	0	0	(R_x, R_y)	$R(dp)$
A_{1u}	1	1	1	1	1	−1	−1	−1	−1	−1		
A_{2u}	1	1	1	−1	−1	−1	−1	−1	1	1	T_z	IR
B_{1u}	1	−1	1	1	−1	−1	1	−1	−1	1		
B_{2u}	1	−1	1	−1	1	−1	1	−1	1	−1		
E_u	2	0	−2	0	0	−2	0	2	0	0	(T_x, T_y)	IR

$\mathscr{D}_{5h}$	E	$2C_5$	$2C_5^2$	$5C_2$	σ_h	$2S_5$	$2S_5^3$	$5\sigma_v$		Ex: planar Cyclopentane
A_1'	1	1	1	1	1	1	1	1		$R(p)$
A_2'	1	1	1	-1	1	1	1	-1	R_z	
E_1'	2	$2\cos 72°$	$2\cos 144°$	0	2	$2\cos 72°$	$2\cos 144°$	0	(T_x, T_y)	IR
E_2'	2	$2\cos 144°$	$2\cos 72°$	0	2	$2\cos 144°$	$2\cos 72°$	0		$R(dp)$
A_1''	1	1	1	1	-1	-1	-1	-1		
A_2''	1	1	1	-1	-1	-1	-1	1	T_z	IR
E_1''	2	$2\cos 72°$	$2\cos 144°$	0	-2	$-2\cos 72°$	$-2\cos 144°$	0	(R_x, R_y)	$R(dp)$
E_2''	2	$2\cos 144°$	$2\cos 72°$	0	-2	$-2\cos 144°$	$-2\cos 72°$	0		

$\mathscr{D}_{6h}$	E	$2C_6$	$2C_3$	C_2	$3C_2'$	$3C_2''$	i	$2S_3$	$2S_6$	σ_h	$3\sigma_d$	$3\sigma_v$		Ex: Benzene
A_{1g}	1	1	1	1	1	1	1	1	1	1	1	1		$R(p)$
A_{2g}	1	1	1	1	-1	-1	1	1	1	1	-1	-1	R_z	
B_{1g}	1	-1	1	-1	1	-1	1	-1	1	-1	1	-1		
B_{2g}	1	-1	1	-1	-1	1	1	-1	1	-1	-1	1		
E_{1g}	2	1	-1	-2	0	0	2	1	-1	-2	0	0	(R_x, R_y)	$R(dp)$
E_{2g}	2	-1	-1	2	0	0	2	-1	-1	2	0	0	0	$R(dp)$
A_{1u}	1	1	1	1	1	1	-1	-1	-1	-1	-1	-1		
A_{2u}	1	1	1	1	-1	-1	-1	-1	-1	-1	1	1	T_z	IR
B_{1u}	1	-1	1	-1	1	-1	-1	1	-1	1	-1	1		
B_{2u}	1	-1	1	-1	-1	1	-1	1	-1	1	1	-1		
E_{1u}	2	1	-1	-2	0	0	-2	-1	1	2	0	0	(T_x, T_y)	IR
E_{2u}	2	-1	-1	2	0	0	-2	1	1	-2	0	0		

F. CHARACTER TABLES FOR THE GROUP $\mathscr{D}_{nd}$

$(n = 2, 3, 4, 5, 6)$

$\mathscr{D}_{2d} = \mathscr{V}_d$	E	$2S_4$	C_2	$2C_2'$	$2\sigma_d$	Ex: Allene	
A_1	1	1	1	1	1		$R(p)$
A_2	1	1	1	-1	-1	R_z	
B_1	1	-1	1	1	-1		$R(dp)$
B_2	1	-1	1	-1	1	T_z	$IR, R(dp)$
E	2	0	-2	0	0	$(T_x, T_y);\ (R_x, R_y)$	$IR, R(dp)$

$\mathscr{D}_{3d}$	E	$2C_3$	$3C_2$	i	$2S_6$	$3\sigma_d$	Ex: Cyclohexane	
A_{1g}	1	1	1	1	1	1		$R(p)$
A_{2g}	1	1	-1	1	1	-1	R_z	
E_g	2	-1	0	2	-1	0	(R_x, R_y)	$R(dp)$
A_{1u}	1	1	1	-1	-1	-1		
A_{2u}	1	1	-1	-1	-1	1	T_z	IR
E_u	2	-1	0	-2	1	0	(T_z, T_y)	IR

$\mathscr{D}_{4d}$	E	$2S_8$	$2C_4$	$2S_8^3$	C_2	$4C_2'$	$4\sigma_d$		
A_1	1	1	1	1	1	1	1		$R(p)$
A_2	1	1	1	1	1	-1	-1	R_z	
B_1	1	-1	1	-1	1	1	-1		
B_2	1	-1	1	-1	1	-1	1	T_z	IR
E_1	2	$\sqrt{2}$	0	$-\sqrt{2}$	-2	0	0	(T_x, T_y)	IR
E_2	2	0	-2	0	2	0	0		$R(dp)$
E_3	2	$-\sqrt{2}$	0	$\sqrt{2}$	-2	0	0	(R_x, R_y)	$R(dp)$

$\mathscr{D}_{5d}$	E	$2C_5$	$2C_5^2$	$5C_2$	i	$2S_{10}^3$	$2S_{10}$	$5\sigma_d$		
A_{1g}	1	1	1	1	1	1	1	1		$R(p)$
A_{2g}	1	1	1	-1	1	1	1	-1	R_z	
E_{1g}	2	$2\cos 72°$	$2\cos 144°$	0	2	$2\cos 72°$	$2\cos 144°$	0	(R_x, R_y)	$R(dp)$
E_{2g}	2	$2\cos 144°$	$2\cos 72°$	0	2	$2\cos 144°$	$2\cos 72°$	0		$R(dp)$
A_{1u}	1	1	1	1	-1	-1	-1	-1		
A_{2u}	1	1	1	-1	-1	-1	-1	1	T_z	IR
E_{1u}	2	$2\cos 72°$	$2\cos 144°$	0	-2	$-2\cos 72°$	$-2\cos 144°$	0	(T_x, T_y)	IR
E_{2u}	2	$2\cos 144°$	$2\cos 72°$	0	-2	$-2\cos 144°$	$-2\cos 72°$	0		

$\mathscr{D}_{6d}$	E	$2S_{12}$	$2C_6$	$2S_4$	$2C_3$	$2S_{12}{}^5$	C_2	$6C_2'$	$6\sigma_d$			
A_1	1	1	1	1	1	1	1	1	1			$R(p)$
A_2	1	1	1	1	1	1	1	−1	−1	R_z		
B_1	1	−1	1	−1	1	−1	1	1	−1			
B_2	1	−1	1	−1	1	−1	1	−1	1	T_z	IR	
E_1	2	$\sqrt{3}$	1	0	−1	$-\sqrt{3}$	−2	0	0	(T_x, T_y)	IR	
E_2	2	1	−1	−2	−1	1	2	0	0			$R(dp)$
E_3	2	0	−2	0	2	0	−2	0	0			
E_4	2	−1	−1	2	−1	−1	2	0	0			
E_5	2	$-\sqrt{3}$	1	0	−1	$\sqrt{3}$	−2	0	0	(R_x, R_y)		$R(dp)$

G. CHARACTER TABLES FOR THE GROUPS $\mathscr{T}$, $\mathscr{O}$, AND $\mathscr{C}_{\infty v}$ AND $\mathscr{D}_{\infty v}$

$\mathscr{T}_d$	E	$8C_3$	$3C_2$	$6\sigma_d$	$6S_4$	Ex: Methane		
A_1	1	1	1	1	1			$R(p)$
A_2	1	1	1	−1	−1			
E	2	−1	2	0	0			$R(dp)$
T_1	3	0	−1	−1	1	R_x, R_y, R_z		
T_2	3	0	−1	1	−1	T_x, T_y, T_z	IR, $R(dp)$	

$\mathscr{O}_h$	E	$8C_3$	$3C_2$	$6C_2$	$6C_4$	i	$8S_6$	3σ	6σ	$6S_4$	Ex: SF$_6$		
A_{1g}	1	1	1	1	1	1	1	1	1	1			$R(p)$
A_{1u}	1	1	1	1	1	−1	−1	−1	−1	−1			
A_{2g}	1	1	1	−1	−1	1	1	1	−1	−1			
A_{2u}	1	1	1	−1	−1	−1	−1	−1	1	1			
E_g	2	−1	2	0	0	2	−1	2	0	0			$R(dp)$
E_u	2	−1	2	0	0	−2	1	−2	0	0			
T_{1g}	3	0	−1	−1	1	3	0	−1	−1	1	R_x, R_y, R_z		
T_{1u}	3	0	−1	−1	1	−3	0	1	1	−1	T_x, T_y, T_z	IR	
T_{2g}	3	0	−1	1	−1	3	0	−1	1	−1			$R(dp)$
T_{2u}	3	0	−1	1	−1	−3	0	1	−1	1			

$\mathscr{C}_{\infty v}$	E	$2C\phi$	σ_v	Ex: HCN	
A_1	1	1	1	T_z	IR, R(p)
A_2	1	1	-1	R_z	
E_1	2	$2\cos\phi$	0	T_x, T_y, R_x, R_y	IR, R(dp)
E_2	2	$2\cos 2\phi$	0		R(dp)
E_3	2	$2\cos 3\phi$	0		

$\mathscr{D}_{\infty h}$	E	$2C\phi$	C_2	i	$2S\phi$	σ_v	Ex: CO_2	
A_{1g}	1	1	1	1	1	1		R(p)
A_{1u}	1	1	-1	-1	-1	1	T_z	IR
A_{2g}	1	1	-1	1	1	-1	R_z	
A_{2u}	1	1	1	-1	-1	-1		
E_{1g}	2	$2\cos\phi$	0	2	$-2\cos\phi$	0	R_x, R_y	R(dp)
E_{1u}	2	$2\cos\phi$	0	-2	$2\cos\phi$	0	T_x, T_y	IR
E_{2g}	2	$2\cos 2\phi$	0	2	$2\cos 2\phi$	0		R(dp)
E_{2u}	2	$2\cos 2\phi$	0	-2	$-2\cos 2\phi$	0		

Values of Overlap and Related Integrals

Overlap integrals often appear in expressions dealing with bonding and spectra, and other quantum chemical integrals, such as the two electron repulsion integrals, are important in the more detailed treatment of π-electron energies and ultraviolet spectra. This appendix consists of tables of some of these quantities. In Table 4A-1, which deals with overlap integrals between two identical $2s$ or $2p$ wave functions, the quantity α is given by

$$\alpha = \frac{Z}{2} \frac{R}{a_0}$$

where Z is the effective nuclear charge (obtained using Slater's rules, p. 26, or in some similar fashion.) For carbon, this is usually taken as 3.18. The distance between nuclei is represented by R, and $a_0 = 0.529$ Å.

The symbols for the overlap integrals are: $S_{s's'}$, the integral between two Slater $2s$ orbitals; S_{ss}, the integral between two hydrogenlike $2s$ orbitals; $S_{s\sigma}$, the integral between a $2s$ orbital and a $2p$ orbital directed toward it; $S_{\sigma\sigma}$, the integral between two $2p$ orbitals directed toward each other; and $S_{\pi\pi}$, the integral between two $2p$ orbitals with edgewise overlap. The table is taken from the compilation by Kopineck[1] which also has values of the Coulombic (J) and exchange (K) integrals.

One often wishes to have the overlap integral between two $2p$ orbitals which have an orientation between that of the σ and π descriptions. The integrals may be obtained by taking the $2p$ components of the starting orbitals in the σ and π directions and summing the overlap integrals for these new orbitals. For example, if the starting orbitals, $2p'$, were given by

$$\psi_{2p'} = 0.199\psi_{2p_\sigma} + 0.980\psi_{2p_\pi}$$

[1] H. Kopineck, Z. Naturforschung, 5a, 420 (1950).

Table 4A-1   Overlap Integrals between $2s$

$\alpha =$	0.5	1.0	1.5	2.0	2.5	3.0
$S_{s's'} =$	0.96287	0.88291	0.80048	0.73081	0.67207	0.61736
$S_{s's'}^2 =$	0.92712	0.77953	0.64077	0.53408	0.45168	0.38113
S_{ss}	0.98645	0.94831	0.88973	0.81502	0.72907	0.63727
$S_{ss}^2 =$	0.97308	0.89929	0.79162	0.66426	0.53154	0.40611
$S_{s\sigma} =$	0.14299	0.27611	0.38647	0.46361	0.50354	0.50878
$S_{s\sigma}^2 =$	0.20446^{-1}	0.76237^{-1}	0.14936	0.21493	0.25355	0.25886
$S_{\sigma\sigma}$	-0.92749	-0.73576	-0.48252	-0.22556	-0.51294^{-2}	0.15932
$S_{\sigma\sigma}^2 =$	0.86024	0.54134	0.23283	0.50877^{-1}	0.26311^{-4}	$0,25383^{-1}$
$S_{\pi\pi} =$	0.97550	0.90744	0.80885	0.69472	0.57802	0.46800
$S_{\pi\pi}^2 =$	0.95160	0.82345	0.65424	0.48264	0.33411	0.21902

then the overlap integral would be given by

$$S_{2p'2p'} = \int \psi_{2p'}\psi_{2p'}\, d\tau = \int (0.199\psi_{2p_\sigma} + 0.980\psi_{2p_\pi})$$

$$\times\ (0.199\psi_{2p_\sigma} + 0.980\psi_{2p_\pi})\, d\tau$$

$$= (0.199)^2 S_{\sigma\sigma} + (0.980)^2 S_{\pi\pi} + 2(0.199)(0.980)S_{\sigma\pi}$$

The overlap integrals for hybrid orbitals may be obtained in the same fashion.

Overlap integrals between two different atoms are usually obtained from the tables of Mulliken, Rieke, Orloff and Orloff.[2] These tables are based on Slater orbitals. The two parameters p and t which reference the tables are given by

$$p = \frac{\frac{1}{2}(\mu_a + \mu_b)R}{a_0}$$

$$t = \frac{\mu_a - \mu_b}{\mu_a + \mu_b}$$

where R is the distance between nuclei, $a_0 = 0.529$ Å, and the μ's are the values given in Table 4A-2. Selected parts of the tables are given as Tables 4A-3 to 4A-14.

In the final tables (4A-11 to 4A-14), *di* refers to a diagonal or *sp* orbital, *tr* refers to a trigonal or sp^2 orbital, and *te* refers to a tetrahedral or sp^3 orbital.

The other integrals of common interest, those used in the Pariser-Parr[3] and Pople[4] treatments of aromatic compounds, have varied considerably from one investigation to the next because of their semiempirical nature. The more recent values are given in Table 4A-15, but it may be expected that small changes in the values will be required as the result of further investigation.

[2] R. S. Mulliken, C. A. Rieke, D. Orloff, and H. Orloff, *J. Chem. Phys.*, **17**, 1248 (1949).
[3] R. Pariser and R. G. Parr, *J. Chem. Phys.*, **21**, 466, 767 (1953); **23**, 711 (1955); R. Pariser, *J. Chem. Phys.*, **24**, 250 (1956).
[4] J. A. Pople, *Trans. Faraday Soc.*, **49**, 1375 (1953).

and 2p Atomic Wave Functions

3.5	4.0	4.5	5.0	5.5	6.0	6.5	7.0
0.56129	0.50185	0.43978	0.37732	0.31708	0.26126	0.21136	0.16815
0.31505	0.25185	0.19341	0.14237	0.10054	0.68257^{-1}	0.44673^{-1}	0.28274^{-1}
0.54485	0.45626	0.37479	0.30246	0.24016	0.18789	0.14502	0.11056
0.29686	0.20817	0.14047	0.91482^{-1}	0.57677^{-1}	0.35303^{-1}	0.21031^{-1}	0.12224^{-1}
0.48613	0.44413	0.39108	0.33390	0.27771	0.22583	0.18007	0.14115
0.23632	0.19725	0.15294	0.11149	0.77123^{-1}	0.50999^{-1}	0.32425^{-1}	0.19923^{-1}
0.26485	0.31869	0.33257	0.31891	0.28863	0.25035	0.20987	0.17143
0.70146^{-1}	0.10156	0.11060	0.10170	0.83307^{-1}	0.62675^{-1}	0.44045^{-1}	0.29388^{-1}
0.37017	0.28694	0.21857	0.16395	0.12134	0.88739^{-2}	0.64209^{-1}	0.46020^{-1}
0.13703	0.82335^{-1}	0.47773^{-1}	0.26880^{-1}	0.14728^{-1}	0.78746^{-2}	0.41228^{-2}	0.21178^{-2}

Table 4A-2   Slater μ Values for Valence Shell s and p Atomic Orbitals[a]

H	1.00	C^-	1.45	O^-	2.10
Li	0.65	C	1.625	O	2.275
Be	0.975	C^+	1.80	O^+	2.45
B^-	1.125	N	1.95	F	2.60
B	1.30	N^+	2.125		
Na	0.733	Si	1.383	Cl	2.033
Mg	0.95	P	1.60	Br	2.054
Al	1.167	S	1.817	I	1.90

[a] For inner shell $1s$ atomic orbitals, $\mu = Z - 0.3$ in all cases where Z is the actual nuclear charge.

Table 4A-3

p	$t = 0.0$	$t = 0.1$	$t = 0.2$	$t = 0.3$	$t = 0.4$	$t = 0.5$	$t = 0.6$	$t = 0.7$	$t = 0.8$
				$S(1s, 1s)$					
0.0	1.000	0.985	0.941	0.868	0.770	0.650	0.512	0.364	0.216
0.5	0.960	0.946	0.905	0.837	0.744	0.630	0.499	0.357	0.213
1.0	0.858	0.847	0.812	0.756	0.678	0.580	0.465	0.337	0.205
1.2	0.807	0.797	0.766	0.715	0.644	0.554	0.447	0.327	0.200
1.3	0.780								
1.4	0.753	0.744	0.717	0.671	0.608	0.526	0.428	0.316	0.196
1.5	0.725								
1.6	0.697	0.689	0.666	0.626	0.570	0.498	0.409	0.305	0.191
1.7	0.669								
1.8	0.641	0.635	0.615	0.581	0.533	0.469	0.388	0.293	0.185
1.9	0.614								
2.0	0.586	0.581	0.565	0.536	0.495	0.439	0.368	0.281	0.180
2.1	0.560								
2.2	0.533	0.529	0.515	0.493	0.458	0.410	0.348	0.269	0.175
2.3	0.508								
2.4	0.483	0.479	0.469	0.451	0.423	0.382	0.328	0.256	0.169
2.5	0.458								
2.6	0.435	0.432	0.425	0.411	0.388	0.355	0.308	0.244	0.164
2.7	0.412								
2.8	0.390	0.388	0.383	0.373	0.356	0.329	0.289	0.233	0.158
2.9	0.369								
3.0	0.349	0.348	0.344	0.338	0.325	0.304	0.271	0.221	0.153
3.2	0.310	0.310	0.309	0.305	0.297	0.281	0.254	0.210	0.148

p	$t = 0.0$	$t = 0.1$	$t = 0.2$	$t = 0.3$	$t = 0.4$	$t = 0.5$	$t = 0.6$	$t = 0.7$	$t = 0.8$
				$S(1s, 1s)$					
3.4	0.275	0.276	0.276	0.274	0.270	0.259	0.237	0.200	0.143
3.5	0.259								
3.6	0.244	0.244	0.246	0.247	0.245	0.238	0.221	0.189	0.138
3.8	0.215	0.216	0.218	0.221	0.222	0.219	0.206	0.180	0.133
4.0	0.189	0.190	0.194	0.198	0.201	0.201	0.192	0.170	0.128
4.2	0.166	0.167	0.171	0.176	0.182	0.184	0.179	0.161	0.123
4.4	0.146	0.147	0.151	0.157	0.164	0.168	0.166	0.152	0.119
4.5	0.136								
4.6	0.127	0.129	0.133	0.140	0.148	0.154	0.155	0.144	0.114
5.0	0.097	0.098	0.103	0.110	0.120	0.129	0.134	0.129	0.106
5.5	0.068	0.069	0.074	0.082	0.091	0.102	0.111	0.112	0.097
6.0	0.047	0.049	0.053	0.060	0.070	0.081	0.092	0.097	0.088
6.5	0.032	0.034	0.037	0.044	0.053	0.064	0.076	0.084	0.080
7.0	0.022	0.023	0.026	0.032	0.040	0.050	0.063	0.073	0.072
7.5	0.015	0.016	0.018	0.023	0.030	0.040	0.052	0.063	0.066
8.0	0.010	0.011	0.013	0.017	0.023	0.031	0.043	0.054	0.059
9.0	0.005	0.005	0.006	0.009	0.013	0.019	0.029	0.040	0.049
10.0	0.002	0.002	0.003	0.004	0.007	0.012	0.019	0.030	0.040
12.0	0.000	0.000	0.001	0.001	0.002	0.004	0.009	0.017	0.027
15.0	0.000	0.000	0.000	0.000	0.000	0.001	0.003	0.007	0.015
20.0	0.000	0.000	0.000	0.000	0.000	0.000	0.000	0.002	0.005

Table 4A-4

$S(1s, 2s)$

p	t = -0.5	t = -0.4	t = -0.3	t = -0.2	t = -0.1	t = 0.0	t = 0.1	t = 0.2	t = 0.3	t = 0.4	t = 0.5	t = 0.6	t = 0.7	t = 0.8	t = 0.9
0.0	0.844	0.933	0.977	0.978	0.938	0.866	0.768	0.652	0.526	0.400	0.281	0.177	0.095	0.037	0.007
0.5	0.829	0.916	0.959	0.960	0.923	0.854	0.760	0.647	0.525	0.401	0.284	0.180	0.097	0.039	0.007
1.0	0.787	0.866	0.906	0.907	0.875	0.814	0.730	0.628	0.516	0.400	0.288	0.186	0.102	0.042	0.008
1.5	0.722	0.790	0.823	0.825	0.799	0.749	0.679	0.593	0.496	0.393	0.290	0.192	0.109	0.046	0.009
2.0	0.644	0.697	0.722	0.723	0.702	0.664	0.610	0.542	0.463	0.376	0.285	0.195	0.114	0.050	0.011
2.2	0.611	0.657	0.679	0.679	0.661	0.627	0.579	0.519	0.447	0.367	0.282	0.196	0.116	0.051	0.011
2.4	0.577	0.617	0.635	0.635	0.619	0.589	0.547	0.494	0.430	0.357	0.277	0.195	0.117	0.053	0.012
2.6	0.543	0.578	0.592	0.591	0.576	0.550	0.514	0.468	0.411	0.345	0.272	0.194	0.119	0.054	0.012
2.8	0.510	0.539	0.550	0.547	0.534	0.512	0.481	0.441	0.392	0.333	0.265	0.192	0.119	0.055	0.013
3.0	0.478	0.501	0.508	0.505	0.493	0.474	0.448	0.414	0.372	0.320	0.258	0.190	0.120	0.057	0.013
3.2	0.446	0.464	0.468	0.464	0.453	0.437	0.416	0.388	0.352	0.306	0.251	0.187	0.120	0.058	0.013
3.4	0.416	0.428	0.430	0.425	0.415	0.402	0.384	0.361	0.331	0.292	0.243	0.184	0.120	0.058	0.014
3.6	0.386	0.395	0.394	0.388	0.379	0.368	0.354	0.336	0.311	0.278	0.234	0.180	0.119	0.059	0.014
3.8						0.335	0.325	0.311	0.291	0.263	0.225	0.176	0.119	0.060	0.014
4.0	0.332	0.333	0.327	0.320	0.312	0.305	0.297	0.287	0.272	0.249	0.216	0.172	0.118	0.060	0.015
4.2						0.276	0.271	0.264	0.253	0.235	0.207	0.167	0.116	0.061	0.015
4.4						0.250	0.246	0.242	0.235	0.221	0.198	0.162	0.115	0.061	0.016
4.5	0.272	0.265	0.256	0.247	0.241										
5.0	0.221	0.209	0.197	0.188	0.183	0.225	0.223	0.221	0.217	0.208	0.189	0.157	0.113	0.061	0.016
5.5						0.181	0.182	0.184	0.185	0.182	0.170	0.147	0.109	0.062	0.017
6.0	0.143	0.127	0.114	0.105	0.101	0.136	0.139	0.144	0.149	0.152	0.149	0.134	0.104	0.061	0.018
6.5						0.101	0.105	0.111	0.119	0.126	0.128	0.120	0.098	0.060	0.018
7.0	0.091	0.075	0.063	0.056	0.053	0.074	0.078	0.085	0.094	0.104	0.110	0.108	0.092	0.059	0.019
7.5						0.054	0.058	0.065	0.074	0.085	0.093	0.096	0.086	0.058	0.019
8.0	0.057	0.044	0.034	0.029	0.027	0.039	0.042	0.048	0.058	0.068	0.079	0.085	0.079	0.056	0.019
9.0						0.027	0.030	0.036	0.044	0.055	0.066	0.075	0.073	0.054	0.020
10.0						0.014	0.016	0.020	0.026	0.035	0.046	0.057	0.061	0.050	0.020
12.0						0.007	0.008	0.010	0.015	0.022	0.032	0.043	0.051	0.046	0.020
15.0						0.001	0.002	0.003	0.005	0.008	0.014	0.023	0.034	0.037	0.019
20.0						0.000	0.000	0.000	0.001	0.002	0.004	0.009	0.017	0.025	0.019

Table 4A-5

$S(1s, 2p\sigma)$

p	t = -0.5	t = -0.4	t = -0.3	t = -0.2	t = -0.1	t = 0.0	t = 0.1	t = 0.2	t = 0.3	t = 0.4	t = 0.5	t = 0.6	t = 0.7	t = 0.8
0.0	0.000	0.000	0.000	0.000	0.000	0.000	0.000	0.000	0.000	0.000	0.000	0.000	0.000	0.000
0.5	0.117	0.155	0.189	0.216	0.234	0.240	0.235	0.218	0.191	0.157	0.119	0.080	0.046	0.022
1.0	0.208	0.276	0.336	0.385	0.417	0.429	0.421	0.394	0.348	0.288	0.220	0.151	0.087	0.038
1.5	0.264	0.348	0.423	0.484	0.525	0.544	0.538	0.507	0.454	0.381	0.296	0.206	0.121	0.054
2.0	0.287	0.375	0.454	0.518	0.564	0.586	0.585	0.558	0.506	0.433	0.344	0.245	0.148	0.067
2.2	0.289	0.375	0.453	0.517	0.563	0.587	0.587	0.563	0.515	0.444	0.355	0.256	0.156	0.071
2.4	0.287	0.371	0.447	0.509	0.554	0.579	0.582	0.561	0.517	0.449	0.363	0.264	0.164	0.076
2.6	0.282	0.363	0.435	0.495	0.540	0.565	0.570	0.553	0.513	0.450	0.368	0.271	0.170	0.079
2.8	0.275	0.352	0.420	0.477	0.520	0.546	0.553	0.540	0.505	0.447	0.369	0.275	0.175	0.083
3.0	0.266	0.338	0.402	0.456	0.497	0.523	0.532	0.522	0.492	0.441	0.368	0.278	0.179	0.086
3.2	0.255	0.323	0.382	0.432	0.471	0.497	0.508	0.502	0.477	0.431	0.364	0.278	0.182	0.089
3.4	0.244	0.306	0.361	0.407	0.443	0.468	0.481	0.479	0.459	0.419	0.359	0.279	0.184	0.091
3.6	0.232	0.289	0.338	0.380	0.414	0.439	0.453	0.454	0.439	0.406	0.351	0.276	0.186	0.093
3.8						0.409	0.424	0.428	0.418	0.390	0.342	0.273	0.186	0.095
4.0	0.207	0.253	0.293	0.327	0.356	0.379	0.394	0.401	0.396	0.374	0.332	0.269	0.186	0.097
4.2						0.349	0.365	0.374	0.373	0.357	0.321	0.264	0.186	0.098
4.4						0.320	0.337	0.348	0.350	0.339	0.310	0.258	0.185	0.099
4.6	0.176	0.210	0.239	0.264	0.286	0.293	0.309	0.322	0.328	0.321	0.298	0.252	0.183	0.100
5.0	0.147	0.171	0.190	0.208	0.225	0.241	0.258	0.273	0.284	0.286	0.272	0.238	0.179	0.101
5.5						0.186	0.202	0.219	0.234	0.243	0.241	0.219	0.172	0.102
6.0	0.099	0.108	0.115	0.122	0.130	0.141	0.155	0.172	0.189	0.204	0.210	0.199	0.163	0.101
6.5						0.105	0.118	0.133	0.151	0.169	0.181	0.179	0.154	0.100
7.0	0.064	0.066	0.066	0.068	0.071	0.078	0.088	0.102	0.120	0.139	0.155	0.160	0.144	0.098
7.5						0.057	0.065	0.077	0.094	0.113	0.132	0.142	0.134	0.095
8.0	0.041	0.039	0.037	0.036	0.037	0.041	0.048	0.058	0.073	0.092	0.111	0.126	0.124	0.092
9.0						0.021	0.025	0.032	0.043	0.059	0.078	0.097	0.104	0.086
10.0						0.010	0.013	0.017	0.025	0.037	0.054	0.073	0.087	0.078
12.0						0.002	0.003	0.005	0.008	0.014	0.025	0.040	0.058	0.063
15.0						0.000	0.000	0.001	0.001	0.003	0.007	0.015	0.030	0.044
20.0						0.000	0.000	0.000	0.000	0.000	0.001	0.003	0.009	0.022

Table 4A-6

S(2s, 2s)

p	t = 0.0	t = 0.1	t = 0.2	t = 0.3	t = 0.4	t = 0.5	t = 0.6
0.0	1.000	0.975	0.903	0.790	0.647	0.487	0.328
0.5	0.986	0.962	0.892	0.782	0.642	0.486	0.328
1.0	0.948	0.926	0.862	0.760	0.629	0.481	0.329
1.5	0.890	0.871	0.815	0.725	0.608	0.472	0.329
2.0	0.815	0.799	0.753	0.678	0.578	0.458	0.327
2.5	0.729	0.717	0.679	0.622	0.540	0.438	0.322
3.0	0.637	0.629	0.603	0.559	0.496	0.413	0.312
3.2	0.600	0.593	0.571	0.533	0.477	0.402	0.308
3.4	0.563	0.557	0.539	0.507	0.457	0.389	0.302
3.6	0.527	0.522	0.507	0.480	0.438	0.377	0.296
3.8	0.491	0.487	0.476	0.454	0.417	0.364	0.290
4.0	0.456	0.454	0.445	0.427	0.397	0.350	0.283
4.2	0.423	0.421	0.415	0.402	0.377	0.336	0.276
4.4	0.390	0.389	0.386	0.376	0.357	0.323	0.268
4.6	0.360	0.359	0.358	0.352	0.337	0.309	0.260
4.8	0.330	0.331	0.331	0.328	0.318	0.295	0.252
5.0	0.302	0.307	0.305	0.305	0.299	0.281	0.244
5.5	0.240	0.242	0.247	0.252	0.255	0.248	0.223

S(2s, 2s)

p	t = 0.0	t = 0.1	t = 0.2	t = 0.3	t = 0.4	t = 0.5	t = 0.6
6.0	0.188	0.190	0.197	0.206	0.215	0.216	0.203
6.5	0.145	0.148	0.155	0.167	0.179	0.187	0.182
7.0	0.111	0.113	0.121	0.133	0.148	0.160	0.163
7.5	0.083	0.086	0.093	0.106	0.121	0.136	0.145
8.0	0.062	0.064	0.071	0.083	0.099	0.116	0.128
8.5	0.046	0.048	0.054	0.065	0.080	0.097	0.112
9.0	0.034	0.035	0.041	0.050	0.064	0.082	0.098
9.5	0.024	0.026	0.030	0.039	0.051	0.068	0.086
10.0	0.018	0.019	0.023	0.030	0.041	0.057	0.075
10.5	0.013	0.014	0.017	0.023	0.032	0.047	0.065
11.0	0.009	0.010	0.012	0.017	0.026	0.039	0.056
11.5	0.006	0.007	0.009	0.013	0.020	0.032	0.048
12.0	0.004	0.005	0.007	0.010	0.016	0.026	0.041
12.5	0.003	0.004	0.005	0.007	0.012	0.021	0.036
13.0	0.002	0.002	0.003	0.006	0.010	0.017	0.030
13.5	0.002	0.002	0.002	0.004	0.008	0.014	0.026
14.0	0.001	0.001	0.002	0.003	0.006	0.012	0.022

Table 4A-7

p	$S(2p\sigma, 2s)$						$S(2s, 2p\sigma)$						
	$t=0.6$	$t=0.5$	$t=0.4$	$t=0.3$	$t=0.2$	$t=0.1$	$t=0.0$	$t=0.1$	$t=0.2$	$t=0.3$	$t=0.4$	$t=0.5$	$t=0.6$
0.0	0.000	0.000	0.000	0.000	0.000	0.000	0.000	0.000	0.000	0.000	0.000	0.000	0.000
0.5	−0.008	0.002	0.020	0.047	0.079	0.112	0.143	0.167	0.180	0.180	0.166	0.139	0.103
1.0	−0.010	0.011	0.047	0.098	0.158	0.220	0.276	0.319	0.343	0.342	0.315	0.265	0.198
1.5	−0.005	0.028	0.081	0.151	0.231	0.313	0.386	0.443	0.473	0.472	0.437	0.369	0.278
2.0	0.006	0.049	0.114	0.197	0.289	0.381	0.464	0.526	0.561	0.560	0.521	0.446	0.340
2.5	0.019	0.070	0.143	0.218	0.327	0.420	0.504	0.567	0.603	0.602	0.569	0.493	0.383
3.0	0.033	0.089	0.163	0.251	0.342	0.431	0.509	0.570	0.606	0.612	0.582	0.513	0.407
3.2	0.037	0.096	0.169	0.254	0.339	0.427	0.503	0.562	0.598	0.606	0.580	0.515	0.412
3.4	0.042	0.099	0.173	0.255	0.335	0.421	0.492	0.549	0.586	0.596	0.573	0.513	0.415
3.6	0.046	0.103	0.175	0.254	0.327	0.411	0.479	0.534	0.570	0.582	0.563	0.509	0.416
3.8	0.049	0.106	0.176	0.252	0.318	0.399	0.463	0.515	0.551	0.565	0.550	0.502	0.415
4.0	0.052	0.109	0.176	0.247	0.307	0.385	0.444	0.494	0.529	0.545	0.535	0.492	0.412
4.2	0.055	0.110	0.174	0.241	0.295	0.369	0.425	0.471	0.505	0.523	0.518	0.481	0.407
4.4	0.057	0.111	0.172	0.234	0.281	0.351	0.402	0.446	0.480	0.500	0.499	0.469	0.401
4.6	0.059	0.111	0.168	0.226	0.267	0.333	0.380	0.421	0.455	0.476	0.479	0.454	0.394
4.8	0.060	0.110	0.164	0.217	0.253	0.314	0.357	0.396	0.428	0.451	0.458	0.439	0.386
5.0	0.061	0.109	0.159	0.208	0.239	0.295	0.334	0.370	0.402	0.426	0.436	0.423	0.377
5.5	0.062	0.104	0.145	0.182	0.216	0.248	0.278	0.308	0.337	0.364	0.382	0.382	0.351
6.0	0.061	0.096	0.129	0.157	0.181	0.203	0.226	0.250	0.277	0.305	0.328	0.339	0.324
6.5	0.058	0.088	0.112	0.132	0.148	0.163	0.180	0.200	0.224	0.251	0.278	0.297	0.295
7.0	0.055	0.079	0.096	0.109	0.119	0.129	0.141	0.157	0.178	0.205	0.233	0.258	0.266
7.5	0.051	0.070	0.082	0.089	0.095	0.101	0.109	0.122	0.140	0.165	0.193	0.222	0.238
8.0	0.047	0.061	0.068	0.072	0.074	0.077	0.083	0.093	0.109	0.131	0.159	0.189	0.212
8.5	0.043	0.053	0.057	0.057	0.057	0.059	0.063	0.070	0.084	0.103	0.130	0.160	0.187
9.0	0.039	0.045	0.047	0.045	0.044	0.044	0.046	0.053	0.064	0.081	0.105	0.135	0.165
9.5	0.035	0.038	0.038	0.036	0.033	0.033	0.034	0.039	0.048	0.063	0.085	0.113	0.144
10.0	0.031	0.033	0.031	0.028	0.025	0.024	0.025	0.029	0.036	0.048	0.068	0.095	0.126
10.5							0.018	0.021	0.027	0.037	0.054	0.079	0.109
11.0	0.024	0.023	0.020	0.016	0.014	0.013	0.013	0.015	0.020	0.028	0.043	0.065	0.095
11.5							0.009	0.011	0.015	0.022	0.034	0.054	0.082
12.0	0.018	0.016	0.012	0.010	0.008	0.007	0.007	0.008	0.011	0.016	0.027	0.044	0.070
12.5							0.005	0.006	0.008	0.012	0.021	0.036	0.060
13.0							0.003	0.004	0.006	0.009	0.016	0.030	0.052
13.5							0.002	0.003	0.004	0.007	0.013	0.024	0.044
14.0							0.002	0.002	0.003	0.005	0.010	0.020	0.038

Table 4A-8

$S(2p\sigma, 2p\sigma)$

p	$t=0.0$	$t=0.1$	$t=0.2$	$t=0.3$	$t=0.4$	$t=0.5$	$t=0.6$
0.0	−1.000	−0.975	−0.903	−0.790	−0.647	−0.487	−0.328
0.5	−0.927	−0.906	−0.840	−0.738	−0.607	−0.461	−0.312
1.0	−0.736	−0.720	−0.673	−0.599	−0.502	−0.389	−0.271
1.5	−0.483	−0.475	−0.452	−0.416	−0.360	−0.292	−0.214
2.0	−0.226	−0.226	−0.222	−0.222	−0.211	−0.188	−0.150
2.5	0.005	−0.007	−0.029	−0.053	−0.076	−0.092	−0.092
3.0	0.159	0.148	0.121	0.079	0.032	−0.011	−0.040
3.2	0.208	0.196	0.167	0.120	0.067	0.016	−0.022
3.4	0.248	0.237	0.204	0.155	0.097	0.040	−0.005
3.6	0.279	0.268	0.235	0.184	0.123	0.061	0.010
3.8	0.303	0.291	0.258	0.207	0.144	0.079	0.023
4.0	0.319	0.308	0.275	0.224	0.161	0.094	0.035
4.2	0.328	0.318	0.286	0.237	0.175	0.107	0.045
4.4	0.332	0.322	0.293	0.245	0.185	0.117	0.054
4.6	0.332	0.322	0.294	0.250	0.191	0.126	0.062
4.8	0.327	0.318	0.293	0.251	0.196	0.132	0.068
5.0	0.319	0.311	0.288	0.249	0.197	0.136	0.074
5.5	0.289	0.282	0.266	0.236	0.193	0.141	0.083

$S(2p\sigma, 2p\sigma)$

p	$t=0.0$	$t=0.1$	$t=0.2$	$t=0.3$	$t=0.4$	$t=0.5$	$t=0.6$
6.0	0.250	0.247	0.235	0.214	0.181	0.138	0.087
6.5	0.210	0.208	0.201	0.187	0.164	0.131	0.087
7.0	0.171	0.171	0.167	0.160	0.145	0.120	0.085
7.5	0.137	0.137	0.137	0.134	0.126	0.109	0.081
8.0	0.107	0.108	0.109	0.110	0.107	0.096	0.075
8.5	0.083	0.084	0.086	0.089	0.090	0.085	0.069
9.0	0.063	0.064	0.067	0.071	0.075	0.073	0.063
9.5	0.047	0.048	0.052	0.057	0.061	0.063	0.057
10.0	0.035	0.036	0.039	0.045	0.050	0.054	0.051
10.5	0.026	0.027	0.030	0.035	0.041	0.045	0.045
11.0	0.019	0.020	0.021	0.027	0.033	0.038	0.040
11.5	0.013	0.014	0.017	0.021	0.026	0.032	0.035
12.0	0.010	0.010	0.012	0.016	0.021	0.027	0.031
12.5	0.007	0.007	0.009	0.012	0.017	0.022	0.027
13.0	0.005	0.005	0.007	0.009	0.013	0.018	0.023
13.5	0.003	0.004	0.005	0.007	0.010	0.015	0.020
14.0	0.002	0.003	0.003	0.005	0.008	0.012	0.017

Table 4A-9

$S(2p\pi, 2p\pi)$

p	$t=0.0$	$t=0.1$	$t=0.2$	$t=0.3$	$t=0.4$	$t=0.5$	$t=0.6$
0.0	1.000	0.975	0.903	0.790	0.647	0.487	0.328
0.5	0.976	0.951	0.882	0.772	0.633	0.478	0.323
1.0	0.907	0.887	0.823	0.723	0.596	0.453	0.308
1.5	0.809	0.790	0.737	0.652	0.542	0.416	0.287
2.0	0.695	0.680	0.638	0.568	0.477	0.372	0.261
2.5	0.578	0.567	0.535	0.481	0.410	0.325	0.233
3.0	0.468	0.460	0.437	0.398	0.345	0.279	0.205
3.2	0.427	0.420	0.401	0.367	0.320	0.262	0.194
3.4	0.389	0.383	0.366	0.337	0.297	0.245	0.183
3.6	0.352	0.348	0.334	0.309	0.274	0.228	0.173
3.8	0.318	0.315	0.303	0.283	0.253	0.213	0.163
4.0	0.287	0.284	0.275	0.258	0.232	0.198	0.153
4.2	0.258	0.255	0.248	0.234	0.213	0.183	0.144
4.4	0.231	0.229	0.224	0.213	0.195	0.170	0.135
4.6	0.207	0.205	0.201	0.193	0.179	0.157	0.127
4.8	0.184	0.183	0.181	0.174	0.163	0.145	0.119

$S(2p\pi, 2p\pi)$

p	$t=0.0$	$t=0.1$	$t=0.2$	$t=0.3$	$t=0.4$	$t=0.5$	$t=0.6$
5.0	0.164	0.163	0.162	0.157	0.149	0.134	0.111
5.2	0.146						
5.4	0.129						
5.5	0.121	0.122	0.122	0.121	0.117	0.109	0.094
5.6	0.114						
5.8	0.101						
6.0	0.089	0.089	0.091	0.092	0.092	0.089	0.079
6.2	0.078						
6.4	0.069						
6.5	0.064	0.065	0.067	0.069	0.072	0.071	0.066
7.0	0.046	0.047	0.049	0.052	0.055	0.057	0.055
7.5	0.033	0.033	0.036	0.039	0.043	0.046	0.046
8.0	0.023	0.024	0.026	0.029	0.033	0.037	0.038
9.0	0.011	0.012	0.013	0.016	0.019	0.023	0.026
10.0	0.005	0.006	0.007	0.008	0.011	0.013	0.018

Table 4A-10

$S(2p\pi, 3p\pi)$

p	t = −0.6	t = −0.5	t = −0.4	t = −0.3	t = −0.2	t = −0.1	t = 0.0	t = 0.1	t = 0.2	t = 0.3	t = 0.4	t = 0.5	t = 0.6
0.0	0.479	0.667	0.826	0.937	0.989	0.979	0.913	0.801	0.659	0.505	0.354	0.222	0.120
0.5	0.473	0.658	0.814	0.923	0.973	0.963	0.899	0.786	0.652	0.500	0.352	0.221	0.120
1.0	0.456	0.632	0.779	0.881	0.928	0.920	0.860	0.758	0.628	0.485	0.344	0.219	0.119
1.5	0.431	0.591	0.724	0.816	0.858	0.851	0.798	0.708	0.591	0.461	0.331	0.213	0.118
2.0	0.399	0.541	0.656	0.735	0.771	0.765	0.720	0.643	0.542	0.429	0.313	0.206	0.117
2.5	0.363	0.484	0.581	0.645	0.676	0.672	0.633	0.569	0.486	0.390	0.290	0.195	0.114
3.0	0.325	0.426	0.503	0.554	0.575	0.571	0.542	0.492	0.426	0.348	0.264	0.182	0.109
3.5	0.287	0.369	0.428	0.466	0.480	0.477	0.454	0.416	0.366	0.303	0.237	0.168	0.104
4.0	0.251	0.315	0.359	0.384	0.394	0.389	0.373	0.345	0.308	0.262	0.209	0.153	0.097
4.5	0.218	0.266	0.297	0.313	0.316	0.312	0.301	0.282	0.255	0.222	0.182	0.137	0.090
5.0	0.187	0.222	0.241	0.250	0.251	0.246	0.238	0.225	0.208	0.185	0.157	0.122	0.083
5.2					0.228	0.223	0.216	0.205	0.191	0.172			
5.4					0.206	0.202	0.195	0.187	0.175	0.159			
5.5	0.160	0.184	0.195	0.198	0.196	0.192	0.186	0.178	0.167	0.153	0.133	0.107	0.076
5.6					0.186	0.182	0.176	0.169	0.160	0.147			
5.8					0.168	0.164	0.159	0.153	0.146	0.135			
6.0	0.136	0.151	0.156	0.155	0.151	0.147	0.143	0.139	0.133	0.125	0.112	0.093	0.069
6.5	0.115	0.123	0.124	0.120	0.115	0.112	0.109	0.107	0.104	0.101	0.093	0.081	0.062
7.0	0.097	0.100	0.097	0.092	0.087	0.084	0.082	0.081	0.081	0.080	0.077	0.069	0.055
7.5	0.082	0.081	0.076	0.070	0.065	0.062	0.061	0.061	0.062	0.064	0.063	0.059	0.049
8.0	0.068	0.065	0.059	0.053	0.049	0.046	0.045	0.046	0.048	0.050	0.052	0.050	0.043
9.0	0.048	0.042	0.036	0.030	0.026	0.024	0.024	0.025	0.027	0.030	0.034	0.035	0.033
10.0	0.033	0.027	0.021	0.017	0.014	0.012	0.012	0.013	0.015	0.018	0.022	0.025	0.025

OVERLAP INTEGRALS BETWEEN HYBRID ORBITALS

Table 4A-11

$S(1s, 2te\sigma)$

p	t = −0.5	t = −0.4	t = −0.3	t = −0.2	t = −0.1	t = 0.0	t = 0.1	t = 0.2
0.0	0.516	0.592	0.643	0.667	0.664	0.433	0.384	0.326
0.5	0.574	0.672	0.744	0.787	0.798	0.635	0.584	0.512
1.0	0.590	0.696	0.778	0.832	0.854	0.779	0.730	0.655
1.5	0.570	0.673	0.754	0.810	0.839	0.845	0.805	0.736
2.0	0.555	0.654	0.732	0.787	0.818	0.840	0.811	0.754
2.2	0.537	0.630	0.705	0.758	0.789	0.822	0.798	0.747
2.4	0.516	0.603	0.673	0.724	0.755	0.796	0.777	0.733
2.6	0.493	0.574	0.639	0.687	0.718	0.765	0.751	0.713
2.8	0.469	0.543	0.603	0.647	0.677	0.729	0.720	0.688
3.0	0.444	0.511	0.565	0.606	0.634	0.690	0.685	0.660
3.2	0.419	0.479	0.527	0.565	0.591	0.649	0.648	0.628
3.4	0.394	0.447	0.490	0.523	0.548	0.606	0.609	0.595
3.6						0.564	0.569	0.561
3.8						0.522	0.530	0.526

$S(1s, 2te\sigma)$

p	t = −0.5	t = −0.4	t = −0.3	t = −0.2	t = −0.1	t = 0.0	t = 0.1	t = 0.2
4.0	0.345	0.385	0.417	0.443	0.464	0.480	0.490	0.491
4.2						0.440	0.452	0.456
4.4						0.402	0.415	0.422
4.5	0.288	0.314	0.335	0.352	0.368			
4.6						0.366	0.380	0.390
5.0	0.238	0.252	0.264	0.274	0.286	0.300	0.314	0.329
5.5						0.229	0.244	0.261
6.0	0.157	0.157	0.157	0.158	0.163	0.173	0.187	0.205
6.5						0.128	0.141	0.158
7.0	0.101	0.094	0.089	0.087	0.088	0.094	0.105	0.121
7.5						0.068	0.077	0.091
8.0	0.064	0.056	0.049	0.046	0.046	0.049	0.056	0.068
9.0						0.025	0.029	0.038
10.0						0.012	0.015	0.020

Table 4A-12

S(1s, 2dσ)

p	t = −0.5	t = −0.4	t = −0.3	t = −0.2	t = −0.1	t = 0.0	t = 0.1	t = 0.2
0.0	0.669	0.757	0.812	0.832	0.818	0.612	0.543	0.461
0.5	0.704	0.807	0.878	0.914	0.913	0.773	0.704	0.611
1.0	0.697	0.804	0.881	0.925	0.936	0.879	0.814	0.723
1.5	0.658	0.758	0.831	0.877	0.895	0.914	0.860	0.778
2.0	0.636	0.730	0.800	0.846	0.865	0.884	0.845	0.778
2.2	0.611	0.699	0.765	0.809	0.829	0.858	0.825	0.765
2.4	0.583	0.665	0.727	0.768	0.789	0.826	0.798	0.746
2.6	0.555	0.630	0.686	0.725	0.746	0.789	0.767	0.722
2.8	0.526	0.593	0.644	0.680	0.700	0.748	0.731	0.694
3.0	0.496	0.556	0.601	0.634	0.654	0.705	0.693	0.662
3.2	0.466	0.519	0.559	0.588	0.607	0.660	0.653	0.629
3.4	0.437	0.483	0.518	0.543	0.561	0.615	0.612	0.594
3.6						0.570	0.570	0.558
3.8						0.526	0.529	0.522

S(1s, 2dσ)

p	t = −0.5	t = −0.4	t = −0.3	t = −0.2	t = −0.1	t = 0.0	t = 0.1	t = 0.2
4.0	0.381	0.414	0.439	0.457	0.472	0.483	0.489	0.486
4.2						0.442	0.450	0.451
4.4						0.403	0.412	0.417
4.5	0.317	0.336	0.350	0.362	0.372			
4.6						0.366	0.377	0.384
5.0	0.260	0.269	0.274	0.280	0.288	0.299	0.311	0.323
5.5						0.228	0.241	0.256
6.0	0.171	0.166	0.162	0.160	0.163	0.171	0.184	0.200
6.5						0.127	0.138	0.155
7.0	0.110	0.100	0.092	0.088	0.088	0.093	0.103	0.118
7.5						0.067	0.076	0.089
8.0	0.070	0.058	0.050	0.046	0.045	0.048	0.055	0.067
9.0						0.024	0.029	0.037
10.0						0.012	0.014	0.020

Table 4A-13

S(1s, 2pσ)

p	t = −0.5	t = −0.4	t = −0.3	t = −0.2	t = −0.1	t = 0.0	t = 0.1	t = 0.2
0.0	0.574	0.655	0.708	0.731	0.727	0.500	0.443	0.376
0.5	0.624	0.725	0.797	0.838	0.845	0.689	0.631	0.551
1.0	0.633	0.740	0.821	0.871	0.890	0.821	0.765	0.684
1.5	0.606	0.708	0.788	0.840	0.866	0.876	0.831	0.756
2.0	0.588	0.686	0.762	0.814	0.841	0.862	0.830	0.769
2.2	0.567	0.659	0.732	0.782	0.810	0.841	0.814	0.759
2.4	0.544	0.630	0.697	0.746	0.773	0.813	0.791	0.743
2.6	0.519	0.598	0.661	0.706	0.733	0.779	0.762	0.722
2.8	0.493	0.565	0.622	0.664	0.690	0.741	0.729	0.696
3.0	0.466	0.531	0.583	0.621	0.646	0.701	0.693	0.666
3.2	0.439	0.497	0.543	0.577	0.601	0.658	0.655	0.634
3.4	0.412	0.463	0.504	0.534	0.557	0.614	0.615	0.599
3.6						0.571	0.574	0.564
3.8						0.527	0.534	0.529

S(1s, 2pσ)

p	t = −0.5	t = −0.4	t = −0.3	t = −0.2	t = −0.1	t = 0.0	t = 0.1	t = 0.2
4.0	0.360	0.399	0.428	0.452	0.471	0.485	0.493	0.493
4.2						0.444	0.455	0.458
4.4						0.405	0.417	0.424
4.5	0.301	0.325	0.343	0.358	0.372			
4.6						0.369	0.381	0.391
5.0	0.247	0.260	0.270	0.278	0.289	0.302	0.316	0.329
5.5						0.231	0.245	0.262
6.0	0.163	0.162	0.160	0.160	0.165	0.174	0.187	0.205
6.5						0.129	0.141	0.158
7.0	0.105	0.097	0.091	0.088	0.089	0.094	0.105	0.121
7.5						0.068	0.077	0.091
8.0	0.067	0.057	0.050	0.046	0.046	0.049	0.056	0.068
9.0						0.025	0.029	0.038
10.0						0.012	0.015	0.020

Table 4A-14

p	$S(2di\sigma, 2di\sigma)$ $t=0.0$	$S(2tr\sigma, 2tr\sigma)$ $t=0.0$	$S(2te\sigma, 2te\sigma)$ $t=0.0$	$S[2(\alpha=\frac{1}{3}), 2(\alpha=\frac{1}{3})]$ $t=0.0$
0.0	0.000	-0.333	-0.500	-0.778
0.5	0.172	-0.155	-0.325	-0.625
1.0	0.382	$+0.086$	-0.076	-0.375
1.5	0.590	0.339	$+0.195$	-0.087
2.0	0.758	0.558	0.436	$+0.181$
2.5	0.871	0.721	0.622	0.402
3.0	0.907	0.798	0.719	0.532
3.2	0.907	0.813	0.742	0.568
3.4	0.898	0.818	0.753	0.593
3.6	0.882	0.813	0.756	0.608
3.8	0.860	0.802	0.750	0.614
4.0	0.832	0.783	0.738	0.613
4.2	0.801	0.761	0.720	0.606
4.4	0.765	0.733	0.696	0.592

p	$S(2di\sigma, 2di\sigma)$ $t=0.0$	$S(2tr\sigma, 2tr\sigma)$ $t=0.0$	$S(2te\sigma, 2te\sigma)$ $t=0.0$	$S[2(\alpha=\frac{1}{3}), 2(\alpha=\frac{1}{3})]$ $t=0.0$
4.6	0.725	0.699	0.668	0.573
4.8	0.685	0.664	0.637	0.552
5.0	0.645	0.628	0.604	0.527
5.5	0.542	0.534	0.517	0.458
6.0	0.445	0.443	0.430	0.385
6.5	0.358	0.358	0.350	0.316
7.0	0.282	0.284	0.278	0.253
7.5	0.219	0.222	0.218	0.199
8.0	0.168	0.170	0.168	0.154
8.5	0.127	0.129	0.128	0.118
9.0	0.095	0.097	0.096	0.089
9.5	0.070	0.072	0.071	0.066
10.0	0.051	0.053	0.052	0.049

Table 4-15   Values of Two Center
Repulsion Integrals[a]

R (Å)	$(pp \mid qq)$
0	10.959
1.39	6.895
2.407	5.682
2.780	4.978
3.687	3.824
4.170	3.390
4.812	2.949
5.012	2.836
5.560	2.563
6.059	2.355
6.370	2.242
7.223	1.981
7.355	1.946
7.739	1.850

[a] R. Pariser, *J. Chem. Phys.*, **24**, 250 (1956). The other commonly needed parameter, β, is given by

$$\beta = -167.9e^{-3.0323R} \text{ ev}$$

(N. Allinger, *J. Org. Chem.*, **27**, 443 (1962)) and has the values −2.80 ev at 1.35 Å and −2.48 ev at 1.39 Å.

Analysis of NMR Spectra

The difficulty in analyzing nmr spectra depends on both the number of protons which are present and on the ratio of the coupling constants to the chemical shifts. If the latter is small (<0.1), the spectrum is usually quite simple and easily interpreted. If the ratio is larger, and the number of protons with different chemical shifts is small (3 or less), the spectrum may usually be analyzed by a trial and error fitting procedure. If the coupling constants are relatively large, and the number of protons is also large, little can be done with the spectrum in most cases.

The simplest spectra arise from the AB and AB_2 cases, and some typical spectra have been given previously (Figs. 1-48 and 1-51). The AB spectrum consists of four lines, two for the A part and two for the B part. The transition energies were obtained in Section 1-19, and it was found that the value of J was given as the spacing between the two lines of either part. If we designated the spacing between lines 1 and 3, or between lines 2 and 4 as Q, the chemical shift was given by

$$\Delta \nu = (Q^2 - J^2)^{1/2}$$

The ratio of the intensities of the inner and outer lines was given by

$$\text{Relative intensity} = \frac{Q - J}{Q + J}$$

The spectrum for the AB_2 case may be obtained as follows. The wave functions for the B protons are $\alpha\alpha$, $\alpha\beta$, $\beta\alpha$, and $\beta\beta$. The first and last of these may be used directly, but the second and third are identical because of the identity of the two nuclei. Therefore, to simplify the secular determinant, we should use the two linear combinations of these wave functions:

$$\frac{1}{\sqrt{2}} (\alpha\beta + \beta\alpha)$$

$$\frac{1}{\sqrt{2}} (\alpha\beta - \beta\alpha)$$

(Remember that with degenerate levels one always gets mixing of the two wave functions in equal proportion if there are off-diagonal elements in the secular determinant; cf. p. 55 and 163.) The first of these is symmetric and the second is antisymmetric.

Each of the four wave functions of the B protons may be associated with either an α or a β for the A proton, giving the wave functions shown in Table 5A-1. Transitions may occur between symmetric states differing by one in F_z, and between antisymmetric states differing by one in F_z, but not between symmetric and antisymmetric states. Thus there are nine possible transitions. One of these (roughly described as between $\alpha\beta\beta$ and $\beta\alpha\alpha$) is of very low intensity, since it involves the simultaneous interchange of three spins.

The matrix elements for the eight diagonal elements of the secular determinant are given in Table 5A-1.[1] The only off-diagonal elements are

$$\int \psi_2 H \psi_3 \, d\tau = \frac{1}{\sqrt{2}} J_{AB}$$

$$\int \psi_4 H \psi_5 \, d\tau = \frac{1}{\sqrt{2}} J_{AB}$$

One may now easily obtain the transition energies and line intensities. Some typical data are tabulated in Table 5A-2.

It can be seen that the observed spectrum consists of eight lines, four for the A part and four for the B part. If J/δ is less than 0.1, the two central lines of the A part merge, giving a triplet, and the four B lines merge into a doublet. In all cases the third line of the spectrum, counting from the far A side, appears at ν_A, and the value of ν_B is given by the average of lines 5 and 7. The ratio of J/δ may now be obtained by

[1] It is instructive to calculate the diagonal elements. If we do this, we must remember to take all the possible integrals, i.e.,

$$2 \int \psi_3 H \psi_3 = \int (\alpha\beta\alpha)H(\alpha\beta\alpha) \, d\tau + \int (\alpha\alpha\beta)H(\alpha\beta\alpha) \, d\tau$$

$$+ \int (\alpha\beta\alpha)H(\alpha\alpha\beta) \, d\tau + \int (\alpha\alpha\beta)H(\alpha\alpha\beta) \, d\tau$$

Table 5A-1 Wave Functions and Diagonal Matrix Elements for the AB$_2$ Case

	Wave Function	F_z	Type	Matrix Element
1	$\alpha\alpha\alpha$	$+\frac{3}{2}$	sym.	$\frac{1}{2}\nu_{\mathrm{A}} + \nu_{\mathrm{B}} + \frac{1}{2}J_{\mathrm{AB}} + \frac{1}{4}J_{\mathrm{BB'}}$
2	$\beta\alpha\alpha$	$+\frac{1}{2}$	sym.	$-\frac{1}{2}\nu_{\mathrm{A}} + \nu_{\mathrm{B}} - \frac{1}{2}J_{\mathrm{AB}} + \frac{1}{4}J_{\mathrm{BB'}}$
3	$\dfrac{1}{\sqrt{2}}\alpha(\alpha\beta + \beta\alpha)$	$+\frac{1}{2}$	sym.	$\frac{1}{2}\nu_{\mathrm{A}} + \frac{1}{4}J_{\mathrm{BB}}$
4	$\dfrac{1}{\sqrt{2}}\beta(\alpha\beta + \beta\alpha)$	$-\frac{1}{2}$	sym.	$-\frac{1}{2}\nu_{\mathrm{A}} + \frac{1}{4}J_{\mathrm{BB'}}$
5	$\alpha\beta\beta$	$-\frac{1}{2}$	sym.	$\frac{1}{2}\nu_{\mathrm{A}} - \nu_{\mathrm{B}} - \frac{1}{2}J_{\mathrm{AB}} + \frac{1}{4}J_{\mathrm{BB'}}$
6	$\beta\beta\beta$	$-\frac{3}{2}$	sym.	$-\frac{1}{2}\nu_{\mathrm{A}} - \nu_{\mathrm{B}} + \frac{1}{2}J_{\mathrm{AB}} + \frac{1}{4}J_{\mathrm{BB'}}$
3'	$\dfrac{1}{\sqrt{2}}\alpha(\alpha\beta - \beta\alpha)$	$+\frac{1}{2}$	antisym.	$\frac{1}{2}\nu_{\mathrm{A}} - \frac{3}{4}J_{\mathrm{BB'}}$
4'	$\dfrac{1}{\sqrt{2}}\beta(\alpha\beta - \beta\alpha)$	$-\frac{1}{2}$	antisym.	$-\frac{1}{2}\nu_{\mathrm{A}} - \frac{3}{4}J_{\mathrm{BB'}}$

comparing the observed spectrum with the calculated spectra in Table 5A-2. For the comparison, ν_{A} should be subtracted from all of the observed values, and then each should be divided by $(\nu_{\mathrm{A}} - \nu_{\mathrm{B}})$.

The ABC spectrum is more difficult to interpret because it involves two chemical shifts, $\Delta\nu_{\mathrm{AB}}$ and $\Delta\nu_{\mathrm{AC}}$, and three coupling constants, J_{AB}, J_{AC}, and J_{BC}. If one of the protons were reasonably separated in chemical

Table 5A-2 Spectra for the AB$_2$ Case[a]

				Line Positions				
J/δ	1	2	3	4	5	6	7	8
0.0	0	0	0	0	1	1	1	1
0.1	−0.105	−0.010	0	0.095	0.950	0.955	1.050	1.055
0.2	−0.218	−0.040	0	0.178	0.904	0.918	1.096	1.122
0.3	−0.338	−0.088	0	0.250	0.862	0.888	1.138	1.200
0.4	−0.463	−0.153	0	0.310	0.826	0.863	1.174	1.290
0.5	−0.593	−0.233	0	0.360	0.797	0.843	1.203	1.390
0.6	−0.726	−0.326	0	0.400	0.774	0.826	1.226	1.500
0.7	−0.862	−0.429	0	0.433	0.755	0.812	1.245	1.617
0.8	−1.000	−0.540	0	0.460	0.740	0.800	1.260	1.740
1.0	−1.218	−0.781	0	0.500	0.719	0.781	1.281	2.000
1.2	−1.560	−1.038	0	0.528	0.706	0.766	1.294	2.272
1.4	−1.855	−1.306	0	0.549	0.696	0.755	1.304	2.551
1.6	−2.146	−1.581	0	0.564	0.690	0.746	1.310	2.836
2.0	−2.732	−2.146	0	0.586	0.682	0.732	1.318	3.414

[a] J. A. Pople, W. G. Schneider, and H. J. Bernstein, *High-Resolution Nuclear Magnetic Resonance*, McGraw-Hill Book Co., 1959, p. 127.

shift from the other two, the spectrum would approach that for the ABX case, and it will help to consider the latter first.

The possible wave functions for the ABX case are:

No.	A	B	X	F_z
1	α	α	α	$\frac{3}{2}$
2	α	α	β	$\frac{1}{2}$
3	α	β	α	$\frac{1}{2}$
4	β	α	α	$\frac{1}{2}$
5	α	β	β	$-\frac{1}{2}$
6	β	α	β	$-\frac{1}{2}$
7	β	β	α	$-\frac{1}{2}$
8	β	β	β	$-\frac{3}{2}$

The wave function 2 will not mix appreciably with 3 or 4, since the off-diagonal element between wave functions with different X spin will be negligible compared to the difference between the diagonal elements. Similarly, wave function 7 will not mix appreciably with 5 or 6. As a result, it is only necessary to solve two 2×2 determinants, and the energy levels are easily found, giving the transition energies shown in Table 5A-3.

Table 5A-3   Line Positions and Intensities for the ABX Case[a]

Line	Energy	Relative Intensity
1	$\nu_{AB} + \frac{1}{4}(-2J_{AB} - J_{AX} - J_{BX}) - D_-$	$1 - \sin 2\phi_-$
2	$\nu_{AB} + \frac{1}{4}(-2J_{AB} + J_{AX} + J_{BX}) - D_+$	$1 - \sin 2\phi_+$
3	$\nu_{AB} + \frac{1}{4}(2J_{AB} - J_{AX} - J_{BX}) - D_-$	$1 + \sin 2\phi_-$
4	$\nu_{AB} + \frac{1}{4}(2J_{AB} + J_{AX} + J_{BX}) - D_+$	$1 + \sin 2\phi_+$
5	$\nu_{AB} + \frac{1}{4}(-2J_{AB} - J_{AX} - J_{BX}) + D_-$	$1 + \sin 2\phi_-$
6	$\nu_{AB} + \frac{1}{4}(-2J_{AB} + J_{AX} + J_{BX}) + D_+$	$1 + \sin 2\phi_+$
7	$\nu_{AB} + \frac{1}{4}(2J_{AB} - J_{AX} - J_{BX}) + D_-$	$1 - \sin 2\phi$
8	$\nu_{AB} + \frac{1}{4}(2J_{AB} + J_{AX} + J_{BX}) + D_+$	$1 - \sin 2\phi_+$
9	$\nu_X - \frac{1}{2}(J_{AX} + J_{BX})$	1
10	$\nu_X + D_+ - D_-$	$\cos^2(\phi_+ - \phi_-)$
11	$\nu_X - D_+ + D_-$	$\cos^2(\phi_+ - \phi_-)$
12	$\nu_X + \frac{1}{2}(J_{AX} + J_{BX})$	1
13	$\nu_X - D_+ - D_-$	$\sin^2(\phi_+ - \phi_-)$
14	$\nu_X + D_+ + D_-$	$\sin^2(\phi_+ - \phi_-)$

$$D_+ = \frac{1}{2}\{[\nu_A - \nu_B \pm \frac{1}{2}(J_{AX} - J_{BX})]^2 + J_{AB}^2\}^{1/2}$$

$$\sin 2\phi_+ = J_{AB}/2D_+ \qquad \sin 2\phi_- = J_{AB}/2D_-$$

$$\cos 2\phi_+ = [2\nu_A - 2\nu_B + J_{AX} - J_{BX}]/4D_+$$

$$\cos 2\phi_- = [2\nu_A - 2\nu_B - J_{AX} + J_{BX}]/4D_-$$

$$\nu_{AB} = \frac{1}{2}(\nu_A + \nu_B)$$

[a] J. A. Pople, W. G. Schneider, and H. J. Bernstein, *High-Resolution Nuclear Magnetic Resonance*, McGraw-Hill Book Co., 1959, p. 134.

One finds that the spectrum consists of two superimposed AB quartets for the A and B part and six lines for the X part. (Here the two outer lines are often so weak that they are not seen.) If one can recognize the two AB quartets (cf. Fig. 5A-1), the analysis is straightforward. The spacing between the outer lines of either AB quartet gives $|J_{AB}|$ but not its sign. The spacing between the first and third lines of one quartet will be designated as D_+ and that between lines one and three of the other quartet will be designated as D_-. The spacing between the centers of the two quartets will be $\frac{1}{2}(J_{AX} + J_{BX})$. In the X part, the spacing between the two most intense lines will give $(J_{AX} + J_{BX})$, and the spacing between the next most intense pair of lines will be $2(D_+ - D_-)$. The spacing between the outer (weak) lines will be $2(D_+ + D_-)$, but these may not be seen because of their low intensity. Four of the lines of the X part are often of about equal intensity, and here the assignment of $(J_{AX} + J_{BX})$ and of $2(D_+ - D_-)$ will be ambiguous. The correct assignment will be a function of the relative signs of J_{AX} and J_{BX}, and this often cannot be determined (unless J_{AX} or $J_{BX} \approx \Delta\nu_{AB}$). In the latter case it may be determined from the intensity distribution and from careful measurement of line positions.

Let us assume that we now have values of J_{AB}, D_+, D_- and $(J_{AX} - J_{BX})$. The remaining quantities may be obtained from the relations:

$$D_+ = \tfrac{1}{2}\{[\nu_A - \nu_B + \tfrac{1}{2}(J_{AX} - J_{BX})]^2 + J_{AB}{}^2\}^{\frac{1}{2}}$$

$$D_- = \tfrac{1}{2}\{[\nu_A - \nu_B - \tfrac{1}{2}(J_{AX} - J_{BX})]^2 + J_{AB}{}^2\}^{\frac{1}{2}}$$

If one had a true ABX spectrum, the parameters would have been determined. However, if it were only a spectrum which approached ABX, the values would be somewhat in error. One calculates the spectrum expected from the approximate parameters (cf. Table 5A-4) and compares the results with the observed spectrum. The parameters are adjusted if necessary and the calculation is repeated. This process is continued until the calculated and observed spectra agree.

For the more difficult ABC cases in which the above approximation is not useful, it is best to compare the observed spectrum with calculated spectra in order to determine approximate values of the spectral parameters.[3] The final values of the parameters are then obtained by trial and error fitting as for the near-ABX case. The process is greatly facilitated by the use of a computer (cf. Appendix 8).

For the four proton case, the AB$_3$ category is the simplest to interpret, since the spectrum depends only on the ratio of J/δ (presumably all AB coupling constants will be equal, and the spectrum will be independent

---

[3] The spectra given in K. B. Wiberg and B. J. Nist, *Interpretation of N.M.R. Spectra*, W. Benjamin, New York, 1962, are valuable for this purpose.

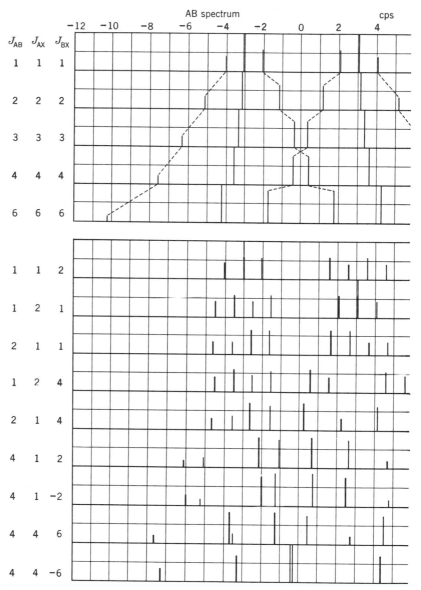

Fig. 5A-1. Effect of spin coupling constants on ABX spectrum ($\Delta \nu_{AB} = 6$ cps). The right-hand part is the X spectrum and the left-hand part is the AB spectrum.

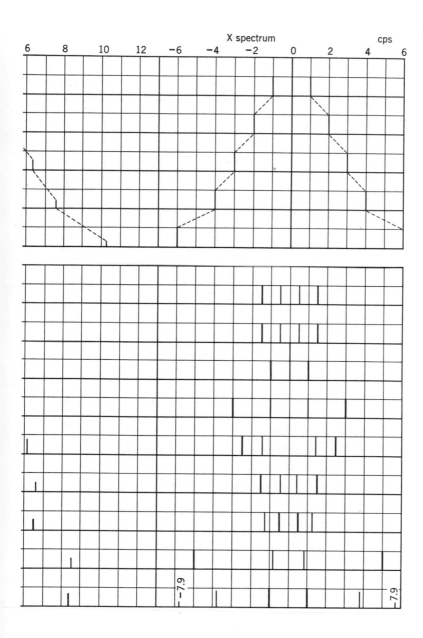

of the BB coupling constant).[4] The value of J_{AB} is usually readily obtained, for it is given as the separation of two lines of the A part. If the spectrum is well resolved, the value of ν_B may be determined as the average of two sets of lines of the B part. The lines to be chosen may best be determined

Table 5A-4 Wave Functions and Diagonal Matrix Elements for the ABC Case

No.	Wave Function	F_z	Diagonal Matrix Element
1	$\alpha\alpha\alpha$	$\frac{3}{2}$	$\frac{1}{2}(\nu_A + \nu_B + \nu_C) + \frac{1}{4}(J_{AB} + J_{BC} + J_{AC})$
2	$\alpha\alpha\beta$	$\frac{1}{2}$	$\frac{1}{2}(\nu_A + \nu_B - \nu_C) + \frac{1}{4}(J_{AB} - J_{BC} - J_{AC})$
3	$\alpha\beta\alpha$	$\frac{1}{2}$	$\frac{1}{2}(\nu_A - \nu_B + \nu_C) + \frac{1}{4}(-J_{AB} + J_{BC} - J_{AC})$
4	$\beta\alpha\alpha$	$\frac{1}{2}$	$\frac{1}{2}(-\nu_A + \nu_B + \nu_C) + \frac{1}{4}(-J_{AB} + J_{BC} - J_{AC})$
5	$\alpha\beta\beta$	$-\frac{1}{2}$	$\frac{1}{2}(\nu_A - \nu_B - \nu_C) + \frac{1}{4}(-J_{AB} + J_{BC} - J_{AC})$
6	$\beta\alpha\beta$	$-\frac{1}{2}$	$\frac{1}{2}(-\nu_A + \nu_B - \nu_C) + \frac{1}{4}(-J_{AB} - J_{BC} + J_{AC})$
7	$\beta\beta\alpha$	$-\frac{1}{2}$	$\frac{1}{2}(-\nu_A - \nu_B + \nu_C) + \frac{1}{4}(J_{AB} - J_{BC} - J_{AC})$
8	$\beta\beta\beta$	$-\frac{3}{2}$	$\frac{1}{2}(-\nu_A - \nu_B - \nu_C) + \frac{1}{4}(J_{AB} + J_{BC} + J_{AC})$

Off-diagonal elements: $\int \psi_2 H\psi_3 \, d\tau = \int \psi_0 H\psi_7 \, d\tau = \frac{1}{2}J_{BC}$

$$\int \psi_3 H\psi_4 \, d\tau = \int \psi_5 H\psi_6 \, d\tau = \frac{1}{2}J_{AB}$$

$$\int \psi_2 H\psi_4 \, d\tau = \int \psi_5 H\psi_7 \, d\tau = \frac{1}{2}J_{AC}$$

by comparing the experimental spectrum with a set of calculated spectra.[3] The value of J/δ will also be obtained from such a comparison, and this will permit a determination of ν_A.

The A_2B_2 case is more difficult in that there are four coupling constants,

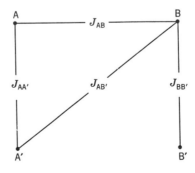

[4] A list of the matrix elements and the transition energies is given in J. A. Pople, W. G. Schneider, and H. Bernstein, *High Resolution Nuclear Magnetic Resonance*, McGraw-Hill Book Co., New York, 1959, pp. 129–130.

Table 5A-5 Wave Functions and Diagonal Matrix Elements for the A_2B_2 case

No.	Wave Function		F_z	Type	Diagonal Matrix Element
	A	B			
1	$\alpha\alpha$	$\alpha\alpha$	2	sym.	$\nu_A + \nu_B + \frac{1}{2}N + \frac{1}{4}K$
2	$\frac{1}{\sqrt{2}}(\alpha\beta + \beta\alpha)$	$\alpha\alpha$	1	sym.	$\nu_B + \frac{1}{4}K$
3	$\alpha\alpha$	$\frac{1}{\sqrt{2}}(\alpha\beta + \beta\alpha)$	1	sym.	$\nu_A + \frac{1}{4}K$
4	$\beta\beta$	$\alpha\alpha$	0	sym.	$-\nu_A + \nu_B - \frac{1}{2}N + \frac{1}{4}K$
5	$\alpha\alpha$	$\beta\beta$	0	sym.	$\nu_A - \nu_B - \frac{1}{2}N + \frac{1}{4}K$
6	$\frac{1}{\sqrt{2}}(\alpha\beta - \beta\alpha)$	$\frac{1}{\sqrt{2}}(\alpha\beta - \beta\alpha)$	0	sym.	$-\frac{3}{4}K$
7	$\frac{1}{\sqrt{2}}(\alpha\beta + \beta\alpha)$	$\frac{1}{\sqrt{2}}(\alpha\beta + \beta\alpha)$	0	sym.	$+\frac{1}{4}K$
8	$\frac{1}{\sqrt{2}}(\alpha\beta + \beta\alpha)$	$\beta\beta$	-1	sym.	$\nu_B + \frac{1}{4}K$
9	$\beta\beta$	$\frac{1}{\sqrt{2}}(\alpha\beta + \beta\alpha)$	-1	sym.	$-\nu_A + \frac{1}{4}K$
10	$\beta\beta$	$\beta\beta$	-2	sym.	$-\nu_A - \nu_B + \frac{1}{2}N + \frac{1}{4}K$
2'	$\frac{1}{\sqrt{2}}(\alpha\beta - \beta\alpha)$	$\alpha\alpha$	1	antisym.	$\nu_B - \frac{1}{4}K - \frac{1}{2}M$
3'	$\alpha\alpha$	$\frac{1}{\sqrt{2}}(\alpha\beta - \beta\alpha)$	1	antisym.	$\nu_A - \frac{1}{4}K + \frac{1}{2}M$
6'	$\frac{1}{\sqrt{2}}(\alpha\beta + \beta\alpha)$	$\frac{1}{\sqrt{2}}(\alpha\beta - \beta\alpha)$	0	antisym.	$-\frac{1}{4}K - \frac{1}{2}M$
7'	$\frac{1}{\sqrt{2}}(\alpha\beta - \beta\alpha)$	$\frac{1}{\sqrt{2}}(\alpha\beta + \beta\alpha)$	0	antisym.	$-\frac{1}{4}K - \frac{1}{2}M$
8'	$\frac{1}{\sqrt{2}}(\alpha\beta - \beta\alpha)$	$\beta\beta$	-1	antisym.	$-\nu_B - \frac{1}{4}K - \frac{1}{2}M$
9'	$\beta\beta$	$\frac{1}{\sqrt{2}}(\alpha\beta - \beta\alpha)$	-1	antisym.	$-\nu_A - \frac{1}{4}K + \frac{1}{2}M$

Table 5A-5 (continued)

Off-Diagonal Elements:

$$\int \psi_2 H \psi_3 \, d\tau = \int \psi_4 H \psi_7 \, d\tau = \int \psi_5 H \psi_7 \, d\tau = \int \psi_8 H \psi_9 \, d\tau = \tfrac{1}{2}N$$

$$\int \psi_5 H \psi_6 \, d\tau = \int \psi_4 H \psi_6 \, d\tau = \tfrac{1}{2}L$$

$$\int \psi_6 H \psi_7 \, d\tau = \int \psi_2' H \psi_3' = \int \psi_6' H \psi_7' \, d\tau = \int \psi_8' H \psi_9' \, d\tau = -\tfrac{1}{2}L$$

$$\int \psi_4 H \psi_5 \, d\tau = 0$$

$J_{AA'}$, $J_{BB'}$, J_{AB}, and $J_{AB'}$. Since these usually occur as sums or differences, we may define a set of new quantities as[5]

$$K = J_{AA'} + J_{BB'} \qquad L = J_{AB} - J_{AB'}$$
$$M = J_{AA'} - J_{BB'} \qquad N = J_{AB} + J_{AB'}$$

The protons come as two pairs, and for both A and B we may write wave functions of the type $\alpha\alpha$, $1/\sqrt{2}(\alpha\beta + \beta\alpha)$, $1/\sqrt{2}(\alpha\beta - \beta\alpha)$ and $\beta\beta$. Taking all possible combinations, we will find sixteen wave functions, as shown in Table 5A-5.

Table 5A-6   Line Positions and Intensities for the A_2X_2 Case[a]

Transition	Position Relative to ν_A or ν_X	Relative Intensity
1	$\tfrac{1}{2}N$	1
2	$\tfrac{1}{2}N$	1
3	$-\tfrac{1}{2}N$	1
4	$-\tfrac{1}{2}N$	1
5	$\tfrac{1}{2}K + \tfrac{1}{2}(K^2 + L^2)^{1/2}$	$\sin^2 \theta_s$
6	$-\tfrac{1}{2}K + \tfrac{1}{2}(K^2 + L^2)^{1/2}$	$\cos^2 \theta_s$
7	$\tfrac{1}{2}K - \tfrac{1}{2}(K^2 + L^2)^{1/2}$	$\cos^2 \theta_s$
8	$-\tfrac{1}{2}K - \tfrac{1}{2}(K^2 + L^2)^{1/2}$	$\sin^2 \theta_s$
9	$\tfrac{1}{2}M + \tfrac{1}{2}(M^2 + L^2)^{1/2}$	$\sin^2 \theta_a$
10	$-\tfrac{1}{2}M + \tfrac{1}{2}(M^2 + L^2)^{1/2}$	$\cos^2 \theta_a$
11	$\tfrac{1}{2}M - \tfrac{1}{2}(M^2 + L^2)^{1/2}$	$\cos^2 \theta_a$
12	$-\tfrac{1}{2}M - \tfrac{1}{2}(M^2 + L^2)^{1/2}$	$\sin^2 \theta_a$
	$\theta_s = \tfrac{1}{2} \cos^{-1} [K/(K^2 + L^2)^{1/2}]$	
	$\theta_a = \tfrac{1}{2} \cos^{-1} [M/(M^2 + L^2)^{1/2}]$	

[a] J. A. Pople, W. G. Schneider and H. J. Bernstein, *High-resolution Nuclear Magnetic Resonance*, McGraw-Hill Book Co., 1959. p. 141.

[5] J. A. Pople, W. G. Schneider, and H. J. Bernstein, *Can. J. Chem.*, **35**, 1060 (1957).

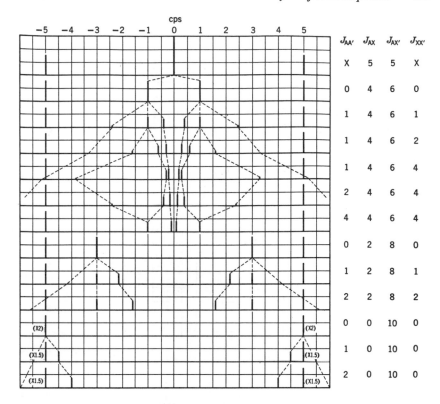

	$J_{AA'}$	J_{AX}	$J_{AX'}$	$J_{XX'}$
X	X	5	5	X
	0	4	6	0
	1	4	6	1
	1	4	6	2
	1	4	6	4
	2	4	6	4
	4	4	6	4
	0	2	8	0
	1	2	8	1
	2	2	8	2
	0	0	(10)	0
	1	0	10	0
	2	0	10	0

Fig. 5A-2. Effect of coupling constants on the A *part of an* A_2X_2 *spectrum, with the parameter* N *kept constant and equal to 10 cps.*

The spectrum is considerably simplified if $\Delta\nu_{AB}$ is large, giving the A_2X_2 case. Here only wave functions in which there is no change in spin for either the A part or the X part will mix appreciably (i.e., wave functions 6 and 7, and 6' and 7'), and a transition is permitted only if $\Delta F_z = 1$ for either the A part or the X part. This reduces the number of transitions to 24, of which 12 are A transitions, centered on ν_A, and the other 12 are an identical set of transitions but centered on ν_X. The transitions may be given in analytical form as shown in Table 5A 6.

It can be seen that each part of the spectrum will consist of a strong doublet (lines 1, 2, 3, and 4) centered on the frequency ν_A (or ν_X) with a separation equal to N and two symmetrical quartets (5, 6, 7, 8, and 9, 10, 11, 12) also centered in ν_A (or ν_X). The arrangement of the lines may be seen in Figs. 5A-2 and 5A-3.

Once we have an assignment of the doublet and the two quartets, values of $|N|$, $|L|$, $|K|$, and $|M|$ may be obtained. However, it is not possible to

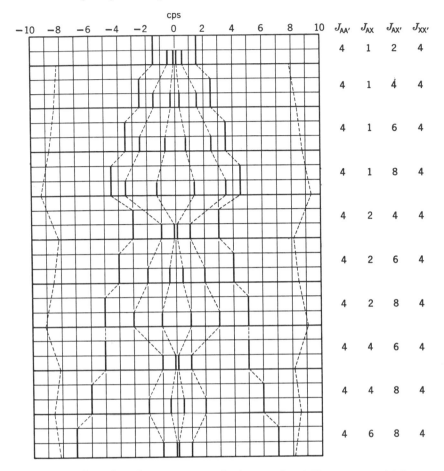

Fig. 5A-3. *Effect of coupling constants on the* A *part of an* A_2X_2 *spectrum, with* $J_{AA'} = J_{XX'} = 4$ *cps.*

distinguish between K and M, and one cannot determine the relative signs of the coupling constants which are derived from these parameters. The analysis is fairly simple, and so, even when the chemical shift between A and B is not quite large enough to give the A_2X_2 case, the above analysis is often helpful in obtaining approximate values for the chemical shifts and coupling constants.

The general A_2B_2 case is often best treated by comparing the experimental spectrum with calculated spectra[3] in order to find approximate values of the spectral parameters. Once these are available, and an assignment of the transitions can be made, it is possible to obtain the correct parameters by a direct analysis,[6] provided the spectrum is well enough resolved.

More complex spectra cannot be satisfactorily treated in the manner described above. However, it is possible to simplify the spectrum experimentally by removing the influence of one or more groups of protons.[7] This may be done by using a second radio frequency which corresponds to the transition frequency for the group of protons in question. If sufficient radio frequency power is introduced, essentially all of the protons of the group will be excited to the upper nuclear state. Since spin-spin coupling depends on these being approximately equal numbers of protons of the two spin states, the second radio frequency will remove the splitting due to spin-spin coupling. Similarly, a third radio frequency may be introduced to remove the effect of a second group of protons, and so on. The first of the radio frequencies referred to is, of course, that used in the normal nuclear magnetic resonance experiments, the one that ultimately results in the observed signal.

[6] B. Dischler and W. Maier, *Z. Naturforsch.*, **169**, 318 (1961).
[7] W. A. Anderson, *Phys. Rev.*, **102**, 151 (1956); R. Freeman, *Mol. Phys.*, **3**, 435 (1960).

Thermodynamic Functions for a

Harmonic Oscillator

We have previously seen that the thermodynamic functions were given by

Translation

$$(H^0 - H_0^0)/T = 4.9680$$
$$(F^0 - H_0^0)/T = -6.8635 \log M - 11.4392 \log T + 7.2820$$
$$C_P^0 = 4.9680$$

Rotation

$$(H^0 - H_0^0)/T = 2.9808$$
$$(F^0 - H_0^0)/T = -2.2878 \log (I_A I_B I_C \times 10^{117})$$
$$- 6.8635 \log T + 4.5757 \log \sigma + 3.0140$$
$$C_P^0 = 2.9808$$

or, for a linear molecule,

$$(H^0 - H_0^0)/T = 1.9872$$

$$(F^0 - H_0^0)/T = -4.5757 \log (I \times 10^{39})$$
$$- 4.5757 \log T + 4.5757 \log \sigma + 2.7676$$
$$C_P^0 = 1.9872$$

Vibration

$$(H^0 - H_0^0)/T = 1.9872 \sum_j (x_j/e^{x_j} - 1)$$
$$(F^0 - H_0^0)/T = 1.9872 \sum_j [\ln (1 - e^{-x_j})]$$
$$C_P^0 = 1.9872 \sum_j [x_j^2 e^{x_j}/(e^{x_j} - 1)^2]$$

The functions for translation and rotation are easily evaluated if one has the mass and the moments of inertia. The vibrational part requires the summation of several terms. In order to facilitate the evaluation of the latter, there follows a table (Table 6A-1) of contributions to each of the thermodynamic functions for a harmonic oscillator in terms of u which is given by $u = h\nu/kT$. The values of u may be obtained from

$$u = 1.4387\nu/T$$

and are tabulated for several temperatures in Table 6A-2.

TABLE 6A-1
THERMODYNAMIC FUNCTIONS FOR A HARMONIC OSCILLATOR

U	C/R	$(H-H_0)/RT$	$(F-H_0)/RT$	S/R
1.000	0.92067	0.58198	0.45868	1.04065
1.005	0.91992	0.58029	0.45578	1.03606
1.010	0.91916	0.57860	0.45290	1.03150
1.015	0.91840	0.57691	0.45005	1.02696
1.020	0.91763	0.57523	0.44722	1.02245
1.025	0.91686	0.57356	0.44441	1.01796
1.030	0.91609	0.57188	0.44162	1.01350
1.035	0.91532	0.57021	0.43886	1.00907
1.040	0.91454	0.56855	0.43611	1.00466
1.045	0.91376	0.56689	0.43339	1.00028
1.050	0.91298	0.56523	0.43069	0.99592
1.055	0.91219	0.56358	0.42801	0.99158
1.060	0.91140	0.56193	0.42535	0.98727
1.065	0.91061	0.56028	0.42270	0.98298
1.070	0.90981	0.55864	0.42008	0.97872
1.075	0.90902	0.55700	0.41748	0.97448
1.080	0.90822	0.55536	0.41490	0.97026
1.085	0.90741	0.55373	0.41234	0.96607
1.090	0.90661	0.55210	0.40980	0.96190
1.095	0.90580	0.55048	0.40728	0.95775
1.100	0.90499	0.54886	0.40477	0.95363
1.105	0.90417	0.54724	0.40229	0.94953
1.110	0.90335	0.54563	0.39982	0.94545
1.115	0.90253	0.54402	0.39737	0.94139
1.120	0.90171	0.54241	0.39494	0.93735
1.125	0.90088	0.54081	0.39253	0.93334
1.130	0.90006	0.53921	0.39013	0.92934
1.135	0.89922	0.53762	0.38776	0.92537
1.140	0.89839	0.53602	0.38540	0.92142
1.145	0.89755	0.53444	0.38305	0.91749
1.150	0.89671	0.53285	0.38073	0.91358
1.155	0.89587	0.53127	0.37842	0.90969
1.160	0.89503	0.52970	0.37613	0.90583
1.165	0.89418	0.52812	0.37385	0.90198
1.170	0.89333	0.52655	0.37160	0.89815
1.175	0.89248	0.52499	0.36935	0.89434
1.180	0.89162	0.52343	0.36713	0.89055
1.185	0.89076	0.52187	0.36492	0.88679
1.190	0.88990	0.52031	0.36272	0.88304
1.195	0.88904	0.51876	0.36055	0.87931

TABLE 6A-1
THERMODYNAMIC FUNCTIONS FOR A HARMONIC OSCILLATOR

U	C/R	$(H-H_0)/RT$	$(F-H_0)/RT$	S/R
1.200	0.88817	0.51722	0.35838	0.87560
1.205	0.88730	0.51567	0.35624	0.87191
1.210	0.88643	0.51413	0.35410	0.86823
1.215	0.88556	0.51259	0.35199	0.86458
1.220	0.88468	0.51106	0.34988	0.86095
1.225	0.88380	0.50953	0.34780	0.85733
1.230	0.88292	0.50801	0.34572	0.85373
1.235	0.88203	0.50648	0.34367	0.85015
1.240	0.88115	0.50497	0.34162	0.84659
1.245	0.88026	0.50345	0.33959	0.84304
1.250	0.87937	0.50194	0.33758	0.83952
1.255	0.87847	0.50043	0.33558	0.83601
1.260	0.87758	0.49893	0.33359	0.83252
1.265	0.87668	0.49743	0.33162	0.82905
1.270	0.87577	0.49593	0.32966	0.82559
1.275	0.87487	0.49443	0.32771	0.82215
1.280	0.87396	0.49294	0.32578	0.81873
1.285	0.87305	0.49146	0.32386	0.81532
1.290	0.87214	0.48998	0.32196	0.81193
1.295	0.87123	0.48850	0.32006	0.80856
1.300	0.87031	0.48702	0.31819	0.80520
1.305	0.86940	0.48555	0.31632	0.80187
1.310	0.86847	0.48408	0.31446	0.79854
1.315	0.86755	0.48261	0.31262	0.79524
1.320	0.86663	0.48115	0.31079	0.79195
1.325	0.86570	0.47969	0.30898	0.78867
1.330	0.86477	0.47824	0.30717	0.78541
1.335	0.86384	0.47679	0.30538	0.78217
1.340	0.86290	0.47534	0.30360	0.77894
1.345	0.86196	0.47389	0.30183	0.77573
1.350	0.86102	0.47245	0.30008	0.77253
1.355	0.86008	0.47102	0.29834	0.76935
1.360	0.85914	0.46958	0.29660	0.76618
1.365	0.85819	0.46815	0.29488	0.76303
1.370	0.85724	0.46672	0.29317	0.75990
1.375	0.85629	0.46530	0.29148	0.75678
1.380	0.85534	0.46388	0.28979	0.75367
1.385	0.85439	0.46246	0.28811	0.75058
1.390	0.85343	0.46105	0.28645	0.74750
1.395	0.85247	0.45964	0.28480	0.74444

TABLE 6A-1
THERMODYNAMIC FUNCTIONS FOR A HARMONIC OSCILLATOR

U	C/R	$(H-H_0)/RT$	$(F-H_0)/RT$	S/R
1.400	0.85151	0.45824	0.28316	0.74139
1.405	0.85055	0.45683	0.28152	0.73836
1.410	0.84958	0.45543	0.27990	0.73534
1.415	0.84861	0.45404	0.27829	0.73233
1.420	0.84764	0.45264	0.27669	0.72934
1.425	0.84667	0.45126	0.27511	0.72636
1.430	0.84570	0.44987	0.27353	0.72340
1.435	0.84472	0.44849	0.27196	0.72045
1.440	0.84374	0.44711	0.27040	0.71751
1.445	0.84276	0.44573	0.26886	0.71459
1.450	0.84178	0.44436	0.26732	0.71168
1.455	0.84080	0.44299	0.26579	0.70878
1.460	0.83981	0.44163	0.26427	0.70590
1.465	0.83882	0.44026	0.26277	0.70303
1.470	0.83783	0.43891	0.26127	0.70017
1.475	0.83684	0.43755	0.25978	0.69733
1.480	0.83584	0.43620	0.25830	0.69450
1.485	0.83485	0.43485	0.25683	0.69168
1.490	0.83385	0.43351	0.25537	0.68888
1.495	0.83285	0.43216	0.25392	0.68609
1.500	0.83185	0.43083	0.25248	0.68331
1.505	0.83084	0.42949	0.25105	0.68054
1.510	0.82984	0.42816	0.24963	0.67779
1.515	0.82883	0.42683	0.24822	0.67505
1.520	0.82782	0.42551	0.24681	0.67232
1.525	0.82681	0.42418	0.24542	0.66960
1.530	0.82580	0.42287	0.24403	0.66689
1.535	0.82478	0.42155	0.24265	0.66420
1.540	0.82377	0.42024	0.24128	0.66152
1.545	0.82275	0.41893	0.23992	0.65885
1.550	0.82173	0.41762	0.23857	0.65620
1.555	0.82071	0.41632	0.23723	0.65355
1.560	0.81968	0.41502	0.23589	0.65092
1.565	0.81866	0.41373	0.23457	0.64830
1.570	0.81763	0.41244	0.23325	0.64569
1.575	0.81660	0.41115	0.23194	0.64309
1.580	0.81557	0.40986	0.23064	0.64050
1.585	0.81454	0.40858	0.22935	0.63793
1.590	0.81350	0.40730	0.22806	0.63536
1.595	0.81247	0.40603	0.22679	0.63281

TABLE 6A-1
THERMODYNAMIC FUNCTIONS FOR A HARMONIC OSCILLATOR

U	C/R	$(H-H_0)/RT$	$(F-H_0)/RT$	S/R
1.600	0.81143	0.40475	0.22552	0.63027
1.605	0.81039	0.40348	0.22426	0.62774
1.610	0.80935	0.40222	0.22300	0.62522
1.615	0.80831	0.40095	0.22176	0.62271
1.620	0.80726	0.39970	0.22052	0.62022
1.625	0.80622	0.39844	0.21929	0.61773
1.630	0.80517	0.39719	0.21807	0.61525
1.635	0.80412	0.39594	0.21685	0.61279
1.640	0.80307	0.39469	0.21565	0.61034
1.645	0.80202	0.39345	0.21445	0.60789
1.650	0.80096	0.39221	0.21326	0.60546
1.655	0.79991	0.39097	0.21207	0.60304
1.660	0.79885	0.38973	0.21089	0.60063
1.665	0.79779	0.38850	0.20972	0.59823
1.670	0.79673	0.38728	0.20856	0.59584
1.675	0.79567	0.38605	0.20740	0.59346
1.680	0.79461	0.38483	0.20625	0.59109
1.685	0.79355	0.38361	0.20511	0.58873
1.690	0.79248	0.38240	0.20398	0.58638
1.695	0.79141	0.38119	0.20285	0.58404
1.700	0.79035	0.37998	0.20173	0.58171
1.705	0.78928	0.37877	0.20061	0.57939
1.710	0.78820	0.37757	0.19951	0.57708
1.715	0.78713	0.37637	0.19841	0.57478
1.720	0.78606	0.37518	0.19731	0.57249
1.725	0.78498	0.37398	0.19623	0.57021
1.730	0.78390	0.37279	0.19514	0.56794
1.735	0.78283	0.37161	0.19407	0.56568
1.740	0.78175	0.37042	0.19300	0.56343
1.745	0.78067	0.36924	0.19194	0.56118
1.750	0.77958	0.36806	0.19089	0.55895
1.755	0.77850	0.36689	0.18984	0.55673
1.760	0.77742	0.36572	0.18880	0.55452
1.765	0.77633	0.36455	0.18776	0.55231
1.770	0.77524	0.36339	0.18673	0.55012
1.775	0.77415	0.36222	0.18571	0.54793
1.780	0.77306	0.36107	0.18469	0.54576
1.785	0.77197	0.35991	0.18368	0.54359
1.790	0.77088	0.35876	0.18267	0.54143
1.795	0.76979	0.35761	0.18167	0.53928

TABLE 6A-1
THERMODYNAMIC FUNCTIONS FOR A HARMONIC OSCILLATOR

U	C/R	$(H-H_0)/RT$	$(F-H_0)/RT$	S/R
1.800	0.76869	0.35646	0.18068	0.53714
1.805	0.76760	0.35532	0.17969	0.53501
1.810	0.76650	0.35418	0.17871	0.53289
1.815	0.76540	0.35304	0.17774	0.53078
1.820	0.76430	0.35190	0.17677	0.52867
1.825	0.76320	0.35077	0.17580	0.52658
1.830	0.76210	0.34964	0.17485	0.52449
1.835	0.76100	0.34852	0.17389	0.52241
1.840	0.75989	0.34740	0.17295	0.52034
1.845	0.75879	0.34628	0.17201	0.51828
1.850	0.75768	0.34516	0.17107	0.51623
1.855	0.75658	0.34405	0.17014	0.51419
1.860	0.75547	0.34294	0.16922	0.51215
1.865	0.75436	0.34183	0.16830	0.51013
1.870	0.75325	0.34073	0.16738	0.50811
1.875	0.75214	0.33962	0.16647	0.50610
1.880	0.75103	0.33853	0.16557	0.50410
1.885	0.74991	0.33743	0.16467	0.50210
1.890	0.74880	0.33634	0.16378	0.50012
1.895	0.74768	0.33525	0.16289	0.49814
1.900	0.74657	0.33416	0.16201	0.49617
1.905	0.74545	0.33308	0.16113	0.49421
1.910	0.74433	0.33200	0.16026	0.49226
1.915	0.74321	0.33092	0.15940	0.49031
1.920	0.74209	0.32984	0.15854	0.48838
1.925	0.74097	0.32877	0.15768	0.48645
1.930	0.73985	0.32770	0.15683	0.48453
1.935	0.73873	0.32664	0.15598	0.48262
1.940	0.73761	0.32557	0.15514	0.48071
1.945	0.73648	0.32451	0.15430	0.47881
1.950	0.73536	0.32345	0.15347	0.47692
1.955	0.73423	0.32240	0.15264	0.47504
1.960	0.73310	0.32135	0.15182	0.47317
1.965	0.73198	0.32030	0.15100	0.47130
1.970	0.73085	0.31925	0.15019	0.46944
1.975	0.72972	0.31821	0.14938	0.46759
1.980	0.72859	0.31717	0.14858	0.46575
1.985	0.72746	0.31613	0.14778	0.46391
1.990	0.72633	0.31510	0.14699	0.46208
1.995	0.72519	0.31406	0.14620	0.46026

TABLE 6A-1
THERMODYNAMIC FUNCTIONS FOR A HARMONIC OSCILLATOR

U	C/R	$(H-H_0)/RT$	$(F-H_0)/RT$	S/R
2.000	0.72406	0.31304	0.14541	0.45845
2.010	0.72179	0.31099	0.14386	0.45484
2.020	0.71952	0.30895	0.14232	0.45127
2.030	0.71725	0.30692	0.14080	0.44772
2.040	0.71497	0.30491	0.13930	0.44420
2.050	0.71269	0.30290	0.13781	0.44071
2.060	0.71041	0.30091	0.13634	0.43725
2.070	0.70813	0.29892	0.13489	0.43381
2.080	0.70584	0.29695	0.13345	0.43041
2.090	0.70356	0.29499	0.13203	0.42703
2.100	0.70127	0.29304	0.13063	0.42367
2.110	0.69897	0.29111	0.12924	0.42035
2.120	0.69668	0.28918	0.12787	0.41705
2.130	0.69438	0.28726	0.12651	0.41377
2.140	0.69209	0.28535	0.12517	0.41053
2.150	0.68979	0.28346	0.12385	0.40731
2.160	0.68749	0.28158	0.12254	0.40411
2.170	0.68518	0.27970	0.12124	0.40094
2.180	0.68288	0.27784	0.11996	0.39780
2.190	0.68058	0.27599	0.11869	0.39468
2.200	0.67827	0.27414	0.11744	0.39158
2.210	0.67596	0.27231	0.11620	0.38851
2.220	0.67365	0.27049	0.11497	0.38546
2.230	0.67134	0.26868	0.11376	0.38244
2.240	0.66903	0.26688	0.11256	0.37944
2.250	0.66672	0.26509	0.11138	0.37647
2.260	0.66441	0.26331	0.11021	0.37351
2.270	0.66210	0.26154	0.10905	0.37059
2.280	0.65978	0.25978	0.10790	0.36768
2.290	0.65747	0.25803	0.10677	0.36480
2.300	0.65515	0.25629	0.10565	0.36194
2.310	0.65284	0.25456	0.10454	0.35910
2.320	0.65052	0.25284	0.10344	0.35629
2.330	0.64821	0.25113	0.10236	0.35349
2.340	0.64589	0.24943	0.10129	0.35072
2.350	0.64358	0.24774	0.10023	0.34797
2.360	0.64126	0.24607	0.09918	0.34525
2.370	0.63895	0.24440	0.09814	0.34254
2.380	0.63663	0.24274	0.09712	0.33985
2.390	0.63432	0.24109	0.09610	0.33719

TABLE 6A-1
THERMODYNAMIC FUNCTIONS FOR A HARMONIC OSCILLATOR

U	C/R	$(H-H_0)/RT$	$(F-H_0)/RT$	S/R
2.400	0.63200	0.23945	0.09510	0.33455
2.410	0.62969	0.23781	0.09411	0.33192
2.420	0.62737	0.23619	0.09313	0.32932
2.430	0.62506	0.23458	0.09216	0.32674
2.440	0.62275	0.23298	0.09120	0.32418
2.450	0.62044	0.23139	0.09025	0.32163
2.460	0.61813	0.22980	0.08931	0.31911
2.470	0.61582	0.22823	0.08838	0.31661
2.480	0.61351	0.22667	0.08746	0.31412
2.490	0.61120	0.22511	0.08655	0.31166
2.500	0.60889	0.22356	0.08565	0.30921
2.510	0.60658	0.22203	0.08476	0.30679
2.520	0.60428	0.22050	0.08388	0.30438
2.530	0.60198	0.21898	0.08301	0.30199
2.540	0.59967	0.21747	0.08215	0.29962
2.550	0.59737	0.21597	0.08130	0.29727
2.560	0.59507	0.21448	0.08046	0.29494
2.570	0.59277	0.21300	0.07962	0.29262
2.580	0.59048	0.21153	0.07880	0.29032
2.590	0.58818	0.21006	0.07798	0.28804
2.600	0.58589	0.20861	0.07718	0.28578
2.610	0.58360	0.20716	0.07638	0.28354
2.620	0.58131	0.20572	0.07559	0.28131
2.630	0.57902	0.20429	0.07481	0.27910
2.640	0.57674	0.20287	0.07404	0.27691
2.650	0.57445	0.20146	0.07327	0.27473
2.660	0.57217	0.20006	0.07252	0.27257
2.670	0.56989	0.19866	0.07177	0.27043
2.680	0.56761	0.19728	0.07103	0.26830
2.690	0.56534	0.19590	0.07029	0.26619
2.700	0.56307	0.19453	0.06957	0.26410
2.710	0.56080	0.19317	0.06885	0.26202
2.720	0.55853	0.19182	0.06814	0.25996
2.730	0.55627	0.19047	0.06744	0.25791
2.740	0.55400	0.18914	0.06675	0.25588
2.750	0.55174	0.18781	0.06606	0.25387
2.760	0.54949	0.18649	0.06538	0.25187
2.770	0.54723	0.18518	0.06471	0.24989
2.780	0.54498	0.18387	0.06405	0.24792
2.790	0.54273	0.18258	0.06339	0.24597

TABLE 6A-1
THERMODYNAMIC FUNCTIONS FOR A HARMONIC OSCILLATOR

U	C/R	$(H-H_0)/RT$	$(F-H_0)/RT$	S/R
2.800	0.54049	0.18129	0.06274	0.24403
2.810	0.53824	0.18001	0.06209	0.24211
2.820	0.53600	0.17874	0.06146	0.24020
2.830	0.53377	0.17748	0.06083	0.23831
2.840	0.53153	0.17623	0.06020	0.23643
2.850	0.52930	0.17498	0.05958	0.23456
2.860	0.52708	0.17374	0.05897	0.23271
2.870	0.52485	0.17251	0.05837	0.23088
2.880	0.52263	0.17128	0.05777	0.22906
2.890	0.52042	0.17007	0.05718	0.22725
2.900	0.51820	0.16886	0.05660	0.22545
2.910	0.51599	0.16766	0.05602	0.22367
2.920	0.51379	0.16646	0.05544	0.22191
2.930	0.51158	0.16528	0.05488	0.22015
2.940	0.50938	0.16410	0.05431	0.21842
2.950	0.50719	0.16293	0.05376	0.21669
2.960	0.50500	0.16177	0.05321	0.21498
2.970	0.50281	0.16061	0.05267	0.21328
2.980	0.50063	0.15946	0.05213	0.21159
2.990	0.49845	0.15832	0.05160	0.20992
3.000	0.49627	0.15719	0.05107	0.20826
3.010	0.49410	0.15606	0.05055	0.20661
3.020	0.49193	0.15494	0.05003	0.20497
3.030	0.48976	0.15383	0.04952	0.20335
3.040	0.48760	0.15272	0.04902	0.20174
3.050	0.48545	0.15163	0.04852	0.20014
3.060	0.48330	0.15053	0.04802	0.19856
3.070	0.48115	0.14945	0.04753	0.19698
3.080	0.47901	0.14837	0.04705	0.19542
3.090	0.47687	0.14730	0.04657	0.19387
3.100	0.47473	0.14624	0.04610	0.19234
3.110	0.47260	0.14518	0.04563	0.19081
3.120	0.47048	0.14414	0.04516	0.18930
3.130	0.46836	0.14309	0.04470	0.18779
3.140	0.46624	0.14206	0.04425	0.18630
3.150	0.46413	0.14103	0.04380	0.18483
3.160	0.46202	0.14001	0.04335	0.18336
3.170	0.45992	0.13899	0.04291	0.18190
3.180	0.45782	0.13798	0.04248	0.18046
3.190	0.45572	0.13698	0.04204	0.17902

TABLE 6A-1

THERMODYNAMIC FUNCTIONS FOR A HARMONIC OSCILLATOR

U	C/R	$(H-H_0)/RT$	$(F-H_0)/RT$	S/R
3.200	0.45363	0.13598	0.04162	0.17760
3.210	0.45155	0.13499	0.04119	0.17619
3.220	0.44947	0.13401	0.04078	0.17479
3.230	0.44740	0.13303	0.04036	0.17339
3.240	0.44533	0.13206	0.03995	0.17201
3.250	0.44326	0.13110	0.03955	0.17065
3.260	0.44120	0.13014	0.03914	0.16929
3.270	0.43915	0.12919	0.03875	0.16794
3.280	0.43710	0.12825	0.03835	0.16660
3.290	0.43505	0.12731	0.03797	0.16527
3.300	0.43301	0.12638	0.03758	0.16396
3.310	0.43098	0.12545	0.03720	0.16265
3.320	0.42895	0.12453	0.03682	0.16135
3.330	0.42692	0.12362	0.03645	0.16007
3.340	0.42490	0.12271	0.03608	0.15879
3.350	0.42289	0.12181	0.03571	0.15752
3.360	0.42088	0.12091	0.03535	0.15626
3.370	0.41887	0.12002	0.03499	0.15502
3.380	0.41688	0.11914	0.03464	0.15378
3.390	0.41488	0.11826	0.03429	0.15255
3.400	0.41289	0.11739	0.03394	0.15133
3.410	0.41091	0.11652	0.03360	0.15012
3.420	0.40894	0.11566	0.03326	0.14892
3.430	0.40696	0.11481	0.03292	0.14773
3.440	0.40500	0.11396	0.03259	0.14655
3.450	0.40304	0.11311	0.03226	0.14537
3.460	0.40108	0.11228	0.03193	0.14421
3.470	0.39913	0.11144	0.03161	0.14306
3.480	0.39719	0.11062	0.03129	0.14191
3.490	0.39525	0.10980	0.03098	0.14077
3.500	0.39331	0.10898	0.03066	0.13964
3.510	0.39139	0.10817	0.03035	0.13853
3.520	0.38946	0.10737	0.03005	0.13741
3.530	0.38755	0.10657	0.02974	0.13631
3.540	0.38564	0.10578	0.02944	0.13522
3.550	0.38373	0.10499	0.02915	0.13413
3.560	0.38183	0.10421	0.02885	0.13306
3.570	0.37994	0.10343	0.02856	0.13199
3.580	0.37805	0.10266	0.02827	0.13093
3.590	0.37617	0.10189	0.02799	0.12988

TABLE 6A-1
THERMODYNAMIC FUNCTIONS FOR A HARMONIC OSCILLATOR

U	C/R	$(H-H_0)/RT$	$(F-H_0)/RT$	S/R
3.600	0.37429	0.10113	0.02770	0.12883
3.610	0.37242	0.10037	0.02742	0.12780
3.620	0.37055	0.09962	0.02715	0.12677
3.630	0.36870	0.09888	0.02687	0.12575
3.640	0.36684	0.09813	0.02660	0.12474
3.650	0.36499	0.09740	0.02633	0.12373
3.660	0.36315	0.09667	0.02607	0.12274
3.670	0.36132	0.09594	0.02581	0.12175
3.680	0.35949	0.09522	0.02555	0.12077
3.690	0.35766	0.09451	0.02529	0.11980
3.700	0.35584	0.09380	0.02503	0.11883
3.710	0.35403	0.09309	0.02478	0.11787
3.720	0.35222	0.09239	0.02453	0.11692
3.730	0.35042	0.09169	0.02429	0.11598
3.740	0.34863	0.09100	0.02404	0.11504
3.750	0.34684	0.09032	0.02380	0.11411
3.760	0.34506	0.08963	0.02356	0.11319
3.770	0.34328	0.08896	0.02332	0.11228
3.780	0.34151	0.08828	0.02309	0.11137
3.790	0.33975	0.08762	0.02285	0.11047
3.800	0.33799	0.08695	0.02262	0.10958
3.810	0.33623	0.08630	0.02240	0.10869
3.820	0.33449	0.08564	0.02217	0.10781
3.830	0.33275	0.08499	0.02195	0.10694
3.840	0.33101	0.08435	0.02173	0.10608
3.850	0.32928	0.08371	0.02151	0.10522
3.860	0.32756	0.08307	0.02129	0.10437
3.870	0.32585	0.08244	0.02108	0.10352
3.880	0.32414	0.08181	0.02087	0.10268
3.890	0.32243	0.08119	0.02066	0.10185
3.900	0.32073	0.08057	0.02045	0.10102
3.910	0.31904	0.07996	0.02024	0.10021
3.920	0.31736	0.07935	0.02004	0.09939
3.930	0.31568	0.07875	0.01984	0.09859
3.940	0.31400	0.07815	0.01964	0.09779
3.950	0.31233	0.07755	0.01944	0.09699
3.960	0.31067	0.07696	0.01925	0.09620
3.970	0.30902	0.07637	0.01905	0.09542
3.980	0.30737	0.07579	0.01886	0.09465
3.990	0.30572	0.07521	0.01867	0.09388

TABLE 6A-1
THERMODYNAMIC FUNCTIONS FOR A HARMONIC OSCILLATOR

U	C/R	$(H-H_0)/RT$	$(F-H_0)/RT$	S/R
4.000	0.30409	0.07463	0.01849	0.09312
4.020	0.30083	0.07349	0.01812	0.09161
4.040	0.29760	0.07237	0.01775	0.09012
4.060	0.29439	0.07126	0.01740	0.08866
4.080	0.29121	0.07017	0.01705	0.08722
4.100	0.28806	0.06909	0.01671	0.08580
4.120	0.28492	0.06803	0.01638	0.08441
4.140	0.28181	0.06699	0.01605	0.08304
4.160	0.27873	0.06596	0.01573	0.08169
4.180	0.27567	0.06494	0.01542	0.08036
4.200	0.27264	0.06394	0.01511	0.07905
4.220	0.26963	0.06295	0.01481	0.07776
4.240	0.26664	0.06198	0.01451	0.07649
4.260	0.26368	0.06102	0.01422	0.07525
4.280	0.26074	0.06008	0.01394	0.07402
4.300	0.25783	0.05915	0.01366	0.07281
4.320	0.25494	0.05823	0.01339	0.07162
4.340	0.25208	0.05733	0.01312	0.07045
4.360	0.24924	0.05644	0.01286	0.06930
4.380	0.24643	0.05556	0.01260	0.06816
4.400	0.24364	0.05469	0.01235	0.06705
4.420	0.24087	0.05384	0.01211	0.06595
4.440	0.23813	0.05300	0.01187	0.06487
4.460	0.23541	0.05217	0.01163	0.06380
4.480	0.23271	0.05136	0.01140	0.06275
4.500	0.23004	0.05055	0.01117	0.06172
4.520	0.22739	0.04976	0.01095	0.06071
4.540	0.22477	0.04898	0.01073	0.05971
4.560	0.22217	0.04821	0.01052	0.05873
4.580	0.21959	0.04745	0.01031	0.05776
4.600	0.21704	0.04671	0.01010	0.05681
4.620	0.21451	0.04597	0.00990	0.05587
4.640	0.21200	0.04525	0.00970	0.05495
4.660	0.20952	0.04454	0.00951	0.05405
4.680	0.20706	0.04383	0.00932	0.05316
4.700	0.20462	0.04314	0.00914	0.05228
4.720	0.20221	0.04246	0.00896	0.05141
4.740	0.19981	0.04179	0.00878	0.05056
4.760	0.19744	0.04112	0.00860	0.04973
4.780	0.19510	0.04047	0.00843	0.04890

TABLE 6A-1
THERMODYNAMIC FUNCTIONS FOR A HARMONIC OSCILLATOR

U	C/R	$(H-H_0)/RT$	$(F-H_0)/RT$	S/R
4.800	0.19277	0.03983	0.00826	0.04809
4.820	0.19047	0.03920	0.00810	0.04730
4.840	0.18819	0.03858	0.00794	0.04651
4.860	0.18593	0.03796	0.00778	0.04574
4.880	0.18370	0.03736	0.00763	0.04498
4.900	0.18149	0.03676	0.00747	0.04424
4.920	0.17929	0.03618	0.00733	0.04350
4.940	0.17712	0.03560	0.00718	0.04278
4.960	0.17498	0.03503	0.00704	0.04207
4.980	0.17285	0.03447	0.00690	0.04137
5.000	0.17074	0.03392	0.00676	0.04068
5.020	0.16866	0.03338	0.00663	0.04000
5.040	0.16659	0.03284	0.00649	0.03934
5.060	0.16455	0.03231	0.00637	0.03868
5.080	0.16253	0.03179	0.00624	0.03803
5.100	0.16053	0.03128	0.00612	0.03740
5.120	0.15855	0.03078	0.00599	0.03678
5.140	0.15659	0.03029	0.00587	0.03616
5.160	0.15465	0.02980	0.00576	0.03556
5.180	0.15273	0.02932	0.00564	0.03496
5.200	0.15083	0.02885	0.00553	0.03438
5.220	0.14895	0.02838	0.00542	0.03380
5.240	0.14709	0.02792	0.00531	0.03324
5.260	0.14525	0.02747	0.00521	0.03268
5.280	0.14343	0.02703	0.00511	0.03213
5.300	0.14162	0.02659	0.00500	0.03159
5.320	0.13984	0.02616	0.00490	0.03106
5.340	0.13808	0.02573	0.00481	0.03054
5.360	0.13633	0.02532	0.00471	0.03003
5.380	0.13461	0.02490	0.00462	0.02952
5.400	0.13290	0.02450	0.00453	0.02903
5.420	0.13121	0.02410	0.00444	0.02854
5.440	0.12954	0.02371	0.00435	0.02806
5.460	0.12789	0.02332	0.00426	0.02759
5.480	0.12626	0.02294	0.00418	0.02712
5.500	0.12464	0.02257	0.00410	0.02666
5.520	0.12304	0.02220	0.00401	0.02622
5.540	0.12146	0.02184	0.00393	0.02577
5.560	0.11990	0.02148	0.00386	0.02534
5.580	0.11836	0.02113	0.00378	0.02491

TABLE 6A-1
THERMODYNAMIC FUNCTIONS FOR A HARMONIC OSCILLATOR

U	C/R	$(H-H_0)/RT$	$(F-H_0)/RT$	S/R
5.600	0.11683	0.02078	0.00370	0.02449
5.620	0.11532	0.02044	0.00363	0.02408
5.640	0.11382	0.02011	0.00356	0.02367
5.660	0.11235	0.01978	0.00349	0.02327
5.680	0.11089	0.01946	0.00342	0.02287
5.700	0.10944	0.01914	0.00335	0.02249
5.720	0.10801	0.01882	0.00329	0.02211
5.740	0.10660	0.01851	0.00322	0.02173
5.760	0.10521	0.01821	0.00316	0.02136
5.780	0.10383	0.01791	0.00309	0.02100
5.800	0.10247	0.01761	0.00303	0.02065
5.820	0.10112	0.01732	0.00297	0.02029
5.840	0.09979	0.01704	0.00291	0.01995
5.860	0.09847	0.01676	0.00286	0.01961
5.880	0.09717	0.01648	0.00280	0.01928
5.900	0.09588	0.01621	0.00274	0.01895
5.920	0.09461	0.01594	0.00269	0.01863
5.940	0.09336	0.01568	0.00264	0.01831
5.960	0.09212	0.01542	0.00258	0.01800
5.980	0.09089	0.01516	0.00253	0.01769
6.000	0.08968	0.01491	0.00248	0.01739
6.050	0.08671	0.01430	0.00236	0.01666
6.100	0.08383	0.01371	0.00225	0.01596
6.150	0.08104	0.01315	0.00214	0.01528
6.200	0.07833	0.01261	0.00203	0.01464
6.250	0.07570	0.01209	0.00193	0.01402
6.300	0.07315	0.01159	0.00184	0.01343
6.350	0.07068	0.01111	0.00175	0.01286
6.400	0.06828	0.01065	0.00166	0.01231
6.450	0.06596	0.01021	0.00158	0.01179
6.500	0.06371	0.00979	0.00150	0.01129
6.550	0.06153	0.00938	0.00143	0.01081
6.600	0.05942	0.00899	0.00136	0.01035
6.650	0.05737	0.00862	0.00129	0.00991
6.700	0.05539	0.00826	0.00123	0.00949
6.750	0.05347	0.00791	0.00117	0.00908
6.800	0.05162	0.00758	0.00111	0.00870
6.850	0.04982	0.00727	0.00106	0.00833
6.900	0.04808	0.00696	0.00101	0.00797
6.950	0.04639	0.00667	0.00096	0.00763

TABLE 6A-1
THERMODYNAMIC FUNCTIONS FOR A HARMONIC OSCILLATOR

U	C/R	$(H-H_0)/RT$	$(F-H_0)/RT$	S/R
7.000	0.04476	0.00639	0.00091	0.00730
7.050	0.04319	0.00612	0.00087	0.00699
7.100	0.04166	0.00586	0.00083	0.00669
7.150	0.04019	0.00562	0.00079	0.00640
7.200	0.03876	0.00538	0.00075	0.00613
7.250	0.03738	0.00515	0.00071	0.00586
7.300	0.03605	0.00493	0.00068	0.00561
7.350	0.03476	0.00473	0.00064	0.00537
7.400	0.03351	0.00453	0.00061	0.00514
7.450	0.03231	0.00433	0.00058	0.00492
7.500	0.03115	0.00415	0.00055	0.00470
7.550	0.03002	0.00397	0.00053	0.00450
7.600	0.02894	0.00381	0.00050	0.00431
7.650	0.02789	0.00364	0.00048	0.00412
7.700	0.02687	0.00349	0.00045	0.00394
7.750	0.02589	0.00334	0.00043	0.00377
7.800	0.02495	0.00320	0.00041	0.00361
7.850	0.02404	0.00306	0.00039	0.00345
7.900	0.02316	0.00293	0.00037	0.00330
7.950	0.02230	0.00280	0.00035	0.00316
8.000	0.02148	0.00268	0.00034	0.00302
8.050	0.02069	0.00257	0.00032	0.00289
8.100	0.01993	0.00246	0.00030	0.00276
8.150	0.01919	0.00235	0.00029	0.00264
8.200	0.01848	0.00225	0.00027	0.00253
8.250	0.01779	0.00216	0.00026	0.00242
8.300	0.01713	0.00206	0.00025	0.00231
8.350	0.01649	0.00197	0.00024	0.00221
8.400	0.01587	0.00189	0.00022	0.00211
8.450	0.01528	0.00181	0.00021	0.00202
8.500	0.01471	0.00173	0.00020	0.00193
8.550	0.01415	0.00166	0.00019	0.00185
8.600	0.01362	0.00158	0.00018	0.00177
8.650	0.01311	0.00152	0.00018	0.00169
8.700	0.01261	0.00145	0.00017	0.00162
8.750	0.01214	0.00139	0.00016	0.00155
8.800	0.01168	0.00133	0.00015	0.00148
8.850	0.01123	0.00127	0.00014	0.00141
8.900	0.01081	0.00121	0.00014	0.00135
8.950	0.01040	0.00116	0.00013	0.00129

TABLE 6A-1
THERMODYNAMIC FUNCTIONS FOR A HARMONIC OSCILLATOR

U	C/R	$(H-H_0)/RT$	$(F-H_0)/RT$	S/R
9.000	0.01000	0.00111	0.00012	0.00123
9.050	0.00962	0.00106	0.00012	0.00118
9.100	0.00925	0.00102	0.00011	0.00113
9.150	0.00889	0.00097	0.00011	0.00108
9.200	0.00855	0.00093	0.00010	0.00103
9.250	0.00823	0.00089	0.00010	0.00099
9.300	0.00791	0.00085	0.00009	0.00094
9.350	0.00760	0.00081	0.00009	0.00090
9.400	0.00731	0.00078	0.00008	0.00086
9.450	0.00703	0.00074	0.00008	0.00082
9.500	0.00676	0.00071	0.00007	0.00079
9.550	0.00649	0.00068	0.00007	0.00075
9.600	0.00624	0.00065	0.00007	0.00072
9.650	0.00600	0.00062	0.00006	0.00069
9.700	0.00577	0.00059	0.00006	0.00066
9.750	0.00554	0.00057	0.00006	0.00063
9.800	0.00533	0.00054	0.00006	0.00060
9.850	0.00512	0.00052	0.00005	0.00057
9.900	0.00492	0.00050	0.00005	0.00055
9.950	0.00473	0.00047	0.00005	0.00052
10.000	0.00454	0.00045	0.00005	0.00050
10.100	0.00419	0.00041	0.00004	0.00046
10.200	0.00387	0.00038	0.00004	0.00042
10.300	0.00357	0.00035	0.00003	0.00038
10.400	0.00329	0.00032	0.00003	0.00035
10.500	0.00304	0.00029	0.00003	0.00032
10.600	0.00280	0.00026	0.00002	0.00029
10.700	0.00258	0.00024	0.00002	0.00026
10.800	0.00238	0.00022	0.00002	0.00024
10.900	0.00219	0.00020	0.00002	0.00022
11.000	0.00202	0.00018	0.00002	0.00020
11.100	0.00186	0.00017	0.00002	0.00018
11.200	0.00172	0.00015	0.00001	0.00017
11.300	0.00158	0.00014	0.00001	0.00015
11.400	0.00146	0.00013	0.00001	0.00014
11.500	0.00134	0.00012	0.00001	0.00013
11.600	0.00123	0.00011	0.00001	0.00012
11.700	0.00114	0.00010	0.00001	0.00011
11.800	0.00104	0.00009	0.00001	0.00010
11.900	0.00096	0.00008	0.00001	0.00009

TABLE 6A-2
VALUES OF U AS A FUNCTION OF VIBRATIONAL FREQUENCY

X	0C	25C	50C	100C	150C	200C	250C	300C
3450.	18.171	16.647	15.359	13.301	11.730	10.490	9.488	8.660
3400.	17.907	16.406	15.137	13.109	11.560	10.338	9.350	8.534
3350.	17.644	16.165	14.914	12.916	11.390	10.186	9.213	8.409
3300.	17.381	15.923	14.692	12.723	11.220	10.034	9.075	8.283
3250.	17.117	15.682	14.469	12.530	11.050	9.882	8.938	8.158
3200.	16.854	15.441	14.246	12.337	10.880	9.730	8.800	8.032
3150.	16.591	15.200	14.024	12.145	10.710	9.578	8.663	7.907
3100.	16.327	14.958	13.801	11.952	10.540	9.426	8.525	7.781
3050.	16.064	14.717	13.579	11.759	10.370	9.274	8.388	7.656
3000.	15.801	14.476	13.356	11.566	10.200	9.122	8.250	7.530
2950.	15.537	14.235	13.133	11.374	10.030	8.970	8.113	7.405
2900.	15.274	13.993	12.911	11.181	9.860	8.818	7.975	7.279
2850.	15.011	13.752	12.688	10.988	9.690	8.666	7.838	7.154
2800.	14.747	13.511	12.466	10.795	9.520	8.514	7.700	7.028
2750.	14.484	13.269	12.243	10.602	9.350	8.362	7.563	6.903
2700.	14.221	13.028	12.020	10.410	9.180	8.210	7.425	6.777
2650.	13.957	12.787	11.798	10.217	9.010	8.058	7.288	6.652
2600.	13.694	12.546	11.575	10.024	8.840	7.906	7.150	6.526
2550.	13.431	12.304	11.353	9.831	8.670	7.754	7.013	6.401
2500.	13.167	12.063	11.130	9.639	8.500	7.602	6.875	6.275
2450.	12.904	11.822	10.907	9.446	8.330	7.450	6.738	6.150
2400.	12.641	11.581	10.685	9.253	8.160	7.297	6.600	6.024
2350.	12.377	11.339	10.462	9.060	7.990	7.145	6.463	5.899
2300.	12.114	11.098	10.240	8.868	7.820	6.993	6.325	5.773
2250.	11.850	10.857	10.017	8.675	7.650	6.841	6.188	5.648
2200.	11.587	10.616	9.794	8.482	7.480	6.689	6.050	5.522
2150.	11.324	10.374	9.572	8.289	7.310	6.537	5.913	5.397
2100.	11.060	10.133	9.349	8.096	7.140	6.385	5.775	5.271
2050.	10.797	9.892	9.127	7.904	6.970	6.233	5.638	5.146
2000.	10.534	9.651	8.904	7.711	6.800	6.081	5.500	5.020

TABLE 6A-2
VALUES OF U AS A FUNCTION OF VIBRATIONAL FREQUENCY

X	0C	25C	50C	100C	150C	200C	250C	300C
1980.	10.428	9.554	8.815	7.634	6.732	6.020	5.445	4.970
1960.	10.323	9.458	8.726	7.557	6.664	5.960	5.390	4.920
1940.	10.218	9.361	8.637	7.480	6.596	5.899	5.335	4.870
1920.	10.112	9.265	8.548	7.402	6.528	5.838	5.280	4.819
1900.	10.007	9.168	8.459	7.325	6.460	5.777	5.225	4.769
1880.	9.902	9.071	8.370	7.248	6.392	5.716	5.170	4.719
1860.	9.796	8.975	8.281	7.171	6.324	5.656	5.115	4.669
1840.	9.691	8.878	8.192	7.094	6.256	5.595	5.060	4.619
1820.	9.586	8.782	8.103	7.017	6.188	5.534	5.005	4.568
1800.	9.480	8.685	8.014	6.940	6.120	5.473	4.950	4.518
1780.	9.375	8.589	7.925	6.863	6.052	5.412	4.895	4.468
1760.	9.270	8.492	7.835	6.786	5.984	5.351	4.840	4.418
1740.	9.164	8.396	7.746	6.708	5.916	5.291	4.785	4.368
1720.	9.059	8.299	7.657	6.631	5.848	5.230	4.730	4.317
1700.	8.954	8.203	7.568	6.554	5.780	5.169	4.675	4.267
1680.	8.848	8.106	7.479	6.477	5.712	5.108	4.620	4.217
1660.	8.743	8.010	7.390	6.400	5.644	5.047	4.565	4.167
1640.	8.638	7.913	7.301	6.323	5.576	4.987	4.510	4.117
1620.	8.532	7.817	7.212	6.246	5.508	4.926	4.455	4.066
1600.	8.427	7.720	7.123	6.169	5.440	4.865	4.400	4.016
1580.	8.322	7.624	7.034	6.092	5.372	4.804	4.345	3.966
1560.	8.216	7.527	6.945	6.015	5.304	4.743	4.290	3.916
1540.	8.111	7.431	6.856	5.937	5.236	4.683	4.235	3.866
1520.	8.006	7.334	6.767	5.860	5.168	4.622	4.180	3.815
1500.	7.900	7.238	6.678	5.783	5.100	4.561	4.125	3.765
1490.	7.848	7.190	6.633	5.745	5.066	4.531	4.098	3.740
1480.	7.795	7.141	6.589	5.706	5.032	4.500	4.070	3.715
1470.	7.742	7.093	6.544	5.668	4.998	4.470	4.043	3.690
1460.	7.690	7.045	6.500	5.629	4.964	4.439	4.015	3.665
1450.	7.637	6.997	6.455	5.590	4.930	4.409	3.988	3.640

TABLE 6A-2
VALUES OF U AS A FUNCTION OF VIBRATIONAL FREQUENCY

X	0C	25C	50C	100C	150C	200C	250C	300C
1440.	7.584	6.948	6.411	5.552	4.896	4.378	3.960	3.615
1430.	7.532	6.900	6.366	5.513	4.862	4.348	3.933	3.589
1420.	7.479	6.852	6.322	5.475	4.828	4.318	3.905	3.564
1410.	7.426	6.804	6.277	5.436	4.794	4.287	3.878	3.539
1400.	7.374	6.755	6.233	5.398	4.760	4.257	3.850	3.514
1390.	7.321	6.707	6.188	5.359	4.726	4.226	3.823	3.489
1380.	7.268	6.659	6.144	5.321	4.692	4.196	3.795	3.464
1370.	7.216	6.611	6.099	5.282	4.658	4.166	3.768	3.439
1360.	7.163	6.562	6.055	5.243	4.624	4.135	3.740	3.414
1350.	7.110	6.514	6.010	5.205	4.590	4.105	3.713	3.389
1340.	7.058	6.466	5.966	5.166	4.556	4.074	3.685	3.364
1330.	7.005	6.418	5.921	5.128	4.522	4.044	3.658	3.338
1320.	6.952	6.369	5.877	5.089	4.488	4.014	3.630	3.313
1310.	6.900	6.321	5.832	5.051	4.454	3.983	3.603	3.288
1300.	6.847	6.273	5.788	5.012	4.420	3.953	3.575	3.263
1290.	6.794	6.225	5.743	4.974	4.386	3.922	3.548	3.238
1280.	6.742	6.176	5.699	4.935	4.352	3.892	3.520	3.213
1270.	6.689	6.128	5.654	4.896	4.318	3.862	3.493	3.188
1260.	6.636	6.080	5.609	4.858	4.284	3.831	3.465	3.163
1250.	6.584	6.032	5.565	4.819	4.250	3.801	3.438	3.138
1240.	6.531	5.983	5.520	4.781	4.216	3.770	3.410	3.113
1230.	6.478	5.935	5.476	4.742	4.182	3.740	3.383	3.087
1220.	6.426	5.887	5.431	4.704	4.148	3.710	3.355	3.062
1210.	6.373	5.839	5.387	4.665	4.114	3.679	3.328	3.037
1200.	6.320	5.790	5.342	4.627	4.080	3.649	3.300	3.012
1190.	6.268	5.742	5.298	4.588	4.046	3.618	3.273	2.987
1180.	6.215	5.694	5.253	4.549	4.012	3.588	3.245	2.962
1170.	6.162	5.646	5.209	4.511	3.978	3.558	3.218	2.937
1160.	6.110	5.597	5.164	4.472	3.944	3.527	3.190	2.912
1150.	6.057	5.549	5.120	4.434	3.910	3.497	3.163	2.887

TABLE 6A-2
VALUES OF U AS A FUNCTION OF VIBRATIONAL FREQUENCY

X	0C	25C	50C	100C	150C	200C	250C	300C
1140.	6.004	5.501	5.075	4.395	3.876	3.466	3.135	2.862
1130.	5.952	5.453	5.031	4.357	3.842	3.436	3.108	2.836
1120.	5.899	5.404	4.986	4.318	3.808	3.405	3.080	2.811
1110.	5.846	5.356	4.942	4.280	3.774	3.375	3.053	2.786
1100.	5.794	5.308	4.897	4.241	3.740	3.345	3.025	2.761
1090.	5.741	5.260	4.853	4.202	3.706	3.314	2.998	2.736
1080.	5.688	5.211	4.808	4.164	3.672	3.284	2.970	2.711
1070.	5.636	5.163	4.764	4.125	3.638	3.253	2.943	2.686
1060.	5.583	5.115	4.719	4.087	3.604	3.223	2.915	2.661
1050.	5.530	5.067	4.675	4.048	3.570	3.193	2.888	2.636
1040.	5.478	5.018	4.630	4.010	3.536	3.162	2.860	2.611
1030.	5.425	4.970	4.586	3.971	3.502	3.132	2.833	2.585
1020.	5.372	4.922	4.541	3.933	3.468	3.101	2.805	2.560
1010.	5.320	4.874	4.496	3.894	3.434	3.071	2.778	2.535
1000.	5.267	4.825	4.452	3.855	3.400	3.041	2.750	2.510
995.	5.241	4.801	4.430	3.836	3.383	3.025	2.736	2.498
990.	5.214	4.777	4.407	3.817	3.366	3.010	2.723	2.485
985.	5.188	4.753	4.385	3.798	3.349	2.995	2.709	2.472
980.	5.162	4.729	4.363	3.778	3.332	2.980	2.695	2.460
975.	5.135	4.705	4.341	3.759	3.315	2.965	2.681	2.447
970.	5.109	4.681	4.318	3.740	3.298	2.949	2.668	2.435
965.	5.083	4.656	4.296	3.721	3.281	2.934	2.654	2.422
960.	5.056	4.632	4.274	3.701	3.264	2.919	2.640	2.410
955.	5.030	4.608	4.252	3.682	3.247	2.904	2.626	2.397
950.	5.004	4.584	4.229	3.663	3.230	2.889	2.613	2.385
945.	4.977	4.560	4.207	3.643	3.213	2.873	2.599	2.372
940.	4.951	4.536	4.185	3.624	3.196	2.858	2.585	2.360
935.	4.925	4.512	4.163	3.605	3.179	2.843	2.571	2.347
930.	4.898	4.487	4.140	3.586	3.162	2.828	2.558	2.334
925.	4.872	4.463	4.118	3.566	3.145	2.813	2.544	2.322

TABLE 6A-2
VALUES OF U AS A FUNCTION OF VIBRATIONAL FREQUENCY

X	0C	25C	50C	100C	150C	200C	250C	300C
920.	4.846	4.439	4.096	3.547	3.128	2.797	2.530	2.309
915.	4.819	4.415	4.074	3.528	3.111	2.782	2.516	2.297
910.	4.793	4.391	4.051	3.508	3.094	2.767	2.503	2.284
905.	4.767	4.367	4.029	3.489	3.077	2.752	2.489	2.272
900.	4.740	4.343	4.007	3.470	3.060	2.737	2.475	2.259
895.	4.714	4.319	3.985	3.451	3.043	2.721	2.461	2.247
890.	4.688	4.294	3.962	3.431	3.026	2.706	2.448	2.234
885.	4.661	4.270	3.940	3.412	3.009	2.691	2.434	2.221
880.	4.635	4.246	3.918	3.393	2.992	2.676	2.420	2.209
875.	4.609	4.222	3.895	3.374	2.975	2.661	2.406	2.196
870.	4.582	4.198	3.873	3.354	2.958	2.645	2.393	2.184
865.	4.556	4.174	3.851	3.335	2.941	2.630	2.379	2.171
860.	4.530	4.150	3.829	3.316	2.924	2.615	2.365	2.159
855.	4.503	4.126	3.806	3.296	2.907	2.600	2.351	2.146
850.	4.477	4.101	3.784	3.277	2.890	2.585	2.338	2.134
845.	4.451	4.077	3.762	3.258	2.873	2.569	2.324	2.121
840.	4.424	4.053	3.740	3.239	2.856	2.554	2.310	2.109
835.	4.398	4.029	3.717	3.219	2.839	2.539	2.296	2.096
830.	4.372	4.005	3.695	3.200	2.822	2.524	2.283	2.083
825.	4.345	3.981	3.673	3.181	2.805	2.509	2.269	2.071
820.	4.319	3.957	3.651	3.161	2.788	2.493	2.255	2.058
815.	4.293	3.933	3.628	3.142	2.771	2.478	2.241	2.046
810.	4.266	3.908	3.606	3.123	2.754	2.463	2.228	2.033
805.	4.240	3.884	3.584	3.104	2.737	2.448	2.214	2.021
800.	4.214	3.860	3.562	3.084	2.720	2.432	2.200	2.008
795.	4.187	3.836	3.539	3.065	2.703	2.417	2.186	1.996
790.	4.161	3.812	3.517	3.046	2.686	2.402	2.173	1.983
785.	4.134	3.788	3.495	3.027	2.669	2.387	2.159	1.970
780.	4.108	3.764	3.473	3.007	2.652	2.372	2.145	1.958
775.	4.082	3.740	3.450	2.988	2.635	2.356	2.131	1.945

TABLE 6A-2
VALUES OF U AS A FUNCTION OF VIBRATIONAL FREQUENCY

X	0C	25C	50C	100C	150C	200C	250C	300C
770.	4.055	3.715	3.428	2.969	2.618	2.341	2.118	1.933
765.	4.029	3.691	3.406	2.949	2.601	2.326	2.104	1.920
760.	4.003	3.667	3.384	2.930	2.584	2.311	2.090	1.908
755.	3.976	3.643	3.361	2.911	2.567	2.296	2.076	1.895
750.	3.950	3.619	3.339	2.892	2.550	2.280	2.063	1.883
745.	3.924	3.595	3.317	2.872	2.533	2.265	2.049	1.870
740.	3.897	3.571	3.294	2.853	2.516	2.250	2.035	1.857
735.	3.871	3.547	3.272	2.834	2.499	2.235	2.021	1.845
730.	3.845	3.522	3.250	2.814	2.482	2.220	2.008	1.832
725.	3.818	3.498	3.228	2.795	2.465	2.204	1.994	1.820
720.	3.792	3.474	3.205	2.776	2.448	2.189	1.980	1.807
715.	3.766	3.450	3.183	2.757	2.431	2.174	1.966	1.795
710.	3.739	3.426	3.161	2.737	2.414	2.159	1.953	1.782
705.	3.713	3.402	3.139	2.718	2.397	2.144	1.939	1.770
700.	3.687	3.378	3.116	2.699	2.380	2.128	1.925	1.757
695.	3.660	3.354	3.094	2.680	2.363	2.113	1.911	1.745
690.	3.634	3.329	3.072	2.660	2.346	2.098	1.898	1.732
685.	3.608	3.305	3.050	2.641	2.329	2.083	1.884	1.719
680.	3.581	3.281	3.027	2.622	2.312	2.068	1.870	1.707
675.	3.555	3.257	3.005	2.602	2.295	2.052	1.856	1.694
670.	3.529	3.233	2.983	2.583	2.278	2.037	1.843	1.682
665.	3.502	3.209	2.961	2.564	2.261	2.022	1.829	1.669
660.	3.476	3.185	2.938	2.545	2.244	2.007	1.815	1.657
655.	3.450	3.161	2.916	2.525	2.227	1.992	1.801	1.644
650.	3.423	3.136	2.894	2.506	2.210	1.976	1.788	1.632
645.	3.397	3.112	2.872	2.487	2.193	1.961	1.774	1.619
640.	3.371	3.088	2.849	2.467	2.176	1.946	1.760	1.606
635.	3.344	3.064	2.827	2.448	2.159	1.931	1.746	1.594
630.	3.318	3.040	2.805	2.429	2.142	1.916	1.733	1.581
625.	3.292	3.016	2.782	2.410	2.125	1.900	1.719	1.569

TABLE 6A-2
VALUES OF U AS A FUNCTION OF VIBRATIONAL FREQUENCY

X	0C	25C	50C	100C	150C	200C	250C	300C
620.	3.265	2.992	2.760	2.390	2.108	1.885	1.705	1.556
615.	3.239	2.968	2.738	2.371	2.091	1.870	1.691	1.544
610.	3.213	2.943	2.716	2.352	2.074	1.855	1.678	1.531
605.	3.186	2.919	2.693	2.333	2.057	1.840	1.664	1.519
600.	3.160	2.895	2.671	2.313	2.040	1.824	1.650	1.506
595.	3.134	2.871	2.649	2.294	2.023	1.809	1.636	1.494
590.	3.107	2.847	2.627	2.275	2.006	1.794	1.623	1.481
585.	3.081	2.823	2.604	2.255	1.989	1.779	1.609	1.468
580.	3.055	2.799	2.582	2.236	1.972	1.764	1.595	1.456
575.	3.028	2.775	2.560	2.217	1.955	1.748	1.581	1.443
570.	3.002	2.750	2.538	2.198	1.938	1.733	1.568	1.431
565.	2.976	2.726	2.515	2.178	1.921	1.718	1.554	1.418
560.	2.949	2.702	2.493	2.159	1.904	1.703	1.540	1.406
555.	2.923	2.678	2.471	2.140	1.887	1.688	1.526	1.393
550.	2.897	2.654	2.449	2.120	1.870	1.672	1.513	1.381
545.	2.870	2.630	2.426	2.101	1.853	1.657	1.499	1.368
540.	2.844	2.606	2.404	2.082	1.836	1.642	1.485	1.355
535.	2.818	2.582	2.382	2.063	1.819	1.627	1.471	1.343
530.	2.791	2.557	2.360	2.043	1.802	1.612	1.458	1.330
525.	2.765	2.533	2.337	2.024	1.785	1.596	1.444	1.318
520.	2.739	2.509	2.315	2.005	1.768	1.581	1.430	1.305
515.	2.712	2.485	2.293	1.986	1.751	1.566	1.416	1.293
510.	2.686	2.461	2.271	1.966	1.734	1.551	1.403	1.280
505.	2.660	2.437	2.248	1.947	1.717	1.536	1.389	1.268
500.	2.633	2.413	2.226	1.928	1.700	1.520	1.375	1.255
495.	2.607	2.389	2.204	1.908	1.683	1.505	1.361	1.243
490.	2.581	2.364	2.181	1.889	1.666	1.490	1.348	1.230
485.	2.554	2.340	2.159	1.870	1.649	1.475	1.334	1.217
480.	2.528	2.316	2.137	1.851	1.632	1.459	1.320	1.205
475.	2.502	2.292	2.115	1.831	1.615	1.444	1.306	1.192

Treatment of Reactions with
Complex Rate Laws

This appendix will be concerned with the practical details of obtaining rate constants from reaction systems involving competitive or consecutive reactions. The simplest is consecutive first order reactions. As we saw previously (Section 3-2), the concentrations of the species A, B, and C

$$A \xrightarrow{k_1} B$$

$$B \xrightarrow{k_2} C$$

are given by

$$A = A_0 e^{-k_1 t}$$

$$B = \frac{A_0 k_1}{k_2 - k_1} (e^{-k_1 t} - e^{-k_2 t})$$

$$C = A_0 - A - B$$

The treatment of the data depends on whether we are able to determine the concentrations of the species as a function of time or if we can only obtain a physical parameter (such as the absorbance) to which all three species may contribute.

If the concentration of A may be followed as a function of time, the rate constant k_1 is readily obtained. If the time at which B reaches its maximum concentration may also be determined, k_2 may be found from the relationship

$$t_{max} = \frac{1}{k_2 - k_1} \ln \frac{k_2}{k_1}$$

Usually, however, we do not have as simple a case as this; rather, we know only the concentration of one compound which may be involved with both reactions, such as with

$$CH_3O_2C(CH_2)_nCO_2CH_3 \xrightarrow{\text{HO}^-} CH_3O_2C(CH_2)_nCO_2^- + CH_3OH$$

$$CH_3O_2C(CH_2)_nCO_2^- \xrightarrow{\text{HO}^-} {}^-O_2C(CH_2)_nCO_2^- + CH_3OH$$

where the hydroxyl ion concentration is in large excess (pseudo-first order conditions) or we know only the total absorbance of the solution.

Several methods have been developed for treating this case analytically.[1] The methods do not have general applicability to all cases but are useful for a case such as the ester hydrolysis mentioned above. A more general procedure, which is now practical because of the availability of computers, is to obtain a set of approximate rate parameters and other parameters necessary to define the observed variable. The expected values of the reaction variable are calculated as a function of time and are compared with the observed values. The average deviation or root mean squared deviation may be used as a criterion of the correctness of the starting parameters. The parameters may then be systematically varied until a minimum deviation between observed and calculated quantities has been reached.

The estimated value of k_1 may be obtained from the initial rate of reaction, for here A is essentially the only reactant. The estimated value of k_2 may often be obtained from the later stages of the reaction, for here the reaction may be approximately described as B going to C. An example of the use of this procedure when the experimental data are obtained in the form of absorbance values is given in Appendix 9.

The foregoing procedure can be used quite generally if one adds an additional step. For the consecutive first order case, the concentrations of A, B, and C could be given an analytical form. With many other cases, this is not possible. Here one may still write the set of differential equations representing the reaction system; and having a set of approximate values of the rate constants and other required parameters, one may obtain the calculated values of the reaction variable being measured by using numerical integration. One of the more satisfactory procedures is fourth order Runge-Kutta integration,[2] which gives very precise results with many types of rate phenomena and which may be used for n simultaneous differential equations.

---

[1] C. G. Swain, *J. Am. Chem. Soc.*, **66**, 1696 (1944); D. French, *J. Am. Chem. Soc.*, **72**, 4806 (1950); A. A. Frost and W. C. Schwemer, *J. Am. Chem. Soc.*, **74**, 1268 (1952); C. Burkhard, *Ind. Eng. Chem.*, **52**, 678 (1960).
[2] Cf. F. B. Hildebrand, *Introduction to Numerical Analysis*, McGraw-Hill Book Co., New York, 1956, pp. 233–239.

As an example, if one had the system

$$A + B \underset{k_2}{\overset{k_1}{\rightleftharpoons}} C$$

$$C + A \xrightarrow{k_3} D$$

one would write

$$\frac{dA}{dt} = -k_1AB + k_2C - k_3AC$$

$$\frac{dB}{dt} = -k_1AB$$

$$\frac{dC}{dt} = k_1AB - k_2C + k_3AC$$

$$\frac{dD}{dt} = k_3AC$$

If approximate values of the three rate constants could be obtained (perhaps by estimating k_1 from the initial rate of reaction, k_2 from an approximate equilibrium constant, and k_3 from data near the end of the run), Runge-Kutta integration would give the values of A, B, C, and D as a function of time. A comparison of the calculated values with the observed parameters, followed by a variation of the rate constants so as to obtain a minimum deviation between observed and calculated values, would lead to the correct rate constants.

An Introduction to Computer
Programming Using
the FORTRAN Compiler

The increasing availability of modern digital computers makes it advisable for many organic chemists to have a reasonable working knowledge of computer programming. It is obviously not possible to give a complete exposition of this subject in a relatively few pages. However, a working knowledge of simple programming methods may be fairly readily obtained.

A digital computer is essentially a device which is capable of adding, subtracting, multiplying, dividing, and of performing certain types of control operations, such as testing to see if a number is smaller than, equal to, or greater than zero. Most mathematical operations may be reduced to a series of these simple operations, and the function of a computer program is to instruct the computer to perform the necessary operations in the required order.

Thus to use a computer one must first know how to solve the problem at hand, using a desk calculator. Certain common operations, such as obtaining the logarithm of a number, obtaining the inverse of a matrix, and obtaining the arctangent of a number, may be effected using subroutines which have been written previously and which may be conveniently introduced into a new program.

Knowing the operations necessary in solving the problem, one is in a position to write the program. If this is written in machine language or in a symbolic form equivalent to machine language (i.e., having a one-to-one correspondence with the operations performed by the computer), it may represent a formidable task. Even a simple problem may require several hundred instructions, whereas more complex problems may require several thousands of instructions.

Fortunately there is a simple alternative to writing a program in machine language. A compiler is a program which will accept arithmetic and control statements, written in a simple form, and which will translate these statements into the appropriate series of machine instructions. One of the most popular compilers is FORTRAN (FORmula TRANslation), which is used with the IBM 704, 709, and related computers, and which may also be used in modified form with the IBM 650 and related computers. This appendix will present a brief introduction to programming using the FORTRAN system; further information may be obtained from the references given at the end of the appendix. The following discussion will apply to the 704, 709, and similar computers using the FORTRAN monitor.

The problem at hand is to prepare a series of FORTRAN statements which will lead to an object program (machine language program) capable of solving the required problem. These FORTRAN statements are punched onto standard cards which have the following format:

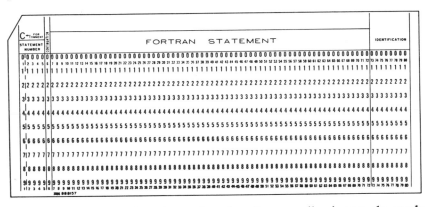

A letter C punched in column 1 makes the compiler ignore the card; however, the statement on the card punched in columns 7–72 will appear in the program list produced by the computer, and therefore these cards may be used to supply comments at appropriate places. Columns 2–5 are used for numbering statements, if they are to be referred to in other statements. The statement itself is punched in columns 7–72. If a statement runs over this limit, a 1 is punched in column 6 of the next card and the statement is continued in columns 7–72.

The preparation of a set of FORTRAN STATEMENTS may be roughly divided into three phases: (1) reading data into the computer, (2) execution of the arithmetic and other operations, and (3) writing the answers to the problem. For each part of the problem we wish to prepare a set of statements, usually on forms such as that shown in the next page, which the computer can interpret. These statements are punched onto cards of the type shown above and then transferred onto magnetic tape by the computer center personnel. The data required for the program are handled in a similar fashion, and all input to the computer is via

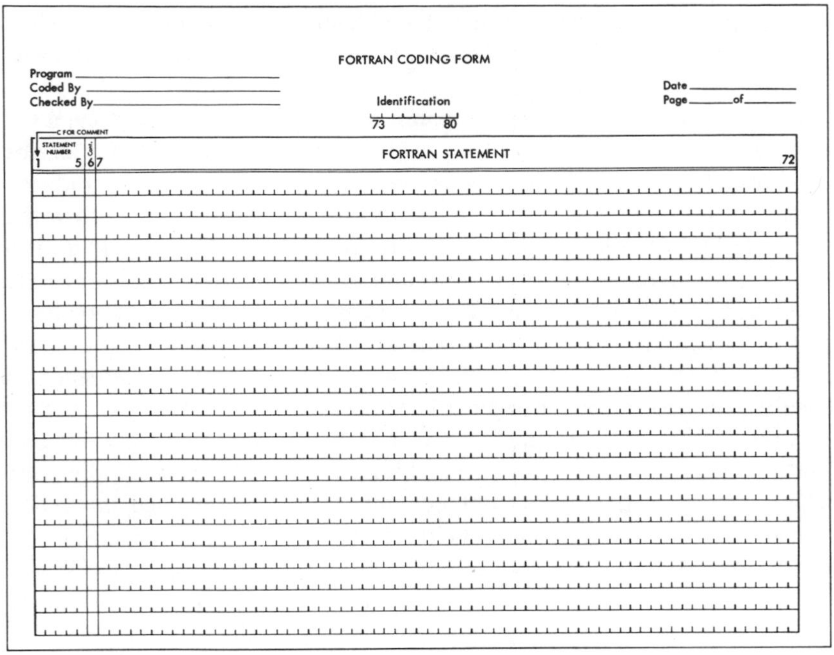

FORTRAN CODING FORM

Program _____
Coded By _____
Checked By _____

Date _____
Page _____ of _____

Identification

73   80

C FOR COMMENT

STATEMENT NUMBER

FORTRAN STATEMENT

1   5 6 7   72

magnetic tape. The output is also written on tape and later converted to a printed record by a separate machine.

A typical statement for reading data into a computer is

READ INPUT TAPE 4, 10, ALPHA, BETA, VALUE, N
10 FORMAT (3F10.0, I10)

The statement says that the values of alpha, beta, value, and n, which were transferred from punched cards to tape unit 4 as mentioned above, are to be read into the computer using the format defined in statement 10.

Before proceeding, we must differentiate between the different types of input data which may be used and must consider the conventions regarding the names of the quantities and the appropriate format designations. Numbers may be introduced into the computer as decimal numbers or as integers; and alphabetic material may also be introduced. The data which are read into or are written by the computer are referred to by mnemonic names such as TIME, VALUE, ABS, DIF. The restriction

526   *An Introduction to Computer Programming*

on the names for decimal numbers is that they must start with a letter other than I, J, K, L, M, or N, that they may not have more than a total of six alphabetic and numerical characters, and that they must not end in the letter F if there are more than three characters. The names starting with I, J, K, L, M, or N represents integers and are usually used for control purposes. Integers and decimal numbers may not be mixed in expressions. The alphabetic data may take the same type of names as decimal numbers.

For decimal numbers, the most common input format is that designated by an F, such as F10.5. The number following the F gives the number of columns on a card which may be occupied by the number, and the number following the decimal point indicates how many digits follow the decimal point. In order to avoid confusion in keypunching the data onto cards, it is advisable to punch the decimal point. If this is done, the number following the decimal point in the format statement has no effect, and we could have written F10.0 just as well. The number may now be punched anywhere within the available field, and for convenience is usually punched starting at the far left-hand side of the field.

A format statement starting with an I, such as I10, is used with integers. The number following the I gives the number of columns of the card which may be used for the number, and it must be punched in the far right-hand side of the available field. The other common format is that designated by an A indicating alphanumeric input. As an example, A6 indicates a name punched in 6 columns of a card. The number following A may be between 1 and 6 but may not be greater than 6.

If a format is to be repeated, this may be indicated by a number before the letter. Thus 3F10.0 means that the first three numbers have F10.0 as their format.

In the foregoing example, the format statement indicates that alpha should be punched in columns 1–10, beta in 11–20, value in 21–30, and *n* in 31–40. If the values of these numbers were 15.376, −9.67, 132.4475, and 21, the data card would be punched as seen on facing page. Note that minus signs must be punched. Numbers which do not have minus signs are automatically taken to be positive.

We may now consider the computing phase. Suppose we wished to obtain the solutions to a series of quadratic equations and that we knew the solutions would be real. The values would be given by

$$X1 = \frac{-b + \sqrt{b^2 - 4ac}}{2a}$$

$$X2 = \frac{-b - \sqrt{b^2 - 4ac}}{2a}$$

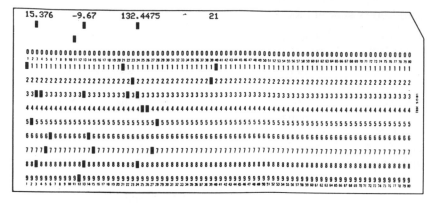

The appropriate FORTRAN statements would be

$$X1 = (-B + SQRTF(B^{**}2 - 4.\ ^*A\ ^*C))/(2.\ ^*A)$$

$$X2 = (-B - SQRTF(B^{**}2 - 4.\ ^*A\ ^*C))/(2.\ ^*A)$$

In the above statements, $+$ and $-$ have their usual significance, $*$ is the symbol for multiplication, $/$ is the symbol for division, and $**$ is the symbol for raising to a power. The parentheses are introduced to define which portions of the expression should be taken as a unit. There are a set of rules which state when parentheses are required, but it is usually simpler for the beginning programmer to use parentheses freely. The main restriction on the operations given above is that one may not indicate two successive operations. Thus

$$A^* - B$$

is incorrect and must be replaced by

$$A^*(-B)$$

It may be noted that most of the constants are given with decimal points. This is in accord with the rule that decimal numbers and integers cannot be mixed in equations. However, when raising a number to an integral power, the exponent need not be written with a decimal point. This is the exception to the rule. It should also be noted that the denominator is enclosed in parentheses so that there is no confusion as to whether division is by $2a$ or by 2 followed by multiplication by a.

The symbol SQRTF indicates that the square root is to be taken of the quantity within the parentheses which follow. This is one of the standard subroutines which are available on the library tape and which will automatically be introduced into one's program as required. The commonly used library subroutines are

SINF(X)	Obtains the sine of the angle X expressed in radians.
COSF(X)	Obtains the cosine of the angle X expressed in radians.
ATANF(X)	Obtains the angle (expressed in radians) whose tangent is X.
TANHF(X)	Obtains the hyperbolic tangent of the angle X expressed in radians.
EXPF(X)	Obtains the value of e^x where $X < 87.3$.
LOGF(X)	Obtains the natural logarithm of X.
SQRTF(X)	Obtains the square root of X.
ABSF(X)	Obtains the absolute value of X.
INTF(X)	Deletes the numbers after the decimal point of X.
FLOATF(X)	Converts the integer X into a decimal number.

(Note that X may be an arithmetic expression. Also, the square root of X may be obtained by stating A = SQRTF(X) or A = X**0.5. Similarly, the cube root of X may be obtained by stating A = X**0.3333.)

A complete program which would effect the above operation would be

```
1 READ INPUT TAPE 4, 2, A, B, C
2 FORMAT (3F10.0)
  X1 = (−B + SQRTF (B**2 − 4. *A*C))/(2. *A)
  X2 = (−B − SQRTF (B**2 − 4. *A*C))/(2. *A)
  WRITE OUTPUT TAPE 2, 3, A, B, C, X1, X2
3 FORMAT (1H 5F10.5)
  GO TO 1
  END
```

Here, the numbers *a*, *b*, and *c* are read from tape unit 4, each number originally having been punched in a field of ten columns on a card, starting with column 1. The values of X1 and X2 are determined, and then the values of all of the quantities are written on tape unit 2. Finally, the program returns to statement 1 and another set of data is read, and this continues until there are no further data. The statement END indicates that there are no further FORTRAN statements in the program.

The output is first placed on tape and later printed on paper. The first part of the output format statement contains information which controls the spacing in the printer output, and it must be an expression such as

1H followed by a blank

1HO

1H+

1H1

The first leads to a single spaced output, and the second gives a double spaced output. The third places the line of output on top of the preceding line and the fourth causes the printer to skip to the top of a page before printing.

Immediately following the control statement there appears the format specifications in terms similar to those given for the input format. The statement F10.5 gives the output in a field of ten characters, five of which are after the decimal point. Thus, since the sign of the number (if negative) and the decimal point must also be printed, a total of eight numbers may be printed, five of which are after the decimal point. The number of characters after the decimal point may be varied at will by changing the number following the decimal point in the format specification—however, it must be remembered that the computer carries a total of eight significant figures. The total number of characters may also be varied, and it is useful to make this large in order to place spaces between successive numbers on a line. Thus, in the above example, if the numbers were between 1000 and 9999 or were negative and between 100–999, all the numbers would run into each other. Since 119 spaces are available for printing, it would be well to make the format statement

3 FORMAT (1H 5F20.5)

in order to space the data across the page.

In some cases the magnitude of the answer is not known, and one wishes to avoid losing significant figures. Here one may use the format specified by E, for example, E14.6. The number is converted to the form

$$0.XXXXXXXX \times 10^N$$

and is printed giving six characters following the decimal, followed by E ± NN where NN is the power to which 10 is raised. Some examples of numbers and the way they are printed using this format are

Number	Format	Printed
199.7657	E14.6	0.199766E 03
0.00775431	E14.6	0.775431E–02
−0.537659	E12.4	−0.5377E 00
−257.392	E12.4	−0.2574E 03

It must be noted that 7 spaces are needed in addition to those used for the numbers, and thus the number following E must be at least 7 greater than the number which follows the decimal point and which controls the number of numerical characters given in the printed record. Again, spaces may be introduced into the output record by increasing the number following E. Thus E20.6 would give seven spaces between the output values.

The formats I and A are the same as for the input statements. The numbers printed using an I specification are placed in the right-hand side of the field. Thus a two digit number printed with a specification I10 would have eight blank spaces preceding it.

Having this much basic information about the FORTRAN system, let us write a series of programs which become progressively more complex. This will permit us to incorporate the control statements of the FORTRAN system.

The calculation of the transition energies and intensities for an A_2X_2 nmr spectrum based on a set of assumed chemical shift and coupling constant parameters is a simple straightforward case. The required equations were given in Appendix 5, and it can be seen that some quantities appear several times. These will be designated by symbols:

$$S = (K^2 + L^2)^{\frac{1}{2}}$$
$$T = (M^2 + L^2)^{\frac{1}{2}}$$
$$THETAS = \tfrac{1}{2}\cos^{-1}(K/S)$$
$$THETAA = \tfrac{1}{2}\cos^{-1}(M/T)$$
$$VAL1 = \sin^2(THETAS)$$
$$VAL2 = \cos^2(THETAS)$$
$$VAL3 = \sin^2(THETAA)$$
$$VAL4 = \cos^2(THETAA)$$

The quantities, K, L, M, and N will be referred to as AK, AL, AM, and AN in order to conform to the rule concerning the names of decimal numbers.

A program which will effect the calculation is shown on the next page. It begins by reading a card giving the identification for the spectrum, which may have 4 × 6 or 24 characters, and then a card having the coupling constants (CAA, CXX, CAX, CAX1). This is followed by the calculation of the values of K, L, M, and N and of the quantities referred to above. Note the use of the $\cos^{-1}$ (ACOSF), sin (SINF), cos (COSF), and square root (SQRTF) subroutines.

Having these quantities, the values of the line positions (POS1 to POS 12) are easily obtained. Certain values repeat (POS1 = POS2), and both need not be calculated. The intensities are given by the quantities designated as VAL1 to VAL4, plus an additional value, VAL5 = 1.0. After all the quantities have been obtained, we may write the results.

The heading is written first and next the line positions and intensities. In order to make the output format more useful and better organized, two additional format designations are added. The first, that designated by the

A$_2$X$_2$ NMR Spectrum Program

```
C       CALCULATE THE SPECTRUM ARISING FROM THE A2X2 CASE
C
1       READ INPUT TAPE 4, 2, TITLE1,  TITLE2,  TITLE3,  TITLE4
2       FORMAT (4A6)
        READ INPUT TAPE 4, 3, CAA, CXX, CAX, CAX1
3       FORMAT (4F10.0)
C
C       CALCULATE CONSTANTS
C
        AK = CAA + CXX
        AL = CAX - CAX1
        AM = CAA - CXX
        AN = CAX + CAX1
        S = SQRTF(AK**2 + AL**2)
        T = SQRTF(AM**2 + AL**2)
        THETAS = 0.5*ACOSF(AK/S)
        THETAA = 0.5*ACOSF(AM/S)
        VAL1 = (SINF(THETAS))**2
        VAL2 = (COSF(THETAS))**2
        VAL3 = (SINF(THETAA))**2
        VAL4 = (COSF(THETAA))**2
        VAL5 = 1.0
C
C       CALCULATE LINE POSITIONS
C
        POS1 = 0.5*AN
        POS3 = -POS1
        POS5 = 0.5*(AK + S)
        POS6 = 0.5*(-AK +S)
        POS7 = -POS6
        POS8 = -POS5
        POS9 = 0.5*(AM + S)
        POS10= 0.5*(-AM + S)
        POS11= -POS10
        POS12= -POS9
C
C       WRITE ANSWERS
C
        WRITE OUTPUT TAPE 2, 10,TITLE1,  TITLE2, TITLE3,  TITLE4
10      FORMAT (1H14A6)
        WRITE OUTPUT TAPE 2, 11, CAA, CXX, CAX, CAX1
11      FORMAT (26HOTHE INPUT PARAMETERS WERE/8HOJ(AA) =F8.3,6X,8H J(XX) =
       1F8.3/8HOJ(AX) =F8.3,6X,8H J(AX*)=F8.3/30H0            LINE
       2   INT/1H0)
        WRITE OUTPUT TAPE 2,12,POS1,VAL5,POS1,VAL5,POS3,VAL5,POS3,VAL5,
       1POS5,VAL1,POS6,VAL2,POS7,VAL2,POS8,VAL1,POS9,VAL3,POS10,VAL4,POS11
       2,VAL4,POS12,VAL3
12      FORMAT (1H 2F15.3)
        GO TO 1
        END
```

Typical Input Data:

```
SAMPLE A2X2 PROBLEM
4.0      2.0      2.0      4.0
```

```
        SAMPLE A2X2 PROBLEM

        THE INPUT PARAMETERS WERE

        J(AA) =    4.000        J(XX) =    2.000

        J(AX) =    2.000        J(AX*)=    4.000

                  LINE              INT

                 3.000            1.000
                 3.000            1.000
                -3.000            1.000
                -3.000            1.000
                 6.162            0.026
                 0.162            0.974
                -0.162            0.974
                -6.162            0.026
                 4.162            0.342
                 2.162            0.658
                -2.162            0.658
                -4.162            0.342
```

letter H, represents material to be written in the output (except for the first character of each line which is the printer control character). The number given before the H indicates the number of characters following the H, all of which are written in the output. Immediately after the last character, the normal format statement is given, without using a comma. The second, designated by X, results in blank spaces in the output, the number preceding the X giving the number of blanks. This is used in order to space the output giving a more readable format. The slash (/) indicates that a new line is to be written.

The next example is the calculation of the slope and intercept for data which fits the equation

$$y = mx + b$$

using the method of least squares. In this procedure, we write the error, F, as

$$F_i = y_i - mx_i - b$$

and we minimize ΣF^2. In order to accomplish this, we set the derivative of ΣF^2 with respect to each variable (m and b) equal to zero:

$$0 = \frac{\partial \sum F_i^2}{\partial m} = \sum F_i \frac{\partial F_i}{\partial m} = \sum -y_i x_i + mx_i^2 + bx_i$$

$$0 = \frac{\partial \sum F_i^2}{\partial b} = \sum F_i \frac{\partial F_i}{\partial b} = \sum -y_i + mx_i + b$$

thus

$$\sum y_i x_i = m \sum x_i^2 + b \sum x_i$$
$$\sum y_i = m \sum x_i + b \sum 1$$

If we designate $\Sigma 1$ as n, the number of values of y and x, and apply Cramer's rule (Appendix 2)

$$m = \frac{\begin{vmatrix} \sum y_i x_i & \sum x_i \\ \sum y_i & n \\ \sum x_i^2 & \sum x_i \\ \sum x_i & n \end{vmatrix}}{} = \frac{n \sum y_i x_i - \sum x_i \sum y_i}{n \sum x_i^2 - (\sum x_i)^2}$$

$$b = \frac{\begin{vmatrix} \sum x_i^2 & \sum y_i x_i \\ \sum y_i & \sum y_i \\ \sum x_i^2 & \sum x_i \\ \sum x_i & n \end{vmatrix}}{} = \frac{\sum y_i \sum x_i^2 - \sum y_i \sum y_i x_i}{n \sum x_i^2 - (\sum x_i)^2}$$

A program for this calculation might start by reading a heading. We often wish to use the full 72 columns available on the card, and if we were to write it out as in the previous example, we would have to write TITLE1 through TITLE12. This may be abbreviated by writing

> READ INPUT TAPE 4, 2, (TITLE(J), J = 1, 12)
> 2 FORMAT (12A6)

Here, a 6 character unit is read as TITLE(1), another is read as TITLE(2) and so on until J has assumed a value greater than 12. At this point, the computer proceeds to the next statement. The title is then stored in 12 pieces which may be reassembled when writing the output.

Whenever we append a subscript to a quantity, as with TITLE above, it is necessary to inform the computer as to the maximum number the subscript may take. This is done using a DIMENSION statement (the first statement in the program):

> DIMENSION TITLE(12), X(40), Y(40), CALCY(40), DIF(40)

and indicates that J in TITLE(J) will never exceed 12, that J in X(J), Y(J), CALCY(J) and DIF(J) will never exceed 40.

Let us designate the summations which are required as

$$\text{SUMX} = \sum x_i$$
$$\text{SUMY} = \sum y_i$$
$$\text{SUMXX} = \sum x_i^2$$
$$\text{SUMXY} = \sum x_i y_i$$

We will first set each of these equal to zero. We may then use a DO statement to effect the summation. In the program which follows, this is effected using the statements

$$
\begin{aligned}
&\text{DO } 10 \ J = 1, N \\
&\text{SUMX } = \text{SUMX} + X(J) \\
&\text{SUMY} = \text{SUMY} + Y(J) \\
&\text{SUMXX} = \text{SUMXX} + X(J)**2 \\
10 \ \ &\text{SUMXY} = \text{SUMXY} + X(J)*Y(J)
\end{aligned}
$$

The DO statement requires the computer to perform all the operations through statement 10 (or whatever other number may be given following the word DO) with the integer J equal first to 1, then to 2 and so on until the value $J = N$ has been used. The computer now proceeds to the next statement in the program. The constant, N, must of course be defined previously in the program. The DO statement is one of the most useful in the FORTRAN vocabulary, and other examples of its use will follow.

Having the values of the summation terms, the slope and intercept are easily calculated. Then the heading, the values of slope and intercept, and the input parameters are written as output. One often wishes to compare the input values of y with those calculated from the equation, and these values and the differences are also calculated (CALCY, DIF) and written in the output. The program and typical input and output are shown on the following pages.

Another example is the calculation of rate constants for first order reactions using the method of least squares. We shall assume that the data were obtained spectrophotometrically and that the rate of disappearance of reactant was followed (i.e., the absorbance decreases with time). In writing such a program, it would be desirable to use the least squares program, written previously, in the form of a subroutine. This may be done by starting the least squares program with the statement

SUBROUTINE LEASQ1 (N, X, Y, SLOPE, B, CALCY, DIF)

The list following the name of the subroutine serves to transmit the values of the quantities given between the main program and the subroutine. (The names used in the subroutine list and the main program list need not be the same. The significance of the names, the order, and the values given in the dimension statements of both must agree. Thus the quantity represented by X in the subroutine might be called TIME in the main program.)

Since the values of n, x, and y are supplied by the main program, and since an identification is no longer required, the read statements in the least squares program may be deleted. Similarly, we may delete the write

Least Squares Program

```
C       CALCULATE M AND B FOR Y =MX + B BY THE METHOD OF LEAST SQUARES
C
        DIMENSION TITLE (12), X(40), Y(40), CALCY(40), DIF(40)
1       READ INPUT TAPE 4,2, (TITLE(J),J=1,12)
2       FORMAT (12A6)
        READ INPUT TAPE 4,3,N
3       FORMAT (I2)
        READ INPUT TAPE 4,4, (Y(J),J=1,N)
        READ INPUT TAPE 4,4, (X(J),J=1,N)
4       FORMAT (7F10.0)
        SUMX =0.0
        SUMY =0.0
        SUMXY =0.0
        SUMXX =0.0
C
C       OBTAIN SUMMATION TERMS
C
        DO 10 J=1,N
        SUMX = SUMX + X(J)
        SUMY = SUMY + Y(J)
        SUMXX = SUMXX + X(J)**2
10      SUMXY = SUMXY+ X(J)*Y(J)
C
C       OBTAIN SLOPE AND INTERCEPT AND WRITE ANSWERS
C
        G = N
        DENOM = SUMX**2 - G*SUMXX
        SLOPE = (SUMX*SUMY - G*SUMXY)/DENOM
        B     = (SUMX*SUMXY - SUMY*SUMXX)/DENOM
        DO 11 J=1,N
        CALCY(J) = SLOPE*X(J) + B
11      DIF(J) = Y(J) - CALCY(J)
        WRITE OUTPUT TAPE 2,15, (TITLE(J),J=1,12)
15      FORMAT (1H112A6)
        WRITE OUTPUT TAPE 2,16,SLOPE, B
16      FORMAT (1HO8X, 3HY =F10.5, 4HX + F10.5/1HO6X,1HY 14X,1HX 11X,
       15HCALCY10X, 3HDIF/1HO)
        WRITE OUTPUT TAPE 2,17,((Y(J),X(J),CALCY(J),DIF(J)), J=1,N)
17      FORMAT (1H 4F13.5)
        GO TO 1
        END
```

Typical Input Data:

```
EXAMPLE OF THE USE OF THE LEAST SQUARES PROGRAM
20
1.752       1.723       1.695       1.662       1.635       1.604       1.578
1.545       1.518       1.459       1.430       1.400       1.312       1.280
1.220       1.154       1.048       0.930       0.811       0.575
0.          1.          2.          3.          4.          5.          6.
7.          8.          9.          10.         12.         14.         16.
18.         20.         24.         28.         32.         40.
```

EXAMPLE OF THE USE OF THE LEAST SQUARES PROGRAM

Y = -0.02937X +   1.74695

Y	X	CALCY	DIF
1.75200	0.	1.74695	0.00505
1.72300	1.00000	1.71757	0.00543
1.69500	2.00000	1.68820	0.00680
1.66200	3.00000	1.65882	0.00318
1.63500	4.00000	1.62945	0.00555
1.60400	5.00000	1.60008	0.00392
1.57800	6.00000	1.57070	0.00730
1.54500	7.00000	1.54133	0.00367
1.51800	8.00000	1.51195	0.00605
1.45900	9.00000	1.48258	-0.02358
1.43000	10.00000	1.45320	-0.02320
1.40000	12.00000	1.39446	0.00554
1.31200	14.00000	1.33571	-0.02371
1.28000	16.00000	1.27696	0.00304
1.22000	18.00000	1.21821	0.00179
1.15400	20.00000	1.15946	-0.00546
1.04800	24.00000	1.04196	0.00604
0.93000	28.00000	0.92447	0.00553
0.81100	32.00000	0.80697	0.00403
0.57500	40.00000	0.57198	0.00302

statements. In order to cause a return to the main program, the subroutine ends with a RETURN statement followed by the always required END statement. The resulting subroutine is given below.

```
      SUBROUTINE LEASQ1(N,X,Y,SLOPE,B,CALCY,DIF)
      DIMENSION          X(40), Y(40), CALCY(40), DIF(40)
      SUMX =0.0
      SUMY =0.0
      SUMXY =0.0
      SUMXX =0.0
      DO 10 J=1,N
      SUMX = SUMX + X(J)
      SUMY = SUMY + Y(J)
      SUMXX = SUMXX + X(J)**2
   10 SUMXY = SUMXY+ X(J)*Y(J)
      G = N
      DENOM = SUMX**2 - G*SUMXX
      SLOPE = (SUMX*SUMY - G*SUMXY)/DENOM
      B     = (SUMX*SUMY - SUMY*SUMXX)/DENOM
      DO 11 J=1,N
      CALCY(J) = SLOPE*X(J) + B
   11 DIF(J) = Y(J) - CALCY(J)
      RETURN
      END
```

The rate constant program is now easily written. It begins with reading identification (card 1), the number of points, and the absorbance at infinite time (card 2), and then values of absorbance from 1 to n, with 7 values per card, each value having ten columns. Finally, the corresponding values of time are read in the same fashion.

The rate constant is given by the expression

$$\ln (A_i - A_\infty) = -kt_i + b$$

where A_i has been designated as ABS(J), A_∞ as AFINAL, $-k$ as SLOPE, t as TIME(J), and b as B. In terms of the least squares subroutine, $Y_i = \ln (A_i - A_\infty)$ or

$$Y(J) = LOGF(ABS(J) - AFINAL)$$

The program then calculates the set of values of Y(J) where J varies from 1 to n, using a DO statement. The LEASQ1 subroutine is called using the statement

CALL LEASQ1 (N, TIME, Y, SLOPE, B, V, W)

giving SLOPE, B, V, and W. The last two are lists of calculated values of y and deviations based on the equation

$$y = mx + b$$

but we are generally more interested in comparing the calculated and observed absorbance values. The calculated values (CALABS) are obtained and the results are written. The rate constant program follows the LEASQ1 subroutine, and an example of the input and output data is also given. It may be noted that the final statement of the program is

GO TO 1

which says that the program is to continue with statement number 1. This will cause another set of data to be read and the calculation to be repeated. If no further data are given, the computer will proceed to the next program.

Subroutines are among the most useful of programs, for if a large number are available, relatively simple main programs may be written and most of the computation may be carried out using the subroutines. As another example of a subroutine, let us write one for matrix multiplication. As shown in Appendix 2, the product of two matrices A and B

$$A \times B = C$$

is given by

$$c_{ij} = \sum_{k=1}^{n} a_{ik} b_{kj}$$

Let us call the subroutine MMULT. The list following the name must contain the size of the matrix (assumed square) or N and the names of the matrices, A, B, and C. Thus we write

SUBROUTINE MMULT (A, B, C, N)

First Order Rate Constant Program

```
C       CALCULATE RATE CONSTANTS FOR FIRST ORDER REACTIONS BY THE METHOD
C       OF LEAST SQUARES. DATA IN THE FORM OF ABSORBANCE, DECREASING WITH
C       TIME.
C
        DIMENSION ABS(40), TIME(40), TITLE(12), Y(40), V(40), W(40)
1       READ INPUT TAPE 4, 2, (TITLE(J), J=1,12)
2       FORMAT (12A6)
        READ INPUT TAPE 4, 3, N, AFINAL
3       FORMAT (I2, 8X, F10.0)
        READ INPUT TAPE 4, 4, (ABS(J), J = 1,N)
        READ INPUT TAPE 4, 4, (TIME(J), J=1,N)
4       FORMAT (7F10.0)
        DO 5 J = 1,N
5       Y(J) = LOGF(ABS(J) - AFINAL)
        CALL LEASQ1 (N, TIME, Y, SLOPE, B, V, W)
        WRITE OUTPUT TAPE 2, 10, (TITLE(J), J=1,12)
10      FORMAT (1H112A6)
        CONST = -SLOPE
        WRITE OUTPUT TAPE 2, 11, CONST, B
11      FORMAT (23H0THE RATE CONSTANT WAS E15.4/19H0THE INTERCEPT WAS E19.
       14/1H0/26H0THE INPUT PARAMETERS WERE/46H0          ABS(J)
       2TIME(J)          CALABS/1H0)
        DO 12 J = 1,N
        CALABS = AFINAL + EXPF(SLOPE*TIME(J) + B)
12      WRITE OUTPUT TAPE 2, 13, ABS(J), TIME(J), CALABS
13      FORMAT (1H 3F15.3)
        GO TO 1
        END
```

Typical Input Data:

```
EXAMPLE OF CALCULATION OF RATE CONSTANT FOR A FIRST ORDER REACTION
 20           0.135
 0.700        0.665        0.626        0.598        0.568        0.535        0.510
 0.489        0.463        0.444        0.425        0.389        0.373        0.327
 0.304        0.278        0.245        0.223        0.200        0.174
 0.           10.          20.          30.          40.          50.          60.
 70.          80.          90.          100.         120.         140.         160.
 180.         200.         240.         280.         320.         400.
```

This must be followed by a **DIMENSION** statement giving the maximum size of the matrices:

$$\text{DIMENSION A(40, 40), B(40, 40), C(40, 40)}$$

The summation must be over the indices I, J, and K, and thus three "nested" DO statements are required, all terminating with the same statement (20). After the indices I and J are set, C(I, J) is set to zero before summing over the index K. The operation of the three DO statements is as follows. All three indices (I, J, and K) initially have the value 1. Then, the last DO loop is executed, K taking all values between 1–N. After this, J is increased by 1 and the last DO loop is executed again. This continues until J = N, after which I is increased by 1, J is set equal to 1, and the last DO loop is again executed. When all these indices attain

Output:

```
EXAMPLE OF CALCULATION OF RATE CONSTANT FOR A FIRST ORDER REACTION
THE RATE CONSTANT WAS        0.6712E-02
THE INTERCEPT WAS           -0.5699E 00


THE INPUT PARAMETERS WERE
      ABS(J)              TIME(J)           CALABS

      0.700               0.                0.701
      0.665               10.000            0.664
      0.626               20.000            0.630
      0.598               30.000            0.597
      0.568               40.000            0.567
      0.535               50.000            0.539
      0.510               60.000            0.513
      0.489               70.000            0.489
      0.463               80.000            0.466
      0.444               90.000            0.444
      0.425               100.000           0.424
      0.389               120.000           0.388
      0.373               140.000           0.356
      0.327               160.000           0.328
      0.304               180.000           0.304
      0.278               200.000           0.283
      0.245               240.000           0.248
      0.223               280.000           0.221
      0.200               320.000           0.201
      0.174               400.000           0.174
```

the value N, the program continues with the next statement which in this case is a return to the main program. The final program is:

```
C      SUBROUTINE FOR MULTIPLYING MATRIX B BY MATRIX A, LEAVING THE
C      PRODUCT IN C
C      THE DIMENSIONS OF THE MATRICES ARE N,N
C      THE DIMENSION STATEMENT IN THE MAIN PROGRAM MUST READ A(40,40),
C      B(40,40),C(40,40)
       SUBROUTINE MMULT (A,B,C,N)
       DIMENSION A(40,40), B(40,40), C(40,40)
       DO 20 I = 1, N
       DO 20 J = 1, N
       C(I,J) = 0.0
       DO 20 K = 1, N
20     C(I,J) = C(I,J) + A(I,K)*B(K,J)
       RETURN
       END
```

Two other statements are required in order to gain an elementary knowledge of computer programming. These are

$$\text{IF (N) I, J, K}$$

$$\text{CONTINUE}$$

The first says that if n is negative, the program continues with statement number I; if it is zero, it continues with statement J; and if it is positive, to continue with statement K. The last says that the program is to continue with the following statement. The last statement of a DO loop cannot be either a GO TO or an IF statement. To avoid ending with one of these, an extra dummy statement CONTINUE may be used as the end of the DO loop.

The use of these two statements may be illustrated by a subroutine which will sort a list of numbers designated as A, of which the total number is N. The subroutine might be written as follows:

```
        SUBROUTINE SORT (A,N)
        DIMENSION A(100)
        DO 10 J = 1,N
        X = A(J)
        K = J
        DO 5 M = J,N
        IF (X-A(M)) 5,5,6
6       X = A(M)
        K = M
5       CONTINUE
        A(K) = A(J)
        A(J) = X
10      CONTINUE
        RETURN
        END
```

It starts by setting a constant X equal to the first value of A. Then it searches the table of A's to see if any following value is larger than A. If it finds a larger value, the computer sets X equal to this larger value and continues to search the table. After the end of the DO loop (statement 5), the first value of A is set equal to X, and the program continues using the second value of A and successive values in the same fashion.

Two other generally useful subroutines are those for inverting a matrix (MATINV) and for diagonalizing a matrix (HDIAG).[1] A listing of these programs is also included in this section. An analysis of these subroutines for the mode of operation is helpful in achieving an understanding of programming principles.

In order to summarize the information given above, the next pages give a list of the FORTRAN statements and a short description of each. Some additional FORTRAN statements which were not discussed above are also given.

SUMMARY OF FORTRAN STATEMENTS

GO TO *n*   Normally the program proceeds from one statement to the next. This statement causes the program to proceed to the statement with the number *n*. One must be careful not to "strand" a portion of the program following a GO

---

[1] This program was written at the MIT computer laboratory and is reproduced with their permission. It uses the Jacobi method for diagonalization (cf. E. Bodewig, *Matrix Algebra*, Interscience Publishers, New York, 1956, pp. 158 ff.)

```
C      SUBROUTINE FOR OBTAINING THE INVERSE OF MATRIX A WHOSE DIMENSIONS
C      ARE M,N.
C      THE DIMENSIONS OF A IN THE MAIN PROGRAM MUST BE 40,40
C      INDEX IS SET EQUAL TO 1 IF A DIVIDE CHECK ERROR OCCURS
C      INDEX IS 0 OTHERWISE
       SUBROUTINE MATINV (A,M,N,INDEX)
       DIMENSION A(40,40), B(40)
       INDEX = 0
       IF DIVIDE CHECK 4, 4
4      M1 = M - 1
       N1 = N - 1
       N2 = 0
       DO 7 L = 1, M
       B(N) = 1.0/A(1,1)
       N2 = N2 + 1
       IF DIVIDE CHECK 9,3
3      DO 5 K = 1, N1
5      B(K) = A(1, K+1)*B(N)
       DO 6 I = 1,M1
       A(I,N) = -B(N)*A(I+1,1)
       DO 6 J = 1, N1
6      A(I,J) = A(I+1, J+1) -B(J)*A(I+1,1)
       DO 7 J = 1, N
7      A(M,J) = B(J)
       GO TO 11
9      WRITE OUTPUT TAPE 2, 10, N2
10     FORMAT (19H DIVIDE CHECK, ROW 12)
       INDEX = 1
11     RETURN
       END
```

TO so that it cannot be reacted by the program. This means that the statement following a GO TO must be numbered, and must be referred to somewhere in the program.

GO TO

$(n_1, n_2 \cdots n_m), i$ This is similar to the ordinary GO TO statement except that one has a choice of which statement the program is to proceed to. This statement is the one corresponding to the value of i. Thus

$$\text{GO TO } (10, 12, 14, 16, 18), I$$

would when $I = 4$ cause the program to go to the fourth statement in the list, or to statement number 16.

IF $(a)\, n_1, n_2, n_3$ If the value of a is negative, the program proceeds to statement n_1. If it is zero, it proceeds to statement n_2, and if it is positive, it proceeds to statement n_3.

DO n

$i = m_1, m_2$ The following section of statements through number n are performed with the value of $i = m_1$, then with $i = m_1 + 1$, with $i = m_1 + 2$, and so on until $i = m_2$. After that the program proceeds to the statement following that numbered n. One normally cannot transfer into the range of a DO statement.

```
C     MIHDI3, FORTAN II DIAGONALIZATION OF A REAL SYMMETRIC MATRIX BY
C     THE JACOBI METHOD.
C     CALLING SEQUENCE FOR DIAGONALIZATION
C     CALL HDIAG( H, N, IEGEN, U, NR)
C     WHERE H IS THE ARRAY TO BE DIAGONALIZED.
C     N IS THE ORDER OF THE MATRIX, H.
C     IEGEN MUST BE SET UNEQUAL TO ZERO IF ONLY EIGENVALUES ARE TO BE
C     COMPUTED.
C     IEGEN MUST BE SET EQUAL TO ZERO IF EIGENVALUES AND EIGENVECTORS
C     ARE TO BE COMPUTED.
C     U IS THE UNITARY MATRIX USED FOR FORMATION OF THE EIGENVECTORS.
C     NR IS THE NUMBER OF ROTATIONS.
C     A DIMENSION STATEMENT MUST BE INSERTED IN THE SUBROUTINE.
C     DIMENSION H(N,N), U(N,N), X(N), IQ(N)
C     COMPUTER MUST OPERATE IN FLOATING TRAP MODE
C     THE SUBROUTINE OPERATES ONLY ON THE ELEMENTS OF H THAT ARE TO THE
C     RIGHT OF THE MAIN DIAGONAL. THUS, ONLY A TRIANGULAR
C     SECTION NEED BE STORED IN THE ARRAY H.
      SUBROUTINE   HDIAG (H,N,IEGEN,U,NR)
      DIMENSION H(40,40), U(40,40), X(40), IQ(40)
      IF (IEGEN) 15,10,15
   10 DO 14 I=1,N
      DO 14 J=1,N
      IF(I-J)12,11,12
   11 U(I,J)=1.0
      GO TO 14
   12 U(I,J)=0.
   14 CONTINUE
   15 NR = 0
      IF (N-1) 1000,1000,17
C     SCAN FOR LARGEST OFF DIAGONAL ELEMENT IN EACH ROW
C     X(I) CONTAINS LARGEST ELEMENT IN  ITH ROW
C     IQ(I) HOLDS SECOND SUBSCRIPT DEFINING POSITION OF ELEMENT
   17 NMI1=N-1
      DO 30 I=1,NMI1
      X(I) = 0.
      IPL1=I+1
      DO 30 J=IPL1,N
      IF(X(I)-ABSF( H(I,J))) 20,20,30
   20 X(I)=ABSF(H(I,J))
      IQ(I)=J
   30 CONTINUE
C     SET INDICATOR FOR SHUT-OFF.RAP=2**-27,NR=NO.OF ROTATIONS
      RAP=7.450580596E-9
      HDTEST=1.0E38
C     FIND MAXIMUM OF X(I) S FOR PIVOT ELEMENT AND
C     TEST FOR END OF PROBLEM
   40 DO 70   I=1,NMI1
      IF (I-1) 60,60,45
   45 IF(XMAX-X(I)) 60,70,70
   60 XMAX=X(I)
      IPIV=I
      JPIV=IQ(I)
   70 CONTINUE
C     IS MAX. X(I) EQUAL TO ZERO, IF LESS THAN HDTEST,REVISE HDTEST
      IF (XMAX) 1000,1000,80
   80 IF( HDTEST) 90,90,85
   85 IF (XMAX - HDTEST) 90,90,148
   90 HDIMIN = ABSF ( H (1,1) )
```

```
          DO 110  I=2,N
          IF (HDIMIN - ABSF ( H (I,I))) 110,110,100
 100 HDIMIN=ABSF (H(I,I))
 110 CONTINUE
          HDTEST = HDIMIN*RAP
C         RETURN IF MAX.H(I,J)LESS THAN(2**-27)ABSF(H(K,K)-MIN)
          IF (HDTEST-XMAX) 148,1000,1000
 148 NR= NR+1
C         COMPUTE TANGENT, SINE AND COSINE,H(I,I),H(J,J)
 150 TANG=SIGNF(2.0,(H(IPIV,IPIV)-H(JPIV,JPIV)))*H(IPIV,JPIV)/(ABSF(H(I
    1PIV,IPIV)-H(JPIV,JPIV))+SQRTF((H(IPIV,IPIV)-H(JPIV,JPIV))**2+4.0*H
    2(IPIV,JPIV)**2))
          COSINE=1.0/SQRTF(1.0+TANG**2)
          SINE=TANG*COSINE
          HII=H(IPIV,IPIV)
          H(IPIV,IPIV)=COSINE**2*(HII+TANG*(2.*H(IPIV,JPIV)+TANG*H(JPIV,JPIV
    1)))
          H(JPIV,JPIV)=COSINE**2*(H(JPIV,JPIV)-TANG*(2.*H(IPIV,JPIV)-TANG*H
    1II))
          H(IPIV,JPIV)=0.
C         PSEUDO RANK THE EIGENVALUES
C         ADJUST SINE AND COS FOR COMPUTATION OF H(IK) AND U(IK)
          IF ( H(IPIV,IPIV) - H(JPIV,JPIV)) 152,153,153
 152 HTEMP = H(IPIV,IPIV)
          H(IPIV,IPIV) = H(JPIV,JPIV)
          H(JPIV,JPIV) =HTEMP
C         RECOMPUTE SINE AND COS
          HTEMP = SIGNF (1.0, -SINE) * COSINE
          COSINE =ABSF (SINE)
          SINE =HTEMP
 153 CONTINUE
C         INSPECT THE IQS BETWEEN I+1 AND N-1 TO DETERMINE
C         WHETHER A NEW MAXIUM VALUE SHOULD BE COMPUTE   SINCE
C         THE PRESENT MAXIMUM IS IN THE I OR J ROW.
          DO 350 I=1,NMI1
          IF(I-IPIV)210,350,200
 200 IF (I-JPIV) 210,350,210
 210 IF(IQ(I)-IPIV) 230,240,230
 230 IF(IQ(I)-JPIV) 350,240,350
 240 K=IQ(I)
 250 HTEMP=H(I,K)
          H(I,K)=0.
          IPL1=I+1
          X(I) =0.
C         SEARCH IN DEPLETED ROW FOR NEW MAXIMUM
          DO 320 J=IPL1,N
          IF ( X(I) -ABSF( H(I,J)) ) 300,300,320
 300 X(I) = ABSF(H(I,J))
          IQ(I)=J
 320 CONTINUE
          H(I,K)=HTEMP
 350 CONTINUE
          X(IPIV) =0.
          X(JPIV) =0.
C         CHANGE THE ORDER ELEMENTS OF H
          DO 530 I=1,N
          IF (I-IPIV) 370,530,420
 370 HTEMP = H(I,IPIV)
          H(I,IPIV)= COSINE*HTEMP + SINE*H(I,JPIV)
```

```
       IF ( X(I) - ABSF( H(I,IPIV)) )380,390,390
   380 X(I) = ABSF(H(I,IPIV))
       IQ(I) = IPIV
   390 H(I,JPIV) = - SINE*HTEMP + COSINE*H(I,JPIV)
       IF ( X(I) - ABSF ( H(I,JPIV)) ) 400,530,530
   400 X(I) = ABSF(H(I,JPIV))
       IQ(I) = JPIV
       GO TO 530
   420 IF(I-JPIV) 430,530,480
   430 HTEMP = H(IPIV,I)
       H(IPIV,I) = COSINE*HTEMP + SINE*H(I,JPIV)
       IF ( X(IPIV) - ABSF(H(IPIV,I)) ) 440,450,450
   440 X(IPIV) = ABSF(H(IPIV,I))
       IQ(IPIV) = I
   450 H(I,JPIV) = - SINE*HTEMP + COSINE*H(I,JPIV)
       IF (X(I) - ABSF( H(I,JPIV)) ) 400,530,530
   480 HTEMP = H(IPIV,I)
       H(IPIV,I) = COSINE*HTEMP + SINE*H(JPIV,I)
       IF ( X(IPIV) - ABSF( H(IPIV,I)) ) 490,500,500
   490 X(IPIV) = ABSF(H(IPIV,I))
       IQ(IPIV) = I
   500 H(JPIV,I) = - SINE*HTEMP + COSINE*H(JPIV,I)
       IF ( X(JPIV) - ABSF( H(JPIV,I)) )510,530,530
   510 X(JPIV) = ABSF(H(JPIV,I))
       IQ(JPIV) = I
   530 CONTINUE
  C    TEST FOR COMPUTATION OF EIGENVECTORS
       IF(IEGEN) 40,540,40
   540 DO 550 I=1,N
       HTEMP=U(I,IPIV)
       U(I,IPIV)=COSINE*HTEMP+SINE*U(I,JPIV)
   550 U(I,JPIV)= -SINE*HTEMP+COSINE*U(I,JPIV)
       GO TO 40
  1000 RETURN
       END
```

CONTINUE

A DO operation cannot terminate in a GO TO or IF statement. If one of these statements would normally be at the end of a DO operation, the dummy statement CONTINUE is placed at the end of the set of instructions. For example

10 DO 15 J = 1, N

A = A + B* C(J)

IF (A − TEST) 15, 15, 20

15 CONTINUE

If the value of N had been defined previously, the set of instructions will be carried out N times, unless A becomes greater than TEST at some point. If this occurs, the program proceeds to statement number 20.

FORMAT

A FORMAT statement gives information on the nature of the data read into or out from the computer. The formats are:

F $a.d$ which gives a decimal output or calls for a decimal input. The field width is a, and the number of figures after the decimal is d.

E *a.d*   which gives a decimal number and the exponent of 10 which indicates the number of decimal positions the number has been shifted. The field width is *a*, and the number of figures after the decimal is *d*. This is normally used as an output format when the magnitude of the number is not known.

A *d*   which gives an alphanumeric output or calls for an alphanumeric input. This format is commonly used for reading titles of sets of data into the computer and writing them on the output. Each "word" in the computer can accommodate six characters and thus *d* is normally six. Longer titles may be read in and written as follows

READ INPUT TAPE 4, 10, (TITLE (J), J $=$ 1, 12)

10   FORMAT (12A6)

WRITE OUTPUT TAPE 2, 15, (TITLE (J), J $=$ 1, 12)

15   FORMAT (1H 12A6)

*n*H   which is an output format. The value, *n*, gives the number of characters which follow, and which are to be printed in the output.

*n*X   which is usually an output format. It causes *n* blanks to appear in the output.

DIMENSION   A dimension statement gives the sizes of the blocks of storage required for each subscripted variable such as DIMENSION TIME (20), VALUE (20), AMATRX (4,4) This reserves a block of twenty locations for values of TIME, twenty locations for values of VALUE, and sixteen locations for the 4 × 4 matrix called AMATRX.

READ INPUT TAPE *n*, *m*, LIST

The data are read from tape unit *n* (set by the computer center) using FORMAT statement *m*, and the names of the data are given in the LIST. For example,

READ INPUT TAPE 4, 25, R, THETA, PHI, VALUE

25   FORMAT (4F10.0)

WRITE OUTPUT TAPE n, m, LIST

> The data in the LIST are written onto tape unit n set by the computer center, using FORMAT statement m.
>
> In the FORMAT statement, a printer control character must appear first:

1H(blank)	single space
1H0	double space
1H+	overprint previous line
1H1	skip to top of a new page

WRITE TAPE n, LIST

> The data in the list are written onto tape unit n, (a list of available tape units may be obtained from the computer center) in binary form. No FORMAT statement is used, since the data are written in the form they appear in storage. This statement is used for storing intermediate data on tape for use in a later step.

READ TAPE n, LIST

> This is the read counterpart of the previous statement.

REWIND n This statement causes the tape on tape unit n to be rewound. This is never used with the input or output tapes or the units having the FORTRAN system tapes.

BACKSPACE n

> This statement causes the tape on the tape unit n to be backspaced one record. A record is the amount of material written using one WRITE TAPE statement.

IF DIVIDE CHECK n_1, n_2

> If a division by zero is attempted, the divide check indicator will be turned on, and the quotient will be given the largest possible value. The results will then be in error, and this condition may be tested for by the use of the IF DIVIDE CHECK statement. The program goes to statement n_1 if the indicator is on and to n_2 if it is off. In either case it is then turned off. The statement might be used as follows:

> IF DIVIDE CHECK 55, 55
>
> 55 A = (SQRTF(B − C))/(D − E)
>
> IF DIVIDE CHECK 57, 56
>
> 57 CALL EXIT

The first DIVIDE CHECK statement turns the indicator off. If $(D - E)$ were equal to zero, the values of A would be in error and the next statement to be executed would be CALL EXIT. Otherwise the program would continue in normal fashion with statement 56.

IF ACCUMULATOR OVERFLOW n_1, n_2

If one tries to develop a number too large for the computer to handle, the accumulator overflow indicator will be turned on. If it is on, the above statement will cause the program to proceed to statement n_1. If an overflow condition did not occur, the program would proceed to statement n_2. In using this statement, the indicator must be turned off before the operation which might produce an overflow by using the statement IF ACCUMULATOR OVERFLOW n_1, n_1, where n_1 is the next statement (see IF DIVIDE CHECK).

COMMON   The COMMON statement is followed by a list of quantities which are to be stored in the high-numbered part of the storage unit. These quantities may be passed from main program to subroutine, and from one subroutine to another by using the same COMMON statement in each and having the corresponding DIMENSION statement for each subscripted variable.

CALL name (arguments)

This statement transfers the program to the subroutine whose name appears after CALL. The variables and constants which must be transferred to the subroutine, and dummy variables whose values will be given by the subroutine, must appear in parentheses after the name of the subroutine. This list must appear in identical form (although the names of the variables may be changed) in the first statement of the subroutine.

SUBROUTINE name (arguments)

This statement is the first of any subroutine. The list of arguments must agree with that of the CALL statement which calls this subroutine, and the dimensions of the subscripted variables in the DIMENSION statement must agree with those in the program which calls it.

RETURN   This is the last statement in a subroutine and causes the computation to return to the program which called the subroutine.

References

General Information Manual, FORTRAN, IBM publication F28-8074-1. (This is a general introductory manual which is applicable to all IBM computers.)

Programmer's Primer for FORTRAN, IBM publication F28-6019.

Reference Manual, 709/7090 FORTRAN Programming System, IBM publication C28-6054-2.

IBM 1620 FORTRAN, IBM publication J28-5598-0.

FOR TRANSIT Automatic Coding System for the IBM 650 Data Processing System, IBM publication C28-4028.

Examples of Computer Programs

This appendix presents five computer programs which will illustrate how more complex programs are built up using FORTRAN statements and subroutines. The first is a program for calculating the transition energies and line intensities for the ABC case in nmr spectroscopy. Here the energy levels cannot be given in an analytical form, and we must set up and diagonalize two 3×3 matrices. Similarly, in order to get the intensities we must first obtain the wave functions. The matrix elements were given previously (p. 490).

The program begins with reading an identification card using 6 character "words" designated as TITLE(1) through TITLE(10). Then the values of the chemical shifts (W1, W2, and W3) and of the coupling constants (A12, A13, A23) are read from the second card using ten columns per number.

The energies corresponding to the wave functions $\alpha\alpha\alpha$ (E_1) and $\beta\beta\beta$ (E_8) may be written directly, since $E_1 = H_{11}$ and $E_8 = H_{88}$. The matrix H collects the elements required for obtaining the energies and coefficients for the wave functions

$$\psi = c_1(\alpha\alpha\beta) + c_2(\alpha\beta\alpha) + c_3(\beta\alpha\alpha)$$

and the matrix HH collects the elements required for

$$\psi = c_1(\alpha\beta\beta) + c_2(\beta\alpha\beta) + c_3(\beta\beta\alpha)$$

Each matrix is converted to the diagonal form by the subroutine HDIAG.[1]

---

[1] This subroutine was given in Appendix 8.

The calling sequence for this subroutine starts with the name of the matrix to be diagonalized, after which follows the order of the matrix (3 in this case), the number 0 or 1 depending on whether or not one wishes the eigenvectors, the name of the matrix collecting the eigenvectors (U or UU in this case), and finishes with NR, which represents the number of times a certain operation was carried out by the subroutine. This is generally not needed but must be included as part of the calling sequence in order to make it correspond to that in the subroutine.

Once one has the eigenvalues and eigenvectors, the transition energies and line intensities may be obtained. The DO loops ending in statements 5 and 6 perform the calculation of the first three transition energies (E1–E2, E1–E3, E1–E4, remembering that after diagonalization $H_{11} = $ E2, $H_{22} = $ E3, and $H_{33} = $ E4), and the corresponding intensities (remembering that the intensities are the squares of the sum of the products of the coefficients of the wave functions).

In the next set of statements, L is an index showing which transition is being calculated. The DO loops ending in statements 7 and 8 perform the calculation of the next nine transition energies in the order E_4–E_7, E_4–E_8, E_4–E_9, E_5–E_7, E_5–E_8, E_5–E_9, E_6–E_7, E_6–E_8, and E_6–E_9 (after diagonalization $HH_{11} = E_7$, $HH_{22} = E_8$ and $HH_{33} = E_9$). The intensities are calculated at the same time. However, here we must not count the product of the coefficients for some wave functions such as $\alpha\alpha\beta$ for E_4 and $\beta\beta\alpha$ for E_7, since a transition between these wave functions involves the simultaneous interchange of two spins and is forbidden. The multipliers FMULT which were defined at the beginning of the program take care of this.

Having the desired data in storage, the computer is now directed to write the answers. A set of typical input data and the resultant output is given after the program.

ABC Spectrum Calculation

```
C       PROGRAM TO CALCULATE THE NMR SPECTRUM ARISING FROM THE ABC CASE
        DIMENSION TITLE(10), H(3,3),U(3,3),HH(3,3),UU(3,3),
       1DEIGEN(15),SUMSQ(15), FMULT(3,3)
        DO 30 J = 1,3
        DO 30 K = 1,3
30      FMULT(J,K) = 1.0
        FMULT(1,3) = 0.0
        FMULT (2,2) = 0.0
        FMULT(3,1) = 0.0
1       READ INPUT TAPE 4,2,(TITLE(J),J=1,10)
2       FORMAT (10A6)
        READ INPUT TAPE 4,3, W1,W2,W3, A12,A13,A23
3       FORMAT (6F10.0)
        E1 = 0.5*(W1+W2+W3) + 0.25*(A12+A23+A13)
        E8 =-0.5*(W1+W2+W3) + 0.25*(A12+A23+A13)
        H(1,1) = 0.5*(W1+W2-W3) +0.25*(A12-A23-A13)
        H(2,2) = 0.5*(W1-W2+W3) +0.25*(-A12-A23+A13)
        H(3,3) = 0.5*(-W1+W2+W3) +0.25*(-A12+A23-A13)
        H(1,2) = 0.5*A23
        H(2,1) = H(1,2)
        H(1,3) = 0.5*A13
        H(3,1) = H(1,3)
        H(2,3) = 0.5*A12
        H(3,2) = H(2,3)
        CALL HDIAG (H,3,0,U,NR)
        HH(1,1) = 0.5*(W1-W2-W3) +0.25*(-A12+A23-A13)
        HH(2,2) = 0.5*(-W1+W2-W3) +0.25*(-A12-A23+A13)
        HH(3,3) = 0.5*(-W1-W2+W3) +0.25*(A12-A23-A13)
        HH(1,2) = 0.5*A12
        HH(2,1) = HH(1,2)
        HH(1,3) = 0.5*A13
        HH(3,1) = HH(1,3)
        HH(2,3) = 0.5*A23
        HH(3,2) = HH(2,3)
        CALL HDIAG (HH,3,0,UU,NR)
        DO 5 J=1,3
        DEIGEN(J) = E1     - H(J,J)
        SUM = 0.0
        DO 6 K=1,3
6       SUM = SUM + U(K,J)
5       SUMSQ(J) = SUM*SUM
        L = 3
        DO 7 J=1,3
        DO 7 K=1,3
        L = L + 1
        DEIGEN(L)= H(J,J)-HH(K,K)
        SUM = 0.0
        DO 8 JJ=1,3
        DO 8 KK = 1,3
8       SUM = SUM + U(JJ,J)* UU(KK,K)*FMULT(JJ,KK)
7       SUMSQ(L) = SUM*SUM
        DO 10 J=1,3
        L = J+12
        DEIGEN(L)= HH(J,J) - E8
        SUM = 0.0
        DO 12 K=1,3
12      SUM = SUM + UU(K,J)
10      SUMSQ(L) = SUM*SUM
        WRITE OUTPUT TAPE 2,15,(TITLE(J),J=1,10)


15      FORMAT (1H110A6)
        WRITE OUTPUT TAPE 2,16,W1,W2,W3,A12,A13,A23
16      FORMAT (1H0/26H0THE INPUT PARAMETERS WERE/ 6H0W1 = F7.2,9H      W2
       1 F7.2, 9H      W3 = F7.2,/ 6H0J12= F7.2, 9H    J13= F7.2,9H      J23
       2F7.2/47H0THE CALCULATED FREQUENCIES AND INTENSITIES ARE/1H0)
        DO 20 J=1,15
20      WRITE OUTPUT TAPE 2, 21, J, DEIGEN(J), J, SUMSQ(J)
21      FORMAT (6H LINE(I2,4H) = F7.2, 9H      INT(I2,4H) = F7.2)
        GO TO 1
        END
```

Input Data:

```
        SAMPLE PROBLEM FOR NMR ABC SPECTRUM PROGRAM
        15.0        25.0        50.0        7.5        2.0        4.5
```

Output:

```
        SAMPLE PROBLEM FOR NMR ABC SPECTRUM PROGRAM


        THE INPUT PARAMETERS WERE

        W1 =    15.00      W2 =    25.00     W3 =    50.00

        J12=     7.50      J13=     2.00     J23=     4.50

        THE CALCULATED FREQUENCIES AND INTENSITIES ARE


        LINE(  1) =    18.54      INT(  1) =    1.68
        LINE(  2) =    31.97      INT(  2) =    0.55
        LINE(  3) =    53.49      INT(  3) =    0.77
        LINE(  4) =    24.48      INT(  4) =    1.80
        LINE(  5) =    51.30      INT(  5) =    0.88
        LINE(  6) =    62.60      INT(  6) =    0.00
        LINE(  7) =    11.05      INT(  7) =    0.45
        LINE(  8) =    37.87      INT(  8) =    0.01
        LINE(  9) =    49.16      INT(  9) =    1.09
        LINE(10) =    -10.46      INT(10) =    0.00
        LINE(11) =     16.35      INT(11) =    1.52
        LINE(12) =     27.65      INT(12) =    0.26
        LINE(13) =     46.98      INT(13) =    1.25
        LINE(14) =     20.16      INT(14) =    1.41
        LINE(15) =      8.86      INT(15) =    0.35
```

The next program is one which is designated to accept kinetic data obtained spectrophotometrically in terms of either percent transmission or absorbance and to calculate the rate constant for either first or second order reactions using the method of least squares. It was written by R. Geer. In order to test for curvature in a plot of log λ vs. t, the rate constant is calculated for the first half life, through two half lives and through three half lives, and the values are compared in the output.

In order to convert percent transmission to absorbance, it will be necessary to obtain the common logarithm. The log subroutine gives only the natural logarithm, but both may be obtained if one begins the program with

$$LOGEF(X) = LOGF(X)$$

$$LOG10F(X) = LOGF(X)/2.30258$$

Then when one writes LOGEF(X) one will obtain the natural logarithm of x and when one writes LOG10F(X) one will obtain the common logarithm.

The program begins by reading a heading from the first card. HED(1) is a four letter (or less) word such as RUN or CASE, HED(2) is a 6 letter (or less) abbreviation for the name of reagent A punched in columns 5–10,

HED(3) is a 6 letter (or less) abbreviation for the name of reagent B punched in columns 11–16, and HED(4) through HED(12) represents 54 columns of identification for the particular set of data and is punched in columns 17–70. The second card contains the run number, R (columns 1–4); the operating mode, M (columns 7–12); the number of data points, N (columns 13–18); the concentrations of A and B (columns 19–26, 27–34) using an E format; the value of the initial absorbance or percent transmission, WZ (columns 35–41); and the value of the final absorbance or percent transmission, WE (columns 42–48). The mode value is 1 for data as percent transmission and a first order reaction, 2 for the same data but a second order reaction, 3 for data as absorbance and a first order reaction, and 4 for the same data but a second order reaction.

The next cards contain the values of absorbance or percent transmission, ten values to a card, seven columns to a number. Then follow the corresponding values of time using the same format.

A set of constants is now set to zero, and the calculation begins. Suppose we were operating with mode three. The computer would go to statement 3 at which point the changes in absorbance through one half life (HL(1)), through two half lives (HL(2)) and three half lives (HL(3)) are calculated.

The computer then enters into a DO loop ending in statement 13 in which Y

$$y_i = \ln (A_i - A_\infty)$$

is calculated. After each value of Y is obtained, the computer goes to statement 32, which effects the evaluation of Σy, Σx, Σxy, Σx^2 (SY, SX, SXY, SXSQ) and then returns to the DO loop. Whenever a half-life period is reached, the computer goes to statement 34 after which the slope (SLP), the rate constant (RC), and the intercept (XZ) are calculated. The calculated values of y (YC) are obtained as well as the differences from the observed values (YD). Finally the root mean squared deviation (RMSE) is calculated. After the 1st and 2nd half-life period, the computation of Y values continues.

Having the values of all of the parameters, the data may now be written. A typical example of input data and the resultant output is shown following the program.

Rate Constant Calculation

```
C       PROGRAM FOR FINDING RATE CONST OF RX BY LEAST SQ, FOR EITHER
C       1 FIRST OR SECOND ORDER RX COMPARED OUT TO 1ST, 2ND, AND 3RD
C       2 HALF LIVES. INPUT EITHER LINEAR OR LOG FUNCTION OF CONC.
        DIMENSION X(20), W(20), C(20),Y(20),YC(20,3), YD(20,3), HL(3),
       1 SLP(3), XZ(3), RMSE(3), RC(3), HED(12)
        LOGEF(X) = LOGF(X)
        LOG10F(X) = LOGF(X)/2.30258
300     FORMAT(A4,11A6)
301     FORMAT(A6,2I6,2E8.3,2F7.0,/(10F7.0))
302     FORMAT (10F7.0)
30      READ INPUT TAPE 4,300,(HED (I), I=1,12)
        READ INPUT TAPE 4,301,R,M,N,A,B,WZ,WE,(W(I),I=1,N)
        READ INPUT TAPE 4,302,(X(I),I=1,N)
50      DO31 I=1,N
        Y(I)=0.
51      DO 31 J=1,3
        YC(I,J) = 0.
31      YD(I,J) = 0.
        SX= 0.
        SY =0.
        SXY =0.
        SXSQ =0.
        J=1
        GO TO (1,2,3,4), M
32      SY = Y(I) + SY
        SX = X(I) + SX
        SXY = X(I) * Y(I) +SXY
        SXSQ = X(I)**2 + SXSQ
        GO TO (11,12,13,14), M
33      I =I + 1
        J= 3
34      P = I - 1
        DV = P*SXSQ -SX**2
        SLP(J) = (P*SXY - SX*SY)/DV
        RC(J) = SLP(J)/D
        XZ(J) = (SXSQ*SY - SX*SXY)/DV
        L = P
        SYDSQ = 0.
52      DO 35 K = 1,L
        YC(K,J) = SLP(J)*X(K) + XZ(J)
        YD(K,J) = Y(K) - YC(K,J)
35      SYDSQ = YD(K,J)**2 + SYDSQ
        RMSE(J) = (SYDSQ/P)** .5
        J = J +1
        IF (J-3) 36,36,37
36      GO TO (21,22,23,24), M
37      GO TO (38,40,38,40), M
38      WRITE OUTPUT TAPE 2,381,HED(1),R,(HED(I),I=2,12),A,B,
       1 (SLP(J),J=1,3),(XZ(J),J=1,3),  (RMSE(J),J=1,3),(X(I),Y(I),(YC(I,J
       2),J=1,3),(YD(I,J),J=1,3),I=1,N)
381     FORMAT(1H1A4,A4,6X,A6,6X,A6,6X,9A6/1H 11X,E12.6,E13.6,//
       143H0    HALF LIVES              FIRST
       253HSECOND      THIRD      FIRST        SECOND      THIRD/
       327H0    RATE CONST  1ST ORDER 3E12.4/
       425H0    INTERCEPT         3F12.4/
       525H0    RMS ERROR         3F12.4//92H0    TIME      Y OBSERVED
       6      Y CALCULATED              DIFFERENCE/
       7(1H0F10.3,F16.4,6F12.4))
        GO TO 30
```

```
 40    WRITE OUTPUT TAPE 2,401,HED(1),R,(HED(I),I=2,12),A,B,(RC(J),J=1,3)
      1,(SLP(J),J=1,3),,(XZ(J),J=1,3),,F,(RMSE(J),J=1,3),,(X(I),Y(I),(YC(I,J
      2),J=1,3),(YD(I,J),J=1,3),I=1,N)
401    FORMAT(1H12A4,11A6/1H 11X,E12.6,E13.6,//
      143H0     HALF LIVES                  FIRST
      253HSECOND       THIRD      FIRST       SECOND       THIRD/
      327H0     RATE CONST  2ND ORDER 3E12.4/
      425H0     SLOPE              3F12.4/
      525H0     INTERCEPT          3F12.4,17H       (THEORETICAL F10.4,1H)/
      625H0     RMS ERROR          3F12.4//92H0    TIME       Y OBSERVED
      7      Y CALCULATED                    DIFFERENCE/
      8(1H0F10.3,F16.4,6F12.4))
       GO TO 30
C      MODE ONE    TRANSMITTANCE TO FIRST ORDER RATE CONSTANT
 1     HL(1) = (LOG10F(WE/WZ))/2.
       HL(2) =HL(1)/2.
       HL(3) =HL(2)/2.
       D = 1.
531    DO 11 I =1,N
       C(I) = LOG10F(WE/W(I))
541    IF(C(I) - HL(J))34,21,21
 21    Y(I) = -LOGEF(C(I))
       GO TO 32
 11    CONTINUE
       GO TO 33
C      MODE TWO    TRANSMITTANCE TO SECOND ORDER RATE CONSTANT
 2     CZ = LOG10F(WE/WZ)
       HL(1) = CZ/2.
       HL(2) = HL(1)/2.
       HL(3) = HL(2)/2.
       D = A-B
       E = D*CZ/A
       F = LOGEF(A/B)
532    DO 12 I = 1,N
       C(I) = LOG10F((WE)/W(I))
542    IF (C(I) - HL(J))34,22,22
 22    Y(I) = LOGEF(C(I)/(C(I)-E))
       GO TO 32
 12    CONTINUE
       GO TO 33
C      MODE THREE    ABSORBANCE TO FIRST ORDER RATE CONSTANT
 3     HL(1) = (WZ -WE)/2.
       HL(2) = HL(1)/2.
       HL(3) = HL(2)/2.
       D = 1.
533    DO 13 I= 1,N
       C(I)= W(I) - WE
543    IF (C(I) - HL(J)) 34,23,23
 23    Y(I) =-LOGEF(C(I))
       GO TO 32
 13    CONTINUE
       GO TO 33
C      MODE FOUR    ABSORBANCE TO SECOND ORDER RATE CONSTANT
 4     CZ= WZ - WE
       HL(1) = CZ/2.
       HL(2) = HL(1)/2.
       HL(3) = HL(2)/2.
       D = A-B
       E = D*CZ/A
```

```
        F = LOGEF(A/B)
534   DO 14 I=1,N
        C(I) = W(I)- WE
544   IF (C(I) - HL(J)) 34,24,24
24      Y(I) = LOGEF(C(I)/(C(I)-E))
        GO TO 32
14    CONTINUE
        GO TO 33
        END
```

Input Data:

```
RUN CU+2   KETOL CUPRIC ION OXIDN OF PHENACYL ALCOHOL IN PYRIDINE WATER
17           3      141.4   -025.0   -010.500   0.019
0.450  0.390  0.325  0.275  0.235  0.200  0.175  0.145  0.125  0.105
0.090  0.070  0.055  0.045
39.    59.    89.    123.   157.   190.   217.   257.   286.   320.
351.   394.   430.   463.
```

The data are: run no. 17, mode 3, 14 data points, $[Cu^{+2}] = 1.4 \times 10^{-2}$, [phenacyl alcohol] $= 5.0 \times 10^{-1}$, initial absorbance $= 0.500$, final absorbance $= 0.019$. The next two lines give the values of absorbance, and the last two give the values to time.

Output:

RUN 17   CU+2   KETOL   CUPRIC ION OXIDN OF PHENACYL ALCOHOL IN PYRIDINE WATER
0.140000E-01 0.500000E 00

	FIRST	SECOND	THIRD
HALF LIVES			
RATE CONST 1ST ORDER	0.6175E-02	0.5522E-02	0.5613E-02
INTERCEPT	0.6164	0.6632	0.6523
RMS ERROR	0.0147	0.0187	0.0188

| TIME | Y OBSERVED | \multicolumn{3}{Y CALCULATED} | | | \multicolumn{3}{DIFFERENCE} | | |

TIME	Y OBSERVED	FIRST	SECOND	THIRD	FIRST	SECOND	THIRD
		Y CALCULATED			DIFFERENCE		
39.000	0.8416	0.8572	0.8785	0.8711	-0.0156	-0.0369	-0.0295
59.000	0.9916	0.9807	0.9890	0.9834	0.0108	0.0026	0.0082
89.000	1.1842	1.1660	1.1547	1.1518	0.0182	0.0295	0.0324
123.000	1.3626	1.3760	1.3424	1.3426	-0.0134	0.0202	0.0200
157.000	1.5325	0.	1.5302	1.5334	0.	0.0023	-0.0010
190.000	1.7093	0.	1.7124	1.7186	0.	-0.0031	-0.0094
217.000	1.8579	0.	1.8615	1.8702	0.	-0.0036	-0.0123
257.000	2.0715	0.	2.0824	2.0947	0.	-0.0109	-0.0232
286.000	2.2443	0.	0.	2.2574	0.	0.	-0.0131
320.000	2.4534	0.	0.	2.4483	0.	0.	0.0051
351.000	2.6451	0.	0.	2.6223	0.	0.	0.0228
394.000	0.	0.	0.	0.	0.	0.	0.
430.000	0.	0.	0.	0.	0.	0.	0.
463.000	0.	0.	0.	0.	0.	0.	0.

In some cases we may have a first order reaction for which the infinity value is not known. One method of handling such a case was given on p. 315. However, if one uses this with a computer, one must build in several tests to prevent the parameters from taking physically impossible values during the set of iterations. This might come about if the shape of the multidimensional space representing the variables and the deviation had an odd shape.

Since large computers are very fast, one may take a simpler approach, that of changing the infinity value in small steps until one has reached a rate constant giving a minimum in the root mean squared deviation between observed and calculated values of the physical property being measured. The next program effects this operation.

The program begins with reading a card having the run number in columns 1–5. The first card for any set of kinetic runs must have the run number zero, or the computation will be deleted. After the zero is read, the computer goes to statement 201, which directs that the names of the reaction components, ANAME, BNAME, and CNAME be read from the next card using columns 1–5, 6–10, and 11–15.

The first card for any given kinetic run has the run number (columns 1–5), an identification for the run (columns 6–25), the number of points, N (columns 34–35), the temperature, T (columns 36–40), the factor converting the units used to seconds, TFACT (columns 41–46), the mode of operation (column 50) and the values of two constants, EQUIV and VOL (columns 51–55 and 56–60). MODE = 1 is used for runs in which the data were obtained titrimetrically, and MODE = 2 is used for those in which the data were obtained spectrophotometrically. If MODE = 1, EQUIV gives the number of equivalents of titrant per mole of A and VOL is the volume of aliquot used. If MODE = 2, EQUIV is the wavelength used, and no entry need be made for VOL.

The second card of a data set gives the values of ACONC (columns 1–10), BCONC (columns 11–20), CCONC (columns 21–30), and DCONC (columns 31–40), which are the concentrations of A, B, and C and a constant. For a true first order reaction, there will be no second or third component (B and C), and no entries need be made for BCONC and CCONC. If MODE = 1, DCONC is the concentration of titrant, and if MODE = 2, DCONC is the absorbancy index of A.

The next cards have the values of time (14 values per card, using five columns per number) and of absorbance or other physical property (VALUE). The last card of a data set gives the infinity value (VINF).

The values of the physical property which is measured may either increase or decrease with time. The sign of the difference (VALUE(N)-VINF) is saved as CONST, since the logarithm must be taken of the absolute value of the difference. The program then calculates the first order rate constant by the method of least squares in a fashion similar to that used in Appendix 8. The values of the parameters are saved as AA (concentration of A), IY (run number), AB (concentration of B), AC (concentration of C), AD (temperature), AE (rate constant), AR (rate constant times 10,000), AF (the rms deviation), and LB (the mode). These values will be printed out in a summary sheet after calculating data for several runs.

If MODE = 1 or 2, the data are written on the output tape in the form shown in the sample output. If MODE = 1 a statement "THE DATA WERE OBTAINED TITRIMETRICALLY" is written, and if MODE = 2, a statement "THE DATE WERE OBTAINED SPECTROPHOTO-METRICALLY" is written. The calculated initial concentration of A is obtained from the intercept (AZ) and the absorbancy index of A (DCONC) for MODE = 2 or from the intercept (AZ), the normality of titrant (DCONC), the volume of aliquot used (VOL) and the equivalents of titrant per mole of A (EQUIV) for MODE = 1. The value is given in the output.

The computer then proceeds to vary VINF by one percent, or 0.002, whichever is larger. After each change in value, the rate constant and intercept are calculated by the method of least squares. This is continued until the rms deviation (DEV) has attained a minimum value. At this point, the resultant values are written on the output tape in the form shown in the typical output which follows. A series of data sets may be run at one time, and if a summary of all of the data is desired, a card having run number O may be used. After the summary has been written, further data sets may be read after first providing a card with ANAME, BNAME, and CNAME.

If a program such as this is used frequently, it is often advisable to make up suitable forms for facilitating the listing of data and subsequent keypunching. A typical form is shown following the program.

First Order Rate Constants by Varying Infinity Value

```
C       CALCULATE RATE CONSTANTS AND INFINITY VALUES
C
C       N IS THE NUMBER OF VALUES, TFACT IS THE FACTOR FOR CONVERTING THE
C       TIME UNITS USED TO SECONDS.  MODE 0 GIVES INTERMEDIATE DATA FROM
C       CALCULATION FOR TESTING PURPOSES, MODE 1 IS USED FOR TITRIMETRIC
C       RUNS AND MODE 2 IS USED FOR SPECTROPHOTOMETRIC RUNS.  EQUIV IS
C       THE EQUIVALENTS OF TITRANT USED, VOL IS THE VOLUME OF ALIQUOT
C       AND DCONC IS THE NORMALITY OF THE TITRANT. T IS THE TEMPERATURE.
C
C       THE INITIAL CARD MUST HAVE 0 IN COLUMNS 1-5, THE SECOND CARD HAS
C       THE ABBREVIATIONS FOR THE NAMES OF COMPOUNDS A, B, AND C USING A
C       FIELD OF 5.
C
C       THE FOLLOWING CARDS ARE AS SETS, WITH RUN NUMBER, IDENTIFICATION,
C       NUMBER OF POINTS, TEMPERATURE, TIME FACTOR, MODE, EQUIVALENT,
C       AND VOLUME ON THE FIRST CARD, CONCENTRATIONS OF A, B, AND C ON THE
C       SECOND CARD, AND VALUES OF TIME AND OF ABSORBANCE OR VOLUME ON THE
C       FOLLOWING CARDS.
C       FOR SPECTROPHOTOMETRIC RUNS, DCONC IS THE ABSORBANCY INDEX OF THE
C       REACTANT.
C
C       THE FINAL CARD OF ANY SET HAS ZEROS IN COLUMNS 1-5. IF MORE DATA
C       SETS FOLLOW, THE NEXT CARD HAS THE NAMES OF THE COMPOUNDS A, B, AND
C       C, AND THE FOLLOWING CARDS ARE DATA SETS AS ABOVE.
C
        DIMENSION DF(28),  Y(28),VALUE(28),TIME(28),F(28),AA(200),AB(200),
       1AC(200),AD(200),AE(200),AF(200),AG(200),AH(200),AI(200),AJ(200),
       1AK(200),LB(200),TITLE(200,4),FMOD(28),Z(28),IY(200),
       1A(40,40),BA(25),BB(25),BC(25),BD(25),NE(25)
        READ INPUT TAPE 4,6,  IRUN,(TITLE(1,J),J=1,4),  N,T,TFACT,MODE,EQUIV
       1, VOL
        IF (IRUN)   200,201,200
  200 CALL EXITM
  201 READ INPUT TAPE 4,9, ANAME, BNAME, CNAME
        LL = 0
    5 LL = LL+1
        I = 1
        READ INPUT TAPE 4,6,IRUN,(TITLE(LL,J),J=1,4),N,T,TFACT,MODE,EQUIV,
       1VOL
    6 FORMAT (I5,4A5, I10,2F5.0, I5,2F5.0)
        IF (IRUN) 100,100,8
    8 READ INPUT TAPE 4, 10, ACONC, BCONC, CCONC,DCONC
   10 FORMAT (4F10.0)
        READ INPUT TAPE 4, 11, (TIME(J),J=1,N)
   11 FORMAT (14F5.0)
        READ INPUT TAPE 4, 11, (VALUE(J),J=1,N)
        READ INPUT TAPE 4, 12, VINF
   12 FORMAT (F5.0)
        IF (VALUE(N) - VINF) 120,121,121
  120 CONST = -1.0
        GO TO 360
  121 CONST = 1.0
C
C       CALCULATE RATE CONSTANTS USING INITIAL VALUE OF V(INF)
C
  360 SUMY = 0.0
        SUMX = 0.0
        SUMXY= 0.0
        SUMXX= 0.0
```

```
      DO 20 J = I ,N
      Y(J) = LOGF(ABSF(VALUE(J) - VINF))
      SUMY= SUMY + Y(J)
      SUMX= SUMX + TIME(J)
      SUMXX= SUMXX+ TIME(J)*TIME(J)
      SUMXY= SUMXY+ TIME(J)*Y(J)
      IF (MODE) 202, 202, 20
  202 WRITE OUTPUT TAPE 2, 203, SUMY, SUMX,SUMXX, SUMXY
  203 FORMAT (1H 4F12.4)
   20 CONTINUE
      G = FLOATF(N-I+1)
      SLOPE= (G*SUMXY - SUMX*SUMY)/(G*SUMXX - SUMX*SUMX)
      B= (SUMX*SUMXY -    SUMY*SUMXX)/(SUMX*SUMX - G*SUMXX)
      FSUM= 0.0
      DO 21 J = I ,N
      F(J)= Y(J) - SLOPE*TIME(J) - B
   21 FSUM = FSUM + F(J)*F(J)
      DEV= SQRTF(FSUM/G)
      AA(LL)= ACONC
      IY(LL) = IRUN
      AB(LL)= BCONC
      AC(LL)= CCONC
      AD(LL)= T
      AE(LL) = ABSF(SLOPE/TFACT)
      AR = 10000.*AE(LL)
      AF(LL)= DEV
      LB(LL) = MODE
      AZ = EXPF(B) + VINF
      IF (MODE-1) 22,22,23
   22 AG(LL) = AZ*DCONC/(EQUIV*VOL)
      GO TO 24
   23 AG(LL) = AZ/DCONC
   24 IF (MODE) 204,204,25
  204 WRITE OUTPUT TAPE 2, 205, AA(LL),AB(LL),AC(LL),AD(LL),AE(LL),AF(LL
     1),AG(LL)
  205 FORMAT (1H 7F12.4).
   25 WRITE OUTPUT TAPE 2, 26, (TITLE(LL,J), J= 1,4),IRUN
   26 FORMAT (1H14A5, 17H        RUN NO I7)
      WRITE OUTPUT TAPE 2,27, ANAME, ACONC, BNAME, BCONC, CNAME, CCONC,
     1T
   27 FORMAT ( 2H0(A5, 3H) =F10.5, 2(5H    (A5, 3H) =F10.5), 6H    T=F6.
     11)
      WRITE OUTPUT TAPE 2,28
   28 FORMAT (47H0     TIME          OBS         CALC        DIF)
      WRITE OUTPUT TAPE 2,29
   29 FORMAT (1H )
      DO 30 J = I ,N
      CALC = EXPF(SLOPE*TIME(J) + B)*CONST + VINF
      DIF    = VALUE(J)- CALC
   30 WRITE OUTPUT TAPE 2, 32, TIME(J), VALUE(J), CALC, DIF
   32 FORMAT (3H   F7.2,F12.3,F14.3,F12.3)
      WRITE OUTPUT TAPE 2, 70, VINF
   70 FORMAT (10H     INF F12.3)
      WRITE OUTPUT TAPE 2, 33, AR
   33 FORMAT (25H0THE RATE CONSTANT IS K =F10.5,8H X 10E-4)
      WRITE OUTPUT TAPE 2, 34, AF(LL)
   34 FORMAT (25H THE RMS DEVIATION IS =  F10.5)
      WRITE OUTPUT TAPE 2, 80, ANAME, AG(LL)
   80 FORMAT (41H THE CALCULATED INITIAL CONCENTRATION OF A5,4H IS F10.5
```

```
    1)
      WRITE OUTPUT TAPE 2, 81, AZ
   81 FORMAT (20H THE INTERCEPT IS = F10.5)
      IF (MODE-1) 35,35,36
   35 WRITE OUTPUT TAPE 2,37
   37 FORMAT (39HOTHE DATA WERE OBTAINED TITRIMETRICALLY)
      GO TO 40
   36 WRITE OUTPUT TAPE 2,38,EQUIV
   38 FORMAT (50HOTHE DATA WERE OBTAINED SPECTROPHOTOMETRICALLY AT F5.0,
    1 3H MU)
C
C     START VARIATION OF V(INF)
C
      CONST2 = 0.01*VINF
      IF (CONST2 - 0.002) 180,40,40
  180 CONST2 = 0.002
   40 LA= 0
      VMOD =VINF
      TEST = DEV
      VMOD = VMOD - CONST2
   76 SUMY = 0.0
      SUMX = 0.0
      SUMXY= 0.0
      SUMXX= 0.0
      DO 82 J = I,N
      Y(J) = LOGF(ABSF(VALUE(J) - VMOD))
      SUMY = SUMY + Y(J)
      SUMX = SUMX + TIME(J)
      SUMXX= SUMXX+ TIME(J)*TIME(J)
   82 SUMXY= SUMXY+ TIME(J)*Y(J)
      SMOD = -(G*SUMXY-SUMX*SUMY)/(G*SUMXX-SUMX*SUMX)
      BMOD = (SUMX*SUMXY-SUMY*SUMXX)/(SUMX*SUMX-G*SUMXX)
      FSUM = 0.0
      DO 83 J = I,N
      F(J) = Y(J) + SMOD*TIME(J)- BMOD
   83 FSUM = FSUM + F(J)*F(J)
      DEV = SQRTF (FSUM/G)
      LA = LA+1
      BA(LA) = SMOD
      BB(LA) = BMOD
      BC(LA) = VMOD
      BD(LA) = DEV
      NE(LA) = N
      IF (TEST-DEV)  84,84,85
   85 TEST = DEV
      DO 86 L = 1,15
      VMOD = VMOD - CONST2
      IF (VMOD) 87,87,88
   88 SUMY = 0.0
      SUMX = 0.0
      SUMXX= 0.0
      SUMXY= 0.0
      DO 89 J = I,N
      Y(J) = LOGF(ABSF(VALUE(J) - VMOD))
      SUMY = SUMY + Y(J)
      SUMX = SUMX + TIME(J)
      SUMXX= SUMXX+ TIME(J)*TIME(J)
   89 SUMXY= SUMXY+ TIME(J)*Y(J)
      SMOD = -(G*SUMXY-SUMX*SUMY)/(G*SUMXX-SUMX*SUMX)
```

```
      BMOD = (SUMX*SUMXY-SUMY*SUMXX)/(SUMX*SUMX-G*SUMXX)
      FSUM = 0.0
      DO 90 J = I,N
      F(J) = Y(J)+ SMOD*TIME(J)- BMOD
   90 FSUM = FSUM + F(J)*F(J)
      DEV = SQRTF(FSUM/G)
      LA = LA+1
      BA(LA) = SMOD
      BB(LA) = BMOD
      BC(LA) = VMOD
      BD(LA) = DEV
      NE(LA) = N
      IF (TEST-DEV) 345,86,86
   86 TEST = DEV
      GO TO 61
   84 VMOD = VMOD + CONST2
      DO 93 L = 1,15
      VMOD = VMOD + CONST2
   94 IF ((VALUE(N) - VMOD)*CONST) 95,95,96
   95 N= N-1
      G = FLOATF(N-I+1)
      GO TO 94
   96 SUMY = 0.0
      SUMX = 0.0
      SUMXX= 0.0
      SUMXY= 0.0
      DO 97 J = I,N
      Y(J) = LOGF(ABSF(VALUE(J) - VMOD))
      SUMY = SUMY + Y(J)
      SUMX = SUMX + TIME(J)
      SUMXX= SUMXX+ TIME(J)*TIME(J)
   97 SUMXY= SUMXY+ TIME(J)*Y(J)
      SMOD = -(G*SUMXY-SUMX*SUMY)/(G*SUMXX-SUMX*SUMX)
      BMOD = (SUMX*SUMXY-SUMY*SUMXX)/(SUMX*SUMX-G*SUMXX)
      FSUM = 0.0
      DO 98 J = I,N
      F(J) = Y(J)+ SMOD*TIME(J)- BMOD
   98 FSUM = FSUM + F(J)*F(J)
      DEV = SQRTF(FSUM/G)
      LA = LA+1
      BA(LA) = SMOD
      BB(LA) = BMOD
      BC(LA) = VMOD
      BD(LA) = DEV
      NE(LA) = N
      IF (TEST-DEV) 345,93,93
  345 LA = LA - 1
      SMOD = BA(LA)
      BMOD = BB(LA)
      VMOD = BC(LA)
      DEV = BD(LA)
      N = NE(LA)
      GO TO 50
   93 TEST = DEV
      GO TO 61
   87 VMOD = 0.0
      GO TO 61
   50 WRITE OUTPUT TAPE 2,52
   52 FORMAT (60HOTHE FOLLOWING DATA WERE OBTAINED USING V(INF) AS A VAR
```

```
      1IABLE)
       WRITE OUTPUT TAPE 2,53, VMOD, LA
   53 FORMAT (31H THE FINAL VALUE OF V(INF) WAS F5.3,14H AND REQUIRED I2
      1, 11H ITERATIONS)
       WRITE OUTPUT TAPE 2,28
       WRITE OUTPUT TAPE 2,29
       AH(LL) = SMOD/TFACT
       AS  =   SMOD*10000./TFACT
       AK(LL)= VMOD
       IF (MODE-1) 55,55,56
   55 AJ(LL) = (EXPF(BMOD)+VMOD)*DCONC/(EQUIV*VOL)
       GO TO 54
   56 AJ(LL) =(EXPF(BMOD)+VMOD)/DCONC
   54 AI(LL)= DEV
       AVDEV = 0.0
       DO 59 J = 1,N
       CALC = EXPF(-SMOD*TIME(J) + BMOD)*CONST + VMOD
       DIF =  VALUE(J) - CALC
       AVDEV = AVDEV + ABSF(DIF)
       DF(J) = DIF
   59 WRITE OUTPUT TAPE 2,32,TIME(J), VALUE(J), CALC, DIF
       WRITE OUTPUT TAPE 2, 33, AS
       WRITE OUTPUT TAPE 2, 34, AI(LL)
       AZ = EXPF(BMOD) + VMOD
       WRITE OUTPUT TAPE 2, 80, ANAME, AJ(LL)
       WRITE OUTPUT TAPE 2, 81, AZ
       AVDEV = AVDEV*2./G
       IF (I-1) 505,505,506
  506 I=1
       IF (MODE) 507,507,508
  508 GO TO 5
  507 DO 509 J = 1,LA
       L = J
  509 WRITE OUTPUT TAPE 2, 65, L, BA(L), BB(L), BC(L), BD(L), NE(L)
       GO TO 5
  505 IF(DF(1) - AVDEV) 501,502,502
  501 IF(MODE) 517,517,518
  518 GO TO 5
  517 DO 519 J = 1,LA
       L = J
  519 WRITE OUTPUT TAPE 2, 65, L, BA(L), BB(L), BC(L), BD(L), NE(L)
       GO TO 5
  502 I = 2
       GO TO 360
   61 WRITE OUTPUT TAPF 2, 62, LA
   62 FORMAT (35H0THE SLOPE HAS NOT CONVERGED AFTER I2,11H ITERATIONS)
       WRITE OUTPUT TAPE 2, 63
   63 FORMAT (51H0 ITERATION     SLOPE      INTERCEPT     VINF       DEV)
       WRITE OUTPUT TAPE 2,29
       DO 64 J = 1,LA
       L= J
   64 WRITE OUTPUT TAPE 2, 65, L, BA(L), BB(L), BC(L), BD(L), NE(L)
   65 FORMAT (1H I6, E13.4,3E12.4,I5)
       GO TO 5
  100 WRITE OUTPUT TAPE 2,101
  101 FORMAT (10H1 SUMMARY)
  102 WRITE OUTPUT TAPE 2,104, ANAME,BNAME,CNAME,ANAME,ANAME
  104 FORMAT (6H RUN A5,5H      A5,5H      A5,29H  TEMP   K          DEV
      1    A5,25H      K       DEV      A5,22H VINF M     REACTANT)
```

```
      DO 109 J = 1, LL
      IF (LB(J) - 1) 105,105,103
105 WRITE OUTPUT TAPE 2, 110,IY(J),AA(J),AB(J),AC(J),AD(J),AE(J),
    1AF(J),AG(J),
    1,AH(J),AI.(J),AJ(J),AK(J),  (TITLE(J,K),K=1,3)
110 FORMAT (1H I3,3E10.3,F4.0,6E10.3,F5.3,3H T 3A5)
      GO TO 109
103 WRITE OUTPUT TAPE 2, 108,IY(J),AA(J),AB(J),AC(J),AD(J),AE(J),
    1AF(J),AG(J),
    1,AH(J),AI(J),AJ(J),AK(J),  (TITLE(J,K),K=1,3)
108 FORMAT (1H I3,3E10.3,F4.0,6E10.3,F5.3,3H S 3A5)
109 CONTINUE
  7 READ INPUT TAPE 4,9, ANAME, BNAME, CNAME
  9 FORMAT (3A5)
      LL = 0
      GO TO 5
      END
```

Input Data:

```
00000
CU(2)KETOLPYRID
00017PHENACYL ALCOHOL              1125.   1.0       2610.
0.0140    0.500     50.       33.
39.   59.   89.   123. 157. 190. 217. 257. 286. 320. 351. 394. 430. 463.
.450 .390 .325 .275 .235 .200 .175 .145 .125 .105 .090 .070 .055 .045
.016
00000
```

The names of compounds A, B, and C are given as CU(2), KETOL, and PYRID, the run no. is 17, there are 11 data points, the temperature was 25°, the time factor was 1, 0, mode was 2, and the data were obtained at 610 mu. The concentration of A was 0.0140, of B 0.500, and of C 50. The absorbancy index of A was 33. The next line gives the absorbance values, and the following line gives the corresponding values of time. The last line gives the infinity absorbance. Note that the data are preceded by a card having 00000, and the final card after several data sets is also 00000.

Output:

```
PHENACYL ALCOHOL                    RUN NO      17

(CU(2)) =   0.01400     (KETOL) =   0.50000     (PYRID) =   50.00000     T=   25.0

        TIME          OBS          CALC          DIF

        39.00        0.450        0.436        0.014
        59.00        0.390        0.392       -0.002
        89.00        0.325        0.335       -0.010
       123.00        0.275        0.280       -0.005
       157.00        0.235        0.235       -0.000
       190.00        0.200        0.199        0.001
       217.00        0.175        0.174        0.001
       257.00        0.145        0.142        0.003
       286.00        0.125        0.124        0.001
       320.00        0.105        0.105       -0.000
       351.00        0.090        0.091       -0.001
        INF          0.016

THE RATE CONSTANT IS K =   55.09842 X 10E-4
THE RMS DEVIATION IS =        0.01792
THE CALCULATED INITIAL CONCENTRATION OF CU(2) IS       0.01627
THE INTERCEPT IS =       0.53679

THE DATA WERE OBTAINED SPECTROPHOTOMETRICALLY AT   610. MU

THE FOLLOWING DATA WERE OBTAINED USING V(INF) AS A VARIABLE
THE FINAL VALUE OF V(INF) WAS 0.010 AND REQUIRED   3 ITERATIONS

        TIME          OBS          CALC          DIF

        39.00        0.450        0.434        0.016
        59.00        0.390        0.391       -0.001
        89.00        0.325        0.335       -0.010
       123.00        0.275        0.281       -0.006
       157.00        0.235        0.236       -0.001
       190.00        0.200        0.200        0.000
       217.00        0.175        0.174        0.001
       257.00        0.145        0.143        0.002
       286.00        0.125        0.124        0.001
       320.00        0.105        0.105       -0.000
       351.00        0.090        0.091       -0.001

THE RATE CONSTANT IS K =   53.17172 X 10E-4
THE RMS DEVIATION IS =        0.01735
THE CALCULATED INITIAL CONCENTRATION OF CU(2) IS       0.01610
THE INTERCEPT IS =       0.53116
```

A third kinetic data program is one which deals with consecutive first order reactions. As indicated previously (Appendix 7), the concentrations of the species involved

$$A \xrightarrow{k_1} B$$
$$B \xrightarrow{k_2} C$$

are given by

$$A = A_0 e^{-kt}$$

$$B = A_0 k_1 (e^{-k_1 t} - e^{-k_2 t})/(k_2 - k_1)$$

$$C = A_0 [1 - (k_1 e^{-k_2 t} - k_2 e^{-k_1 t})/(k_1 - k_2)]$$

The kinetic data are commonly obtained in the form of absorbance as a function of time. If ϵ_A is the absorbancy index of A, ϵ_B is the absorbancy index of B and ϵ_C is the absorbancy index of C, the observed absorbance of the solution is given by

$$A_{obs} = \epsilon_{obs} A_0 = \epsilon_A A + \epsilon_B B + \epsilon_C C$$

and thus

$$\epsilon_{obs} = \epsilon_A e^{-k_1 t} + \epsilon_B k_1 (e^{-k_1 t} - e^{-k_2 t})/(k_2 - k_1)$$
$$+ \epsilon_C [1 - (k_1 e^{-k_2 t} - k_2 e^{-k_1 t})/(k_1 - k_2)]$$

If one has a set of approximate values of k_1, k_2, ϵ_A, ϵ_B, and ϵ_C, one may now calculate the apparent absorbancy index of the solution as a function of time. The average deviation from the observed values may be used as criterion of accuracy for the assumed values, and they may be varied so as to minimize the deviation. The "best values" thus obtained should be close to the true values.

The program begins by reading an identification card, and then a card having the number of points, N (columns 1–10), absorbancy index of A, EA (columns 11–20), of B, EB (columns 21–30), of C, EC (columns 31–40), the rate constant k_1, AK (columns 41–50) and k_2, BK (columns 51–60). The next cards have the values of the observed absorbancy index (OBSE) using 14 five column fields per card, and then the corresponding values of time (T) are read.

The statements through number 4 affect the calculation of the absorbancy index from the starting parameters (CALE) and the differences from the observed values (DIF). This allows the deviation (DEV) to be obtained.

The computer writes the identification which was read from the first card, the starting parameters and the calculated average deviation. It also writes the iteration number (L), and a constant M, which indicates which parameter is being varied.

The computation now proceeds with statement 10. The value of EB is saved as CONST1, and EB is increased by one percent. So long as L is less than 200, the computer proceeds to statement 3 which repeats the preceding calculation. Now L is greater than zero, and the computer goes to statement 6. If the deviation has decreased, the value of ϵ_B is again increased by one percent and the calculation repeated. If the deviation has increased, ϵ_B is set back to its previous value and M is increased by 1. The operation of M is as follows:

M = 1	Increase ϵ_B by 1%
M = 2	Decrease ϵ_B by 1%
M = 3	Increase k_1 by 1%
M = 4	Decrease k_1 by 1%
M = 5	Increase k_2 by 1%
M = 6	Decrease k_2 by 1%
M = 7	Increase ϵ_C by 1%
M = 8	Decrease ϵ_C by 1%
M = 9	Increase ϵ_A by 1%
M = 10	Decrease ϵ_A by 1%

After M has been set equal to 10, it is reset to 1. Thus the computation may cycle through the possible variations of values of ϵ_B, k_1, k_2, ϵ_C, and ϵ_A. When one cycle through all of the parameters produces no further decrease in DEV (determined via statement 45 and the following one), the computation ceases and the data are written on the output tape. Typical input and output data are given after the program.

Consecutive First Order Rates Calculation

```
C     PROGRAM FOR OBTAINING RATE CONSTANTS FOR CONSECUTIVE FIRST ORDER
C     REACTIONS    MODIFICATION 1
      DIMENSION  OBSE(30), CALE(30), DIF(30), T(30), A(30),
     1 B(30), C(30), TITLE(12), DEV(201)
  100 READ INPUT TAPE 4, 28, (TITLE(J), J=1,12)
   28 FORMAT (12A6)
      M= 1
      L= 0
      READ INPUT TAPE 4, 1, N, EA, EB, EC, AK, BK
    1 FORMAT (I10,5F10.0)
      READ INPUT TAPE 4, 2, (OBSE(J),J=1,N)
    2 FORMAT (14F5.0)
      READ INPUT TAPE 4, 2, (T(J), J=1,N)
    3 SUM = 0.0
      DO 4 J = 1,N
      EK1 = EXPF(-AK*T(J))
      EK2 = EXPF(-BK*T(J))
      CALE(J) = EA*EK1 + EB*AK*(EK1-EK2)/(BK-AK) +EC*(1.+
     1 (BK*EK1-AK*EK2)/(AK-BK))
      DIF(J) = ABSF(OBSE(J) -CALE(J))
    4 SUM = SUM+DIF(J)
      G = N
      L1 = L+1
      DEV(L1) = SUM/G
      IF (L) 5,5,6
    5 L= 1
      TEST = DEV(L1)
      WRITE OUTPUT TAPE 2, 29, (TITLE(J), J = 1,12)
   29 FORMAT (1H112A6)
      WRITE OUTPUT TAPE 2, 42
   42 FORMAT (1H0)
      WRITE OUTPUT TAPE 2, 43
   43 FORMAT (102H0          E(A)          E(B)          E(C)
     1K1          K2          DEV    SECT  ITER)
      CONST2 = AK
      CONST3 = BK
      CONST4 = EC
      CONST5 = EA
      WRITE OUTPUT TAPE 2, 42
      WRITE OUTPUT TAPE 2, 7, CONST5, EB, CONST4, CONST2,
     1 CONST3, TEST, M, L
    7 FORMAT (1H 3F15.5, 2E15.4, F15.5, 2I5)
      GO TO 10
    6 L= L+1
      IF (TEST - DEV(L)) 8, 9, 9
    8 EB = CONST1
      AK = CONST2
      BK = CONST3
      EC = CONST4
      EA = CONST5
      DEV(L) = TEST
      M=M+1
      IF (M-11) 45,51,51
   51 M = 1
   45 IF (L-11) 40,41,41
   41 L2 = L - 10
      IF (DEV(L2) - DEV(L)) 16,16,40
    9 TEST = DEV(L)
   40 IF (M-2) 10,11,12
```

```
  10 CONST1 = EB
     EB = 1.01*EB
     IF (L - 200) 3, 3, 16
  11 CONST1 = EB
     EB = 0.99*EB
     IF (L - 200) 3, 3, 16
  12 IF (M-4) 18,19,20
  18 CONST2. = AK
     AK = 1.01*AK
     IF (L - 200) 3, 3, 16
  19 CONST2 = AK
     AK = 0.99*AK
     IF (L - 200) 3, 3, 16
  20 IF (M-6) 23,24,50
  23 CONST3 = BK
     BK = 1.01*BK
     IF (L - 200) 3, 3, 16
  24 CONST3 = BK
     BK = 0.99*BK
     IF (L - 200) 3, 3, 16
  50 IF (M-8) 151, 52, 166
 151 CONST4 = EC
     EC = 1.01*EC
     IF (L - 200) 3, 3, 16
  52 CONST4 = EC
     EC = 0.99*EC
     IF (L - 200) 3, 3, 16
 166 IF (M-10) 180, 190, 16
 180 CONST5 = EA
     EA = 1.01*EA
     IF (L - 200) 3, 3, 16
 190 CONST5 = EA
     EA = 0.99*EA
     IF (L - 200) 3, 3, 16
  16 WRITE OUTPUT TAPE 2, 7, CONST5, CONST1,CONST4, CONST2,
   1 CONST3, TEST, M, L
     WRITE OUTPUT TAPE 2, 42
     WRITE OUTPUT TAPE 2, 30
  30 FORMAT (104H0         V(OBS)         V(CALC)         DIF
   1   TIME         (A)         (B)         (C))
     EB = CONST1
     AK = CONST2
     BK = CONST3
     EC = CONST4
     EA = CONST5
     DO 35 J=1,N
     EK1 = EXPF(-AK*T(J))
     EK2 = EXPF(-BK*T(J))
     CALE(J) = EA*EK1 + EB*AK*(EK1-EK2)/(BK-AK) +EC*(1.+
   1 (BK*EK1-AK*EK2)/(AK-BK))
     DIF(J) = ABSF(OBSE(J) -CALE(J))
     A(J)= EK1
     B(J) = AK*(EK1-EK2)/(BK-AK)
  35 C(J) = 1. - A(J) - B(J)
     WRITE OUTPUT TAPE 2, 42
     WRITE OUTPUT TAPE 2, 31, (OBSE(J), CALE(J), DIF(J),
   1 T(J), A(J), B(J), C(J), J=1,N)
  31 FORMAT (1H 7F15.5)
     GO TO 100
```

Input Data:

```
CHROMYL ACETATE OXIDATION OF BENZALDEHYDE
        280.78        1.90        0.85        0.75        0.35
1.0281.0751.1181.1581.2301.2831.3251.3501.3651.3761.3891.3981.3981.397
1.3951.3911.3821.3711.3601.3451.3351.2991.2621.2221.1901.1581.0971.044
0.30 0.40 0.50 0.60 0.80 1.00 1.20 1.40 1.50 1.60 1.80 2.00 2.20 2.40
2.50 2.60 2.80 3.00 3.20 3.40 3.50 4.00 4.50 5.00 5.50 6.00 7.00 8.00
```

The second card indicates that there are 28 data points, that the absorbance of A is 0.78, of B 1.90, and of C 0.85. The estimated rate constants are $k_1 = 0.75$ and $k_2 = 0.35$. The next two cards give the absorbance values, and the final two cards give the corresponding values of time.

Output:

CHROMYL ACETATE OXIDATION OF BENZALDEHYDE

E(A)	E(B)	E(C)	K1	K2	DEV	SECT	ITER
0.7800	1.9000	0.8500	0.750E 00	0.350E-00	0.0409	1	1
0.8277	1.9184	0.9023	0.671E 00	0.323E-00	0.0032	4	122

V(OBS)	V(CALC)	DIF	TIME	(A)	(B)	(C)
1.0280	1.0177	0.0103	0.3000	0.8176	0.1736	0.0088
1.0750	1.0692	0.0058	0.4000	0.7645	0.2203	0.0152
1.1180	1.1154	0.0026	0.5000	0.7148	0.2622	0.0230
1.1580	1.1568	0.0012	0.6000	0.6684	0.2995	0.0321
1.2300	1.2266	0.0034	0.8000	0.5844	0.3620	0.0535
1.2830	1.2813	0.0017	1.0000	0.5110	0.4105	0.0786
1.3250	1.3231	0.0019	1.2000	0.4468	0.4469	0.1063
1.3500	1.3541	0.0041	1.4000	0.3906	0.4733	0.1361
1.3650	1.3661	0.0011	1.5000	0.3653	0.4832	0.1515
1.3760	1.3760	0.0000	1.6000	0.3415	0.4912	0.1673
1.3890	1.3901	0.0011	1.8000	0.2986	0.5020	0.1994
1.3980	1.3979	0.0001	2.0000	0.2611	0.5069	0.2320
1.3980	1.4004	0.0024	2.2000	0.2283	0.5070	0.2647
1.3970	1.3985	0.0015	2.4000	0.1996	0.5030	0.2974
1.3950	1.3962	0.0012	2.5000	0.1866	0.4998	0.3136
1.3910	1.3931	0.0021	2.6000	0.1745	0.4958	0.3297
1.3820	1.3848	0.0028	2.8000	0.1526	0.4860	0.3614
1.3710	1.3742	0.0032	3.0000	0.1334	0.4742	0.3924
1.3600	1.3618	0.0018	3.2000	0.1166	0.4608	0.4226
1.3450	1.3480	0.0030	3.4000	0.1020	0.4461	0.4519
1.3350	1.3407	0.0057	3.5000	0.0954	0.4385	0.4662
1.2990	1.3017	0.0027	4.0000	0.0682	0.3981	0.5337
1.2620	1.2610	0.0010	4.5000	0.0487	0.3566	0.5947
1.2220	1.2210	0.0010	5.0000	0.0348	0.3162	0.6490
1.1900	1.1831	0.0069	5.5000	0.0249	0.2782	0.6969
1.1580	1.1481	0.0099	6.0000	0.0178	0.2432	0.7390
1.0970	1.0880	0.0090	7.0000	0.0091	0.1834	0.8075
1.0440	1.0407	0.0033	8.0000	0.0046	0.1365	0.8588

A modification of this program written by P. Lepse (Modification 2) follows. Instead of varying each parameter one at a time, the effect of changing each parameter is determined using the subroutine EVAL. Then all parameters are simultaneously changed in proportion to their effect of the average deviation. The computation proceeds along this "vector" until no further decrease in deviation is found. A new "vector" is obtained and the calculation is repeated—and this process continues until no further decrease in deviation is possible. The results are then written. The input and output format are similar to those used for the first modification.

```
C       PROGRAM FOR OBTAINING RATE CONSTANTS FOR CONSECUTIVE FIRST ORDER
C       REACTIONS    MODIFICATION 2
        DIMENSION  OBSE(30), CALE(30), DIF(30), T(30), A(30),
      1 B(30), C(30), TITLE(12), DEV(501)
        COMMON  N, OBSE, T
  100 READ INPUT TAPE 4, 28, (TITLE(J), J=1,12)
   28 FORMAT (12A6)
        M= 2
        L= 0
        R = 0.1
        READ INPUT TAPE 4, 1, N, EA, EB, EC, AK, BK
    1 FORMAT (I10,5F10.0)
        READ INPUT TAPE 4, 2, (OBSE(J),J=1,N)
    2 FORMAT (14F5.0)
        READ INPUT TAPE 4, 2, (T(J), J=1,N)
        WRITE OUTPUT TAPE 2, 29, (TITLE(J), J = 1,12)
   29 FORMAT (1H112A6)
        WRITE OUTPUT TAPE 2, 42
   42 FORMAT (1H0)
        WRITE OUTPUT TAPE 2, 43
   43 FORMAT (102H0       E(A)        E(B)            E(C)
      1K1            K2            DEV   SECT   ITER)
        WRITE OUTPUT TAPE 2, 42
        GO TO 3
   55 WRITE OUTPUT TAPE 2, 117, EA, EB, EC, AK, BK, TEST, M, L
  117 FORMAT (1H 3F15.5, 2E15.4, F15.5, 2I5)
    5 IF (M - 2) 7, 8, 8
    8 EB1 = 1.0001*EB
        EC1 = 1.0001*EC
        AK1 = 1.0001*AK
        BK1 = 1.0001*BK
        EA1 = 1.0001*EA
        CALL EVAL (EA1, EB , EC , AK , BK , DEA)
        CALL EVAL (EA , EB1, EC , AK , BK , DEB)
        CALL EVAL (EA , EB , EC1, AK , BK , DEC)
        CALL EVAL (EA , EB , EC , AK1, BK , DAK)
        CALL EVAL (EA , EB , EC , AK , BK1, DBK)
        H1 = (-EB*100.)*(DEB - DEV(L))
        H2 = (-EC*100.)*(DEC - DEV(L))
        H3 = (-EA*100.)*(DEA - DEV(L))
        H4 = (-AK*100.)*(DAK - DEV(L))
        H5 = (-BK*100.)*(DBK - DEV(L))
        M = 1
        S = 10.0
        GO TO 11
    6 M = M + 1
   11 TEST = DEV(L)
  200 IF (L - 500) 10, 10, 87
   10 CONST1 = EB
        CONST4 = EC
        CONST2 = AK
        CONST3 = BK
        CONST5 = EA
        EB = EB + H1*S
        EC = EC + H2*S
        EA = EA + H3*S
        AK = AK + H4*S
        BK = BK + H5*S
    3 L= L+1
```

```
      CALL EVAL  (EA,  EB,  EC,  AK,  BK,  DEV(L))
201 IF (L-1) 14, 14, 15
 14 TEST = DEV(L)
 15 IF (TEST - DEV(L)) 13,55, 6
 13 EB = CONST1
    EC = CONST4
    AK = CONST2
    BK = CONST3
    EA = CONST5
 20 DEV(L) = TEST
    S = S/10.0
202 IF (S - R) 5, 5, 11
  7 R = R/10.0
    M = M + 100
204 IF (R - 0.0001) 87, 87, 11
 87 WRITE OUTPUT TAPE 2, 117, EA, EB, EC, AK, BK, TEST, M, L
    WRITE OUTPUT TAPE 2, 30
 30 FORMAT (104H0          V(OBS)             V(CALC)           DIF
  1 TIME          (A)               (B)               (C))
205 DO 35 J=1,N
    EK1 = EXPF(-AK*T(J))
    EK2 = EXPF(-BK*T(J))
    CALE(J) = EA*EK1 + EB*AK*(EK1-EK2)/(BK-AK) +EC*(1.+
  1 (BK*EK1-AK*EK2)/(AK-BK))
    DIF(J) = OBSE(J) - CALE(J)
    A(J)= EK1
    B(J) = AK*(EK1-EK2)/(BK-AK)
 35 C(J) = 1. - A(J) - B(J)
    WRITE OUTPUT TAPE 2, 42
    WRITE OUTPUT TAPE 2, 31, (OBSE(J), CALE(J), DIF(J),
  1 T(J), A(J), B(J), C(J), J=1,N)
 31 FORMAT (1H 7F15.5)
    GO TO 100
    END



    SUBROUTINE EVAL (EA, EB, EC, AK, BK, VAL)
    DIMENSION OBSE(30), T(30), CALE(30), DIF(30)
    COMMON  N, OBSE, T
    SUM = 0.0
208 DO 4 J = 1,N
    EK1 = EXPF(-AK*T(J))
    EK2 = FXPF(-BK*T(J))
    CALE(J) = EA*EK1 + EB*AK*(EK1-EK2)/(BK-AK) +EC*(1.+
  1 (BK*EK1-AK*EK2)/(AK-BK))
    DIF(J)= ABSF(OBSE(J) - CALE(J))/ABSF(OBSE(J))
  4 SUM = SUM+DIF(J)
    G = N
    VAL = SUM/G
    RETURN
    END
```

The final program of this appendix is one which obtains the Hückel energy levels and wave functions for π-electronic systems. The program is based on the use of a numerical list to indicate which atoms are joined together. As an example if we had the hydrocarbon and numbered it as shown (each π-electronic center must have a number), the structure could be represented by the lists

1 2 3 4 5 6 7 8 9 10 11 12 13 14 15 16 17 18 1

3 8

9 18

12 17

provided all of the rings were assumed to be regular hexagons. This assumption is usually made.

The program begins with the reading of an identification card (columns 1–72), followed by a card having the number of nitrogen atoms, M1 (columns 1–5), the number of oxygen atoms, M2 (columns 6–10), the number of π-electronic centers, N (columns 10–15), the number of electrons, NELECT (columns 16–20), the number of entries in the first list of numbers above, N2 (columns 21–25), in the second list, N3 (columns 26–30), and so on. Finally, the value of MODE is written in columns 65–70. If MODE = 1, the H and S matrices are read from cards (twelve five column entries per card), if MODE = O, the matrices are formed automatically, and if MODE = 2, the matrices are formed automatically and are written in the output.

The next cards contain the lists given above (as many as required up to a maximum of 7) using two columns per number. Remember that integers must be punched in the right-hand side of the field. Then, if there are nitrogen atoms, their numbers are read from a card, and if these are oxygen atoms, their numbers are read from a card. Finally, a card giving the overlap integral, SC (assumed to be the same for all pairs of atoms which are joined together), the value of ξ for nitrogen (AN) and the value of ξ for oxygen (AO):

$$\alpha_N = \alpha_C + \xi\gamma$$
$$\alpha_O = \alpha_C + \xi\gamma$$

Common values are $\xi_N = 0.5$ and $\xi_O = 1.0$.

The diagonal elements for the H matrix (called A in the program) are obtained by setting $\alpha_C = O$ and by introducing the appropriate values in every position corresponding to a nitrogen or oxygen atom. The off-diagonal elements of H are obtained by the series of statements from 20–35 which examine the lists of joined atoms and write a 1 for the matrix element joining the two atoms.

The off-diagonal elements for the S matrix (called B in the program) are obtained by multiplying the off-diagonal elements of H by the overlap integral, SC. The diagonal elements are unity. The main program now calls the subroutine SECN which handles the calculation of the eigenvalues and eigenvectors. Note that the subroutines MMULT and MATINV used by SECN are different than those given in Appendix 8.

The locations of the matrices are transferred from the main program to the subroutine using the COMMON statement. The COMMON statement must be identical in the main program and subroutines, and the dimension statements must agree in each. The SECN subroutine inverts the matrix S giving S^{-1}, and effects the multiplication

$$C = S^{-1}H$$

As shown in Appendix 2, the eigenvalues and eigenvectors of C are the required ones, and the subroutine calls HDIAG to effect the diagonalization of C and the calculation of the eigenvectors.

A return to the main program is effected and subroutine OUTPUT is called. This subroutine obtains the electron density for each atom in the π-electronic system (DEN), the bond orders (BOND), the π-electronic energy (PI), and the delocalization energy (PJ). The latter is correct only if the overlap integral were set equal to 0.25. The use of the statement

PJ = PI − FLOATF (IBOND)*0.8*2.

may be noted. FLOATF(N) converts the integer N into a decimal number. It will be remembered that integers and decimal numbers may not be mixed in algebraic expressions.

The final return to the main program directs the computer to read another set of data cards. If no further cards are supplied, it proceeds to the next program. A set of typical input and output data is shown following the program. The program works satisfactorily for all-carbon systems. However, if heteroatoms are present, and an overlap integral other than zero is used, the matrix C will not be symmetrical, and a matrix diagonalization program other than HDIAG must be used. Further, the delocalization energy will not be correct if heteroatoms are present, although the total π-electronic energy will be correct.

Hückel M.O. Wave Functions and Energies

```
C     EIGENVALUE-EIGENVECTOR PROGRAM FOR 40 CENTER AROMATIC SYSTEMS
C
C     THE FIRST CARD CONTAINS THE NAME OF THE COMPOUND.
C
C     THE SECOND CARD CONTAINS THE NUMBER OF NITROGEN ATOMS IN THE CON-
C     JUGATED SYSTEM IN THE FIRST FIELD, THE NUMBER OF OXYGEN ATOMS IN
C     THE SECOND FIELD, THE NUMBER OF ATOMS IN THE CONJUGATED SYSTEM IN
C     THE THIRD FIELD, THE NUMBER OF ELECTRONS IN THE FOURTH FIELD, THE
C     CONSTANTS FOR THE ATOM CONNECTION STATEMENTS IN THE NEXT SEVEN
C     FIELDS, AND THE MODE CONSTANT IN THE TWELFTH FIELD. THE FIELD
C     WIDTH IS FIVE.
C
C     IF MODE=0, THE H AND S MATRICES ARE FORMED AUTOMATICALLY.
C     IF MODE IS=1, THE H AND S MATRICES ARE READ IN AFTER THE ATOM
C     CONNECTION STATEMENTS.
C     IF MODE=2, THE PROGRAM PROCEEDS ACCORDING TO MODE 0, BUT THE
C     MATRICES WHICH ARE FORMED ARE PRINTED OUT.
C
C     THE NEXT CARDS CONTAIN THE ATOM CONNECTION STATEMENTS, EACH WITH A
C     FIELD WIDTH OF TWO.
C
C     IF MODE IS 0, AND THERE ARE NITROGEN ATOMS THE NEXT CARD GIVES THE
C     LOCATIONS OF THE NITROGEN ATOMS USING A FIELD WIDTH OF TWO.
C
C     IF MODE IS 0, AND THERE ARE OXYGEN ATOMS THE NEXT CARD GIVES THE
C     LOCATION OF THE OXYTEN ATOMS USING A FIELD WIDTH OF TWO.
C
C     IF MODE=1, THE NEXT CARDS GIVE THE H MATRIX ELEMENTS USING
C     A FIELD WIDTH OF FIVE, AND PLACING EACH SET OF VALUES FOR A GIVEN
C     ROW ON A SEPARATE CARD(S).
C     THE S MATRIX IS THEN READ IN A SIMILAR FASHION.
C
C     THIS PROGRAM REQUIRES THE SUBROUTINES SECN, AND OUTPUT.
C
      COMMON A,B,C,N,ENERGY,TITLE, NELECT, NATOM
      DIMENSION A(40,40),B(40,40),C(40,40),ENERGY(40),NATOM(7,40),IAN(35
     1),IAO(35),TITLE(12)
    1 READ INPUT TAPE 4,52, (TITLE(J),J=1,12)
      READ INPUT TAPE 4,2, M1,M2,N,NELECT,N2,N3,N4,N5,N6,N7,N8, MODE
    2 FORMAT (14I5)
      READ INPUT TAPE 4,3, (NATOM(1,J),J=1,N2)
    3 FORMAT (35I2)
      IF (N3) 10,10,4
    4 READ INPUT TAPE 4,3,(NATOM(2,J), J=1,N3)
      IF (N4) 10,10,5
    5 READ INPUT TAPE 4,3,(NATOM(3,J), J=1,N4)
      IF (N5) 10,10,6
    6 READ INPUT TAPE 4,3,(NATOM(4,J), J=1,N5)
      IF (N6) 10,10,7
    7 READ INPUT TAPE 4,3,(NATOM(5,J), J=1,N6)
      IF (N7) 10,10,8
    8 READ INPUT TAPE 4,3,(NATOM(6,J), J=1,N7)
      IF (N8) 10,10,9
    9 READ INPUT TAPE 4,3,(NATOM(7,J),J=1,N8)
   10 IF (MODE-1) 110,60,110
  110 IF (M1) 13,13,11
   11 READ INPUT TAPE 4,3,(IAN(J), J=1,M1)
   13 IF (M2) 15,15,12
   12 READ INPUT TAPE 4,3,(IAO(J), J=1,M2)
```

```
      15 READ INPUT TAPE 4,16, SC, AN, AO
      16 FORMAT (3F10.3)
         DO 53 J=1,N
         DO 53 K=1,N
         A(J,K)=0.0
         B(J,K)=0.0
      53 C(J,K)=0.0
    C    DIAGONAL ELEMENTS OF MATRIX A
         IF (M1) 17,17,18
      18 DO 19 J=1,M1
         L=IAN(J)
      19 A(L,L)=AN
      17 IF (M2) 20,20,21
      21 DO 22 J=1,M2
         L=IAO(J)
      22 A(L,L)=AO
    C    OFF DIAGONAL ELEMENTS OF MATRIX A
      20 NN=N2-1
         DO 23 L=1,NN
         J=NATOM(1,L)
         L1=L+1
         K=NATOM(1,L1)
         A(J,K)=1.0
      23 A(K,J)=1.0
         IF (N3) 40,40,24
      24 NN=N3-1
         DO 25 L=1,NN
         J=NATOM(2,L)
         L1=L+1
         K=NATOM(2,L1)
         A(J,K)=1.0
      25 A(K,J)=1.0
         IF (N4) 40,40,26
      26 NN=N4-1
         DO 27 L=1,NN
         J=NATOM(3,L)
         L1=L+1
         K=NATOM(3,L1)
         A(J,K)=1.0
      27 A(K,J)=1.0
         IF (N5) 40,40,28
      28 NN= N5-1
         DO 29 L=1,NN
         J=NATOM(4,L)
         L1=L+1
         K=NATOM(4,L1)
         A(J,K)=1.0
      29 A(K,J)=1.0
         IF(N6) 40,40,30
      30 NN=N6-1
         DO 31 L=1,NN
         J=NATOM(5,L)
         L1=L+1
         K=NATOM(5,L1)
         A(J,K)=1.0
      31 A(K,J)=1.0
         IF (N7) 40,40,32
      32 NN= N7-1
         DO 33 L=1,NN
```

```
         J=NATOM(6,L)
         L1=L+1
         K=NATOM(6,L1)
         A(J,K)=1.0
   33 A(K,J)=1.0
         IF (N8) 40,40,34
   34 NN=N8-1
         DO 35 L=1,NN
         J=NATOM(7,L)
         L1=L+1
         K=NATOM(7,L1)
         A(J,K)=1.0
   35 A(K,J)=1.0
C        OFF DIAGONAL ELEMENTS OF MATRIX B
   40 DO 41 J=1,N
         DO 41 K=1,N
   41 B(J,K)= A(J,K)*SC
C        DIAGONAL ELEMENTS OF MATRIX B
         DO 43 J=1,N
   43 B(J,J)=1.0
         IF (MODE-1) 80,60,90
   80 CALL SECN(INDEX)
         IF(INDEX) 50,50,51
   50 CALL OUTPUT (N2,N3,N4,N5,N6,N7,N8)
   51 GO TO 1
   52 FORMAT (12A6)
   60 DO 61 K=1,N
         DO 61 J=1,N
         A(J,K) =0.0
         B(J,K)=0.0
   61 C(J,K) =0.0
C        READ MATRIX
         DO 65 J=1,N
   65 READ INPUT TAPE 4,72, (A(J,K),K=1,N)
   72 FORMAT (12F5.0)
         DO 78 J=1,N
   78 READ INPUT TAPE 4,72, (B(J,K), K=1,N)
   90 WRITE OUTPUT TAPE 2,91
   91 FORMAT (26H1 THE H MATRIX ELEMENTS ARE)
         DO 75 J=1,N
         WRITE OUTPUT TAPE 2,73
   73 FORMAT (1H )
   75 WRITE OUTPUT TAPE 2,76, (A(J,K), K=1,N)
   76 FORMAT ( 1H 12F5.2)
         WRITE OUTPUT TAPE 2, 92
   92 FORMAT (26H0THE S MATRIX ELEMENTS ARE)
         WRITE OUTPUT TAPE 2, 73
         DO 77 J=1,N
   77 WRITE OUTPUT TAPE 2,76, (B(J,K), K =1,N)
         GO TO 80
         END
```

```
      SUBROUTINE SECN (INDEX)
      DIMENSION A(40,40),B(40,40),C(40,40),ENERGY(40), TITLE(12)
      COMMON A,B,C,N,ENERGY,TITLE
      CALL MATINV(N,N,INDEX)
      IF (INDEX) 3,3,4
3     CALL MMULT(N)
      CALL HDIAG(C,N,0,A,NR)
4     RETURN
      END
```

```
      SUBROUTINE MATINV (M,N,INDEX)
      DIMENSION A(40,40), C(40,40), D(40,40), B(40)
      COMMON D, A, C
      INDEX = 0
      IF DIVIDE CHECK 4, 4
4     M1 = M - 1
      N1 = N - 1
      N2 = 0
      DO 7 L = 1, M
      B(N) = 1.0/A(1,1)
      N2 = N2 + 1
      IF DIVIDE CHECK 9, 3
3     DO 5 K = 1, N1
5     B(K) = A(1, K+1)*B(N)
      DO 6 I = 1, M1
      A(I,N) = -B(N)*A(I+1,1)
      DO 6 J = 1, N1
6     A(I,J) = A(I+1, J+1) - B(J)*A(I+1,1)
      DO 7 J = 1, N
7     A(M,J) = B(J)
      GO TO 11
9     WRITE OUTPUT TAPE 2, 10, N2
10    FORMAT (19H DIVIDE CHECK, ROW I2)
      INDEX = 1
11    RETURN
      END
```

```
      SUBROUTINE MMULT (N)
      COMMON B, A, C
      DIMENSION A(40,40), B(40,40), C(40,40)
      DO 20 I = 1,N
      DO 20 J = 1,N
      C(I,J) = 0.0
      DO 20 K = 1,N
20    C(I,J) = C(I,J) + A(I,K)*B(K,J)
      RETURN
      END
```

```
       SUBROUTINE OUTPUT  (MM,MN,MO,MP,MQ,MR,MS)
       COMMON A,B,C,N,ENERGY,TITLE, NELECT, NATOM
       DIMENSION ENERGY(40), A(40,40),TITLE(12),DEN(40),
      1B(40,40), C(40,40), NATOM(7,40), MM(7)
       MM(1) = MM
       MM(2) = MN
       MM(3) = MO
       MM(4) = MP
       MM(5) = MQ
       MM(6) = MR
       MM(7) = MS
       WRITE OUTPUT TAPE 2,1,(TITLE(J),J=1,12)
1      FORMAT (1H112A6)
       WRITE OUTPUT TAPE 2,2
2      FORMAT (1H )
       J = 1
4      WRITE OUTPUT TAPE 2, 5, J, C(J,J), J, (A(K,J),K, K=1,6)
5      FORMAT (8H ENERGY(I2, 3H) =F8.4, 8H    PSI(I2, 3H) =F7.4,
      1 2H (I2, 1H)5(2H +F7.4,  2H (I2, 1H)))
       IF (N-6) 130,130,9
9      IF (N-12) 7,7,10
7      WRITE OUTPUT TAPE 2, 8, (A(K,J), K, K= 7,N)
8      FORMAT ( 32H                           6(2H +F7.4, 2H (I2,1H)
      1) )
       GO TO 130
10     WRITE OUTPUT TAPE 2, 8, (A(K,J), K, K= 7,12)
12     IF (N-18) 14,14,15
14     WRITE OUTPUT TAPE 2, 8, (A(K,J), K, K= 13, N)
       GO TO 130
15     WRITE OUTPUT TAPE 2, 8, (A(K,J), K, K= 13, 18)
20     IF (N-24) 21,21,22
21     WRITE OUTPUT TAPE 2, 8, (A(K,J), K, K= 19, N)
       GO TO 130
22     WRITE OUTPUT TAPE 2, 8, (A(K,J), K, K= 19, 24)
25     IF (N-30) 26,26,27
26     WRITE OUTPUT TAPE 2, 8, (A(K,J), K, K= 25, N)
       GO TO 130
27     WRITE OUTPUT TAPE 2, 8, (A(K,J), K, K= 25, 30)
30     WRITE OUTPUT TAPE 2, 8, (A(K,J), K, K= 31, 36)
130    IF (J-N) 133,132,132
133    J = J+1
       GO TO 4
132    WRITE OUTPUT TAPE 2, 131
131    FORMAT (1H0)
       WRITE OUTPUT TAPE 2,32
32     FORMAT (28H0          ELECTRON DENSITIES)
       WRITE OUTPUT TAPE 2,2
       NE = NELECT/2
       NF = NELECT - NE*2
       NEP1 = NE + 1
       DO 62 K = 1,N
       DEN(K)=0.0
       DO 35 L = 1,NE
35     DEN(K) = DEN(K) +(A(K,L)**2)*2.
       IF (NF) 62,62,61
61     DEN(K) = DEN(K) + A(K,NEP1)**2
62     CONTINUE
       WRITE OUTPUT TAPE 2,36, (K, DEN(K),K=1,N)
36     FORMAT(1H 6( 7H  ATOM(I2, 2H)=F6.4))
```

```
      WRITE OUTPUT TAPE 2, 131
      WRITE OUTPUT TAPE 2, 37
37    FORMAT (21H0          BOND ORDERS)
      WRITE OUTPUT TAPE 2, 2
      DO 45 II= 1,7
      MT = MM(II)
      DO 41 M = 2, MT
      M1 = M-1
      K = NATOM(II,M1)
      L = NATOM(II,M)
      BOND = 0.0
      DO 42 J = 1, NE
42    BOND = BOND + A(K,J)*A(L,J)*2.
      IF (NF) 41,41,70
70    BOND = BOND + A(K,NELECT)*A(L,NELECT)
41    WRITE OUTPUT TAPE 2, 48, K, L, BOND
      IJ = II+1
      IF (MM(IJ)) 46,46,45
45    CONTINUE
46    CONTINUE
48    FORMAT (7H  BOND(I2, 1H,I2, 2H)=F6.4)
      IBOND = N/2
      PI = 0.0
      DO 50 J = 1, NE
50    PI = PI + 2.*C(J,J)
      IF (NF) 52,52,53
53    PI = PI + C(NEP1,NEP1)
52    PJ = PI - FLOATF(IBOND)*0.8*2.
      WRITE OUTPUT TAPE 2, 131
      WRITE OUTPUT TAPE 2, 51, NELECT, PI
51    FORMAT (25H THE TOTAL PI ENERGY FOR I2, 14H ELECTRONS IS F7.3)
      WRITE OUTPUT TAPE 2, 250, PJ
250   FORMAT (30H THE DELOCALIZATION ENERGY IS F7.3,6H GAMMA)
      RETURN
      END
```

Input Data:

```
AZULENE        S = 0.25
      0      0     10     10     11      2      0      0      0      0      0
010203040506070809100 1
0105
0.25          0.5          1.0
```

Output:

```
AZULENE       S = 0.25

ENERGY( 1) =  1.4645    PSI( 1) = 0.4670 ( 1) + 0.3233 ( 2) + 0.2799 ( 3) + 0.3233 ( 4) + 0.4670 ( 5) + 0.2886 ( 6)
                                 + 0.1730 ( 7) + 0.2234 ( 8) + 0.1730 ( 9) + 0.2886 (10)

ENERGY( 2) =  1.1689    PSI( 2) = 0.1180 ( 1) + 0.2678 ( 2) + 0.5247 ( 3) + 0.2678 ( 4) + 0.1180 ( 5) +-0.1909 ( 6)
                                 +-0.4333 ( 7) +-0.3243 ( 8) +-0.4333 ( 9) +-0.1909 (10)

ENERGY( 3) =  1.0125    PSI( 3) =-0.2992 ( 1) +-0.2207 ( 2) +-0.0000 ( 3) + 0.2207 ( 4) + 0.2992 ( 5) + 0.4841 ( 6)
                                 + 0.3571 ( 7) +-0.0000 ( 8) +-0.3571 ( 9) +-0.4841 (10)

ENERGY( 4) =  0.7260    PSI( 4) =-0.3536 ( 1) + 0.2585 ( 2) + 0.5527 ( 3) + 0.2585 ( 4) +-0.3536 ( 5) +-0.2186 ( 6)
                                 + 0.2675 ( 7) +-0.2697 ( 8) + 0.2675 ( 9) +-0.2186 (10)

ENERGY( 5) =  0.4264    PSI( 5) = 0.2591 ( 1) + 0.5428 ( 2) + 0.3157 ( 3) + 0.5428 ( 4) + 0.2591 ( 5) +-0.1601 ( 6)
                                 + 0.1023 ( 7) +-0.3157 ( 8) + 0.1023 ( 9) +-0.1601 (10)

ENERGY( 6) = -0.4449    PSI( 6) = 0.2904 ( 1) + 0.0632 ( 2) +-0.0000 ( 3) +-0.0632 ( 4) +-0.2904 ( 5) + 0.4699 ( 6)
                                 + 0.4372 ( 7) +-0.0000 ( 8) +-0.4372 ( 9) +-0.4699 (10)

ENERGY( 7) = -0.9044    PSI( 7) =-0.2207 ( 1) + 0.2992 ( 2) + 0.3416 ( 3) + 0.2992 ( 4) +-0.2207 ( 5) +-0.3571 ( 6)
                                 +-0.2697 ( 7) + 0.4045 ( 8) +-0.2697 ( 9) +-0.3571 (10)

ENERGY( 8) = -2.6094    PSI( 8) =-0.1365 ( 1) + 0.4364 ( 2) +-0.0000 ( 3) +-0.4364 ( 4) + 0.1365 ( 5) +-0.0844 ( 6)
                                 + 0.5527 ( 7) +-0.0000 ( 8) +-0.5527 ( 9) + 0.0844 (10)

ENERGY( 9) = -3.5090    PSI( 9) = 0.1998 ( 1) +-0.2500 ( 2) + 0.4045 ( 3) +-0.2500 ( 4) + 0.1998 ( 5) +-0.3233 ( 6)
                                 +-0.3233 ( 7) +-0.3157 ( 8) +-0.3233 ( 9) +-0.3233 (10)

ENERGY(10) = -4.4002    PSI(10) = 0.5428 ( 1) +-0.2591 ( 2) +-0.1601 ( 3) +-0.2591 ( 4) + 0.5428 ( 5) +-0.3355 ( 6)
                                 +-0.1601 ( 7) + 0.1601 ( 8) +-0.1601 ( 9) +-0.3355 (10)


            ELECTRON DENSITIES

ATOM( 1)=1.0274   ATOM( 2)=1.1729   ATOM( 3)=1.0466   ATOM( 4)=1.1729   ATOM( 5)=1.0274   ATOM( 6)=0.8549
ATOM( 7)=0.9864   ATOM( 8)=0.8700   ATOM( 9)=0.9864   ATOM(10)=0.8549


            BOND ORDERS

BOND( 1, 2)=0.5956
BOND( 2, 3)=0.6560
BOND( 3, 4)=0.6560
BOND( 4, 5)=0.5956
BOND( 5, 6)=0.5858
BOND( 6, 7)=0.6640
BOND( 7, 8)=0.6389
BOND( 8, 9)=0.6389
BOND( 9,10)=0.6640
BOND(10, 1)=0.5858
BOND( 1, 5)=0.4009


THE TOTAL PI ENERGY FOR 10 ELECTRONS IS  9.597
THE DELOCALIZATION ENERGY IS  1.597 GAMMA
```

Index

585